ROCK MECHANICS: CAVERNS AND PRESSURE SHAFTS
FELSMECHANIK: KAVERNEN UND DRUCKSCHÄCHTE
MÉCANIQUE DES ROCHES: LES CAVERNES ET LES PUITS SOUS PRESSION

1

ISRM SYMPOSIUM / AACHEN / 1982.05.26-28

ROCK MECHANICS: CAVERNS AND PRESSURE SHAFTS

FELSMECHANIK: KAVERNEN UND DRUCKSCHÄCHTE

MECANIQUE DES ROCHES: LES CAVERNES ET LES PUITS SOUS PRESSION

Editor / Redakteur / Rédacteur
W.WITTKE
*Institut für Grundbau, Bodenmechanik, Felsmechanik
und Verkehrswasserbau, Aachen*

VOLUME 1
*Rock Mechanical Investigations / Large Span Caverns
Felsmechanische Untersuchungen / Hohlräume mit grosser Spannweite
Recherches en mécanique des roches / Cavités de grandes portées*

*Published for / Herausgegeben für / Publié pour
Deutsche Gesellschaft für Erd- und Grundbau e.V., Essen*
A.A.BALKEMA / ROTTERDAM / 1982

The texts of the various papers in this volume were set individually
by typists under the supervision of each of the authors concerned

For the complete set of three volumes, ISBN 90 6191 232 6
For Volume 1, ISBN 90 6191 233 4
For Volume 2, ISBN 90 6191 234 2
For Volume 3, ISBN 90 6191 235 0

ISRM SYMPOSIUM / AACHEN / 1982.05.26-28

ROCK MECHANICS RELATED TO CAVERNS AND PRESSURE SHAFTS
FELSMECHANIK IN VERBINDUNG MIT KAVERNEN UND DRUCKSCHÄCHTEN
MÉCANIQUE DES ROCHES EN LIAISON AVEC LES CAVERNES ET LES PUITS SOUS PRESSION

CHAIRMAN / VORSITZENDER / PRÉSIDENT

Prof. Dr.-Ing. W. Wittke   President of the International Society for Rock Mechanics
Präsident der Internationalen Gesellschaft für Felsmechanik
Président de la Société Internationale de Mécanique des Roches

ADVISORY COMMITTEE / BEIRAT / COMITÉ DE PATRONAGE

Direktor H. Heiderhoff   Vorstandsmitglied des Rheinisch-Westfälischen Elektrizitätswerkes AG, Essen
Dr.-Ing. W. Krabbe   Vorstandsmitglied der Philipp Holzmann AG, Frankfurt
Direktor L. Meyer   Geschäftsführer, Lahmeyer International GmbH, Frankfurt
Prof. Dr.-Ing. K. Roske   Kreditanstalt für Wiederaufbau, Frankfurt

SCIENTIFIC COMMITTEE / WISSENSCHAFTLICHER BEIRAT / COMITÉ SCIENTIFIQUE

Prof. Dr.-Ing. H. Blind   Lehrstuhl für Wasserbau und Wassermengenwirtschaft, TU München
Prof. Dr. K.H. Heitfeld   Lehrstuhl für Ingenieurgeologie und Hydrogeologie, RWTH Aachen
Prof. Dr.-Ing. H.J. Kayser   Lehrstuhl für Strassenwesen, Erd- und Tunnelbau, RWTH Aachen
Prof. Dr.-Ing. G. Rouvé   Lehrstuhl für Wasserbau und Wasserwirtschaft, RWTH Aachen

ORGANIZING COMMITTEE / ORGANISATIONSKOMITEE / COMITÉ D'ORGANISATION

Dipl.-Ing. S. Babendererde   Leiter der Zentralen Tiefbauabteilung der Hochtief AG, Essen
Prof. Dr.-Ing. K.H. Idel   Geschäftsführer der Deutschen Gesellschaft für Erd- und Grundbau e.V., Essen
Prof. Dr. M. Langer   Bundesanstalt für Geowissenschaften und Rohstoffe, Hannover
Dr. R. Wolters †   Generalsekretär der Internationalen Vereinigung für Ingenieurgeologie, Krefeld

Assistance at the organization: / Mitwirkung bei der Organisation: / Organisé avec le concours de:

Mitarbeiter des Instituts für Grundbau, Bodenmechanik, Felsmechanik und Verkehrswasserbau, RWTH Aachen

CONTENTS / INHALT / TABLE DES MATIÈRES

2 PART TEIL PARTIE
Underground caverns with large span
Untertägige Hohlräume mit grosser Spannweite
Cavités souterraines de grandes portées

PREFACE

Underground structures in rock are being erected to an increasing extent in connection with the construction of power stations and the storage of liquids, gases and waste materials. Thus, particularly as a result of economic requirements, it has been necessary to present scientific and technical knowledge and developments in a readily useable form for the designers and contractors. It is in this context that the German Geo-technical Society - DGEG - is organizing an International Symposium in Aachen from the 26th - 28th May, 1982 on the subject of "Rock Mechanics related to Caverns and Pressure Shafts". The event is taking place under the sponsorship of the International Society for Rock Mechanics - ISRM - which will be celebrating its 20th anniversary.

In the conference's 1st Bulletin the experts in the field were invited to submit papers on the following topics:

1. Rock Mechanical Investigation Programs for Large Caverns in Rock Masses
2. Underground Caverns With Large Span
3. Load Sharing Capacity of the Rock Mass for Pressure Tunnels and Shafts
4. Limitation of the Applicability of Tunnel Boring Machines as seen from the Rock Mechanical Point of View
5. Rock Mechanical Problems in Association With Underground Storage.

The submission of more than 130 papers from 30 countries indicates that these topics are of great interest. The papers are being published in three volumes of the Proceedings, two of which will be available at the conference.

I would like to express my most sincere gratitude to all the authors and to the colleagues, who will be chairing meetings, for their efforts. In particular my thanks go to the members of the Conference Advisory and Organisation Committees for their valuable support and assistance in the planning and organisation of the event.

Walter Wittke
President of the International
Society for Rock Mechanics

VORWORT

In zunehmendem Umfang werden im Zusammenhang mit dem Bau von Kraftwerken und der Lagerung von Flüssigkeiten, Gasen und Abfällen unterirdische Fels- bauten errichtet. Hieraus ist, insbesondere aus wirtschaftlichen Erfor- dernissen, die Notwendigkeit entstanden, wissenschaftliche und technolo- gische Erkenntnisse und Entwicklungen im Felsbau dem Planer und Bauaus- führenden nutzbar zu machen. In diesem Zusammenhang veranstaltet die Deutsche Gesellschaft für Erd- und Grundbau e.V. - DGEG - vom 26. - 28. Mai 1982 in Aachen ein Internationales Symposium zum Thema: "Fels- mechanik in Verbindung mit Kavernen und Druckschächten". Die Veranstal- tung steht unter der Schirmherrschaft der Internationalen Gesellschaft für Felsmechanik - ISRM -, deren 20-jähriges Bestehen im Rahmen der Tagung gewürdigt werden soll.

Mit dem 1. Bulletin zur Tagung, das im Frühjahr 1981 erschien, wurden die Fachleute um Beiträge zu den folgenden Einzelthemen gebeten:

1. Felsmechanische Untersuchungsprogramme für große Felskavernen
2. Untertägige Hohlräume mit großer Spannweite
3. Mittragende Wirkung des Gebirges bei Druckstollen und Druckschächten
4. Einsatzgrenzen von Tunnelvortriebsmaschinen aus felsmechanischer Sicht
5. Felsmechanische Probleme im Zusammenhang mit der untertägigen Spei- cherung.

Mehr als 130 eingegangene Beiträge aus 30 Ländern zeigen, daß diese Themen in der Fachwelt ein großes Interesse gefunden haben. Die Beiträge werden in drei Bänden der Proceedings veröffentlicht, wobei 2 Bände bereits zur Tagung erscheinen.

Ich möchte mich bei allen Autoren und den Kollegen, die die Leitung von Sitzungen übernommen haben, sehr herzlich für ihre Mühen bedanken. Ins- besondere gilt mein Dank den Mitgliedern des Tagungsbeirates und des Or- ganisationskomitees für deren wertvolle Unterstützung und Mithilfe bei der Planung und Durchführung der Veranstaltung.

Walter Wittke
Präsident der Internationalen
Gesellschaft für Felsmechanik

AVANT-PROPOS

En rapport avec la construction de centrales électriques et le stockage de liquides, de gaz et de déchets, des constructions en roches souterraines sont érigées en un nombre croissant. Il en résulte, notamment de par les exigences économiques, la nécessité de rendre les connaissances scientifiques et technologiques et les évolutions dans la construction en roches, utiles au projeteur et au constructeur. C'est dans ce but que la Société Allemande des Travaux de Terrassements et de Fondations S.A. - DGEG - organise du 26 au 28 Mai 1982 à "l'Eurogress" d'Aix-la-Chapelle un symposium international ayant pour thème: mécanique des roches en liaison avec les cavernes et les puits sous pression. Ce symposium est placé sous le patronage de la Société Internationale de Mécanique des Roches - ISRM - dont on honorera la 20e année de son éxistence.

Dans le 1er bulletin relatif au symposium qui a été publié au printemps 1981, il a été demandé aux experts de présenter des exposés sur les différents thèmes suivants.

1. Programmes de recherches en mécanique des roches dans le cas de cavernes rocheuses de grandes dimensions

2. Cavités souterraines de grandes portées

3. Effet de la portance du terrain dans le cas des galeries forcées et des puits sous pression

4. Limites d'emploi de foreuses pour le creusement de tunnels, du point de vue de la mécanique des roches

5. Problèmes de mécanique des roches en relation avec le stockage souterrain.

Plus de 130 exposés venant de 30 pays ont été déjà reçus, ce qui prouve que les experts montrent un grand intérêt pour ces thèmes. Ces exposés seront publiés dans les trois volumes des comptes-rendus dont deux paraîtront déjà pour le symposium.

J'aimerais remercier très cordialement les auteurs et les collègues, qui ont pris la direction d'une séance, pour leurs peines. Mes remerciements vont particulièrement aux membres du comité consultatif du symposium et à ceux du comité d'organisation pour leur précieux soutien et leur assistance dans la planification et la réalisation de cette conférence.

Walter Wittke
Président de la Société
Internationale de Mécanique des Roches

* 1 *

ROCK MECHANICAL INVESTIGATION PROGRAMS FOR LARGE CAVERNS IN ROCK MASSES

Felsmechanische Untersuchungsprogramme für grosse Felskavernen

Programmes de recherches en mécanique des roches dans le cas de cavernes rocheuses de grandes dimensions

ROCK MASS CHARACTERIZATION METHODS
FOR NUCLEAR WASTE REPOSITORIES IN JOINTED ROCK
Gebirgsklassifikationen für Lagerstätten von radioaktiven Stoffen in geklüftetem Fels
Méthodes de classification des massifs rocheux pour le dépôt des déchets nucléaires dans les roches à diaclases

NICK BARTON & RICHARD LINGLE
Terra Tek Inc., Salt Lake City, Utah, USA

SUMMARY:

The planned isolation of nuclear waste in mined rock repositories poses unusual require-ments for rock mass characterization. This paper describes recently developed block test methods for characterizing and quantifying the thermal, mechanical and hydraulic proper-ties of rock masses. The heated block test, recently conducted in situ on an $8m^3$ block of jointed gneiss, provides normal stress and temperature-dependent data such as defor-mation modulus, joint stiffness, joint permeability, thermal expansion, thermal conduc-tivity and dynamic elastic modulus. Simpler tests conducted on singly jointed blocks or on jointed drill core provide joint roughness data. This is incorporated in recently developed constitutive models which describe the coupling of normal displacement, shear displacement, shear strength, dilation and permeability.

ZUSAMMENFASSUNG:

Die geplante Isolierung von radioaktivem Abfall in abgebauten Gesteinsabfällen stellt ungewöhnliche Anforderungen an Felsgesteinkennzeichnung. Dieser Bericht beschreibt kürzlich entwickelte Blocktestmethoden zur Kennzeichnung und quantitativen Bestimmung der Wärmeeigenschaften und der mechanischen und hydraulischen Eigenschaften der Fels-masse. Der Heißblocktest, der kürzlich "in-situ" auf einem $8m^3$ großen Block von gek-lüftetem Gneis durchgeführt wurde, gibt normale Spannungs- und Temperaturabhängigkeits-werte wie Verzerrungsmodul, Verbindungssteifigkeit, Verbindungsdurchlässigkeit, Wärme-usdehnung, Wärmeleitfähigkeit und Dynamik elastizitätsmodul. Einfachere Messungen, die an einzeln geklüfteten Blcoks oder an geklüfteten Bohrkernen vorgenommen wurden, geben Kluftrauhigkeitswerte an. Diese sind miteingeschlossen in kürzlich entwickelte zusam-menfassende Modelle, die die Kupplung normaler Verlagerung, Scherverlagerung, Scher-festigkeit, Dehnung und Durchlässigkeit beschreiben.

RESUME:

L'isolation projetée des déchets nucléaires dans des dépôts de roche extraites présente des exigences peu commune pour la caractérisation de la masse de roche. Cette étude décrit les méthodes, récemment développées, des essais des blocs pour caractériser et pour quantifier les propriétés thermiques, méchaniques et hydrauliques des masses de roche. L'essai du bloc chaud, récemment conduit in situ sur un bloc de gneiss jointé (de $8m^3$) fournit l'indication normale qui dépend de la force et de la température par exemple, le coéfficient de la déformation, la dureté de la jointure, la perméabilité de la jointure, l'expansion thermique, la conductivité thermique et le coéfficient dynam-ique et élastique. Des essais plus simples qu'on a conduits sur des blocs individuelle-ment jointés ou sur le centre jointé d'un trepan fournissent les indications de la rugosité des jointures. Tout ça est incorporé dans des modèles de base, récemment dé-veloppés, qui décrivent le couplage du déplacement normal, du déplacement du cisaille-ment, de la force du cisaillement, de la dilation et de la perméabilité.

1 INTRODUCTION

Characterization of rock masses is usually associated with construction and excavation projects such as dams, tunnels, mines, etc. In general the parameters of most importance are associated with deformation moduli, shear strength and permeability, each a function of stress and orientation. Civil engineering experience suggests that the natural joint sets have most effect on the magnitude of these parameters. Jointing is also responsible for their directional anisotropy.

The planned isolation of nuclear waste in mined rock repositories poses additional problems in rock mass characterization. The extended time scale and the thermal load associated with long-term isolation add to the number of significant parameters that need to be quantified. Numerical modeling of potential groundwater and radionuclide transport through changing stress and temperature regimes demands an advanced level of input data. Particular emphasis falls on accurate joint characterization, in particular on the manner in which the hydraulic, thermal and mechanical properties should be coupled.

2 THE HEATED BLOCK TEST

The schematic block diagram shown in Figure 1 represents the 8 m^3 in situ test recently completed by Terra Tek for the Office of Nuclear Waste Isolation. The objective was to demonstrate a suitable method for obtaining appropriate hydro-thermomechanical data for modeling and designing a repository in jointed rock. The particular test was performed in jointed gneiss. Flat-jacks were used to apply uniaxial and biaxial loading, and a line of borehole heaters were used to heat the block and to generate a temperature gradient. An extensive suite of borehole instruments were evaluated over a range of stress and temperature cycles, as indicated in Figures 2 and 3. The list below indicates average block temperatures relevant to the joint permeability tests described later.

Ambient Tests

1. Equal biaxial, cycle to 6.9 MPa.
2. N-S uniaxial, cycle to 6.9 MPa.
3. E-W uniaxial, cycle to 6.9 MPa.
4. Equal biaxial, load to 6.9 MPa.

Heating and Cooling Cycles

5. Equal biaxial, 41°C.

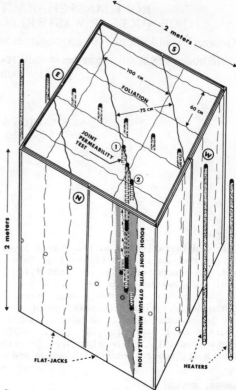

Fig. 1 Schematic of Terra Tek's 8 m^3 in situ heated block test in jointed gneiss.

6. Equal biaxial, cycle, 6.9-3.45-6.9 MPa, 56°C.
7. Equal biaxial, cycle, 6.9-3.45-6.9 MPa, 74°C.
8. Equal biaxial, , unload, 17°C.
9. Unconfined, 56°C, cycle, 0-3.45-0 MPa.
10. Unconfined, ambient.

The ability to load and unload or heat and cool the block independently exposed the instrumentation to a large number of operating cycles and pinpointed several areas where improvements to existing instrumentation could be achieved.

2.1 Deformation behavior

The deformability of the block was measured over several different base lengths, ranging from 25 cm with the Whittemore gage, to the full 2 meters dimension using the multiple position borehole extensometers (MPBX). Whittemore gage points were specifically located to measure the deformation across individual joints, and to record the deformation of the intact rock

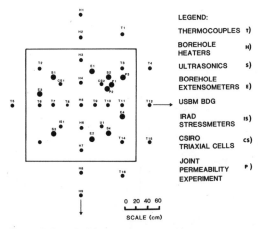

INSTRUMENT BOREHOLE ARRAY

LEGEND:

THERMOCOUPLES T)

BOREHOLE HEATERS H)

ULTRASONICS S)

BOREHOLE EXTENSOMETERS E)

USBM BDG

IRAD STRESSMETERS IS)

CSIRO TRIAXIAL CELLS CS)

JOINT PERMEABILITY EXPERIMENT P)

0 20 40 60

SCALE (cm)

Fig. 2 Borehole instrument array.

between joints. Figure 4 shows a typical stress-strain loop from EW uniaxial loading at ambient temperature. Whittemore gage measurements aligned within ±10° of drift E-W were used. Eight measurements at each stress level (1.75, 3.45, 5.25, 6.9 MPa) were averaged to compute the strain values. Six of the eight gages spanned joints. The "S" shaped hysteritic loop is typical of much of the loading data obtained on jointed rock, signifying low moduli on first loading and final unloading, and consistently high moduli on initial unloading.

Block deformation could actually be detected visually, by observing the growth and closure of cracks above each flatjack, round the four vertical sides of the block. These cracks were monitored with several gages. In effect the surrounding rock mass acts as the loading "platten" and deforms outwards, while the block itself shortens, each contributing to the total crack width. An elastic solution given by Poulos and Davis (1973) was used to relate stress level and crack width to the modulus:

$$E = \frac{\Delta P \cdot 1920}{\delta} \qquad (1)$$

where E = deformation modulus (MPa)
ΔP = stress increment (MPa)
δ = total crack opening (mm)

A value of Poisson's ratio of 0.2 was assumed in deriving the equation. Figure 5 illustrates the results obtained following four ambient load cycles, which had stiffened the block to an effective deformation modulus of approximately 40 GPa.

Unloading loops at 50°C and 80°C showed an interesting reversal of hysteresis which has yet to be satisfactorily explained. Perhaps the most significant result is the tendency for extremely high unloading moduli at elevated temperature and also when cooling.

Observations of joint deformation reported later, indicate that joints interlock tightly at elevated temperature, and remain tightly closed until almost unloaded. This behavior has potentially serious consequences for the long-term hydraulic integrity of a repository, since it is likely to facilitate the development of sporadic large aperture joints during the cooling-unloading phase. This may also be contemporary with the canister failure phase.

2.2 Poisson's ratio

Values of Poisson's ratio for horizontal transverse to axial strain were calculated using Whittemore strain data acquired during uniaxial loading at ambient temperature. The results show the characteristic non-elastic response of jointed rock to uniaxial stress. Individual measurements of Poisson's ratio fell in the range of ≤0 to ≥2.0, probably because of shear displacement along joints. Average values ranged from -0.441 to +0.472, the negative values occurring during the reversed shear caused by the EW loading.

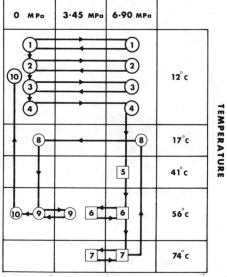

Fig. 3 Test matrix for the present series of block tests.

5

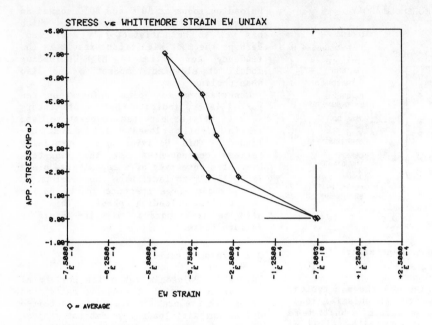

Fig. 4 Typical stress-strain loop obtained from Whittemore points.

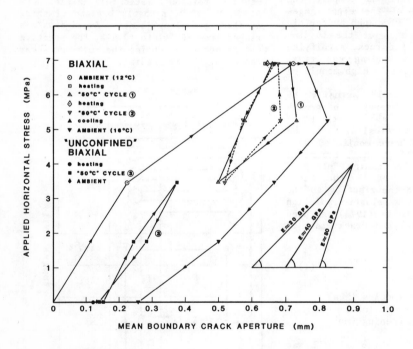

Fig. 5 Block deformation measured from boundary crack monitoring,
under elevated temperatures.

Values of Poisson's ratio were also calculated from the vertical strains measured by the two vertical MPBX gauges, during biaxial and uniaxial loading. The following values were obtained during ambient loading:

Biaxial   0-6.9 MPa   0.246
               6.9-0 MPa   0.171

NS uniaxial 0-6.9 MPa   0.063
               6.9-0 MPa   0.058

EW uniaxial 0-6.9 MPa   0.071
               6.9-0 MPa   0.059

The absence of joint shearing is evident in these moderate vertical strains.

2.3 Dynamic elastic moduli

Crosshole ultrasonic velocity (compressional and shear wave) measurements were made in the block at different loads and temperatures. The equipment used to make the ultrasonic measurements is shown in Figure 6.

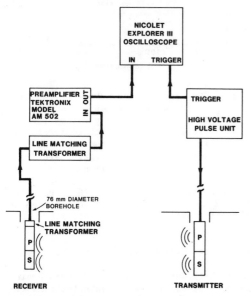

RECEIVER   TRANSMITTER

Fig. 6 Diagram of crosshole ultrasonic equipment.

Piezoelectric transducers were bonded to the downhole assemblies, which were in turn mechanically loaded against the side of the borehole at the location of each measurement, to provide acoustic coupling to the rock. The transit time between the transmitted pulse and the received signal was obtained from the oscilloscope display.

Each wave form was also recorded on a magnetic disk built into the oscilloscope, for future reference.

The dynamic Young's modulus and Poisson's ratio were calculated in accordance with elastic theory, using the following equations:

$$E = \frac{\rho V_s^2 (3V_p^2 - 4V_s^2)}{V_s^2 - V_p^2} \qquad (2)$$

$$\nu = \frac{V_p^2 - 2V_s^2}{2(V_p^2 - V_s^2)}, \qquad (3)$$

where E = dynamic Young's modulus
  ν = Poisson's ratio
  V_p = P-wave (longitudinal) velocity
  V_s = S-wave (shear) velocity
  ρ = bulk density of the rock

Figure 7 shows examples of some of the data obtained during ambient temperature loading. The trend for higher modulus at greater depth in the block, and at higher stress (confinement) levels is apparent. Note also the reduced dynamic modulus on final unloading, a result consistent with the moduli obtained from static measurements.

Laboratory measurements of dynamic Young's modulus on intact samples indicated a small increase with confining stress. For example, the dynamic modulus increased from 72 to 73 GPa parallel to foliation, and from 76 to 77 GPa perpendicular to foliation, over the range of confining stress 0-7 MPa. The dynamic modulus reduced from 69 to 64 GPa in the temperature range 20-140°C, under a confining stress of 7 MPa. The dynamic moduli obtained from the cross-hole ultrasonic tests reflected

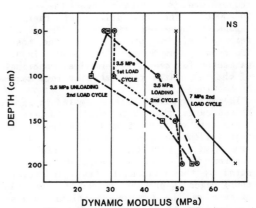

Fig. 7 Dynamic Young's modulus calculated from the ultrasonic data, as a function of depth in the block at different load conditions.

the effect of jointing and blast damage or stress relief. At 50 cm depth in the block values under ambient loading ranged from 10-49 GPa, while at 200 cm depth at the base of the block, where there was presumably improved confinement, values ranged from 27-68 GPa.

Under ambient biaxial loading the average dynamic modulus measured at the highest stress level (6.9 MPa, 1000 psi) was 53 GPa. Under N-S uniaxial loading, the first occasion in which the block was subjected to shear along the diagonal joints, the average dynamic modulus in the lateral (expanding) E-W direction was only 34 GPa. In the loaded N-S direction it remained high at 50 GPa. However, when the shear stress was reversed in the E-W uniaxial test, the average dynamic modulus in the lateral N-S direction was only slightly lower than in the loaded direction (47 GPa compared to 53 GPa). This is presumably due to the re-closing of joints during reversed shear.

Under elevated temperature biaxial loading, the general tendency for increased modulus with depth remained. However, there was a marked increase in the range of modulus values in the E-W direction, parallel to foliation. At elevated temperature, high confinement (6.9 MPa) produced 10-30 GPa increase in modulus in this sensitive E-W direction.

2.4 Thermal Expansion

Thermal property data for intact samples of Stripa (Swedish) granite presented by Chan, et al. (1980), indicate reduced values of Young's modulus, thermal conductivity and Poisson's ratio as rock temperature is increased over the range 20-200°C. The coefficient of thermal expansion increased over the same range of temperature, and proved to be the most important temperature dependent input parameter for realistic numerical modeling of the mechanical response of a rock mass to heating.

Thermal expansion data assembled in Figure 8 indicates that both small and large scale data obtained from the heated block test follow the trends of laboratory data from similar rock types. An initial reduction in (α) at low temperatures measured by the horizontal strain indicator (HSI) gages is probably caused by improved closure of the numerous vertical joints sampled by these gages. The strongly foliated nature of the granitic gneiss is reflected in the relative magnitudes of the expansion coefficients. Those mea-

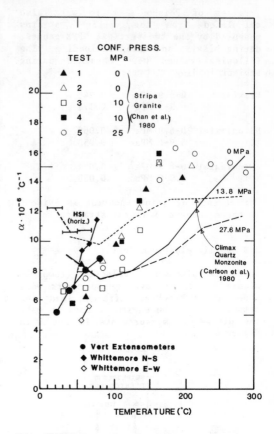

Fig. 8 Overlay of major laboratory tests of (α) as a function of temperature and confining pressure for granitic rocks. Block test results from the rod extensometers, Whittemore pins and HSI gages are plotted for comparison.

sured parallel to foliation (E-W) were 1/3 to 1/2 the magnitude of those measured in the perpendicular (N-S) direction.

2.5 Stress Monitoring Discrepancies

A significant objective of the heated block test was to investigate the performance of several stress gages in a known (applied) stress field, under conditions of cycling stress and temperature. As it turned out, the strongly foliated nature of the granitic gneiss caused considerable discrepancies between applied and measured stress, presumeably due to the extremely large strength and stiffness contrast caused by the quartz lenses. Schmidt hammer rebound values reported by Hardin, et al. (1981) indicated rebounds as high as 96%, which theoretically convert to unconfined compression strengths well in excess of 400 MPa. The strength contrast was certainly evident in the problems experienced in percussive drilling of the slots. Hole alignment was so irregular that the slots eventually had to be diamond cored with overlapping holes, using drill-guides.

Data taken with the USBM three component borehole deformation gage during ambient equal biaxial loading indicated that the applied horizontal N-S and E-W stresses were in a ratio 4:1. This result was incompatible with the known equal stress distribution of 6.9 MPa, and may have been caused by locating the gage in a borehole paralleling a hard quartz lense.

IRAD vibrating wire stressmeters responded to stress changes somewhat differently than they did during laboratory calibration in a 157 mm (6.0 inches) core of gneiss taken from the block. Although installed in the block with special attention given to alignment, the N-S gage perpendicular to foliation was roughly 300% more sensitive than the laboratory calibration, and the E-W gage showed only a 20% sensitivity to the known applied stresses of 6.9 MPa. This is equivalent to the core used for calibration being stiffer, in the N-S direction, than the block in the vicinity of the stress meters. This difference indicates that the foliation and quartz lenses in the block were not satisfactorily represented by the core. A more detailed knowledge of the inhomogeneity of the deformation modulus within this foliated lenticular body of rock would be required for improved results to be obtained from these gages.

2.6 Joint Permeability

The location of the joint permeability test is indicated in Figure 1. The rough mineralized joint was first flow tested before the flatjack slots were drilled, then after drilling, and finally during successive stages of loading and unloading. The results of one of the ambient tests are shown in Figure 9. In this test, flat-jack loading was equal and biaxial, and the joint was therefore under the influence of pure normal stress, with no shear component at this stage. A result which was common to previous ambient temperature block tests, was the difficulty of closing the natural joint beyond some limiting aperture. In this case it appeared that the conducting aperture of 30 microns could not easily be reduced by

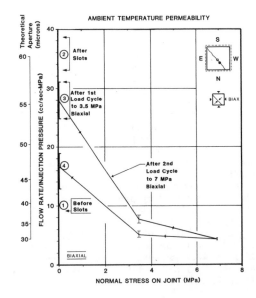

Fig. 9 Effect of normal stress on the flowrate and on the theoretical smooth wall aperture (e).

the influence of stress alone. This theoretical smooth wall aperture is derived from the well known "cubic" flow law for parallel plates:

$$q = \frac{de^3}{12\mu} \cdot \frac{dP}{dy} \qquad (4)$$

where: $\frac{dP}{dy}$ = pressure gradient

μ = absolute viscosity (1.2×10^{-5} gm.sec/cm^2 at 12°C)

d = width of flow path

q = flow rate

A second ambient biaxial test (points 9, 10 and 11 in Figure 10) showed a similar minimum aperture of 30 μm at a maximum normal stress of 6.9 MPa. However, when the block temperature was raised to 55°C following 22 days heating at 500 watts/heater, and to 74°C following a further 13 days at 700 watts/heater, the conducting aperture was found to reduce considerably, despite controlled boundary stresses.

In summary, the test joint exhibited a four-fold reduction in permeability when loaded from 0 to 6.9 MPa under ambient conditions, and a thirty-fold reduction when temperature was also increased to 74°C. Increased temperature alone, with no change in the normal stress, reduced permeability ten-fold.

This remarkable reduction of flow aperture is interpreted as improved mating of the opposed joint walls. The diagonal joints are quite rough, and they were undoubtedly formed at elevated temperature, though how high is uncertain. A roughness profile of a joint measured at ambient temperature will not exactly match a profile measured while the joint is at elevated temperature, due to anisotropic thermal expansion. Elevated temperature and pressure partially recreate formation conditions.

The improved mating of the asperities is almost maintained by pressure alone during cooling, probably due to the high shear strength of the tightly mated walls. Significant lack of fit was not reestablished until the aperture rebounded from 16.1 to 42.2 μm, which occurred somewhere between 3.45 MPa and 0 MPa (points 20 and 21 in Figure 10).

2.7 Shear Displacement Constraints

Two of the ambient temperature tests involved uniaxial loading, which was achieved by activating the N-S flat-jacks and E-W flat-jacks separately. Figure 11 indicates that the N-S loading develops clockwise shear along the diagonal test joint, and shear reversal when activating the E-W flat-jacks.

Careful shear strength estimates which are described later, indicated that the maximum applied shear and normal stress components would be sufficient to shear the joint in the absence of the stiff intact base of the block. A specific limitation of the flat-jack-loaded in situ block test is indicated by the small magnitudes of shear displacement and the artificially high shear stiffness. Only 0.25 mm of shear displacement was recorded, and reversal through the origin did not occur.

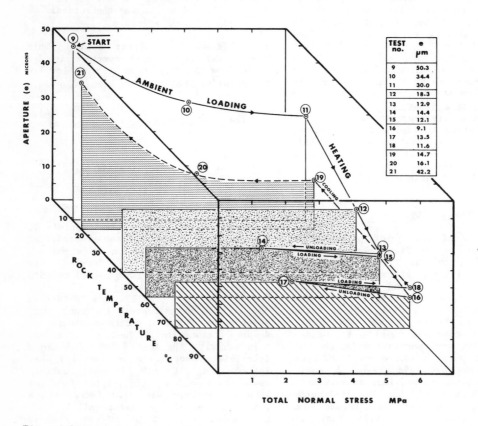

Fig. 10 Biaxial loading at elevated temperatures facilitates hydrothermomechanical coupling, causing dramatic reductions in flow aperture.

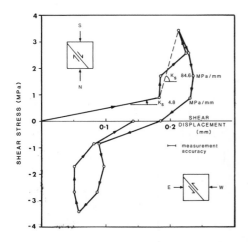

Fig. 11 Shear displacement and reversal
measured along the diagonal, permeability test joint, during the
N-S and E-W uniaxial tests that
were conducted at ambient temperature.

Despite the limited shear displacements,
there was an indication of "aperture
strain", and the beginnings of dilation,
as seen in the flowrate-stress data shown
in Figure 12. Once again conducting apertures were only reduced to marginally less
than 30 μm. The reduced aperture achieved
during the E-W test is probably a function
of slightly improved joint "seating"
caused by asperity damage during the
reversal.

A significant finding from these tests
was the lack of equality between measured
changes of joint aperture and calculated
changes of flow aperture. The former
always exceeded the latter by a factor of
2 to 7. This effect is presumeably due to
roughness and tortuosity, and is consistent with other data reported in the
literature (Barton, 1981).

2.8 Laboratory Cube Test

Limited shear displacements are difficult
to avoid in an in situ block test, unless
extreme measures are taken to "disconnect"
the block from the underlying rock mass,
using wire sawing or hydraulic fracturing

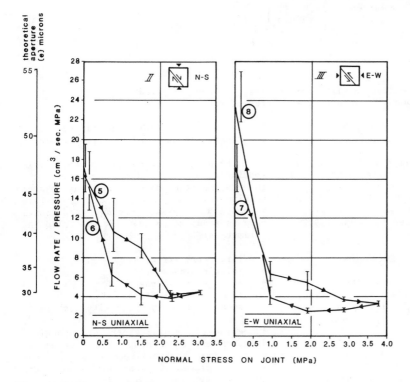

Fig. 12 Effect of proportional shear and normal stress on flow rate and theoretical smooth wall aperture, under ambient temperature.

11

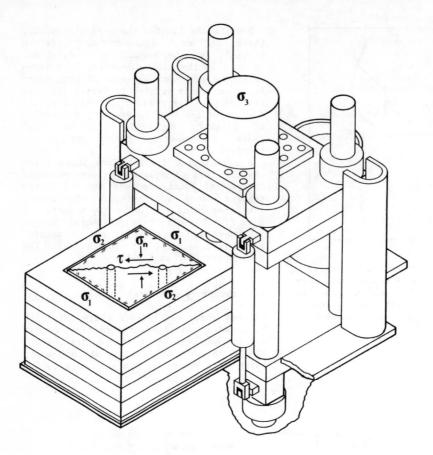

Fig. 13 Laboratory cube test facility for investigating hydrothermomechanical
coupling phenomena in jointed 1 m^3 blocks of rock.

of the base. Terra Tek's 1 m^3 cube machine depicted in Figure 13 is not subject to these shear displacement limitations and is capable of applying elevated temperature, polyaxial loading up to 35 MPa (5000 psi). Sample acquisition is facilitated by pre-bolting the joint to be tested, and wire sawing the sample using the five-side release method described by Londe (1972).

3 SHEAR STRENGTH CHARACTERIZATION

The heated block test described in the preceding pages provides quite reliable characterization of the following stress and temperature dependent parameters on a large scale:

1. intact and jointed rock modulus
2. joint normal stiffness
3. joint permeability and conducting aperture
4. coefficient of thermal expansion

5. thermal conductivity and diffusivity
6. dynamic Young's modulus (cross-hole)

With the possible exception of the dynamic modulus each of the above parameters represents important direct input for comprehensive modeling of near-field repository response to thermal loading. Additional data is required to quantify the following parameters:

7. joint wall strength
8. joint roughness
9. joint shear strength
10. joint shear stiffness
11. shear-dilation-permeability coupling

Tunneling and mining experience, physical joint models and numerical models demonstrate the possibility of significant shear displacement along joints that are exposed by excavation in anisotropic stress regimes. The potential migration of groundwater across a repository will be

strongly influenced by the zones of reduced permeability caused by joint closure, and by the zones of increased permeability caused by shear displacements.
Data is required so that a coupled model
of thermal-mechanical-hydraulic behavior
can be formulated and quantified.

3.1 Quantitative Joint Characterization

A simple, though quite complete method of
characterizing the shear behavior of rock
joints has been developed in recent years.
It consists of three components: ϕ_b, JRC
and JCS. A basic or residual friction
angle (ϕ_b or ϕ_r) for flat non-dilatent
surfaces in fresh or weathered rock,
respectively, forms the limiting value of
shear strength. To this is added a roughness component (i). This is normal stress
dependent and varies with the magnitude of
the joint wall compressive strength (JCS),
and with the joint roughness coefficient
(JRC). The latter varies from about 0 to
20 for smooth to very rough surfaces
respectively. The peak drained angle of
friction (ϕ') at any given effective normal stress (σ'_n) is expressed as follows:

$$\phi' = \phi_r + i = JRC \log(JCS/\sigma'_n) + \phi_r \quad (5)$$

Example

$\phi_r = 25°$, JRC = 10, JCS = 100 MPa,

$\sigma'_n = 1$ MPa

equation 5 gives $\phi' = 45°$

The compression strength of the joint
walls (JCS) has increased influence on the
shear strength as the joint roughness increases. Values of JCS and its variation
with weathering are measured with the
Schmidt (L) hammer. Experimental details
are given by Barton and Choubey (1977).
The residual friction angle (ϕ_r) of
weathered joints is very difficult to
determine experimentally due to the large
displacements required, particularly if
only small joint samples are available. A
simple empirical approach has been developed as shown below.

$$\phi_r = (\phi_b - 20) + 20 \, r_1/r_2 \quad (6)$$

where:

ϕ_b = basic (minimum) friction angle of
flat unweathered rock surfaces
(obtained from tilt tests on sawn
blocks, or from triple core tilt
tests - see Figure 14)

r_1 = Schmidt rebound on saturated, weathered joint walls

r_2 = Schmidt rebound on dry unweathered
rock surfaces (i.e., saw cuts, fresh
fracture surfaces, etc.)

Example:

$\phi_b = 30°$, $r_1 = 30$, $r_2 = 40$

equation 6 gives: $\phi_r = 25°$

The value of JRC can be back-calculated
directly from a tilt test on jointed core,
as depicted in Figures 14 and 15. The
shear strength equation is rearranged to
give:

$$JRC = \frac{\alpha° - \phi_r}{\log(JCS/\sigma'_{no})} \quad (7)$$

where

$\alpha°$ = tilt angle when sliding occurs ($\alpha°$
= arctan τ/σ'_{no} = ϕ')

σ'_{no} = effective normal stress acting
across joint when sliding occurs

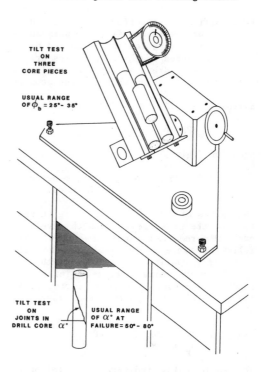

TILT TEST
ON
THREE
CORE PIECES

USUAL RANGE
OF ϕ_b = 25°- 35°

TILT TEST
ON
JOINTS IN
DRILL CORE $\alpha°$

USUAL RANGE
OF $\alpha°$ AT
FAILURE= 50°- 80°

Fig. 14 Tilt tests of axially jointed core
provided estimates of the full-
scale shear strength of joints,
after correction for scale effects.

13

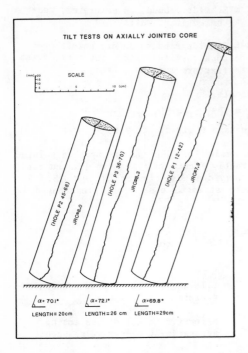

TILT TESTS ON AXIALLY JOINTED CORE

SCALE

Fig. 15 Tilt tests performed on jointed
cores obtained from the permeability test holes in the heated block.
Measured roughness profiles are
shown, drawn at the mean angles of
tilt measured when sliding occurred.

Example: $\alpha = 75°$, $\phi_r = 25°$, JCS = 100

MPa, $\sigma_{no}' = 0.001$ MPa

equation 7 gives:

JRC = $(75° - 25°)/5 = 10$ (i.e., moderately
rough, undulating)

The values of JRC, JCS, and ϕ_r can be used
to generate peak shear strength envelopes
over the required range of stress. The
following table of values shows how the
value of ϕ' varies inversely with the log
of effective normal stress. This is a
fundamental result for rock joints, rock-
fill, gravel, etc. (Barton and Kjaernsli,
1981).

Example: JRC = 10, JCS = 100 MPa,
$\phi_r = 25°$

The table below indicates the following
relation between stress level and friction
angle:

Type of Test	σ_n' MPa	$\phi'*$
Approx. lab tilt test	0.001	75°
Approx. field tilt test	0.01	65°
	0.1	55°
Approx. design loading	1.0	45°
	10.0	35°

*Note: ϕ' varies by JRC degrees (°) for
each ten-fold change in stress, in
this case, 10°.

3.2 Scale Effects

Large-scale shear tests of joints in
quartz diorite (Pratt, et al. 1974) and a
comprehensive series of tests performed by
Bandis (1980) have indicated that larger
shear displacements are required to mobilize peak strength as the length of joint
sample is increased. This means that
larger but less steeply inclined asperities tend to control peak strength as the
length of sample is increased.

Tests by Bandis (1980) indicate that
during a shear test, the block size will
determine both the distribution, number
and size of contact areas. While this
level of detail can obviously not be
modeled numerically, its effect on joint
behavior must be taken into account. The
following possible size-dependent properties have to be considered:

1. shear displacement to mobilize peak
   strength (δ peak)
2. joint roughness coefficient (JRC)
3. joint wall compression strength (JCS)
4. shear stiffness (K_s)
5. dilation during shear (d_n)

A method of estimating (or measuring) the
size-dependency of these parameters is
needed, before a satisfactory constitutive
law of behavior can be developed.

Figure 16 shows schematically but quite
realistically how the shear strength,
stiffness, peak displacement and dilation
are changed by increasing block size, for
the case of non-planar joints. However,
there is strong evidence to suggest that
these scale effects do not extend beyond
the natural block size in a jointed rock
mass (Bandis, et al. 1981). Large scale
tilt and pull tests on natural blocks as
depicted in Figure 17 are therefore recommended for obtaining scale free values of
the joint roughness coefficient (JRC).

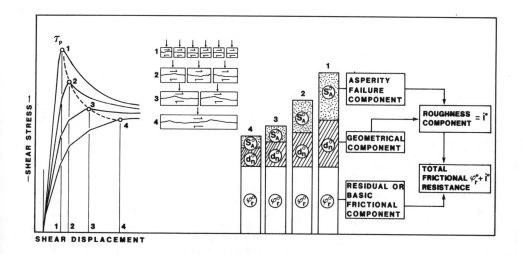

Fig. 16 Size dependence of shear strength components, after Bandis, et al. 1981.

TILT TEST   **PULL TEST**

Fig. 17 Self-weight tilt and pull tests are used to quantify the joint roughness
component of shear strength at full-scale.

3.3 Strength-Displacement-Size Coupling

Frequently it will not be possible to extract or test natural scale blocks, and smaller scale tests such as tilt tests on jointed core or shear box tests have to be relied upon. Recent work reported by Bandis, et al. (1981) and Barton (1981) has provided a method for predicting how the values of JCS and JRC obtained from small scale tests reduce with increasing block size. Numerous shear box tests indicate that the values of these parameters reduce most strongly in the case of rough undulating joints having high values of JRC on a laboratory scale. Values of δ(peak) are found to increase with in-

15

creasing block size, the increase being most marked for the case of rough joints.

The table inset in Figure 18 gives examples of the quantitative changes of JRC, JCS and δ(peak) that occur with increasing block size, for a rough joint that exhibits a JRC value of 15 on a laboratory size (10 cm long) sample. Scale dependent values such as these are used to generate complete stress-displacement and dilation-displacement curves for any given block size. Validations with experimental data indicate an excellent degree of fit (Barton, 1981).

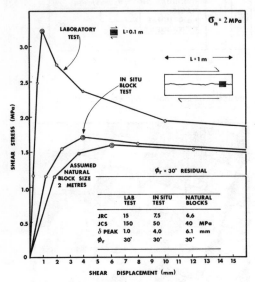

Fig. 18 A constitutive model relating stress, displacement, dilation and block size has recently been developed (Barton, 1981).

3.4 Permeability-Displacement Coupling

Normal stress and shear stress perturbations may cause changes in the undisturbed aperture of a joint, which would be superimposed on the initial aperture and cause corresponding changes in permeability. The undisturbed conducting aperture may be estimated from carefully controlled borehole pump-in tests, using accurately located, closely spaced packers, or using the statistical method proposed by Snow (1968). This method provides estimates of the mean theoretical smooth wall conducting aperture (e) (equation 4) and estimates of the mean spacing (S) of water conducting joints, assuming the rock mass

can be idealized as a cubic network of water conducting joints.

In the case of the heated block test described earlier, the value of (e) and its variation with normal stress and temperature can be studied directly. The problem lies in generating similar data at the bottom of a 1000 meter deep borehole, and including the coupling between shear displacement and permeability. This data will usually be required before access is made available for actually extracting blocks, for tests such as depicted in Figure 13.

Recent constitutive modeling and experimental data indicates that the parameters JRC and JCS determine the magnitudes of both normal closure and the dilation induced by shear. In the case of normal closure, laboratory scale values of JRC and JCS determine behavior, as shown by Bandis (1980) and Barton (1981). Only when shearing occurs do the lower, size-dependent values of JRC and JCS dominate behavior.

Comparison of the predicted aperture and permeability reductions with measurements obtained in the heated block experiment show good agreement. However, the limited shear displacement (0.25 mm) achieved in the heated block test was insufficient to test the predictive capabilities of the JRC-JCS shear-flow model. The only coupled shear-flow data known to the authors is Maini's data, which was reported by Maini and Hocking (1977).

This test was performed under extremely low normal stress, generated by the self-weight of a block of slate of 160 cm² area. The joint was a planar cleavage parting. The flow rate was monitored as shear displacement was increased in steps to about 6 mm. The initial conducting aperture was found to increase significantly, resulting in two orders of magnitude increase in permeability. This experimental result and our prediction are compared in Figures 19 and 20. The method shows promising agreement. Closeness of fit could possibly have been improved if Schmidt hammer and tilt tests had been performed. The values of JRC and JCS shown in Figure 19 are best estimates only, representing realistic values for smooth, almost planar cleavage surfaces in a moderate strength slate.

4 CONCLUSIONS

1. Heated in situ tests of jointed rock using flat-jacks to load several m³ of rock can provide the majority of the

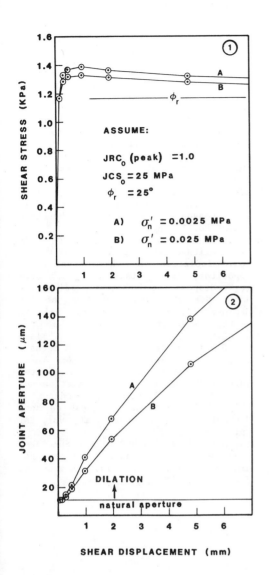

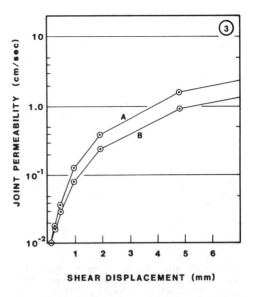

Fig. 19 An example of stress-displacement
and dilation-displacement modeling
(graphs 1 and 2).

Fig. 20 Comparison of permeability-dis-
placement modeling (graph 3) with
the results of a coupled flow-
shear test reported by Maini and
Hocking (1977).

hydrothermomechanical input data needed
for rock mass characterization of potential nuclear waste repositories.

2. The potentially low stiffness and high
permeability of joints under conditions
of shear can be measured in a large cube
testing machine capable of applying
polyaxial mechanical loading, and thermal loading to jointed blocks of up to 1
m^3 volume. Access to the repository
horizon, or to an equivalent rock mass,
is assumed in both the above block
tests.

3. Useful data can also be obtained prior
to site access, using jointed pieces of
drill core. Tilt tests and Schmidt
hammer tests to quantify the roughness
(JRC) and wall strength (JCS) of the
joints can provide the necessary data
for preliminary constitutive modeling.
These parameters determine the magnitudes of joint deformability and shear
strength, and the critically important
coupling between permeability, normal
closure, shear, dilation and size
effects.

17

5 ACKNOWLEDGEMENTS

Funding for the heated block test and for the constitutive joint modeling was provided by the Office of Nuclear Waste Isolation. This support is gratefully acknowledged. Ernie Hardin, Mark Board and Mike Voegele were major contributors to the success of the heated block test.

6 REFERENCES

Bandis, S., 1980. "Experimental Studies of Scale Effects on Shear Strength, and Deformation of Rock Joints," Ph.D. Thesis, University of Leeds, Dept of Earth Sciences.

Bandis, S., A.C. Lumsden and N. Barton, 1981. "Experimental Studies of Scale Effects on the Shear Behavior of Rock Joints," Int. J. Rock Mech. Min. Sci. and Geomech. Abstr., Vol. 18, pp. 1-21.

Barton, N. and V. Choubey, 1977. "The Shear Strength of Rock Joints in Theory and Practice," Rock Mechanics, Vol. 10, pp. 1-54.

Barton, N. and B. Kjaernsli, 1981. "Shear Strength of Rockfill," Journal of the Geotechnical Engineering Division, American Society of Civil Engineers, Vol. 107, No. GT7, Proc. Paper 16374, July, pp. 873-891.

Barton, N., 1981, "Modeling Rock Joint Behavior From In Situ Block Tests: Implications for Nuclear Waste Repository Design," Office of Nuclear Waste Isolation, Columbus, Ohio, 96 p.

Chan, T., M. Hood and M. Board, 1980. "Rock Properties and Their Effect on Thermally Induced Displacements and Stress," Proc. American Society of Mechanical Engineers, Energy Sources Technology Conf., New Orleans.

Hardin, E.L., N. Barton, R. Lingle, M.P. Board and M.D. Voegele, 1981. "A Heated Flatjack Test Series to Measure the Thermomechanical and Transport Properties of In Situ Rock Masses," Office of Nuclear Waste Isolation, Columbus, Ohio, 193 p.

Londe, P., 1972. "The Mechanics of Rock Slopes and Foundations," Imperial College London, Rock Mechanics Research Report No. 17, April 1972, 89 p.

Maini, T. and G. Hocking, 1977. "An Examination of the Feasibility of Hydrologic Isolation of a High Level Waste Repository in Crystalline Rock," Geologic Disposal of High-Level Radioactive Waste Session, Annual Meeting of the Geological Society of America, held in Seattle, Washington.

Poulos, H.G. and E.H. Davis, 1973. "Elastic Solutions for Soil and Rock Mechanics," John Wiley and Sons, New York.

Pratt, H.R., A.D. Black and W.F. Brace, 1974. "Friction and Deformation of Jointed Quartz Diorite," Proceedings of the 3rd International Congress on Rock Mechanics, held in Denver, CO, Vol. 2A, pp. 306-310.

Snow, D.T., 1968. "Rock Fracture Spacings, Openings, and Porosities," Proceedings, American Society of Civil Engineers, Vol. 96, No. SM 1, pp. 73-91.

A GEOTECHNICAL INVESTIGATION METHODOLOGY FOR CAVERNS IN ROCK
Eine Methode für die geotechnische Untersuchung von Kavernen in Fels
Une méthodologie pour l'étude géotechnique des cavernes dans les roches

ANTÓNIO P.CUNHA
Laboratorio Nacional de Engenharia Civil (LNEC), Lisbon, Portugal

SUMMARY:
In the submitted paper, some of the most recent results of rock mass investigations carried out by LNEC are summarized, involving the evaluation of the initial state of stress and the deformability and resistance characteristics of rock masses. Statistical analysis of joint behaviour and scale effects connected to in situ deformability tests are also mentioned. Finally, a proposal of methodology for caverns in rock, mainly based on the use of LNEC test techniques, is expounded by the author.

ZUSAMMENFASSUNG:
In dem eingereichten Referat werden einige der jüngsten Ergebnisse von Felsuntersuchungen zusammengefasst, die durch das LNEC durchgeführt wurden und die Abschätzung des ursprünglichen Spannungszustandes und der Verformungs- und Festigkeitseigenschaften von Felsen betreffen. Statistische Kluftverhaltensanalysen und mit den In-Situ-Verformbarkeitsversuchen verbundene Skaleneffekte werden auch erwähnt. Schliesslich wird eine Untersuchungsmethodologie für Kavernen in Felsen, die hauptsächlich auf der Benutzung von LNEC-Versuchsverfahren fusst, vom Verfasser vorgeschlagen und im einzelnen dargestellt.

RESUME:
Des résultats récents de recherches conduites au LNEC sur la déformabilité, la résistance des massifs rocheux et l'état de contrainte sont présentés dans cet article, en même temps qu'une méthodologie pour l'étude géotechnique des cavernes rocheuses, fondée essentiellement sur l'emploi des techniques développées au LNEC est proposée par l'auteur.

1 INTRODUCTION

Concerning the geotechnical study of rock masses for caverns, a commendable rule should be the testing of every zone of the surrounding rock mass, the mechanical characteristics of which one should expect to have some kind of influence on the behaviour of the underground structure to be designed.

However, the technological and economical limitations of the in situ and laboratory testing techniques generally prevent a sufficiently detailed mechanical investigation and recommend a criterious employment of the available resources, in order to get the maximum of results with a minimum of investment.

The heterogeneity and anisotropy of the rock, as well as the scattering of the geometric and mechanical characteristics of the discontinuities give the rock masses a complex mechanical behaviour, the analysis of which requires the use of simplified models. It should always be borne in mind that mechanical parameters to be determined are strictly connected with morphological and structural characteristics of the rock mass and consequently, with the model of analysis to be used in design.

As far as underground structures are concerned, models reproducing the rock mass as a continuous medium and models allowing individualized representation of discontinuities have been used. In this case, due to practical reasons, only the individual simulation of the most important discontinuities, namely the principal joint sets and faults, is possible, the rock mass between these discontinuities being represented as a continuous, isotropic or anisotropic medium. Therefore, the study of the

surrounding rock mass for the design of ca
verns requires the difinition of the geotechnically relevant discontinuities and
their geometrical and mechanical proper -
ties, and the definition of the properties
of the continuous medium equivalent to the
rock mass comprised within these discontinuities. Rock properties, usually determin
ed in the laboratory, constitute the upper
most limit of such medium.

The definition of the mechanical behaviour of this equivalent continuous medium
has to be made by means of in situ tests,
on representative samples of the rock mass,
that is, on volumes which, owing to their
size, include rock and discontinuities in
such proportions as to reproduce the mutu
al mean influence of these two components
in the test zone. As to the mechanical cha
racterization of the discontinuities, it
may be carried out, mainly by means of la
boratory and in situ shear tests,which, al
though similar, differ in the size of the
test samples and, therefore, in the representativeness of their results.

2 GEOMETRICAL AND MECHANICAL PROPERTIES OF ROCK MASSES

In the following lines,some recent results
of rock mechanics investigations carried
out in LNEC are summarized, involving the
geometrical description and the evaluation
of the initial state of stress, deformability and resistance of rock masses.

2.1 Geometrical properties of rock masses

Rock mass loosening around underground
works is in many cases essentially governed by the sliding, along pre-existing or
blast— induced joints, of blocks which the
excavation allows to move under the action
both of their weight and the forces transmitted by adjacent blocks.The behaviour of
the opening thus depends on the geometri -
cal characteristics of the discontinuities,
particularly on their orientation,spacing,
aperture, persistence, roughness and fillings.

The definition of joint sets is based on
the statistical analysis of the   fracture
orientations (Grossmann 1977), obtained,at
the LNEC, chiefly by means of the integral
sampling method. Jointing density diagrams
such as that of fig 1a (Cunha 1980) are ob
tained, by using a stereographic projection and a counting unit, the area of which
has been modified at grid counting points
with the probability of intersection   of
discontinuities with a given orientation
by the borehole. Fig. 1b shows the corresponding stereographic pole diagram where,
for each joint set and admitting a normal
bivariated distribution of the projections
of the respective poles on the plane tangent to the auxiliary sphere, at the point
that corresponds to the mean attitude of
the set, were drawn the ellipses of probability (N-1)/N (N - number of fractures of
each joint set) that should contain 100 x
x (N-1)/N % of the poles belonging to the

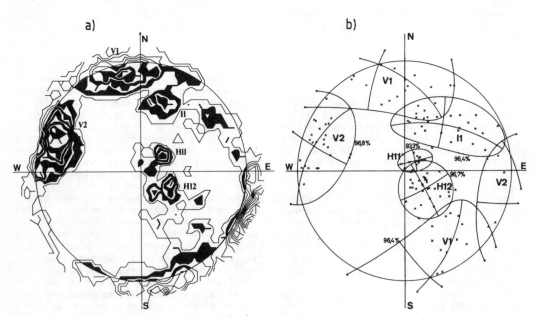

Fig. 1 Definition of the rock mass jointing system

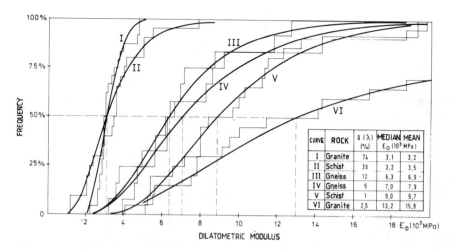

CURVE	ROCK	Q (λ) (%)	MEDIAN E_D (10³ MPa)	MEAN (10³ MPa)
I	Granite	74	3,1	3,2
II	Schist	39	3,2	3,5
III	Gneiss	12	6,3	6,9
IV	Gneiss	5	7,0	7,9
V	Schist	1	9,0	9,7
VI	Granite	2,5	13,2	15,8

Fig. 2 Experimental and most probable log-normal cummulative curves of dilatometric moduli

same joint set.

Concerning the distribution of joint spacings, its statistical analysis has been performed at LNEC, through the drawing of spacing cummulative curves and the use of tests to assess the adaptability of certain theoretical distributions to their representation. The results obtained (Grossmann 1977, Cunha 1980) show a good adjustment of log-normal and negative exponential distributions to the statistical description of spacing in rock masses. As regards the aperture of joint sets, analyses of similar type show that they are well represented by log-normal distributions.

2.2 Mechanical properties of rock masses

The in situ characterization of the deformability of rock masses has been made at LNEC chiefly by dilatometer (BHD) tests in boreholes, and conventional jack load tests and large flat jack (LFJ) tests in galleries. The values of the dilatometric moduli at a given site usually fit log-normal distributions rather closely, as shown in fig. 2, where results regarding different kinds of rock and various places are given (Cunha 1980). It should be noted that the dilatometric modulus with a 50% probability of being exceeded (median) is, for this distribution, lower than the average.

Conventional hydraulic jack tests inside galleries are now hardly ever used, replaced by the large flat jack tests, because of the advantages of the diamond disc slot opening process, which does not disturb the rock significantly, and because of the possibility of involving larger volumes in the tests, thereby increasing their representativeness.

Dilatometric moduli, considering the small volumes affected by the tests, the influence of fractures existing in the neighbourhood of the borehole and the effect of the tangential developed stresses are regarded more as deformability index, allowing the zoning of the rock mass, than as real elasticity moduli. The results of LNEC correlations of dilatometer tests with LFJ tests, which have a merely local meaning are shown in fig. 3 (Cunha 1980). Such correlations make it possible to ascertain the deformability moduli for zones of the rock mass where only dilatometer tests, which are much quicker and cheaper, have

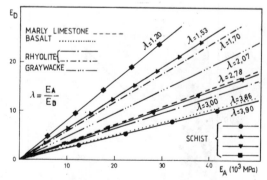

Fig. 3 Correlation between dilatometric and LFJ moduli

been carried out. The figure shows that dilatometric moduli E_D are as a rule lower than deformability moduli E_A obtained with LFJ, as it should be expected, owing to the

above referred factors which affect dilato
meter tests.

Concerning the mechanical behaviour of
discontinuities, fig. 4 shows and compares
the values obtained for the normal (K_N)
and tangential (K_T) stiffness of 45 discon
tinuities (Cunha 1980), where the relation
K_N/K_T stands between one and thirteen. The
absolute values of K_N are within the range
25-810 kg/cm^3 and those of K_T in the inter
val 6-188 kg/cm^3. The site was a heterogeneous rock mass, where tested discontinuities corresponded to low strength surfaces,
joints and contacts between formations,
showing different infillings and roughnes-
ses, which account for the marked scattering of the obtained values.

The adopted values of K_N are secant values corresponding to the constant normal
stress of the shear test. For the defini -
tion of K_T a criterion of area compensa -
tion between the experimental diagrams and
the bi-linear or tri-linear models which,
according to the type of $\tau - \delta_T$ diagrams,
approximate the experimental curves, was
choosen. This procedure leads to adopting
diagrams equivalent to the real ones, from
the point of view of the energy involved
in tests. Note that the information avail
able on these matters is not only scarce
but also omits the criteria adopted for

the definition of K_T and K_N, and that different criteria may determine appreciable
differences in the calculated values. An
effort should be made to uniformize criteria in this field.

At another site, in a schistous rock mass,
a study was carried out about the jointing
system, which made it possible to define three main joint sets, approximately
perpendicular to one another, designated
by H (sub-horizontal), V (sub-vertical) and
X (coincident with the schistosity, also
sub-vertical). Forty four joints were submitted to laboratory or in situ shear
tests and the distribution of the K_T values for the first slidings was studied
for each set. Fig. 5 shows the corresponding cumulative curves and the most proba -
ble log-normal distribution for each case.
The figure, where the mean and median values are presented, shows the good agree -
ment of log-normal distribution to the des
cription of the tangential stiffness va -
lues of the different joint sets, all of
them showing the same order of K_T values.
Concerning their strength characteristics,
all sets also show rather similar values
for cohesion and friction angle. The mean
peak values of C correspond to 1.4 MPa,
1.5 MPa and 1.1 MPa and those of φ to 38°,
39° and 35°, for joint sets H, V and X,
respectively.

2.3 Initial state of stress

It is well known that the state of stress
in rock masses, pre-existent to the excava
tion, is a fundamental parameter for the
behaviour of underground structures. The
discontinuous, anisotropic and heterogeneous morphology of rock masses, and the
lack of knowledge about their geologic his
tory, make it generally impossible to evaluate the initial state of stress by any
means other than in situ measurements.

The principal methods for determining
the state of stress in rock masses are based on the release of the stresses that
are going to be measured by the opening of
slots or overcoring. The former have the
advantage of not requiring the knowledge
of the deformability characteristics of
the rock mass, since they carry out the di
rect measurement of the stresses, but they
involve the execution of major accesses to
the rock mass (shafts and galleries). Over
coring methods, on the other hand, are ap
plicable in boreholes but, as they are bas
ed on the measurement of deformations for
the determination of stresses, the mechanical characteristics of the rock must be
known which, together with the small volu-

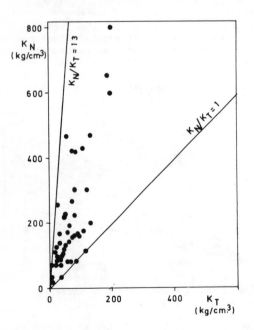

Fig. 4 Correlation between normal and tangential stiffness

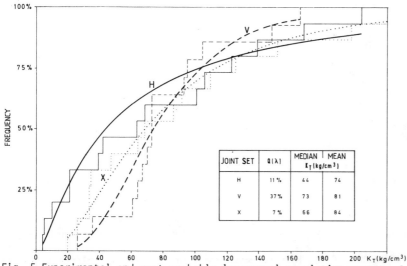

FREQUENCY

100%
75%
50%
25%

JOINT SET	Q(λ)	MEDIAN K_T (kg/cm³)	MEAN K_T (kg/cm³)
H	11%	44	74
V	37%	73	81
X	7%	66	84

0 20 40 60 80 100 120 140 160 180 200 K_T(kg/cm³)

Fig. 5 Experimental and most probable log-normal cumulative curves of K_T

mes involved, constitutes their chief draw back.

Concerning the technology developed by LNEC, with the small flat jack method(SFJ) stresses applied by flat jacks are used to cancel the deformations due to slot cutting. A minimum of three slots must be used to determine the state of stress in the plane normal to the slots at the measuring point. By repeating this procedure in two more planes with a distinct orientation, it becomes possible to make a complete determination of the state of stress at the testing site. As this state of stress does not correspond to the initial one but rather to the state of stress after excavation, expressions for the evaluation of the the most probable components of the initial stress tensor using circular,square and elliptic section galleries, which correspond to current situations in practice,were developed (Pinto and Graça 1979). Another LNEC technique, based on an over-coring process is the stress tensor tube (STT) which, by using a single borehole (fig. 6), allows the thourough determination of the state of stress at the measuring point. It consists essentially of a plastic cylinder provided with three electric strain gauge rosettes cemented onto the walls of a narrow installing borehole. The strains corresponding to overcoring are converted into stresses by convenient analytical expressions. Fig. 7 sums up the results obtained by LNEC concerning stress determination using the above described techniques. The variation of the vertical stress σ_V is represented with the mean ho-

rizontal stress σ_H and with the depth H. The left diagram show relations σ_V/σ_H to be frequent at interval 0.25-4, including hydrostatic state. The right diagram shows that the weight of overburden is not always a good estimator of σ_V, higher and lower values beeing common, possibly due to either the Poisson's effect connected with tectonic actions or erosive processes which act in opposite senses. The scattering of the results, clearly indicates the need of in situ stress determinations and point out reasonable enveloping situations for the σ_V/σ_H and σ_V/H ratios which can be used in design.

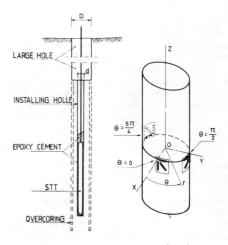

Fig. 6 Stress tensor tube (STT)

23

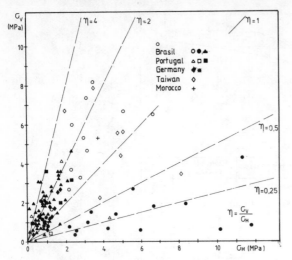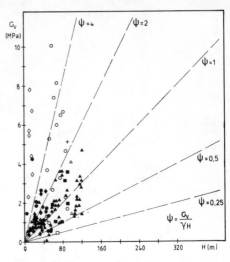

Fig. 7 Computation of results of the in situ measurement of the state of stress

3 INVESTIGATION METHODOLOGY FOR CAVERNS IN ROCK

The optimization of geotechnical studies of rock masses for caverns necessarily im- plies, given the limits imposed by depth to the in situ techniques, that advantage should be taken of every access to the in- terior of the rock mass (boreholes, explo- ration galleries and shafts and even cons- truction accesses), using for each kind of access as many investigation techniques as are compatible with its dimensions.

The establishment of statistical correla tions between large and small volume in si tu testing results and between such tests and laboratory ones, is also a suitable me thod of reducing investigation investment with a minor compromise of the information level required by design.

In the following lines is outlined a rock mechanics investigation methodology for caverns in rock, mainly based on the use of LNEC testing techniques and on the conceptions expounded above. Geotechnical studies for caverns necessarily imply a suf ficiently detailled description of litholo gical, structural and hydrogeological fea- tures of the zone where the underground construction is foreseen. Reconnaissance, geophysical and mechanical exploration are available tools for obtaining a comprehen- sive geological zoning of the surrounding rock mass.

Concerning the definition of the geotech nical parameters for the design, we can use, in the same borehole, conventional ro tative drilling and, for economical reasons, in the neighbourhood of the future excava-

tion, just in the lenght of some diameters in the vicinity of the cavern, the integral sampling method, which provides the comple te and oriented sampling of the rock mass and the study of the geometrical features of joints, namely orientation and spacing. The same borehole will allow dilatometer tests, which make use of 76 mm diameter, suitable for integral sampling. Moreover, the cores extracted between successive in- tegral samples or by conventional boring may be submitted to laboratory tests for determination of deformability and stren - ght properties of the rock and fractures, allowing the establishment of empiric cor- relations between the laboratory and in si tu measured values. The same borehole can also be used to carry out seismic tests.It has recently been found (Rodrigues 1979) a good correlation between the elasticity moduli of the rock masses, determined with LFJ and the shear wave frequency and also between the dynamic modulus and the dilato metric modulus, in the same borehole.

It should be noted that LNEC has been us ing boreholes for the determination of the initial state of stress by the STT method. As for technical reasons it is only possi- ble to use the STT with boreholes larger than those needed by the dilatometer, the initial state of stress may be determined either in other boreholes with suitable diameters or in the same borehole, above the zone of the dilatometer tests,so as to allow the required reduction in diameter. In this case the STT should be aimed at es tablishing, by means of tests carried out at different points, a law of variation, with depth, of the initial state of stress,

24

that may be extrapolated to the zone of the future construction.

As regards the depth of the caverns, it will be easier to make a more thorough investigation for those within the reach of surface testing techniques than for deeper caverns, in which case two alternative courses, of decreasing accuracy, are pos - sible.

a. the opening of direct accesses to the cavern, for exploration or construction purposes, and the application, from there, of all methods that may be used in galle - ries, or from the surface. Such accesses can thus be used to determine in the ca - vern site the initial state of stress (SFJ or STT), to characterize the strength pro perties of rock and joints by means of in situ shear tests and to determine the de- formability (LFJ or BHD tests).

b. the carrying out of an exploration and testing programme in the overlying rock mass, starting at the surface and working down to depths acceptable from the economic and technologic point of view, and then extrapolating the results to the depths at which the envisaged underground work is to be located.

The importance of these structures and the safety requirements generally involved, in most cases largely justify the adoption of the former alternative.

In any case, the geotechnical study of caverns should always be regarded as an iterative process, in which the gathering of geologic and geotechnical data may very often reveal the need of carrying out fur- ther, more detailed studies, in order to obtain a reasonable knowledge of the condi tions that will affect the envisaged work.

4 ACKNOWLEDGEMENTS

This paper contains a methodology of geo - technical investigation and some geotechni cal data, which were included in a thesis initiated under the supervision of Prof. Rocha and submitted at LNEC a short time before his death. It is now presented in tri bute to the memory of this prominent scien tist.

5 REFERENCES

Cunha, A.P. 1980, Aplicação de modelos ma- temáticos ao estudo de túneis em maci - ços rochosos (Mathematical modelling of rock tunnels), Research Officer Thesis. Lisbon, LNEC.

Grossman, N.F. 1977, Contribuição para o estudo da compartimentação dos maciços rochosos (Contribution to the study of jointing in rock masses), Research Offi- cer Thesis. Lisbon, LNEC.

Pinto, J.L., Graça, J.C. 1979, Determina - ção do estado de tensão dos maciços ro- chosos por meio de macacos planos de pe- quena área (Evaluation of the state of stress in rock masses by the small flat jack system), Geotecnia 27 : 75-94.

Rocha, M. 1976, Estruturas Subterrâneas (Underground structures). Lisbon, LNEC.

Rodrigues, L.F. 1979, Métodos de prospec- ção sísmica em geologia de engenharia — — a importância da onda de corte (The importance of shear wave in engineering geology), Research Officer Thesis. Lis- bon, LNEC.

LANGZEIT-KRAFTMESSUNGEN AN VORGESPANNTEN FELSANKERN
Long term load measurements on prestressed rock anchors
Mesures des forces à long terme dans les boulons d'ancrage

H.DIETRICH
Losinger AG, Bern, Schweiz

SUMMARY:
The force of a selected number of permanent rock anchors must be continuously monitored. This is required by various standards. Six structures are described and the measured figures graphicly represented. The results are interpreted from the anchor manufacturer's point of view. The results of all measuring anchors checked essentially corresponded to the expected values.

ZUSAMMENFASSUNG:
Die Vorspannkraft einer Auswahl von permanenten Ankern muss dauernd überwacht werden. Dies verlangen verschiedene Normen. 6 Bauwerke werden beschrieben und die Messwerte grafisch dargestellt. Die Resultate werden aus der Sicht des Ankerherstellers interpretiert. Die Resultate aller untersuchten Messanker entsprachen im wesentlichen den Erwartungen.

RESUME:
Les normes de différents pays requièrent un contrôle permanent de la force effective d'un certain nombre de tirants d'ancrages assurant une structure. Cet exposé présente les mesures effectuées sur 6 chantiers différents. Les résultats y sont interprêtés selon les critères du fournisseur des tirants et répondaient aux exigences posées par le cahier des charges.

1 EINFUEHRUNG

Vorgespannte Anker in bedeutenden Bauwerken werden heute dauernd überwacht. Dies verlangt z.B. die schweizerische Norm SIA 191 sowie die DIN Norm 4125.

Die wichtigste Messgrösse ist die Ankerkraft. Sie wird an einer Auswahl von Ankern, welche mit Kraftmessdosen versehen sind, periodisch abgelesen.

Diese sogenannten Messanker sind in der Regel Freispielanker, d.h. ohne Verbund über der Spannstrecke.

Gleichzeitig mit der Kraftmessung ist es zweckmässig, noch Verformungs- und Bewegungsmessungen am gesamten Bauwerk vorzunehmen. Dies kann mit Extensometern oder mit geodaetischen Mitteln erfolgen.

Ich will mich in diesem Vortrag auf das Langzeitverhalten der Ankerkräfte beschränken.

Wir sind Unternehmer und stellen Anker her. Ich möchte deshalb aus der Sicht des Unternehmers die Resultate betrachten.

2 HAUPTANFORDERUNGEN UND SOLLVERHALTEN VON DAUERANKER

Die wesentlichen Anforderungen an vorgespannte Anker sind:
- Sichere Verankerung der Spannstähle im Boden sowie im Spannanker.
- Umfassender, dauernder Korrosionsschutz.
- Exakte initiale Vorspannung.

Diese Anker werden nun auf ihren Lebensweg geschickt. Bezüglich der Vorspannkraft unterliegen sie nun den verschiedensten Einflüssen.

Kraftänderungen aus Verformungen des Bodens sind ausserhalb der Verant-

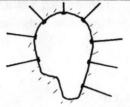

Kaverne Waldeck	Anzahl Messanker : 65
BR Deutschland	Anzahl Anker total : 800
	Ankertyp, Gebrauchslast : VSL 1350 kN
	Spannstahl : Draht Ø 8
	Spannstahlausnutzung : 0,50 β_z
	Verankerungszone : 4,6 m im Fels
	Kraftmessdose : VSL G250;

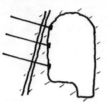

Kaverne Hotzenwald	Anzahl Messanker : 7
BR Deutschland	Anzahl Anker total : 82
	Ankertyp, Gebrauchslast : VSL 1350 kN
	Spannstahl : Draht Ø 8
	Spannstahlausnutzung : 0,50 β_z
	Verankerungszone : 6 m im Fels
	Kraftmessdose : VSL G250;

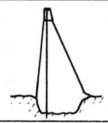

Staumauererhöhung	Anzahl Messanker : 4
El Kansera	Anzahl Anker total : 77
Marokko	Ankertyp, Gebrauchslast : VSL 2600 kN
	Spannstahl : Litzen 13 mm
	Spannstahlausnutzung : 0,70 β_z
	Verankerungszone : 5 m im Fels
	Kraftmessdose : VSL G280;

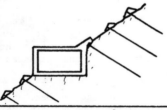

Hangsicherung	Anzahl Messanker : 5
Schallberg VS	Anzahl Anker total : 224
Schweiz	Ankertyp, Gebrauchslast : VSL 1630 kN
	Spannstahl : Litzen 13 mm
	Spannstahlausnutzung : 0,68 β_z
	Verankerungszone : 5 m im Fels
	Kraftmessdose : VSL G200;

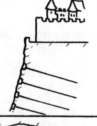

Sicherung Schlossfelsen	Anzahl Messanker : 4
Burgdorf	Anzahl Anker total : 50
Schweiz	Ankertyp, Gebrauchslast : VSL 650 und 1100
	Spannstahl : Litzen 13 mm
	Spannstahlausnutzung : 0,55 β_z
	Verankerungszone : 4,5 m in Sand-
	Kraftmessdose : VSL G100 und G200;

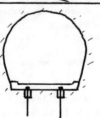

Auftriebssicherung	Anzahl Messanker : 32
Autobahntunnel	Anzahl Anker total : 720
Seelisberg	Ankertyp, Gebrauchslast : VSL 630 kN
Schweiz	Spannstahl : Litzen 13 mm
	Spannstahlausnutzung : 0,50 β_z
	Verankerungszone : 4 m im Mergel
	Kraftmessdose : VSL G100

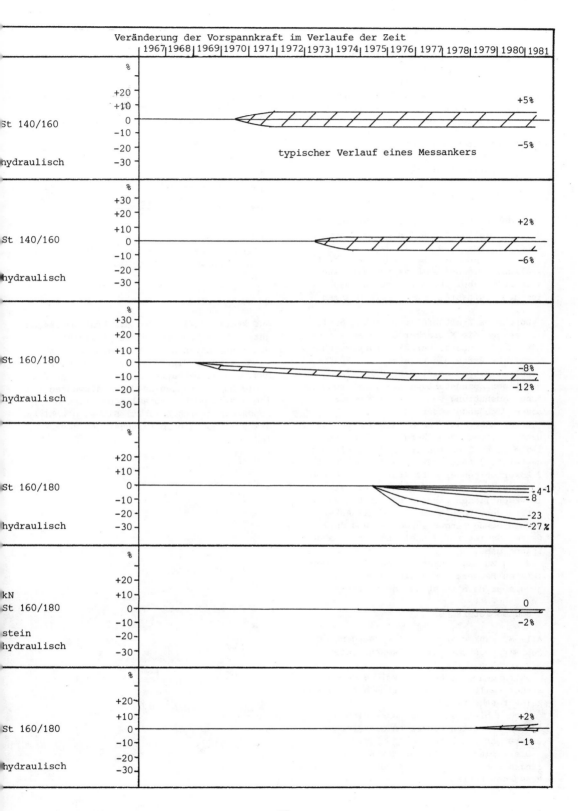

Veränderung der Vorspannkraft im Verlaufe der Zeit

| 1967 | 1968 | 1969 | 1970 | 1971 | 1972 | 1973 | 1974 | 1975 | 1976 | 1977 | 1978 | 1979 | 1980 | 1981 |

St 140/160
hydraulisch

typischer Verlauf eines Messankers

+5%
−5%

St 140/160
hydraulisch

+2%
−6%

St 160/180
hydraulisch

−8%
−12%

St 160/180
hydraulisch

−4−1
−8
−23
−27 %

kN
St 160/180
stein
hydraulisch

0
−2%

St 160/180
hydraulisch

+2%
−1%

29

wortung des Unternehmers.

Schlagartige Kraftabfälle jedoch ohne
Bewegung der Umgebung sind schon eher dem
Konto des Ankerherstellers anzulasten. Es
könnte sich hier um Störungen in den Verankerungen handeln, z.B. Schlupf der
Spannstähle. Auch Korrosionsschäden würden
sich auf diese Weise bemerkbar machen.

3 MESSWERTE VON 6 BAUWERKEN

(Siehe grafische Darstellung)

4 BEURTEILUNG DER MESSWERTE

Fünf der 6 untersuchten Bauwerke weisen
geringe Kraftänderungen auf. Dies über
eine Zeitdauer von bis 13 Jahren.

Eine erfreuliche und beruhigende Feststellung. Die beiden Kavernen verhalten
sich recht ähnlich. Wir stellen sowohl
leichte Kraftabfälle wie Kraftzunahmen
fest.

Durchwegs Kraftabfälle zwischen 8 bis
12% zeigen die Messanker der Staumauerer-
höhung El Kansera, Marokko. Hauptverant-
wortlich dürfte die relativ hohe Spann-
stahlrelaxation sein. Eine Folge der
damaligen Spannstahlqualität, der recht
hohen Ausnutzung von 70% sowie einer
hohen Umgebungstemperatur.

Etwas näher ansehen muss man sich die
Hangsicherung Schallberg. Die Kraftver-
läufe aller 5 Messanker sind einzeln dargestellt. 3 Anker verhalten sich normal.
2 Anker weisen erhöhte Kraftverluste von
23 respektive 27% auf. Diese Verluste sind
im wesentlichen während der ersten Jahre
entstanden. Dazu kommt, dass die Anker
verschiedene Längen aufweisen und über ein
weites Gebiet auf Einzelfundamenten abge-
spannt sind.

Wenig zu sagen gibt es über die beiden
letzten Bauwerke. Sie sind noch etwas
jung aber doch recht gut gestartet.

5 SCHLUSSFOLGERUNGEN

Alle Messanker erfüllen ihre Aufgabe. Die
Messwerte entsprechen im wesentlichen den
Erwartungen.

Störungen oder Schäden welche der An-
kerhersteller zu verantworten hätte wurden
keine festgestellt.

Nach 2 bis 7 Jahren ab Ankereinbau
kommen bei allen Bauwerken die Kraftänderungen zur Ruhe.

Die typische Hüllkurve der Kraftänderungen über alle Bauwerke und bis 13 Jahre
Messdauer beträgt +5% und -12%.

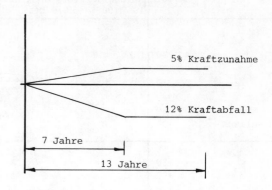

Hüllkurve der Kraftänderungen über
6 Bauwerke während 13 Jahren

Auf keinen Fall sollten die Kraftmessungen
jetzt abgeschlossen werden. Allfällige
Schäden könnten nunmehr zuverlässig er-
fasst werden. Die Messintervalle sollen
max. 1 Jahr betragen.

Die Anforderungen an die Kraftmessan-
lagen sind hoch. Hydraulische Kraftmessdosen haben sich bewährt. Sie sind wohl
etwas altmodisch aber robust und zuverlässig.

30

DEEPHOLE PREEXCAVATION STRESS MEASUREMENTS FOR THE DESIGN OF UNDERGROUND POWERHOUSES IN THE SIERRA NEVADA MOUNTAINS

Tiefliegende Primärspannungsmessungen für den Entwurf unterirdischer Kraftwerke in der Sierra Nevada

Mesures en profondeur des contraintes primaires pour le dimensionnement des centrales électriques souterraines du Sierra Nevada

BEZALEL C.HAIMSON

Department of Metallurgical & Mineral Engineering, Madison, Wisconsin, USA

SUMMARY:
The objectives of large rock cavern design are to establish the most suitable location, the optimum shape and size, the best orientation, and the necessary support or reinforcement. Most of these design objectives can be better accomplished if the virgin state of stress is known and its effects properly considered. The stress regime, however, is generally unknown and has to be determined at each project site. In North America it has become quite common to use the deep-hole hydrofracturing method in the preliminary stages of site exploration in order to determine the preexcavation stress condition in the rock at the depth of the planned cavern. In particular, hydrofracturing has been used in many underground hydro projects. Three such projects, namely Helms, Kerckhoff 2 and Balsam Meadow are all situated in the Sierra Nevada Mountains just east of Fresno, California. The preexcavation stress measuements in each case are described together with the specific use of the results in the design process of the underground powerhouses and other components. It is shown that knowledge of the state of stress was critical in making important design decisions, and that site specific stress measurements were necessary in each case despite the relative proximity of the three projects.

ZUSAMMENFASSUNG:
Die Ziele in der Planung grosser Steinhölen sind gute Lage, Grösse, und Orientierung, sowohl wie die nötige Stützung oder Verstärkung. Diese Ziele sind einfacher to erreichen wenn der ursprüngliche Belastungszustand bekannt ist und dessen Einfluss berücksichtigt werden kann. Weil Belastungen aber im allgemeinen unbekannt sind, müssen sie für jede Lage einzeln bestimmt werden. In Nord Amerika wird üblicherweise die "deep-hole hydrofracturing" Methode benutzt um den Belastungszustand im Stein an der geplanted Tiefe zu bestimmen. "Hydrofracturing" wurde an drei Lagen für unterirdische Wasserwerke benutzt (Helms, Kerchhoff, und Balsam Meadow), die alle in den Sierra Nevada Bergen östlich von Fresno, California sind. Die Stressmessungen vevor Aushölung sind für alle drei Lagen beschrieben, zusammen mit dem Gebrauch der Resultate in der Planung unterirdischer Kraftwerke. Es wird gezeigt dass ein Kenntniss des Belastungszustandes kritisch ist um Beschlüsse zu fassen über den Entwurf, und dass Messungen an allen drei Lagen nötig waren, obwohl diese nahe zu einander liegen.

RESUME:
La connaissance des contraintes in-situ dans les roches facilite l'étude des projets de construction de grandes cavitées souterraines. Les contraintes ne sont généralement pas connues. La méthode d'hydro-fracturation dans des trous profonds est souvent utilisée en Amérique du Nord pour explorer les sites de construction. Les sites de Helms, Kerchoff 2 et Balsam Meadow sont tous les trois situés dans les Sierra Nevadas à l'est de Fresno en Californie. Les mesures de contraintes et leurs utilisations dans les études de ces sites sont présentées. Dans certains cas, ces mesures ont eu une influence determinante sur les décisions prises. Malgré la proximité des trois sites, les mesures des contraintes à chacun des sites ont été nécessaires.

1 ROCK STRESSES AND THE DESIGN OF UNDER-GROUND HYDRO PROJECTS

A hydro project in which the powerhouse is located underground will typically have in the subsurface all of its main components between the inlet and discharge reservoirs (such as headrace tunnel, pressure tunnel, penstock, surge chamber, transformer and machine halls, tailrace tunnel). The major objectives of the design process of these underground components are to establish for each of them:

a – the most suitable location
b – the optimum shape and size
c – the best orientation
d – the most efficient and safe
    sequence of excavation
e – the necessary lining, support and
    reinforcement.

Most, if not all, of these design objectives can be better accomplished if the state of stress in the area of the project is measured and its effect is properly considered. For example, the location of the underground tunnels and chambers is usually assumed to be a function of the site geography and topography (minimize volume of excavation between upper and lower reservoirs), and of the rock mass conditions (seek zones of high rock quality, avoid major shear zones or other large discontinuities). The state of stress becomes an important factor if the surface topography is varied over the distance between the two reservoirs. The section of a tunnel located just under a steeply inclined mountain slope will behave quite differently from the segment going under the toe of a slope, or the cavern located well below a flat plateau. In each case knowledge of the stress conditions will enable the estimation of the stress concentrations and will affect the final positioning of the tunnel.

The shape and dimensions of some of the important underground caverns are dictated by the mechanical and electrical equipment and by hydraulic requirements. In those cases where there is flexibility in designing the shape of the entire opening (e.g. headrace and tailrace tunnels) or of parts of it (e.g. the arch in the machine hall), a major objective is to enhance stability and minimize artificial support. A principal role in selecting the optimum shape is played by the state of stress, and specifically by the ratio of the vertical to horizontal stresses. To minimize stress concentrations around the walls, a circular cross sectional shape, for example, is recommended when the ratio is approximately 1:1. In zones of sparce jointing and where

the horizontal stress is much larger than the vertical a cross-section whose width is larger than the height may be preferred (ideally, in a linear elastic unjointed rock, this should be an ellipse for which the ratio between the horizontal and the vertical axes is equal to the ratio between the respective stresses).

The orientation of rock openings is primarily a function of the hydraulic requirements, the joint set directions and the stress ellipsoid. Ignoring the effects of discontinuities, the best orientation is that in which the cavern axis subparallels the maximum horizontal stress. Such an orientation minimizes the stress concentrations at and around the walls, thus optimizing stability. Jointing may, however, dictate cavern orientation if some preferred directions reduce excessive block release into the excavation, or as in the case of pressure tunnels, if by proper alignment of the excavation axis leak-off through discontinuities can be controlled. In most situations the orientation dictated either by stresses or by the joint sets are in close proximity; otherwise a compromise is sought.

Regardless of the utilization of in situ stress measurements in the previous design steps, their use is imperative in the calculation of stress distribution around underground openings and in the resulting estimation of the amount of support or reinforcement required. There is simply no substitute to measured in situ stresses when the real boundary conditions are to be set for stability evaluations around openings. Only a few of the documented case histories show how knowledge of in situ stresses was used in the orientation of tunnels and caverns (Haimson, 1977a; Haimson and Lee 1980) or their shape (Martna 1979); all of the published literature, however, emphasizes the use of the measured stress regime in the evaluation of cavern stability and reinforcement.

2 METHODS OF STRESS MEASUREMENTS

In the last 2 decades or so, the stresses in the vicinity of future underground hydroelectric projects have been almost routinely measured using one of the available overcoring methods (such as 'borehole deformation', 'doorstopper', 'triaxial strain cell' and others). Because of distance limitations of these methods, exploratory boreholes are not typically used for overcoring stress measurements. Rather, pilot tunnels are first driven into the planned powerhouse area. From these tunnels, short boreholes are drilled specifically for over-

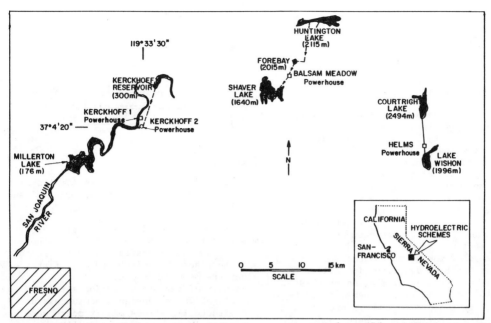

Fig. 1 The sites of three recent hydroelectric projects in the central Sierra Nevada Mts.

coring tests. These methods prove satisfactory in most cases. However, their two major disadvantages are the necessity to drive a pilot or an access tunnel, and the subsequent delay in obtaining the stress values. Moreover, in some cases the powerhouse location could be far enough from the top and the slope of the mountain so as to render pilot tunneling unfeasible. In such cases, the design would have to proceed by making some intelligent assumptions regarding stresses and directions. These are to be checked later during the actual excavation, rendering any change in shape or orientation of the opening extremely expensive.

In a small number of projects no overcoring was conducted; rather the flat-jack method was used to determine the stress concentrations at the wall of the excavation. This method does not enable the measurement of the preexcavation virgin stress, but rather that of the disturbed, often relaxed, stress produced by the excavation. The measured values can be used only for the opening where they were taken.

Some ten years ago a new method of stress measurement was developed and used in the field. It is the hydrofracturing method (Haimson 1968; 1974; 1978a) which requires no overcoring and is limited in depth of measurement only by the length of the borehole. The technique consists of sealing-off a section of a borehole at the required depth by means of two rubber pack-

ers, and hydraulically pressurizing the packed-off segment. When the 'breakdown pressure' is reached, the rock surrounding the borehole fails in tension and develops a fracture. This fracture can be extended away from the hole by continuous pumping. When pumps are shut-off with the hydraulic circuit kept closed, a 'shut-in' pressure is recorded. This is the pressure necessary to keep the fracture open. The breakdown and shut-in pressure can be related to the prevailing in situ stresses. A commercial impression packer is finally used to determine the exact direction and inclination of the hydrofracture. In this manner, both the magnitudes and the directions of the principal stresses can be evaluated. The hydrofracturing technique can be used in deep holes (the deepest measurement to date was at 5000 m beneath the earth surface) or in short holes around tunnels (Haimson 1978b; Haimson et al 1974).

At sites of future underground hydro projects hydrofracturing is used directly in exploration holes drilled into the general area of the planned caverns. Thus, no additional expenses are needed for drilling special holes for stress measurements. Moreover, the stresses are estimated as part of the preliminary investigation prior to actual design and excavation, causing no delays, and requiring no design changes of the kind described above. If necessary, overcoring tests can also be conducted later on when the pilot or access tunnels

are excavated. They can provide a check
on the hydrofracturing results and increase
confidence in the stress boundary conditions used in design.

3 HYDROELECTRIC PROJECTS IN THE SIERRA NEVADA MOUNTAINS

In the last 8 years we were given the opportunity of measuring the preexcavation
in situ stress by hydrofracturing at three
different sites of planned underground
hydroelectric schemes in the Sierra Nevada
Mountains. All of the sites are northeast
of Fresno, California (Fig. 1). The first
measurements chronolgically were conducted
for the design of the Helms Pumped Storage
Project. This is the only project the
excavation of which has been completed.
The direct use of the measured stress in
the design of the Helms Project underground
openings has been described in earlier
publications (Haimson 1977a, Haimson 1981,
Strassburger et al 1978, Sweeney et al 1980).
The other two projects where preexcavation hydrofracturing tests were conducted,
Kerckhoff 2 and Balsam Meadow, are now at
different stages of construction but have
already utilized the measured stresses in
important design decisions. These neighboring projects are described also in order
to emphasize the importance of specific
stress determination at each site.

3.1 The Helms Pumped Storage Project

The Helms Project of the Pacific Gas and
Electric Company is located some 80 km
east-northeast of Fresno, California in
the Sierra Nevada mountains. Briefly it
is a three-unit 1050 MW plant which will
connect two existing reservoirs,
Courtright Lake (el. 2494 m) and Lake
Wishon (el. 1996 m). Starting from
Courtright the project incorporates a 4000
m-long (8 m diameter) concrete-lined
tunnel, and a 61 m (6.7 m diameter) steel-
lined tunnel leading to 55° inclined penstock shaft (dropping 400 m) which connects
to a penstock manifold. The manifold
bifurcates into three steel-lined conduits
(about 180 m long) passing under the transformer vault and into the powerhouse. On
the other side of the powerhouse the three
conduits are joined into the tailrace
tunnel (1200 m long, 8 m diameter) leading
to Lake Wishon. The powerhouse is 25 m
wide, 44 m high, and 102 m long (Fig. 2)
and is separated by a 15 m pillar from
the transformer chamber (12m x 12m x 92m).
These openings are 300 m below the surface
(Strassburger et al 1978; Sweeney 1980).
The location of the powerhouse was dictated

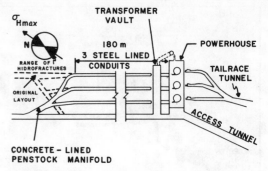

Fig. 2 Underground powerhouse complex in
the Helms Project, showing the original and
final layouts of the penstock manifold.

partly by rock conditions (the granodiorite
was preferred to the quartzite), by the
site of two surge shafts and by the necessity to place the switchyard on a flat spot
along the mountain slope.
As part of the preexcavation site
investigation and design nine successful
hydrofracturing stress measurements were
conducted in granite in two drillholes,
seven in a vertical NX size hole between
the depths of 119 and 326 m, and two in
an inclined hole at depths 239, and 271 m
(Haimson 1977a). The inclined hole was
30° off the vertical in the N27°E direction
which parallels the general direction of
the hydrofractures in the vertical hole
(N25°E). Hence, vertical axial hydrofractures in the inclined hole would have
confirmed the results obtained in the
vertical hole. The fractures induced were
indeed nearly axial, with subvertical
dips (80°SE). The tests in the inclined
hole increased our confidence in the
results obtained in the vertical hole and
reinforced the assertion that the principal
stresses were approximately vertical and
horizontal, with the maximum horizontal
stress (σ_{Hmax}) oriented at N25°E. Figure
3 gives the hydrofracturing results as a
function of depth. The steady increase
with depth of all the stresses can be
approximated by linear regression:

$$\sigma_V = 0.027 \times D$$
$$\sigma_{Hmin} = 3.5 + 0.006 \times D \quad \text{at N65°W}$$
$$\sigma_{Hmax} = -0.65 + 0.035 \times D \quad \text{at N25°E}$$

where stresses are in megapascals and D
is depth in meters.
The vertical stress is based on measured
rock density. The uniqueness of these
measurements was that for the first time
an inclined hole was used for hydrofracturing tests in order to verify the orientation of the principal stresses. As shown

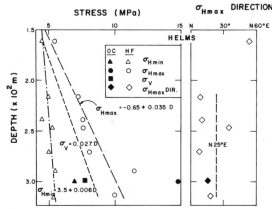

STRESS (MPa)

σ_{Hmax} DIRECTION

HELMS

OC	HF	
▲	△	σ_{Hmin}
●	○	σ_{Hmax}
■	□	σ_V
◆	◇	σ_{Hmax} DIR.

$\sigma_{Hmax} = -0.65 + 0.035\ D$

$\sigma_V = 0.027\ D$

$\sigma_{Hmin} = 3.5 + 0.006\ D$

N 25°E

Fig. 3 Variation of principal hydrofracturing stress magnitudes and
σ_{Hmax} direction with depth, and
comparison with overcoring results
at powerhouse depth-Helms Project.

in Figure 3 the inclined hole results
cannot be distinguished from those obtained
in the vertical hole.

The results of the preexcavation hydrofracturing tests were very important in
that they immediately called attention to
some design problems, and were used to
make necessary changes in the original
layout, long before any construction work
began. Thus, it was discovered that the
minimum principal stress is apparently
lower than the transient pressure expected
in the concrete lined penstock (7.5 MPa).
This internal pressure may not have been
sufficient to induce fracturing in the
wall of the penstock, but it might have
been high enough to open up existing
joints which are perpendicular to the
direction of σ_{Hmin}. To prevent excessive leakage of pressurized water from
weakening the rock mass around the powerhouse a drainage gallery and drain holes
were provided. They were meant to cut off
the migration of the water through the
northeast trending joints. The high upstream pressures were mitigated by lining
the three 180 m-long water conduits with
steel. Another direct result of the early
stress measurements was the change in the
geometry of the penstock manifold. The
original layout called for the manifold to
be orientated at N30°E. The stress measurements revealed that this direction parallels
that of the obtained hydrofractures. Joints
belonging to the NE set which would traverse
the manifold axially could be opened by internal pressure. To minimize the potential
leaking, the layout was inverted so that
the manifold axis was directed to NW and
the problematic joints would thus cross the

tunnel transversally (Fig. 2).

No changes were made in the original
layout of the powerhouse; its orientation
is E-W, that is, bisecting the angle
between σ_{Hmax} and σ_{Hmin} as well as
between the two major subvertical joint
sets. The measured stresses were incorporated, however, in the finite element
analysis aimed at predicting stresses and
displacements at critical areas of excavation such as the crown and corners of the
large caverns. The results were used to
establish the stability conditions of the
underground openings and the required
support. No serious problems were predicted by the numerical model. Nevertheless
a number of mild rock bursts were encountered in excavation. This served as an
inducement to run a series of independent
stress measurements using the more conventional techniques of overcoring (borehole
deformation) and flat jacking. The tests
were conducted from a drift just off the
powerhouse access tunnel, some 100 m from
the site of the hydrofracturing measurements.

The flat jack tests were inconclusive;
the overcoring measurements, however, gave
reasonable results which showed the
principal stresses to be somewhat inclined
(15° to 30°) but basically similar to the
hydrofracturing values (Sweeney et al 1980,
Haimson 1981). Figure 3 juxtaposes the
overcoring secondary principal stresses
in the vertical and horizontal planes
against the hydrofracturing results in
the powerhouse area. Other than a
noticeable difference in σ_{Hmax} value
there is a remarkable agreement with
respect to both magnitudes and directions.
The successful corroboration of the two
methods served first to provide additional
confidence in the reliability of hydrofracturing; second to reassure the designers
that their use of preexcavation stress
measurements using a new method (hydrofracturing) was justified; and third, to
provide a check on the design decisions
and calculations originally based on hydrofracturing alone.

3.2 The Kerckhoff 2 Hydroelectric Project

The Kerckhoff 2 Hydroelectric Project of
Pacific Gas and Electric Company is located
in the western foothills of the Central
Sierra Nevada Mountains of California, on
the eastern side of San Joaquin River,
some 30 km north-east of Fresno (Fig. 1).

When completed the project will work in
tandem with Kerckhoff 1, using the
Kerckhoff 1 reservoir and discharging
into Millerton Lake. The capacity of

Kerckhoff 2 will be 140 MW. The present
project will use a 6700 m concrete lined
main tunnel connecting the intake
reservoir to a 55° inclined penstock. This
concrete lined shaft is 188 m long and
averages 5 m in diameter. The powerhouse
is cylindrical in shape so as to
house the one 140 MW generator, and its
dimensions are 29 m diameter by 45 m
height. The discharge tunnel is
175 m long and 7.5 m diameter (Zayakov 1981,
Zayakov - personal communication 1982).

The surface topography is dominated by
the Squaw Leap Mountain (elevation 711 m)
to the east and the San Joaquin River
(elevation 168 m) to the west. The average
dip of the mountainside above the proposed
underground powerhouse of the Project and
toward the river is 15° to S55°W, but is
substantially steeper to the east as the
mountain peak is approached. The local
topography is shown in Fig. 4 together
with the site of the powerhouse and that
of the two NX test holes 1B and 1C.

The rock penetrated by the two testholes is a medium grained, medium gray
Cretaceous granodiorite cut by many aplite
dikes. The core is generally of excellent
quality, sparsely to moderately jointed
with numerous segments of 0.5 m length of
more. Surface surveys show that most
joints in the powerhouse area strike
northwesterly at dips varying from 30° to

90° toward either SW or NE. The rock
shows a moderate amount of foliation
striking northerly to northeasterly and
dipping 35°-90° to the SW. No faults
have been encountered in the area.

Encouraged by the success of the preexcavation stress measurements at Helms,
and unwilling to assume that the stress
regime there extends to the site of the
new Project, some 50 km west, the company
decided to proceed with hydrofracturing
tests from the surface to the depth of
the future powerhouse in the early stages
of Kerckhoff 2 design. Again two exploratory testholes were used, one vertical
and one inclined, with the latter selected
from among several based on the proximity
of its axis direction to that of the hydrofractures in the vertical hole.

The significance of the hydrofracturing
tests conducted in the inclined hole (1B)
is that they confirmed that the 3 principal
stresses act in the vertical and horizontal
planes (within 10°). Fig. 5 is a stereographic projection of the hydrofractures
obtained in the 7 successful tests in the
vertical hole (1C) and 4 successful tests
in the inclined hole (1B). It is clearly
seen that all hydrofractures are vertical
or subvertical and strike in the NW
direction. The average strike direction
is N45°W ± 15° (rounded to nearest 5°).

The stress magnitudes have been plotted in
Fig. 6. Significantly the results obtained in the inclined hole match closely those
of the vertical hole (1C). As expected
all three principal stresses increase with
depth. The values of σ_{Hmin} are clustered

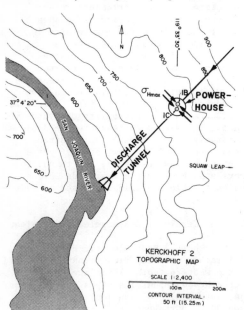

Fig. 4   Topographic map around the
          Kerckhoff 2 powerhouse and test-
          holes 1B and 1C, showing the
          direction of σ_{Hmax}.

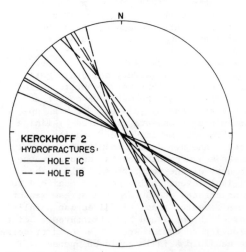

Fig. 5   Stereographic projection of
          hydrofractures (equivalent to the
          direction of σ_{Hmax}) at
          Kerckhoff 2.

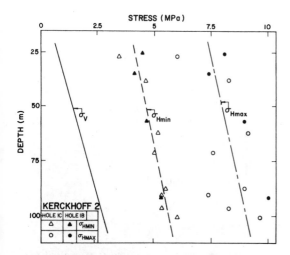

Fig. 6 Variation of principal stress
        magnitudes with depth in vertical
        testhole (1C) and inclined hole
        (1B) - Kerckhoff 2 Project.

closely around the average stress-depth
line obtained by linear regression. The
values of σ_{Hmax} are considerably more
spread out (as is usually the case) but
their linear regression is approximately
parallel to σ_{Hmin}.

For the depth range of 25-105 m the
following values were obtained by linear
regression (Haimson 1979):

$$\sigma_V \quad = \quad 0.027 \times D$$

$$\sigma_{Hmin} = 3.60 + 0.020 \times D \qquad \text{at N45°E}$$

$$\sigma_{Hmax} = 6.90 + 0.022 \times D \qquad \text{at N45°W}$$

where D is depth in meters and stresses
are in megapascals.

The stress regime at Kerckhoff 2 as
given by these equations (and shown in
Figs. 5 and 6) has two outstanding
features: (a) both horizontal principal
stresses are larger than the vertical
component and (b) the direction of the
major horizontal compressive stress is
generally N45°W. The first feature is
becoming less surprising and more common
as more stress measurements are conducted.
At shallow depths the vertical stress is
naturally small in magnitude and usually
lower than the other two principal stresses.
Note, that in the neighboring Helms the
vertical stress was clearly the intermediate
component and, thus, radically different
from Kerckhoff 2. However, extrapolation
upward of the Helms results indicate that
at depths of 0-150 m σ_V becomes the
least principal stress (Fig. 3).

The second feature of the described
tests is considerably less expected. The
regional trend of the maximum horizontal
stress direction changes gradually from
approximately N-S along the San Andreas
fault to about N25°E in the central Sierra
Nevada Mountains (at Helms, California) to
N45°E at the Nevada Test Site (Haimson
1977b, 1978c, and Fig. 7) based on both
hydrofracturing tests and focal mechanism
solutions, with an additional confirmation
by overcoring in Nevada. The direction
of σ_{Hmax} at Kerckhoff 2 is definitely
decoupled from the regional stress characteristics and clearly different from
the conditions at Helms. This apparent
90° rotation can be partially explained by
use of Fig. 5. The surface topography is
clearly one that would indicate a least
horizontal compressive stress acting in a
northeastern direction and parallel to the
mountain slope direction. On the other
hand the direction parallel to the slope
axis (northwest) is one along which the
stress component is unaffected by the
nearby free boundary and is expected to be

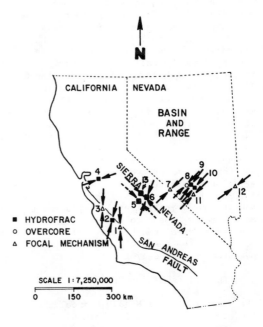

Fig. 7 Directions of σ_{Hmax} in California-
        Nevada as determined by hydro-
        fracturing, overcoring and focal
        mechanism solutions (Haimson 1978c).
        The results at Kerckhoff 2 (5) and
        Balsam Meadow (13) are clearly
        at odds with the regional trend.
        Helms results (6) are in accord
        with the trend.

37

a major principal stress direction. The topographic effect remains the only reasonable explanation for the unexpected N45°W direction of σ_{Hmax}.

The results at Kerckhoff 2 help illustrate the pitfalls avoided by not using neighboring measurements (such as those at Helms in this case) in order to predict stress regimes at specific sites. Such extrapolations could be particularly unreliable in mountaineous terrain. The direct in situ stress measurements at Kerckhoff 2 were clearly the only way to determine the state of stress there.

The data provided by the hydrofracturing stress measurements at a very early stage of planning has been extremely valuable in the rational design of the underground works. In particular, the stress results were used in comparing the two suggested layouts for the single unit (140 MW) powerhouse: circular and rectangular. The circular (or cylindrical) cavern with a dome shaped ceiling was found to offer more advantages, including lower stresses in the wall and roof and thus resulting in less rockbolt reinforcement (Zayakov, 1981). A finite element analysis, using the measured stresses as boundary conditions, showed that in the cylindrical cavern no tensile stresses developed in the walls or the dome. The rectangular opening would have developed in its walls tensile stresses reaching 1 MPa. The stress measurement results were also used in deciding to concrete line the 55° inclined penstock, to concrete line and rock bolt the surge chamber and to rock bolt and grout the headrace tunnel.

Construction has been underway since 1980 and the only major component still unexcavated is the main tunnel.
The powerhouse dome has been completed and its early instrumental displacement measurements appear to confirm the magnitudes predicted by the analysis resulting from the preexcavation stress measurements (Zayakov 1981).

3.3 The Balsam Meadow Project

The proposed Balsam Meadow Hydroelectric Project of Southern California Edison Company is located just north of Shaver Lake, California, on the western flank of the Sierra Nevada Mountains and halfway between the Helms Project on the east and Kerckhoff 2 Project on the west (Fig. 1). The Balsam Meadow Project is a peaker plant designed to be used only where Huntington Lake is overfull (mainly during spring runoff). The Project complements the existing Huntington Lake -

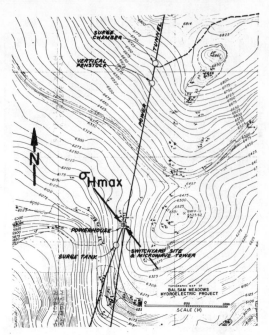

Fig. 8 Topographic map around the Balsam Meadow powerhouse showing the direction of σ_{Hmax} - (scale and contours in ft; 1 ft = 0.3048 m).

Shaver Lake hydroelectric scheme which produces electricity for the Los Angeles area. The feeder reservoir will be the Balsam Meadow Forebay into which the excessive water from Huntington Lake will be channeled through a diversion tunnel. From the inlet portal at 2015m elevation a straight line power tunnel will lead to the underground powerhouse (Fig. 8) via a surge chamber and a vertical penstock. The powerhouse is designed to accommodate one single generator producing 200 MW. The system will have pumped storage capability but in the foreseeable future it will be used only for generating power. The switchyard will be immediately above the 300 m deep powerhouse. A tailrace tunnel will lead from the powerhouse via a surge tank to the outlet portal on the northern shore of Shaver Lake at an elevation of 1640 m.

The planned underground powerhouse (Fig. 8), which is reached by the lower portion of the vertical testhole PH-1 at some 300m below the surface (elevation of which is 1920m), is in massive granitic rock of excellent quality. The most prominent joints are vertical trending N60°E, N20°W, N40°W and N60°W, with spacing averaging 5 m. Moderately developed foliation strikes in the range of N20°W

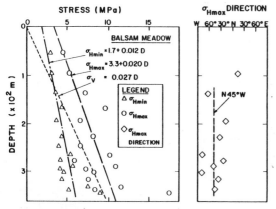

Fig. 9 Variation of principal stress
magnitudes and σ_{Hmax} direction
with depth-Balsam Meadow Project.

to N60°W and dips 70° to 90°.

The results of 16 hydrofracturing tests
indicate the following variation of stress
with depths:

$$\sigma_V = 0.027 \times D$$

$$\sigma_{Hmin} = 1.7 + 0.0125 \times D \quad \text{at N45°E}$$

$$\sigma_{Hmax} = 3.35 + 0.02 \times D \quad \text{at N45°W}$$

where stresses are in megapascals and D is
depth in meters. Fig. 9 gives the individual measurement results and the linear
approximation of stress vs. depth with
respect to both magnitudes and directions.
As can be seen in Fig. 8 the direction of
σ_{Hmax} cannot be easily related to the
local topographical relief which in the
testhole - powerhouse area is a mountainside sloping directly to the west. The
depth of the proposed powerhouse may be
sufficiently far so as not to be affected
by the topography. Clearly the stress
directions are again not coupled to
the regional trend (Fig. 7).

Comparing the results at 300 m depth
with the other two sets of measurements in
the Sierras it appears that the stress
magnitudes in the powerhouse area at
Balsam Meadow are similar to those at Helms,
while the stress directions are close to
those at Kerckhoff 2. Significantly, such
a state of stress could not have been
predicted without site specific measurements.

In the preliminary design considerations
the measured state of stress at Balsam
Meadow was deemed moderate when compared
to the high strength of the granite. This
in itself was an important observation

which could not have been established
without stress measurements. The direction
of the powerhouse axis has tentatively
been selected at east-west, approximately
bisecting the angle between the direction
of the predominant joint set (N60°E) and
that of σ_{Hmax} (S45°E). Moreover, it has
been concluded that the transient water
pressure in the conduits leading to the
powerhouse will probably not exceed the
magnitude of σ_{Hmin} and thus no particular
danger of joint opening is envisaged. The
results of the hydrofracturing stress
measurements are being used as boundary
conditions in a finite element program
designed to calculate the stress concentrations around the powerhouse. This
program will assist in selecting the proper
geometry of opening, as well as in defining the areas of potential stability
problems. The present plans call for
light construction to commence in 1982,
with heavy underground construction to
follow in 1983.

4   CONCLUSIONS

In this paper we reemphasize the important
role of rock stress measurements in each
step of the design process of large underground openings such as those required in
hydro projects. We selected 3 case
histories of recent hydroelectric projects,
all located within 50 km or so in the
central Sierra Nevada Mountains of
California. The three projects are at
different stages of construction and the
direct impact of the preexcavation stress
measurements on different aspects of each
scheme design is reported. The three
sets of hydrofracturing tests are summarized in order to emphasize that preexcavation
stress measurements are now being conducted
almost routinely in the U.S. to help in
the design of large underground projects.
Moreover, the considerably different
results obtained at these three neighboring sites in California serve as a
reminder that extrapolation of stress
regimes from one site to the next, regardless of distance, can be risky and that
for specific use of the local stress in
design there is no substitute to actual
measurements.

7   REFERENCES

Haimson, B.C. 1968, Hydraulic fracturing
in porous and nonporous rock and its
potential for determining in situ
stresses at great depth, Ph.D. Thesis
and Technical Report 4-68, Missouri
River Division Corps of Engineers.

Haimson, B.C. 1974, A simple method for estimated in situ stresses at great depth, in Field Testing and Instrumentation of Rock, Am. Soc. Testing and Materials (ASTM) Special Tech. Publ. 554, p. 156-182.

Haimson, B.C. 1977a, Design of underground powerhouses and the importance of pre-excavation stress measurements, in Design Methods in Rock Mechanics, Edited by C. Fairhurst and S. L. Crouch, Am. Soc. Civil Engr., N.Y., p. 197-204.

Haimson, B.C. 1977b, Crustal stress in the continental United States as derived from hydrofracturing tests, Geophysical Monograph 20, The Earth Crust, Am. Geophys. Union, Washington, D.C., p. 576-592.

Haimson, B.C., 1978a, The hydrofracturing stress measuring method and recent field results, Int. J. Rock Mech. Min. Sci. and Geomech. Abstr., 15: 167-178.

Haimson, B.C. 1978b, Crustal stress in the Michigan Basin, Journal of Geophysical Research, 83, No. B12: 5857-5863.

Haimson, B.C. 1978c, Crustal stress measurements by hydrofracturing, Memoire du B.R.G.M. no. 91, Science de la Terre Mesures, Paris, p. 163-172.

Haimson, B.C. 1979, New hydrofracturing measurements in the Seirra Nevada Mountains and the relationship between shallow stresses and surface topography, in Proceeding of the 20th U.S. Symposium on Rock Mechanics, Austin, Texas, p. 675-682.

Haimson, B.C., J. LaComb, S.J. Green and A.H. Jones 1974, Deep stress measurements in tuff at the Nevada Test Site, in Advances in Rock Mechanics (Proceedings of the 3rd Congress of the Int'l. Soc. for Rock Mechanics), Vol. II, p. 557-562.

Haimson, B.C. and C.F. Lee 1980, In Situ stress and rock thermal properties in underground nuclear plant design, in Subsurface Space, edited by M. Bergman, Pergamon Press, Vol. II, p. 623-631.

Martna, J. 1979, Selective overbreak in the Suorva-Vieta Tunnel caused by rock pressure, in Proceedings of the International Symposium on Underground Openings, edited by H. Grob and K. Kovari, A.A. Balkema, Rotterdam, p. 141-145.

Strassburger, A.G., R.R. Friedricks and J.A. Davis 1978, California pumped-storage project advances state of the art in high-head tunneling, Tunneling Technology, Newsletter of the U.S. National Committee on Tunneling Technology, No. 22, p. 2-7.

Sweeney, N.F., J.A. Davis and A.G. Strassburger 1980, A practical/economic rock mechanic program, in Proceedings of the 21st U.S. Rock Mechanics Symposium, Rolla, Missouri, p. 729-740.

Zayakov, D. 1981, Circular underground powerhouse for USA's Kerckhoff 2, Int. Water Power and Dam Construction, 33: 21-24.

EVALUATION OF THE MECHANICAL STABILITY OF UNDERGROUND STORAGE FACILITIES USING MICROSEISMIC TECHNIQUES

Die Bewertung der mechanischen Stabilität von Untertagespeichern durch mikroseismische Methoden

L'évaluation de la stabilité mécanique des usines de stockage souterraines par la méthode microsismique

H.REGINALD HARDY, Jr.
Pennsylvania State University, University Park, USA

SUMMARY:

There is little doubt that during the latter part of this century considerable use will be made of the underground for storage of solids, liquids, and gases. At present commercial and government owned facilities for underground storage of such products as natural gas, LNG, crude oil, compressed air and radioactive wastes are in use, or are under development, in many countries. Although techniques for the design and construction of such facilities have developed rapidly in recent years, procedures for monitoring the mechanical stability of these facilities are in their infancy. Due to the size and often inaccessible nature of such large underground storage facilities, the microseismic technique appears to offer one of the most suitable methods for stability monitoring of such structures. The present paper will include a brief outline of the microseismic concept, a discussion of the associated monitoring and data analysis procedures, and a review of a number of current applications in the area of underground storage.

ZUSAMMENFASSUNG:

Es besteht kaum Zweifel daran, daß zum Ende dieses Jahrhunderts die Benutzung von Untertagespeichern für die Lagerung von Festkörpern, Flüssigkeiten and Gasen beträchtig sein wird. Im Augenblick sind in vielen Ländern kommerzielle und staatliche Einrichtungen für die Untertagespeicherung von Erdgas, verflüssigtem Ergas, Rohöl, verdichteter Luft und radioaktiven Abfallstoffen in Betrieb oder in der Entwickelung. Obgleich sich die Technik für den Entwurf und den Bau solcher Anlagen in den letzten Jahren schnell entwickelt hat, sind die Methoden zur Überwachung ihrer mechanischen Stabilität noch in einem frühen Stadium der Entwickelung. In Anbetracht der Größe und oft unzugänglichen Lage von solchen Speichern scheint sich die mikroseismische Methode als eine günstige Methode zur Überwachung ihrer Stabilität anzubieten. Dieser Vortrag schliesst sowohl einen kurzen Abriß des mikroseismischen Konzepts, eine Diskussion der Überwachung und der Datenanalyse ein, als auch einen Überblick über die heutigen Anwendungen auf dem Gebiet der Untertagespeicherung.

RESUME:

Il y a peu de doute que d'ici la fin du siècle, l'espace souterrain verra un usage important pour le stockage des solides, liquides et gaz. Présentement, plusieurs entreprises commerciales ainsi que des organismes gouvernementaux sont propriétaires d'usines en exploitation ou en ont en développement et sous étude pour fins de stockage; du gaz naturel, du GNL, du pétrole brut, de l'air comprisé et les déchets radioactifs. Bien que les méthodes de conception et de réalisation de tels usines ont progressé rapidement ces dernières années, les méthodes de contrôle du comportement sont à leurs débuts. En vue des grandes dimensions et des emplacements souvent inaccessibles de ces usines, la méthode microsismique semble être des plus prometteuses pour la contrôle de leurs comportement. Cette communication traitera brièvement du concept microsismique, discutera des procedures de vérification du comportement et de l'analyse des données et rendra compte de plusieurs applications pratiques de cette technique dans le domaine du stockage souterrain.

1 INTRODUCTION

There is little doubt that during the latter part of this century considerable use will be made of the underground for storage of solids, liquids, and gases. At present commercial and government owned facilities for underground storage of such products as natural gas, LNG, crude oil, compressed air and radioactive wastes are in use, or are under development in many countries. Although techniques for the design and construction of such facilities have developed rapidly in recent years, procedures for monitoring the mechanical stability of these facilities are in their infancy. Due to their size and often inaccessible nature the microseismic technique appears to offer one of the more suitable methods for stability monitoring of such structures.

The phenomenon of microseismic activity is associated with the fact that when a structure composed of materials such as rock is loaded the resulting deformation and/or localized failure cause the generation of seismic signals within the structure. These signals are indicative of the overall stability of the structure, and with suitable instrumentation they may be detected at considerable distances from their source. Basic and applied microseismic research has been underway for some 40 years, although the major developments in the subject have taken place since about 1965.

In recent years, extensive use has been made of microseismic techniques for evaluating the stability of such geologic structures as mines, rock and soil slopes, tunnels, earth filled dams, and more recently underground gas storage facilities. A detailed discussion of the microseismic concept and information on a variety of applications is available in a number of recent publications [for example, Hardy (1981) and Hardy and Leighton (1977, 1980, 1982)].

As noted by the writer in an earlier paper (Hardy, 1978), one of the major problems associated with the accelerating use of underground storage is the fact that the development of techniques for monitoring the long-term mechanical stability of such structures are lagging seriously behind developments in other associated areas such as excavation. There can be little doubt that suitable techniques are required to evaluate the long-term mechanical stability of underground storage facilities during their development and later operation. Such techniques are necessary to insure first, that the storage cavern itself is suitably stable, and second, that the surrounding environment is not influenced significantly by the storage operation. Looking into the future (possibly the near future), it is not unrealistic to anticipate the time when those involved in using the underground for storage purposes will be held legally responsible for verifying that their storage operations do not seriously disturb the equilibrium of nature outside their specific area of operation.

Although in recent years there has been increased interest in the stability evaluation of underground storage facilities, progress in this area has been relatively limited. There is little doubt that this is at least partially due to the indirect nature and apparent complexity of such methods as the microseismic technique. Furthermore, although in recent years an increasing number of papers dealing with various applications of the microseismic technique have appeared in the literature, the technique remains generally unfamiliar to the majority of the rock mechanics fraternity. A prime purpose of the present paper, therefore, is to promote increased interest in this technique, and in particular to consider its application in the stability evaluation of underground storage facilities. The paper will include a brief outline of the microseismic concept, a discussion of the associated monitoring and data analysis procedures, and a review of a number of current applications in the areas of underground storage including those developed using both conventional and solution mining methods.

2 MICROSEISMIC CONCEPT

In geologic materials the origin of microseismic activity is not well understood, but it appears to be related to processes of deformation and failure which are accompanied by a sudden release of strain energy. In such materials, microseismic activity may originate at the micro-level as a result of dislocations; at the macro-level by twinning, grain boundary movement, or initiation and propagation of fractures through and between mineral grains; and at the mega-level by fracturing and failure of large areas of material and/or relative motion between structural units. It is assumed that the sudden release of stored elastic strain energy accompanying these processes generates an elastic stress wave (seismic wave) which travels from the point of origin within the material to a boundary where it is observed as a microseismic signal or a discrete microseismic event. Figure 1 illustrates a number of typical microseismic signals monitored at a number of Penn State field sites.

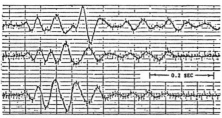

A. Event Recorded on Three Transducers Above a Long-wall Coal Mine Site.

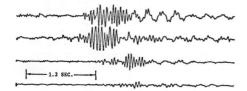

B. Event Recorded on Four-Transducers at a Shallow Underground Gas Storage Site.

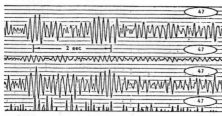

C. Events Recorded on Three Transducers at a Scenic Cavern Site.

Figure 1. Typical microseismic signals and discrete events monitored at a number of different Penn State field sites.

The fundamental frequency character of an observed microseismic signal in general depends on the source, and the distance between the source and the detector (transducer). Frequencies below 1 Hz have been observed at large scale field sites, whereas in laboratory studies microseismic signals have often been observed to contain frequencies greater than 500 kHz. It should also noted that most microseismic signals contain both a compressional (p-wave) and shear (s-wave) component, although in many field situations these are difficult to distinguish.

Frequency analysis of an individual microseismic event indicates that it contains a spectrum of different frequencies.

The form of the observed spectrum is a result of two separate factors, namely: the spectrum of the event at its source, and modifications incurred during its propagation from the source location to the point of observation (transducer location). Attenuation, which in geologic materials is often highly frequency dependent, plays a major role in modifying the microseismic source spectrum. The ability to detect microseismic events at a distance from their source is thus dependent on the source spectrum, the degree and frequency of the attenuation, the distance of the transducer from the source, and the band-width and sensitivity of the transducer and the associated monitoring system. Figure 2 illustrates typical range versus frequency data for microseismic signals. As a general rule, attenuation increases with frequency, thus at a large distance from the source only the low frequency components of the event will be observed.

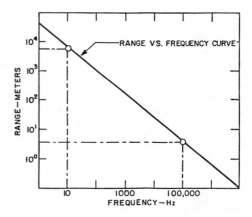

Figure 2. Typical range versus frequency data for microseismic signals.

One of the major advantages of the microseismic technique over more conventional geotechnical monitoring techniques is its ability to delineate the area of instability. From a fundamental point-of-view, therefore, accurate microseismic source location is extremely important. First, unless the actual source is accurately located, it is impossible to estimate the true magnitude of an observed microseismic event. For example, a series of small observed events may be due to a weak source located close to the transducer or due to a strong source located a considerable distance away. Secondly, in order to determine the mechanism responsible

43

for the observed activity, it is necessary that the location of the source be accurately known. In general, source location techniques involve the use of a number of monitoring transducers located at various points throughout the structure under study. Such a set of transducers is termed an array.

Figure 3 illustrates, for example, a typical field situation where microseismic techniques are being employed to monitor the mechanical stability of an underground storage cavern. Here suitable transducers have been installed at accurately known locations, and data from these are monitored during product input, output, and long-term storage. Microseismic activity occurring during such an evaluation is detected at each transducer at a different time depending on the distance between the particular transducer and the microseismic source. The difference in arrival-time between the closest transducer and each of the others yields a set of arrival-time-difference values which, along with the geometry of the transducer array and the velocity of propagation in the material, may be used to determine the spatial coordinates of the microseismic source. In such a study, source location makes it possible to determine the location of any instabilities which may influence the safety and operating performance of the facility and, furthermore, it provides a means (spatial filtering) of eliminating from subsequent analysis any activity occurring outside the immediate area of the facility.

In review then, from an application point-of-view, the important microseismic concepts are as follows:

(1) Microseismic activity originates at locations where the material is mechanically unstable.

(2) It propagates through the surrounding material undergoing attenuation as it moves away from the source.

(3) With suitable instrumentation such activity may be detected at locations a considerable distance from its source.

(4) The rate of occurrence and magnitude of the observed microseismic activity provides indirect evidence of the type and degree of instability.

(5) Microseismic data obtained from a number of transducers (array) make it possible to determine the actual location of the associated instability.

3 MONITORING AND ANALYSIS TECHNIQUES

3.1 General

At a field site microseismic signals are obtained by installing a suitable transducer, or usually a number of transducers (an array), in locations where they can detect any activity which may be originating in the structure under study. The overall monitoring system involves a transducer, an amplifying and filtering system, and a recorder. Figure 4 illustrates a typical system which might be used, for example, to monitor the microseismic activity occurring in a shallow underground storage cavern. In such an application the transducer could be a geophone (velocity gage) located in a suitable borehole perhaps 8-30 m below surface. In this case the transducer would monitor ground velocities due to microseismic activity occurring in, or around, the cavern structure.

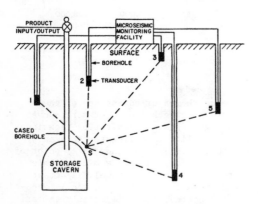

Figure 3. Transducer array installed to monitor the stability of an underground storage cavern.

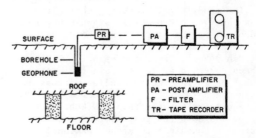

Figure 4. Block diagram of a typical system for microseismic field monitoring.

The output of the transducer, resulting from the presence of typical microseismic activity, is normally only of the order of a few microvolts, and it is necessary to amplify this small signal, without introducing noise and distortion, for subsequent processing and/or recording. Furthermore, to properly match the impedance of the transducer to the relatively low input impedance of the post-amplifier, it is necessary to employ an intermediate preamplifier. A band-pass filter is also normally included in such systems in order to eliminate undesirable extraneous low and high frequency signals. Past experience has shown that a magnetic tape recorder often provides the most satisfactory means for direct recording of microseismic signals, since it introduces a minimum of distortion and makes it possible to conveniently analyze the recorded data at a later date.

3.2 Transducers

The purpose of the transducer is to convert the mechanical energy associated with microseismic event into a suitable electrical signal. Microseismic activity at a specific point in a structure may be detected by monitoring the displacements, velocities or accelerations generated by the associated mechanical signals at that point using a suitable transducer. Where signals containing relatively high frequency components (f > 2000 Hz) are involved, accelerometers are usually employed, in contrast low frequency signals (f < 1 Hz) are usually detected with displacement gages. Signals between these extremes (1 Hz < f < 2000 Hz) are conveniently detected using velocity gages (geophones). Typical geophones and accelerometers have sensitivities in the range 40-400 V/m/s and 2-100 mV/g, respectively. Although both geophones and accelerometers have been used in monitoring such geologic structures as mines, tunnels, and caverns, in the majority of cases, geophones are normally employed. These geophones are less expensive than accelerometers and are generally more sensitive in the lower frequency range where much of the microseismic energy associated with large structures occurs. Two different types of geophones utilized in recent Penn State microseismic field studies are shown in Figure 5.

A limited number of field studies have also been conducted using hydrophones as microseismic transducers. Such transducers are effectively ultra-sensitive

pressure transducers and when installed in a fluid-filled borehole they sense the presence of minute pressure changes in the borehole fluid resulting from mechanical instabilities occurring in the surrounding strata. Although hydrophones are not suitable as microseismic transducers in most geotechnical applications, they have proven to be extremely useful in a number of special applications.

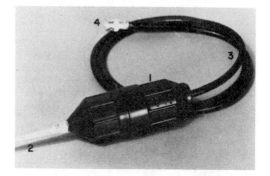

(A) Typical marsh-type geophone unit (1-marsh case, 2-spike, 3-electrical cable, and 4-electrical connector)

(B) Low frequency geophone with remote calibration capabilities

Figure 5. Two types of geophones utilized in recent Penn State microseismic field studies.

Optimum transducer locations and associated installation methods are highly site specific. For example, Figure 6 illustrates a simplified field situation where

45

it is desired to monitor microseismic activity associated with an underground geologic structure (ST). This structure, which could be for example an underground storage facility, is assumed to be located at an average depth below surface of d_1. It is also assumed that the site is overlain with a layer of unconsolidated material, for example soil, to a depth of d_2. One possible mode of transducer installation would involve installing a suitable number of transducers on the surface of the structure (A) and/or in holes drilled outwards from it (B). This would require access to the structure. A second mode of installation would involve installing transducers from ground surface above the structure (C1-C4). A detailed description of various methods for installing transducers both underground and from surface has been presented elsewhere (Hardy, 1981).

associated microseismic activity. A review of the literature indicates that a wide variety of equipment has been developed by various workers in the geotechnical field for this purpose [see for example, Hardy and Leighton (1977, 1980, 1982)]. In general, as illustrated in Figure 7A, a single channel system regardless of its apparent complexity consists of only three major sections, namely, the transducer, the signal conditioning unit, and the readout unit. In such a system, microseismic activity is detected by the transducer, the resulting electrical signals are suitably modified by the signal conditioning section, and these are finally displayed and/or recorded in the readout section. In general, two totally different types of signal conditioning are in common use; for the purpose of this paper these will be denoted as "basic" and "parametric."

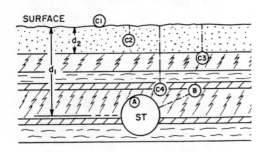

Figure 6. Simplified field situation illustrating various possible locations for microseismic transducers.

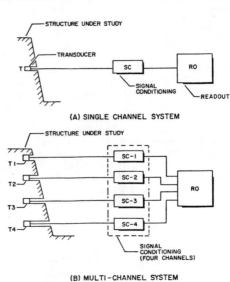

Figure 7. Simplified block diagrams of a single- and a multi-channel microseismic monitoring facility.

The type of transducer, and the location and depth of the installation, will depend on a number of factors including, amongst others, the depth of the structure (d_1), the depth of the overburden (d_2), the thickness and properties of the strata overlying the structure, the expected energy of the microseismic events to be detected, the desired source location accuracy, and the funds available. It should be noted at this point that there appears to be no one single type of transducer or installation technique which is suitable for all studies; experience has shown that the optimum arrangement must be tailored to the specific application.

3.3 Monitoring facilities

After the required transducer or transducer array has been installed, suitable facilities must be provided to monitor the

As noted earlier in the paper, an array of transducers and an associated multichannel monitoring system is normally required to obtain meaningful field data. A simplified four-channel system is illustrated in Figure 7B. It is important to note that in most cases such a system merely involves additional transducers and signal conditioning units, with the total data from all channels being recorded on a single multi-channel readout system. Regardless of the number of monitoring channels involved the various components of the system must be selected to provide the frequency response, signal-to-noise ratio (SNR), amplification, parametric processing, and data recording capacity necessary for the specific study.

As indicated earlier, two different types of signal conditioning are commonly in use in microseismic monitoring facilities, namely, basic and parametric. Figure 8A illustrates a simplified block diagram of a basic system. In such a system microseismic signals detected by a suitable transducer (e.g., a geophone) are first passed through a preamplifier located near the transducer. A field cable carries the amplified signal to the monitoring facility where the signal is further amplified, filtered, and finally recorded on a multi-channel tape recorder. The important feature of the basic signal conditioning system is that the microseismic data, although amplified and filtered, still retains much of its original analog form.

In contrast to the basic system, the parametric system incorporates additional signal conditioning facilities which further process the amplified and filtered microseismic signals to provide a series of specific parameters. For example, Figure 8B illustrates the block diagram of a single channel monitoring system incorporating a parametric signal conditioning system which automatically provides microseismic event rate data. Such systems are commercially available to provide one or more microseismic parameters such as total number of events, event rate, event energy, amplitude distribution, etc. For the most part these parameters are determined using digital techniques. Although such signal conditioning systems are extremely useful in certain specific situations, they have a serious disadvantage in that the original analog form of the microseismic data is permanently lost.

Depending on the type of signal conditioning system utilized, a variety of readout systems are available for storage and display of microseismic data. If basic-type signal conditioning is employed, the most flexible system is one incorporating a tape recorder along with an associated strip chart recorder (usually a high speed U-V recorder) for detailed visual examination of the data. Storage-type oscilloscopes and transient recorders are also useful for evaluation of selected microseismic signals. When parametric-type signal conditioning is employed, the data (such as microseismic rate) may be displayed on a simple panel meter, or on a digital display, printer, or graphics unit.

In many respects the type of readout system employed is intimately related to the method of data processing to be utilized for later analysis of the collected data.

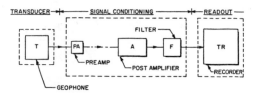

(A) Basic signal conditioning

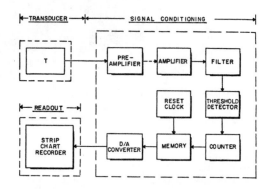

(B) Parametric signal conditioning

Figure 8. Single-channel microseismic monitoring systems incorporating basic and parametric signal conditioning.

As noted earlier, systems similar to those shown in Figure 8 are suitable for monitoring data from only a single transducer. In most field cases, however, the actual source of the microseismic activity is required and this can only be obtained using data from an array of transducers (normally a minimum of five), and a multi-channel monitoring system is therefore required. Details on the design and construction of a variety of such systems are available elsewhere (e.g., see Hardy, 1981). The multi-channel mobile monitoring facility (Mark I) developed at Penn State in the early 1970s is a typical example of such a system. Figure 9 shows a photograph of this system, which was originally designed to handle up to seven channels of microseismic data but was later expanded to 10 channels. A new system (Mark II) presently under construction, will have a 14-channel capability.

Figure 9. Penn State multi-channel microseismic monitoring facility (Mark I).

In general, at those field sites where more or less continuous on-site monitoring is undertaken, the monitoring facilities are usually located in a suitable enclosure underground or on surface. The tendency, however, in most recently reported studies has been to locate monitoring facilities above ground regardless of whether the transducers themselves are installed underground or from surface. Furthermore, as field sites under investigation become more numerous and remote, and the structures under study increase in dimensions, new techniques for transmitting microseismic signals from the various transducer sites to the monitoring facility are being investigated. For example, at one underground gas storage site under study by the writer (Hardy et al., 1981), signals from a number of transducer sites were transmitted by FM radio telemetry for distances of the order of two miles to the monitoring facility.

3.4 Data analysis

Once the necessary microseismic monitoring facilities have been designed, constructed and tested, a suitable transducer array has been installed, and the overall monitoring system optimized, it is possible to begin acquiring microseismic data. In general, the storage and processing of such data presents a number of difficulties,

namely:
(1) In most cases it is necessary to deal simultaneously with at least five channels of data, often seven or more.
(2) Microseismic events occur randomly in both time and amplitude.
(3) The frequency content of microseismic signals from the same field site may vary considerably from point to point.
(4) Considerable effort may be required to separate microseismic signals from the ambient or background noise.

In the past, analysis of microseismic field data has been for the most part based on manual and/or "hardwired" techniques. In recent years, with the increasing availability of compact and relatively inexpensive computers, the use of computer-based data analysis systems have become more common. Such systems make it possible to carry out on-line evaluation of such parameters as microseismic rate, amplitude, and source location. Unfortunately, the simpler forms of on-line processing involves parametric signal conditioning and as a result analog data, necessary for more sophisticated analysis, are often not recorded. In general, the type of analysis system required for a specific application is dependent on a number of factors including the following:
(1) Purpose of study (basic research/engineering).
(2) Degree of objectivity desired.

48

(3) Signal-to-noise ratio of typical microseismic data to be analyzed.

(4) Desired analysis speed and accuracy.

(5) Funds available.

Figure 10 illustrates a number of different types of microseismic data analysis systems. Although a tape recorder is shown as providing the input to the various systems, under suitable circumstances, all systems could be operated on-line to provide real time output data.

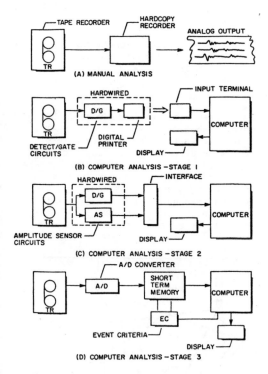

Figure 10. Various types of microseismic data analysis systems.

Figures 10B to 10D illustrate a number of stages in the historical development of computer-based microseismic analysis systems. The first stage (Figure 10B) involved the use of a suitable hardwired pre-processor unit to provide digital information on arrival times for source location analysis. In this type of system digital data is provided by the pre-processing unit which is then manually entered into a small computer for further processing and display. The next stage of development (stage 2) involves the direct interfacing of the pre-processor with the computer as shown in Figure 10C. Here both arrival-time and event-amplitude

data is generated in the pre-processor and fed directly to the computer for further processing, storage, and display.

The third stage in data analysis system development is shown in Figure 10D. Here the pre-processor unit has been eliminated, and microseismic signals entering the system are first digitized and put in a short-term digital memory. Using suitable software (event criteria), the computer then edits the digitized data, selects suitable signals, stores these in permanent memory, and then processes them to provide various microseismic parameters such as source location, amplitude, energy, etc., for each event. An important feature of this type of data analysis system is that the original form of the selected signals is retained within the computer, or in disc or tape storage, so that it may be examined in more detail later, and other parameters such as frequency spectra, event duration, etc., determined if desired.

4 APPLICATION TO MINED CAVERNS

4.1 General

It should be obvious at this stage in the paper that the microseismic technique for detection and location of instabilities in geologic structures has in recent years progressed to the status of a respectable geotechnical field tool. Such techniques are presently used routinely in a number of applications and there should be no serious difficulties in adapting this technique to the monitoring of conventional and solution mined cavern stability. Certainly all the required elements (transducers, transducer installation techniques, monitoring and data acquisition systems, data analysis techniques, etc.) for the development of suitable cavern stability monitoring systems are now generally available, and in the writer's opinion, the only factors that require further study are those associated with optimal array design, transducer selection, and installation. A number of aspects of these are considered in the following sections.

4.2 Transducer selection

A variety of commercial transducers are presently available which may be utilized for underground monitoring of microseismic activity associated with cavern stability. The most suitable one will depend to a great degree on the specific details of the cavern site. In the majority of cases it is recommended that geophones (velocity gages) rather than accelerometers be utilized.

For source-to-transducer distances of less than 500 feet relatively inexpensive geophones developed for geophysical exploration may be suitable. For those situations where source-to-transducer distances are greater than 500 feet, or where low-level microseismic sources are involved, more sensitive and lower frequency geophones (seismometers) will be necessary. In the writer's opinion the later type of transducer should be utilized where possible since these are available with internal calibration systems which allow the mechanical and electrical components of the transducer to be remotely calibrated on a regular basis.

Finally one of the most critical factors to be considered in selection of suitable transducers is their long-term stability. This is mainly a function of the design of the transducer case and the associated electrical connectors and cable. Since most transducers will be installed semi-permanently, particular attention must be given to insuring that the transducer and its accessory connectors and cables are intrinsically moisture proof and capable of withstanding rust and other possible corrosion for long periods of time.

4.3 Transducer array design

Figure 3, presented earlier, illustrates the general microseismic concept applied to cavern stability monitoring. The transducer array illustrated is however highly simplified and a number of important factors must be considered in designing an optimum transducer array for cavern stability monitoring. A number of the more critical factors will be considered here.

(1) Three-dimensional requirement--If the overall monitoring system is to be capable of accurately locating the sources of microseismic activity the transducer array must as nearly as possible surround the cavern in 3-dimensions. Figure 11 illustrates an example of both satisfactory and unsatisfactory (planar) array geometry.

(2) Shadow effects--Even with what appears to be a suitable 3-dimensional array, the presence of the cavern itself will create so-called "shadow effects" preventing one or more of the transducers from receiving direct signals from certain areas of the structure. For example,

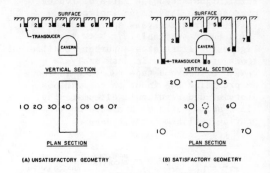

Figure 11. Typical satisfactory and unsatisfactory microseismic transducer array geometries.

Figure 12 illustrates the shadow areas associated with two transducers. Furthermore it should be noted in this example that neither transducer is capable of receiving direct signals from the floor region of the cavern. In general, therefore, an optimum transducer array must incorporate a sufficient number of properly located transducers so that all critical points in the structure may be "seen" directly by at least five transducers.

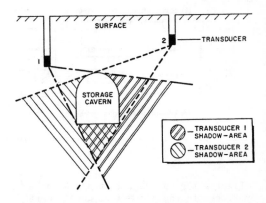

Figure 12. Microseismic "shadow-areas" associated with the presence of the storage cavern.

(3) Distance limitations--As microseismic signals travel from their source to the various transducers they are attenuated, with the highest frequencies being attenuated most rapidly. Under normal conditions the detection limits (which depend to a large part on the signal-to-noise ratio of the overall monitoring system) are of the order of 2000-3000 feet, and

50

at such distances the primary signal frequencies are of the order of 5-40 Hz. If possible, the transducer array should be designed so that the maximum source-to-transducer distances are of the order of 1000 feet.

4.4 Transducer installation

Most transducer installations associated with storage cavern stability monitoring will of necessity be at least semi-permanent in nature. Bearing in mind the restrictions placed on the design of the transducer array (see section 4.3) careful consideration must be given to the types of transducer installations employed. Furthermore, since a cavern stability monitoring system must be capable of long-term operation, considerable thought should be given to the difficulties which may be involved in replacing defective transducers. For example, the replacement of a transducer installed in the floor of the cavern will be considerably more difficult, and expensive, than replacing an equivalent one in a deep borehole drilled from surface. In general three types of installation, as illustrated diagrammatically in Figure 13, appear applicable, namely: shallow burial, deep borehole mounting, and in-cavern mounting. Further details on these are available elsewhere (Hardy, 1978, 1981).

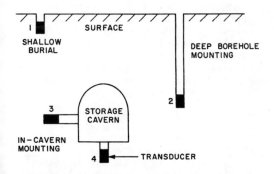

Figure 13. Various types of microseismic transducer installations suitable for storage cavern monitoring.

4.5 System optimization and calibration

Experience has shown that after the transducers are installed and the associated monitoring system is operational a number of important preliminary studies are required at a new microseismic field site

before meaningful results are obtained. In particular studies are required to optimize the overall system, and to develop a suitable velocity model for the associated rock strata.

(1) System optimization--Essentially this involves a detailed analysis of the ambient background, and selection of suitable system gains and filter setting to insure a maximum signal-to-noise ratio in the frequency range expected. If possible such studies should be initiated while access to the cavern is still available so that mechanical calibration signals may be applied at various locations in the cavern for evaluation of overall system response and sensitivity.

(2) Velocity model--In order to accurately locate microseismic sources it is necessary to have detailed information on the propagation velocities associated with the various rock strata in which the storage cavern is located. Space here does not permit a detailed discussion of the necessary procedures, however, they basically involve using the existing microseismic monitoring system to record seismic signals generated by small explosive charges detonated at precise times and locations in and around the cavern, and the analysis of the resulting data to provide a suitable velocity model. In this regard there is a considerable advantage if the monitoring system can be installed prior to completion of cavern excavation so that blasts occurring during the construction phase can be at least partially utilized.

4.6 Operational history

Once the stability monitoring system has been installed, optimized and calibrated, and a suitable velocity model developed, routine, continuous recording of microseismic data can be initiated. Since it is normal for even highly stable structures to emit some microseismic activity, initial studies must be carried out to determine the microseismic behavior of the storage cavern while it is empty and during various phases of its operation (filling, long-term storage, emptying, etc.). Furthermore in order to evaluate the stability of a specific storage cavern at a future date it will be necessary to develop a detailed knowledge of its operational history, from a microseismic point-of-view, which can then serve as a reference for future evaluation.

5 RECENT CAVERN STUDIES

As noted earlier in this paper to date there has been relatively few studies undertaken to evaluate the overall stability of caverns specifically developed for the purpose of underground storage. However, a limited number of related, although somewhat specialized, studies have been underway in which microseismic techniques have been, or are scheduled to be, utilized to evaluate structural stability. A brief review of a number of these studies, the majority of which are related to the problem of radioactive waste isolation, are included.

5.1 Radioactive waste isolation

In recent years the U.S. Department of Energy has been evaluating the potential of salt, granite, and basalt as a radioactive waste isolation medium, and small scale underground test caverns have been constructed in granite and basalt for preliminary experiments. Consideration has been given to utilizing microseismic techniques as a means of monitoring structural stability in such storage facilities. A variety of associated field studies have been underway, and others are in the planning stage.

In a recent paper by Majer et al. (1982), an experiment has been underway to investigate the discrete failure and behavior of hard rock in response to storage of high-level nuclear waste. Data are presently being collected from a 15-station, three-dimensional array of microseismic transducers surrounding 11 canisters of spent nuclear fuel and six electrically heated simulator canisters. The canisters are arranged in a linear array 420 meters beneath the surface in the Climax Granite at the Nevada Test Site. During the study, the microseismic signals are digitized and analyzed on-site using an Automated Seismic Processor (ASP) developed for microearthquake studies. Although the observed discrete microseismic events are high frequency in nature (1 kHz to 10 kHz) their behavior and appearance are typical of shear failure observed in microearthquake sequences.

The authors report that the preliminary results are encouraging, and indicate that the automated processor developed during the study should provide the desired monitoring and analysis sophistication necessary to characterize the response of the repository rock to the imposed thermal and radiation sources. The experiment is continuing and future studies will address questions relating to ongoing physical processes within the storage area through observation of their effects on the observed microseismic activity. Similar studies are also contemplated at the near-surface test facility associated with the basalt waste isolation project near Richland, Washington (Thirumalai, 1981).

West Germany has two major repositories for radioactive wastes: the Konrad site, located within an abandoned limestone mine, is used exclusively for low-level waste; and the Asse site, located in an abandoned salt mine, is used for both low- and medium-level waste. Both sites are situated in northeastern Germany near the city of Hannover.

In West Germany the Gesselschaft für Strahlen- and Unweltforschung (GSF), a Government organization, is concerned with the safety of nuclear operations and the problems of radioactive waste disposal. Studies associated with the latter aspect were initiated in 1965. At present GSF has basic and applied research underway at the Asse and Konrad sites. In order to monitor the overall structural stability of these repositories, a suitable microseismic monitoring system has been installed at both sites (Hardy, 1980A). As of mid-1980, detailed microseismic studies were already underway at the Konrad site, and similar studies at the Asse site were scheduled to begin later in 1980. At both sites microseismic signals from the various transducers, installed on concrete pads or directly on the floor of the underground entries, are first pre-processed using an event detector and then recorded on magnetic tape. The resulting tapes are later processed using a computer system developed specifically for this purpose. Preliminary analysis of data from these sites indicates that the observed microseismic events have major frequency components up to 50-100 Hz, and that the general microseismic background occurs in the same general frequency range.

Plans are presently underway to install "close-in" facilities to monitor in detail the microseismic activity in the actual storage areas. In particular, studies are planned at an experimental high-level waste disposal area at the Asse site where electrical heaters are presently being used to simulate the thermal effect of high-level waste. The purpose of these studies will be to determine if the motion of the associated thermal front can be traced using microseismic transducers installed at various distances from the location of the simulated waste (heaters).

According to a recent paper by Majer et al. (1981), during studies conducted by the University of California, at the Stripa mine in Sweden, electric heaters were used for the study of thermal stress effects in the associated granite. Unfortunately, microseismic studies were started well after heater turn-on, and only one transducer was used. However, it was observed that considerable microseismic activity occurred during the heating phase, and that such activity increased during the cool-down period.

5.2 Salt cavern storage

Extensive research and industrial development in the areas of salt cavern storage is presently underway in the USA and elsewhere. In particular, the use of solution mined caverns for the storage of such materials as crude oil, petroleum products, natural gas, and compressed air has accelerated rapidly during the last 10 years. Recent laboratory and field studies have indicated that under stress salt does generate microseismic activity. The microseismic technique, therefore, appears to offer a unique method of monitoring the structural behavior and stability of salt cavern storage facilities which are normally inexcessible. A number of current field applications of microseismic techniques in the area of salt cavern storage are those related to strategic petroleum storage, compressed air energy storage, and storage of natural gas.

In the USA, over the past several decades, a large number of caverns have been solution mined in Texas and Louisiana salt domes for the production of brine for use in the chemical industry. A number of these caverns are now being used to store strategic reserves of petroleum. In 1978 depressurization experiments were carried out at one of these storage sites, which consisted of an interconnected upper and lower cavern. During these studies, microseismic activity was monitored by a team from the Los Alamos Scientific Laboratory (Albright and Pearson, 1982) using a down-hole transducer package similar to that utilized in their geothermal fracture mapping program. Although these studies indicated essentially no microseismic activity prior to depressurization, an abrupt increase in such activity was noted immediately following partial depressurization. Maps of hypocenter distribution for the microseismic events indicated a concentration of sources at a thick ledge of salt located between the upper and lower caverns, where theory predicted possible structural instabilities could occur. These studies concluded that "the presence of detectable acoustic emissions [microseismic events] strongly indicates material fracture on at least a very localized scale. Further research is required to isolate the source mechanisms of these acoustic signals. It may be, especially if microcracking is the source, that repeated load cycles could cause localized failures to coalesce into macroscopic rock falls within the cavern." To the writer's knowledge, the preceding study was the first successful one in which it was possible to evaluate the stability of a solution mined salt cavern using microseismic techniques.

In recent years Dr. R. L. Thoms, and others at the Louisiana State University, have been involved in a number of research programs related to the engineering behavior of salt. At present this group is actively involved in the problem of designing solution mined caverns for compressed air energy storage (CAES), and have made extensive use of microseismic techniques both in the laboratory and underground (Gehle and Thoms, 1982).

The increasing worldwide use of solution mined salt caverns for the storage of natural gas presents another area where microseismic stability monitoring may well play an important role. Since 1975 the American Gas Association has supported a research program in the Penn State Rock Mechanics Laboratory relative to the design and performance of salt caverns for the storage of natural gas (Hardy, 1980B). During this program microseismic techniques have proven extremely useful for laboratory evaluation of salt properties, and in the future it is planned to evaluate their applicability for field monitoring of operating natural gas storage caverns.

Similar studies relative to salt cavern storage of natural gas have been underway in Denmark (Hardy, 1980A). Recent discussions with Professor Vagn Askegaard, director of the Structural Research Laboratory (SRL) at the Technical University of Denmark, indicate that his laboratory has been involved in a variety of microseismic related projects and recent studies have been associated with the design of facilities for the underground storage of natural gas in Danish salt domes. Although to date microseismic studies on salt have been limited to laboratory tests consideration is being given to the possibility of employing "down-hole" microseismic techniques in full-scale field measurements of salt cavern stability, possibly at depths of up to 5000 feet.

53

5.3 Other related studies

Recently a number of other microseismic studies have been underway, the results of which should be applicable to the evaluation of mined cavern stability. These include studies of natural caverns and gas storage reservoirs.

(1) Natural caverns--The detection and location of mechanical instabilities in an underground structure as complex as a natural cavern presents a large number of difficulties even with the highly sophisticated instrumentation available today. Regardless, the microseismic technique appears to be the only method presently available to realistically quantify the mechanical stability of such a structure. Recently, microseismic studies have been carried out in two scenic caverns located in the USA. Although the basic object of both studies were similar, the two studies are distinguished by the frequency range over which the studies were conducted. In the first, a high-frequency study, microseismic activity was monitored in the range 100 Hz to 45 kHz range; in the second, a low-frequency study, a frequency range of 1-50 Hz was employed. A relatively detailed description of both studies are presented elsewhere (Hardy, 1981), however, a brief summary of the two studies is included here.

The high-frequency study was carried out by Leaird (1980) and involved a series of experiments in which microseismic techniques were evaluated for the purpose of monitoring possible roof instabilities in a scenic cavern complex originally opened to the public in 1970. As noted by Leaird, the caverns under study had been formed by ground water solution of limestone strata containing interbedded layers of shale and clay. Bed separations, when they occurred, were generally along these weaker clay and shale layers. In one area of the cavern, separation of the roof strata had occurred and in a number of places the roof had developed 6 m long tension cracks, although it was noted that several of these had apparently stabilized. Recently, the agency responsible for the development and operation of the cavern felt it was necessary, from a safety point-of-view, to monitor roof rock stability in order to develop criteria for the prediction of possible later roof collapse.

During the study microseismic activity at the cavern site was monitored underground using commercially available equipment. Evaluation of the results indicated that the microseismic activity occurred in a discontinuous fashion, with periods of low-activity being followed by a short period of high-activity. It was Leaird's opinion that this observed behavior was a result of the cavern roof structure deforming in a "slip-and-hold" manner. Furthermore, he noted that the observed increase in the low-level activity just prior to the initiation of a period of high-activity appeared to provide the basis of a meaningful method for roof failure prediction.

The low-frequency cavern study was recently carried out by the Penn State Rock Mechanics Laboratory in another scenic cavern located in central USA. One area of this cavern complex had been closed to the public for nearly 15 years; however, due to an increased number of visitors in recent years the possibility of reopening this area to allow a more efficient flow of visitors through the cavern is currently under consideration. Since the area had been closed to the public for some years, and since minor structural instabilities had been noted in the past at this site, it was felt that a microseismic evaluation of the safety of the area should be undertaken as a preliminary step in the reactivation of the area for public use. Since the mechanical stability of a relatively large area (approximately 100 x 100 x 70 m) was to be evaluated, it was decided to employ an array of surface, borehole, and underground transducers, and to restrict the measurements to the low-frequency range in order to obtain a suitable monitoring range and an optimum signal-to-noise ratio.

At the site, commercially available geophones were utilized as transducers. Single element units were installed in a number of borehole locations and in two underground locations, and a single tri-axial geophone was also installed in a shallow borehole (0.6 m deep) near the center of the sink-area overlying the cavern under study. Monitoring at the cavern test site was carried out using the Penn State mobile microseismic monitoring facility (see Figure 9 presented earlier in this paper). As a consequence of the system configuration employed, and the extensive associated filtering, very high monitoring system sensitivities were attained. In general, the system was capable of sensing ground velocities as small as 5×10^{-8} m/s. During a four-day monitoring period a number of small microseismic events were recorded, however, the ground motions associated with largest events rarely exceed 12.5×10^{-6} m/s.

Based on the study it was concluded that the site, from a mechanical point-of-view, was highly stable. It was recommended, however, that if and when it was decided that the site would be renovated for regular use by cavern visitors, further microseismic studies should be undertaken to evaluate the long-period stability of the site both during and following the necessary renovation work.

(2) Reservoir storage--Since 1966 the Penn State Rock Mechanics Laboratory has been involved in research associated with the mechanical stability of underground gas storage reservoirs. Such reservoirs are regions of highly porous and permeable rock, often located at considerable depths (300-2000 m), which are utilized by the natural gas industry for storage of compressed natural gas for use during the periods of peak demand. During Phase I of the research, laboratory, model, and theoretical studies were conducted, and since 1971 an extensive microseismic field program (Phases II and III) has been underway to evaluate the mechanical stability of full-scale operating reservoirs.

A recent six-year field study (Phase III) involved a detailed investigation of the microseismic activity associated with the injection-withdrawal cycle of a relatively shallow (≈300 m) underground storage reservoir specifically selected to provide optimum experimental conditions. A total of six transducers (high sensitivity geophones) were permanently installed in boreholes, ranging in depth from 1-300 m, over the central section of the reservoir. In order to rapidly and objectively analyze the large volume of microseismic data obtained during the studies (some 70,000 m of multichannel tape), it was necessary to design and develop a suitable computer-based analysis system. With this system it has been possible to edit, manipulate and store large volumes of microseismic field data along with detailed information on various reservoir storage parameters, such as wellhead pressures, injection rates, gas in storage, etc. These data were later analyzed in order to evaluate possible correlations between observed activity and storage parameters. Analysis was also carried out to investigate the approximate source of the observed microseismic signals. In general the recent study was highly successful, and a two-volume monograph was recently published which provides a detailed description of all aspects of the project (Hardy and Mowrey, 1981; Hardy et al., 1981).

6 DISCUSSION

In this paper the writer has attempted to indicate the importance and need for storage cavern stability monitoring. It is obvious that with the rapidly accelerating use of underground storage, particularly in areas of high population and industrial development, methods must be perfected for the evaluation of the mechanical stability of such structures. Although the paper has specifically emphasized the need for such methods in relation to underground storage, these methods would also find considerable application in the construction and post-construction phases associated with such structures as pressure shafts, tunnels, and a wide range of other types of underground openings.

At present it appears that the most promising technique for this purpose is that based on microseismic phenomena. In this paper the writer has briefly reviewed the fundamentals of the microseismic technique and has presented a brief outline of how these techniques could be applied specifically to the monitoring of underground storage cavern stability. As indicated early in the paper, the microseismic technique is at present commonly utilized in a wide range of geotechnical applications, and its use in many fields of mining, in particular strata stability evaluation, have become almost routine. It is the writer's opinion that the application of microseismic techniques to other areas, such as underground storage, are long overdue.

Finally, although there is little doubt that microseismic measurements are somewhat more sophisticated and expensive then those involving conventional rock mechanics instrumentation, such measurements provide data unobtainable by any other method. Furthermore, due to the size and often inaccessible nature of many large underground structures, such as storage facilities, tunnels, pressure shafts, etc., the microseismic technique appears to provide the only practical means for overall stability monitoring of such structures.

7 ACKNOWLEDGEMENTS

The major financial support for the microseismic research carried out at The Pennsylvania State University has been provided by the Pipeline Research Committee of the American Gas Association (Projects PR-12-43 and PR-12-75), and the U.S. Bureau of Mines (Projects G0101743 and G0144013). During the more than 10 years that the writer has been involved in microseismic field investigations, he has been fortunate to have the assistance of a hardworking and enthusiastic group of staff and graduate assistants, including Dr. A. W. Khair, Dr. R. Y. Kim, and Dr. W. Zuberek, research associates; Dr. G. Mowrey, research assistant; E. Kimble, research aide; and A. Mangolds, L. Beck, J. Berezniak, W. Comeau, D. Roberts, and A. Richardson, graduate assistants. These persons have all contributed immeasurably to the Penn State microseismic field research program.

8 REFERENCES

Albright, J. N. and C. Pearson, (1982), "Microseismic Activity Observed During Decompression of an Oil Storage Cavern in Rock Salt," Proceedings Third Conference on Acoustic Emission/Microseismic Activity in Geologic Structures and Materials, H. R. Hardy, Jr. and F. W. Leighton – Editors, Trans Tech Publications, Clausthal, Germany (In Press).

Gehle, R. M. and R. L. Thoms, (1982), "Monitoring Cyclic Load Effects on Salt In-Situ," Proceedings Third Conference on Acoustic Emission/Microseismic Activity in Geologic Structures and Materials, H. R. Hardy, Jr. and F. W. Leighton – Editors, Trans Tech Publications, Clausthal, Germany (In Press).

Hardy, H. R., Jr., (1978), "Application of Microseismic Techniques to the Monitoring of Storage Cavern Stability," Storage in Excavated Rock Caverns, Vol. 2, M. Bergman – Editor, Pergamon Press, New York, pp. 321-328.

Hardy, H. R., Jr., (1980A), "Outline of Activities During 1980 Sabbatical Leave," Internal Report RML-IR/80-17, Geomechanics Section, Department of Mineral Engineering, The Pennsylvania State University, 204 pp.

Hardy, H. R., Jr., (1980B), "Development of Design Criteria for Salt Cavern Storage of Natural Gas," Proceedings Fifth International Symposium on Salt, Vol. 2, A. H. Coogan and L. Hauber – Editors, Northern Ohio Geological Society, Inc., Cleveland, pp. 13-20.

Hardy, H. R., Jr., (1981), "Applications of Acoustic Emission Techniques to Rock and Rock Structures: A State-of-the-Art Review," Acoustic Emissions in Geotechnical Engineering Practice, Editors – V. P. Drnevich and R. E. Gray, ASTM, STP 750, American Society for Testing and Materials, Philadelphia, Pennsylvania, pp. 4-92.

Hardy, H. R., Jr. and F. W. Leighton, Editors, (1977), Proceedings First Conference on Acoustic Emission/Microseismic Activity in Geologic Structures and Materials, Trans Tech Publications, Clausthal, Germany, 489 pp.

Hardy, H. R., Jr. and F. W. Leighton, Editors, (1980), Proceedings Second Conference on Acoustic Emission/Microseismic Activity in Geologic Structures and Materials, Trans Tech Publications, Clausthal, Germany, 491 pp.

Hardy, H. R., Jr. and F. W. Leighton, Editors, (1982), Proceedings Third Conference on Acoustic Emission/Microseismic Activity in Geologic Structures and Materials, Trans Tech Publications, Clausthal, Germany (In Press).

Hardy, H. R., Jr. and G. L. Mowrey, (1981), "A Microseismic Study of an Underground Natural Gas Storage Reservoir, Volume II - Field Data, Analysis and Results," American Gas Association, Arlington, Virginia, 372 pp.

Hardy, H. R., Jr., G. L. Mowrey, and E. J. Kimble, Jr., (1981), "A Microseismic Study of an Underground Natural Gas Storage Reservoir, Volume I - Instrumentation and Data Analysis Techniques, and Field Site Details," American Gas Association, Arlington, Virginia, 343 pp.

Leaird, J. D., (1980), Personal Communication, Acoustic Emission Technology Corporation, Sacramento, California, November 1980.

Majer, E. L., T. V. McEvilly, and M. S. King, (1982), "Monitoring an Underground Repository with Modern Seismological Methods," International Journal of Rock Mechanics and Mining Sciences (In Press).

Thirumalai, K., (1981), Personal Communication, Rockwell Hanford Operations, Richland, Washington, Feburary 1981.

EFFECT OF GEOLOGICAL STRUCTURE AND STRESSED CONDITIONS OF ROCK MASS IN DESIGNING UNDERGROUND POWER HOUSE

Berücksichtigung der geologischen Struktur und des Primärspannungszustandes im Gebirge bei der Projektierung von Maschinenkavernen für Wasserkraftwerke

Effet de la structure géologique et de l'état de contraintes primaire des massifs rocheux dans le dimensionnement du bâtiment des turbines souterrain

A.V.KOLICHKO
'Hydroproject' Institute (Middle Asia Branch), Tashkent, USSR
I.A.PARABOUCHEV
'Hydroproject' Institute, Moscow, USSR
V.J.STEPANOV
Rock Mechanics & Physics Institute, Kirgiz Academy of Sciences, Frúnzè, USSR

SUMMARY:

The problem of siting the underground powerhouses in the environment which is most favourable for construction and operation of the powerhouse necessitates maintaining stability of large-size caverns. Excavation of such caverns in the mountain regions which are still tectonically active and are characterized by high seismisity sets some special requirements for the minuteness of investigations in elements of engineering geology and their consideration in locating of the underground works, configuration and orientation of the caverns. In the USSR, like detailed investigations are carried out for all proposed hydro-developments with underground powerhouses and deep-set water-conveying tunnel systems. The paper deals with some results of investigations of the above factors and their accounting in design of the Rogun project on the Vakhsh River whose power house cavern is proposed to be 28 m wide, 68 m high and 200 m long.

ZUSAMMENFASSUNG:

Das Problem der bau-und betriebsgünstigen Lage von Maschinenkavernen für Wasserkraftwerke steht im Zusammenhang mit der dauerhaften Standsicherheit von Hohlräumen grosser Abmessungen. Der Bau derartiger Hohlräume in Gebirgsgebieten, die durch rezente tektonische Aktivitäten und starke Erdbebenwirkung gekennzeichnet sind, erfordert die umfassende Erforschung von mehreren ingenieur-geologischen Einflüssen und deren Berücksichtigung bei der Auswahl des Standortes, der Querschnittsform und Raumstellung dieser unterirdischen Hohlräume. In der USSR werden derartige Untersuchungen für all zu projektierenden Wasserkraftanlagen mit Maschinenkavernen und tiefliegenden Umleitungsstollen durchgeführt. Im Bericht werden einige Untersuchungsergebnisse und deren Ausnutzung für die Projektierung der Wasserkraftanlage Rogun am Wachsch mit der Maschinenkaverne von 28 x 68 x 200 m beschrieben.

RESUME:

L'implantation des centrales hydroélectriques souterraines dans les conditions les plus favorables pour leur construction et exploitation exige la stabilité de longue durée des cavernes de grandes dimensions. La création de telles cavernes dans les régions montagneuses, qui se caractèrisent par une activité tectonique récente et par une sismicité élevée, impose des exigences particulières à l'étude détaillée de divers facteurs géologiques et à leur considération pendant le choix des emplacements des ouvrages souterrains, de la forme de leur section et de leur orientation dans l'espace. En URSS, les études de ce genre s'effectuent pour tous les aménagements hydrauliques projetés avec les centrales en caverne ou les dérivations en souterrain de grande profondeur. Dans le rapport sont examinés certains résultats d'étude des facteurs indiqués et leur considération pendant l'élaboration du projet de l'aménagement hydraulique de Rogoune sur le Vakch dont la caverne pour la salle des machines a une largeur de 28m, une hauteur de 68 m et, une longueur de 200m.

Construction of underground structures having large sections and which are to be constructed in mountainous regions characterized with great seismicity, modern tectonic movements at fructures and with availability of great natural stresses, has on the one hand to meet the particular engineering and geological requirements when substantiating the design, and on the other hand to take into account all peculiarities and abilities of the rock mass when designing. In this sense the Rogoun hydroelectric station is extremely demonstrative; the construction of this station has been started some years ago on the Vakhsh river in Tajikistan, USSR.

The project consists of the following structures: a rock and earth dam 320 m high, a water intake structure, inlet tunnels, an underground power house which is located in upstream at a depth of 420m from the surface of the ground, and the outlet tunnels. The power house has a two-room layout: the machine room of the power house and the premises for transformers are located in parallels and have the following size: they are 28 m wide, 68 m high, and 200 m long.

From geological point of view the Rogoun project area is located within the zone of a joint of the two largest structural-facial regions of Middle Asia - south-west Tien Shan and east Pamirs - and it is characterized with highly active modern tectonic movements. Seismicity of the region regists 9 degrees on the 12-degree scale.

The project site itself is located in a narrow steep-sloped canyon, the slopes rise above the river for 400-600 meters. The basic rocks forming the site here are of Early Cretaceous age, and they are represented here with an irregular interstratification of sand stone and aleurolites with interlayers of argillites. The rocks deposit here monoclinally, and they are inclined to the downstream pool at the angle of 65-75°.

The sand stone as well as aleurolites and argillites are hard rocks, and they are characterized with the following strength abilities: temporary resistance to the uniaxial compression under water saturation is 100-120 and 60-80 MPa, tension resistance is equal to 7.5-11.0 MPa and 2-5 MPa respectively. The value of Poisson's ratio is 0.15-0.22. Under conditions of all-side compression (the value of side compression is some 20 MPa) the sand rock strength increases up to 300, while with aleurolites it rises up to 150-200 MPa.

The sand rocks and aleurolites have medium and heavy jointing: the jointing modulus here is equal to 3-6, while the value of volumic joint hollowness at a depth of 20-30 meters and more does not exceed some 0.3-0.5%.

At the places of the underground structures location the permeability of the rock mass is very poor (less than 0.01 l/min) as well as its ability for deformations (deformation modulus of the rock mass is some 6000-8000 MPa).

Apart from tectonic fissures which are united into four systems, there are developed various rupture faults in the rock mass here. Small ruptures (rupture thrusts) 100-300 meters long and which have shifts from 1 to 10 meters are available everywhere. Actual distances between those ruptures here are equal to some 20-60 meters. All of them are inclined to upstream at an angle of 20-30°. It is a plumage of more developed faults N° 1 and N° 2 (see Fig. 1).

Fault N° 1 is a steep upthrow fault with a shift of some 2000 meters, and its length is almost the same as the length of the rocks here. It is accompanied by a detritus zone which is well seen in plan and it is some 60 meters thick. The joint of the fracture is 1.0-1.5 meters wide and it is represented with breccia and clay.

Fault N° 2 is a gentle upthrow with a shift of some 120 meters, it is inclined to upstream at an angle of 50°, and it is a plumage of the fault N° 1. Thickness of the detritus zone which accompanies the said fault is some 30 meters; the joint of the fault is represented with friction clay of 10-15 cm wide.

Analysis of peculiarities of tectonic structure of the region allows to make a supposition that there are significant horizontal stresses inside the rock mass here,

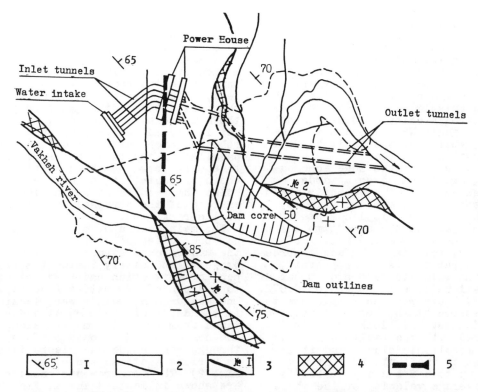

Fig. 1. Scheme of tectonic structure and layout of the main structures
of the Rogoun hydroelectric station.

1 - Orientation of rock layers; 2 - Small tectonic ruptures;
3 - Faults N° 1 and N° 2; 4 - Detritus zone; 5 - Prospecting adit.

and as a result of this, modern displacements at main fractures of the area (N° 1 and N° 2) are possible. In order to check up this supposition, as well as to make quantity analysis of velocity and direction of those movements, there were arranged stationary observations. Those observations included the following: precise geodetic levelling (accuracy ± 0.1 mm), levelling with the help of hydrostatic levels (± 0.01 mm), measuring of the surface inclination with the help of the two-component inclinometers (± 0.5-1.0 degree/year), while the deformations were being measured with deformation meters (± 0.2 mkm/m). Levelling has been carried on twice a year (geodetic one) and monthly, while inclinations and deformations were being measured continuously. The measuring lines and

points of observations were located both within the faults Nos 1,2 zones and near smaller fractures, and outside those zones. The total period of observations exceeded 12 years.

It should be noted that the directions and velocity of the tectonic movements which were being measured at the same points with different methods have practically coincided.

The main results of the carried on observations are as follows:

1.1. There exists a relative displacement of the rock mass blocks which are devided by the faults Nos 1 and 2, and it is constant in time. The direction of this movement coincides with the direction of those displacements which have been found with the help of geological indications (at Fig. 1 the rising blocks are marked with a sign +, and the settling blocks are marked with a sign -). The average velocity of the displacement movement at the fault N° 1 is equal to 1.6 mm/year, while at the fault N° 2 it is equal to 0.9 mm/year. In some individual years which are distinct for their heightened seismic activity of this region the velocity of displacement at the fault N° 1 amounts to 3 mm/year, while for the fault N° 2 it comes to 2 mm a year.

1.2. The detritus zone accompanying fractures moves upwards (squeezes out) at a velocity which exceeds 1.5-2 times the velocity of the relative displacements of the blocks; at the same time there were observed some relative deformations, both tensions and compressions, but the tensions prevail, and the relative values of those deformations come to some 0.03-0.07%.

1.3. There were no displacements registered at the lesser fractures and faults. The block which is limited with the faults Nos 1 and 2 is a monolithic block, and it inclines to the fault N° 1 at a velocity up to 6-8 sec a year (it is the average velocity of the whole region inclination), but at the same time the values of inclination reach some 40-110 sec a year in the zones of detritus.

Natural locked-up stresses of the rock mass were being measured by a method of relief in the butt-end version in the boreholes, 6-10 m deep, which have been drilled from the prospecting adits. At each point the measurements were being carried out in two mutual perpendicular boreholes which have been oriented in parallel to the rock layers. Simultaneously there has been carried on the ultrasonic logging of the boreholes the results of which also give an idea of the stressed conditions of the rock mass.

The main volume of measurements has been effected at the stretch of the underground structures of the project, and namely inside the prospecting adit which had been driven to a depth of 620 meters (see Fig.1). The measurement points were located in the depth of the mass at a distance from 40 to 360 meters along the normal to the ground surface through sand stone and aleurolites, in various tectonic zones (see Fig. 2). The measurements results are shown in Table 1 and at Fig. 2.

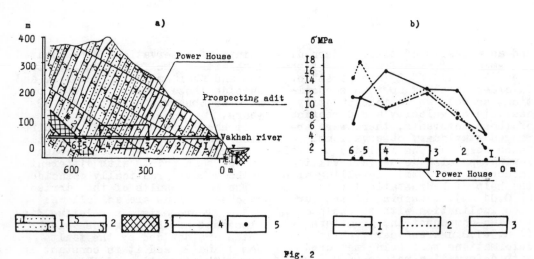

Fig. 2

a) Geological section at prospecting adit and location of points where have been measured internal stresses of rock mass.

1 - sand rock; 2 - aleurolites; 3 - detritus zones; 4 - line of small ruptures; 5 - measurement point and its number.

b) Absolute values of stresses:

1 - in vertical direction;
2 - perpendicular to rock layers;
3 - along rock layers.

Table 1.

Point N°	Distance, m		Lithologic-tectonic peculiarities of stretch	Average values of stresses, MPa		
	from borehole mouth	along normal from surface		vertical	horizontal	
					normal to rock layers	along rock layers
1	57	40	aleurolites and sand stone	$5.1^{\pm}1.6$	$2.4^{\pm}2.1$	$5.3^{\pm}1.7$
2	176	130	sand stone	$8.3^{\pm}5.7$	$9.2^{\pm}1.9$	$13.7^{\pm}3.7$
3	308	270	aleurolites with inter-layers of sand rock	$13.1^{\pm}6.7$	$14.0^{\pm}5.9$	$14.2^{\pm}2.7$
4	470	320	sand rock	$10.1^{\pm}4.7$	$10.1^{\pm}6.8$	$17.2^{\pm}9.9$
5	570	360	sand stone, 20 m from fault N° 2 joint (hang-ing wing)	$12.1^{\pm}7.3$	$19.1^{\pm}11.8$	$12.0^{\pm}4.8$
6	600	360	sand stone in detritus zone of fault N° 2 (lying wing at a distance of 10m from joint)			

For estimation of alterations which take place in natural stressed conditions of the rock mass in time there were arranged stationary observations. They are being carried on with the help of photoelastic transducers having resolving power of 0.2 MPa. The transducers are set in the same boreholes where the stresses conditions have been measured. During two years of observations there were found no alterations in the values of stresses.

Analysis of the results of the natural stresses measuring at the area of the underground structures of the project allows to come to the following conclusions:

2.1. For the rock mass of the Rogoun project the compressive stresses are typical, and their values are significantly higher than those which had been calculated for above lying rocks according to their weight (H). In the subsurface part of the slope down to the depth of 130-150 meters those stresses are less thanks to the process of relief.

2.2. In the part of the rock mass where relaxation has not taken place the horizontal stresses are everywhere 1.2-1.5 times greater than those vertical ones, and they exceed the horizontal stresses which had been calculated in accordance with H by 5-6 times. Actual vertical stresses also exceed the stresses which are caused by the weight of the above lying rocks. An exception to this is a part of the lying wing of the fault N° 2 (point 6 at Fig. 2) where the measured vertical stresses are less than those calculated with H. This exception can be explained with the fact that the weight of rocks in the hanging wing of the fault is being transferred to the lying wing through the forces of Coulomb friction, and this brings with itself a significant decrease in the vertical component of stresses tensor in the rocks below the faults.

2.3. Outside the fault N° 2 influence zone the horizontal components of stresses tensor which are oriented along the rock layers are greater than those normal to the layers, and they exceed them by 1.5 times; while next to the fault this ratio becomes vice versa (see observation points 5 and 6, Table 1). Alike relations are typical also for velocity of spreading of an elastic longitudinal wave which has been defined with the help of seismographic prospecting.

Analysis of fissures parameters at the above described stretches shows that at the direction of maximum value of the horizontal component of stress tensor the jointing modulus is less than in the perpendicular direction to it by 1.2-1.3 times. Thus, anisotropy of the rock mass stresses reflects the anisotropy of its deformation features.

Orientation of the maximum compressive stresses's vector for the rock mass is, as a whole, next to horizontal one.

2.4. Parameters of natural stresses field of the rock mass can be considered as constant ones in time. Growth of the stresses caused by deep seismic processes is being realized in the form of deformations at the faults. Thus, for the rock mass the state of dynamic equilibrium between stresses and deformations is typical.

As it is seen from the above described, the area of the Rogoun project is devided with the faults Nos 1 and 2 into three blocks which are subjected to relative displacements. There are no modern tectonic deformations inside the blocks. Rocks which serve a foundation of the dam and the media for the underground structures of the project are represented with hard rocks which are compressed from all sides. Field of the natural stresses is characterized with constant parameters in time and with their alterations in space, with excess of the horizontal stresses over the vertical ones. All these circumstances have significantly affected the layout and some other designing decisions of the underground structures of the project.

First of all, the whole complex of the project structures (water intakes, penstocks and the power house) as well as the dam core are located within the limits of one tectonic block which is outlined with the faults Nos 1 and 2. The outlet gravity tunnels intersect the fault N° 2 (Fig. 1) at which modern movement is fixed. To ensure safety operation of the tunnels they will be provided with "flexible" lining of special design which will be capable of withstanding the forcast tectonic deformations. The underground excavation for the power house (namely for the machine room and the transformer premises) is located within the limits of the part of the rock mass which has two peculiarities of the parameters of the stress field (Fig. 2):

3.1. Within the limits of this area the stress value in the rock mass is practically the same.

3.2. The value of the stresses tensor components ($\sigma_x = 14.0^{-2}_{+5}$ MPa; $\sigma_y = 14.0^{\pm}1.4$ MPa; $\sigma_z = 5^{\pm}1.5$ MPa) and the values of the main stresses directed in parallel (σ_{II}) and normal to (σ_I) the rock layers ($\sigma_{IImax} = 20.0^{\pm}5.0$ MPa, $\sigma_{IImin} = 5.5.^{\pm}3.0$ MPa, $\tau_{IImax} = 7.0^{\pm}3.5$ MPa; $\sigma_{Imax} = 19.0^{\pm}6.5$ MPa, $\sigma_{Imin} = 6.6^{\pm}4.0$ MPa; $\tau_{Imax} = 5.5^{\pm}3.5$ MPa) are practically equal to each other.

Thus, the part of the rock mass which has been chosen for the underground excavation of the power house is characterized with all-side and uniform significant compression which creates the best conditions for the breaking out stability. The parts of the rock mass next to the surface or to the fault N° 2 (Fig. 2) have a significant gradient of tensor stress values, and it is less favourable for stability of the breaking out space.

The long axes of the two excavation hollows are oriented almost "in a cross" to the rocks spreading, and this is favourable for stability of their long walls. For bracing of the walls it is supposed to use the prestressed anchors made of steel having high plastic limit, and those anchors will be able to withstand the residual deformations of the rock mass due to its relaxation. When estimating the carrying capacity of that part of the rock mass into which there should be embedded the said anchors the increase of its strength under the conditions of all-side compression has been taken into account.

The underground power house will be located in upstream pool, under reservoir waters, and with due regard to this it is necessary to implement some measures for protection of the underground excavations against entering of water into them in operation period of the station. Application of anti-seepage grouting of the rock mass around the underground premises, and it is usually being done in hydroengineering construction, in this case in ineffective because of being under conditions of the all-side compression the fissures in the rock mass are very narrow. Poor permeability of the rock mass in the area of the power house (specific water saturation does not exceed here 0.01 l/min) confirms this. A drainage-grouting curtain has been accepted as the main version of protection against infiltration of water: the grouting is being effected in close vicinity to the structure outlines in the zone of the rock mass relaxation; the drainage which is a network of boreholes having optimum orientation to the fissures and faults developped in the mass is located at the head side of the underground excavations.

The present paper deals with the most essential aspects of the design decisions which have been caused by some geological peculiarities and the stressed conditions of the rock mass in the foundation and around the underground Rogoun hydroelectric station.

However, the fundamentals of those design decisions, as we believe, are enough true for underground project structures which are designed under complicated geological conditions.

ROOF-ROCK BREAKING PREDICTION OF UNDERGROUND CHAMBERS DRIVEN IN SEDIMENTARY ROCKS

Die Prognose des Hangendbruches in untertägigen Hohlräumen in Sedimentgestein

Le pronostic de l'effondrement subite de matières rocheuses dans les cavités souterraines de la roche sédimentaire

S.T.KUZNETSOV, N.A.FILATOV & N.F.DONZYL
VNIMI, Leningrad, USSR

SUMMARY:
A method for the prognosis of mechanism of deforming and destroying in a stratified mine roof is described. The method concerning near rooms driven in sedimentary rocks includes the real pattern strength of rocks. The practical direction of this report including the use of its results for the estimation of the stability of rooms erected underground is shown.

ZUSAMMENFASSUNG:
Es handelt sich um eine Prognose der Verformungen und Zerstörungen des vielschichtigen Hangendgebirges über den benachbarten Kavernen im Sedimentgestein mit Anwendung der reellen Festigkeitskennwerte der Gesteine. Es wird eine praktische Bedeutung dieser Arbeiten hervorgehoben, einschließlich der Anwendung ihrer Ergebnisse für die Beurteilung der Standsicherheit von untertägigen Kavernen.

RESUME:
La méthode de la prédiction du méchanisme de la déformabilité et de la destruction des formations multicouches du toit est considerée conformément aux chambres rapprochées dans les roches sédimentaires avec l'utilisation de la solidité réele des roches. La tendance pratique des recherches en question parmi eux l'utilisation leur résultats pour l'évaluation de la stabilité des chambres souterrains est notée.

1 INTRODUCTION

The mechanical processes, occuring in a solid when underground workings are driven through it depend, to a great extent, upon the heterogenity of the solid structure as well as on the presence of surface weakening and fracturing. The weakened contacts in sedimentary bedded solids possess little cohesion with the angles of friction being small. These features are to be taken into account when solving the problems connected with rock stability estimation, the prediction of the breaking points within the cover of the solid and the choice of the type of support in workings being also taken into consideration.

A number of analytical and experimental investigations in this field were carried out by Kuznetsov (1961), Mc Niven and Ewoldsen (1969), Rachimov (1980).

The paper studies some aspects of the prediction in the roof-rock breaking processes of underground chambers. These processes commence under the influence of the tangential stresses due to the shear, (the processes are commonly known as lamination). Sometimes they are due to scaling when the contact relations of the adjacent (strata) layers are disturbed. Extended are the conceptions previously advanced by Donzyl (1974, 1975), Kuznetsov (1968), Kuznetsov, Filatov, Donzyl (1980), i.e. the authors of the paper.

2 CALCULATIONS OF ROOF ROCK LAMINATION AND SCALING

The complex problem of elasticity theory dealing with the stress-strain condition of the heterogeneous roof of adjacent chambers is solved by two methods. At first the calculation for initial rock lamination is performed, then the rock scaling possibility is determined.

The diagram for the calculation is shown in Fig. 1.

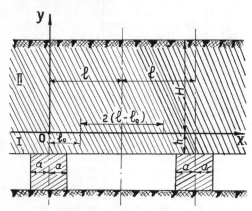

Fig. 1. The diagram for stress-strain condition determination of the back.

The roof considered consists of two layers. The bottom layer (I) represented by the strip has h_1 (m) thickness and the upper layer (II) simulated by half-plane stretches to the surface through the whole H (m) rock cover. The elastic modulus and Poisson's ratio for both layers are considered to be known.

Since the stability between the layers mentioned is essentially less than that of the layers themselves, the slot is formed in mining, its d length being equal to $2(l - l_0)$. The slot position is unknown beforehand and it wants estimating.

The quantity values of the ρ angle of friction (deg.) and C cohesion (MPa) are taken as factors of the volume stability of the contact layers interaction. The calculation is done on the basis of Coulomb's law:

$$|\tau_n| = \sigma_n \cdot tg\rho + c \qquad (1)$$

The σ_n normal value and tangential stresses obtained from elastic solutions are substituted into condition 1, thus locating the contour of the zone where shears occur along the plane of weakening.

The investigation of the problems resulted in revealing the initial lamination along the weakened contact occurs not only in the back itself and sometimes over the pillars. The pillar width, the span of the working and the angle of friction along the layer contacts affect most essentially the lamination zone height.

The rock scaling problem of layer I (Fig. 1) is solved by the method of successive approximation from two diagrams.

Diagram I. Taking into account the formation of the AA' slot, the relation between the contact surfaces of layers I and II along vertical displacements is given by:

$$V_I(X) = V_{II}(X) + \Delta V(X) \qquad (2)$$

where $V_I(X)$, $V_{II}(X)$ are the displacements of the contact surfaces of the layers, $\Delta V(X)$ is the function presenting the profile of the slot.

Diagram II. Let the equation of the vertical displacements under boundary conditions in the $0 \leqslant X \leqslant l_0$ section be:

$$V_I(X) = V_{II}(X) \qquad (3)$$

Let the normals to the boundary of stress in the $l_0 < X \leqslant l$ section be equal to zero:

$$\sigma_{yII}(X) = 0 \qquad (4)$$

As a result of these calculations, obtained from both diagrams, it was found that the length of the slot formed in scaling depends, to a great extent, upon the thickness of the h_1 layer and, to some extent

it is determined by the mechanical characteristics of the layer.

Analytical methods for solving the problem of rock lamination and scaling are computerized. These can be effectively used in the practice of calculation. The me methods enable the h (m) height of the rock lamination zone, the d (m) length of the scaling zone and the stress condition of the layers to be determined.

For the predicted estimation of roof-rock condition the simplified approximated formulae for $\bar{h}$, $\bar{d}$, σ_i determining on the empirical basis along with the methods calculated, can be used, the latter being computerized.

The application field of such solutions is limited by the following conditions: $9° \leqslant \rho \leqslant 36°$, $0.2 \leqslant a/_l \leqslant 0.5$, $0.2 \leqslant h_{I/(1-a)} \leqslant 0.5$

$$2(1-a)(\beta - \varkappa C') - 0.15 l > 0 \qquad (5)$$

where $C' = C/\gamma H$, β and $\varkappa$ are empirical coefficients obtained from Fig. 2.

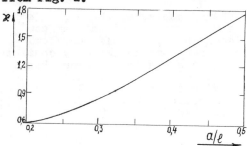

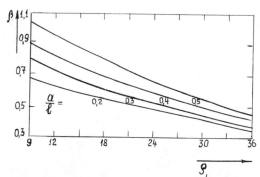

Fig. 2. The change of the $\varkappa$ and β coefficients as a function of ρ and $a/_l$.

The h height of the rock lamination zone for the cases, determined by the ratio s (5) is given by the following formula:

$$\bar{h} = 2(1-a)(\beta - \varkappa C') \qquad (6)$$

The formula for the determination of the $\bar{d}$ rock scaling zone length with regard to the given thickness of the h_n layer is the following:

$$d = 2(1-a) \sqrt{1 - \frac{h_n/(1-a)}{0.50 + 0.36 a/_l}} \qquad (7)$$

where

$$h_n = h_I \sqrt[3]{\frac{E_I(1-\gamma_{II})}{E_{II}(1-\gamma_I)}}$$

When calculating the stress condition of the roof bearing layer with the approximated formulae, the influence of the rock cover supplementary load, the inherent weight of the layer and the efforts of boundary friction should be taken into consideration as it was done by Donzyl in his work (1974).

To evaluate the accuracy of the approximated methods of calculation, a correlation was made with the data obtained from computerized solutions as well as with the results of the experiments carried out in mines and model experiments, the models being made of equivalent and optically sensitive materials. A good match ranging from 15 to 20% was obtained. This match suggests the representation and reliability of the original positions of the work presented (Skosobzev et.al. 1974).

3 CALCULATION OF ROCK LAMINATION SEQUENCE ALONG THE WEAKENED CONTACTS

The above methods of the calculation for two-layer systems dealing with the processes of lamination and scaling in roof-rock of the underground chambers are generalized for the case of more complicated problem with n-layer cover.

To characterize the excess of $|\tau'_n(x, y_i)|$ dimensionless stresses over the $\sigma'_n(x, y_i)$ value that prevents shear at the i-point of the weakened contact, the following

$$R_{m_i}(x, y_i) = |\tau'_n(x, y_i)| - \sigma'_n(x, y_i) \operatorname{tg} \rho_i - c'_i \qquad (8)$$

expression is introduced, where

$$\tau'_n = \tau_n/\gamma H \; ; \quad \sigma'_n = \sigma_n/\gamma H \; ; \quad c' = c/\gamma H$$

y_i – is the lamination from the i-contact to the surface of the pillar closure with roof-rock (m).

Since the discontinuity of the weakened contacts in a cover is, as a rule, due to mining and connected with the chamber span increase, the maximum $R_{m_i}(x, y_i)$ value specifies the lamination crack starting point on the contact studied.

$$\eta_{1,i}(x,y_i) = \max R_{mi}(x,y_i) \qquad (9)$$

The calculations demonstrate that the criterion (9) enables the diagnostic estimation to be carried out under a wide range of condi - tions. The diagrammatic plotting of the predicted specified strength permits the sequence of possible rock lamination along the weakened contacts to be determined. Such diagrams are graphic illustrations to the analysis.

The roof-rock cover, taken as an example, involves three types of contacts in multilayer measures. The information on these contacts is given in Table 1 for the a/l parameter that is equal to 0.4

Table 1. The contact characteristic

Contact types	y_i/l	ρ deg.	c'	$\eta_{1,i}$
I	0.12	24	0.3	0.07
II	0.18	9	0.0	0.56
III	0.54	24	0.4	-0.29

According to the conceptions advanced by Fisenko (1959), the estimation of surface breaking along the weakened contacts is conducted with regard to the dis- cription of specific ultimate con- dition and the diagrammatic plot- ting, characterizing the nominal infinite strength.

The $\eta_{1,i}(x,y_i)$ criterion values are found (Table 1).

Fig. 3 demonstrates that the lamination cracks appearing due to shear is primarily possible at the first and then at the second type of the contacts, whereas the third contact type is not subject to any lamination at all. By means of $\eta_{1,i}(x,y_i)$ values the dis - turbance of contact discontinuity is predicted even in the cases when only separate sections are laminated.

To find out the contact along which the first lamination crack will appear, it is necessary to analyse the K_i values of tangen- tial stress acting along the

$$K_i = \int_{l'_i}^{l} |\tau_n(x,y_i)| dx , \qquad (10)$$

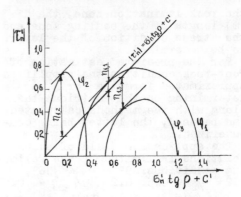

Fig. 3. The specification of contact layers strength.

weakened contacts, where l'_i is the x-coordinate of the surface discontinuity in solid and lami - nated sections weakened by contacts.

Fig. 4 shows the diagram change of the $K_i/(\gamma H l)$ values as h/l function for various values of the a/l ratios: 1=0.1, 2=0.2, 3=0.3, 4=0.4, 5=0.5 when l'_i is equal to 0.

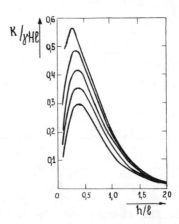

Fig. 4. The change diagram of $K_i/\gamma H l$ value as h/l function.

To predict possible cracks widen- ing within the rock lamination zone it is necessary to find how many times the tangential stress exceeds the sum of Γ_i friction efforts and μ_i cohesion along the weaken- ed contacts, i.e.

$$\eta_{2,i} = \frac{K_i}{\Gamma_i + \mu_i} , \qquad (11)$$

where $\Gamma_i = \Gamma_i \, tg \, \rho_i$; $\Gamma_i' = \int_{t_i}^{t} \sigma_n(x, y_i) \, dx$,
$\mu_i = C_i(1 - t_i')$

Thus criterion (11) permits to follow the crack development and movement in the solid. The calculations prove that in the above cases the sequence of cracks lamination widening along the weakened contacts also coincide with that of $\eta_{2,i}(x, y_i)$ decreasing changes.

It is not difficult to obtain $\eta_{2,1} = 0.21$; $\eta_{2,2} = 3.6$ as the values of the above mentioned example. One should not define $\eta_{2,3}$ parameter as $R_{m,3} < 0$ Consequently, the first lamination crack widens along the whole span of the chamber merely at contact II whereas at contact I the crack will only appear without developing at full length because of the sufficient high values of friction and cohesion strength at the contact.

4 EXPERIMENTAL INVESTIGATIONS

Some experimental investigations were carried out to check up and refine a number of methodical conceptions of the calculation on the sequence of roof-rock lamination. The layer models, representing the schematic part of the problem were made of optically sensitive materials. The experiments were carried out at room temperature under stress plane condition. The contact layer surfaces imitating the rock thickness, were cemented by rosin, the latter being an indicator to shear deformation. The technique of optical investiga - tions is given in the paper by Filatov et al. (1975).

Despite the relative character of the prerequisites assumed the results of the experimental in - vestigations were of great interest. These allowed to find graphically both the qualitative agreement of the predicted estimation for pos- sible roof-rock crack formation and the section length of contact discontinuity.

5 REFERENCES

Donzyl N.F. Calculation of stress-strain condition of one layer back in a stope, VNIMI Trans - actions, Vol. 91, p.p. 159-164, 1974.

Donzyl N.F., Afanasiev U.S., Filatov N.A. Calculation of roof-rock lamination in room and pillar without extraction of pillars, VNIMI Transactions, Leningrad, Vol. 95, p.p. 83-88, 1975.

Kuznetsov G.N. Ultimate tensile strength of solid rocks with regard to space orientation of the natural surface weakening, VNIMI Transactions, Leningrad, Vol. 43, p.p. 198-221, 1961.

Kuznetsov S.T. On calculation of sedimentary rock cover stability, VNIMI Transactions, Leningrad, Vol. 68, 1968.

Kuznetsov S.T. , Filatov N.A., Donzyl N.F. On problem of roof-rock chamber lamination predic- tion, Physicotechnical Problems of Natural Resources Mining, No. 4, p.p. 23-26, 1980.

Mc Niven H.D., Ewoldsen H.M.,1969. Rockbolting of tunnels for struc- tural support, J. of Rock Mech. and Min. Sci., V.6, No. 5, p.p. 24-28.

Rachimov V.P. Mechanical processes in solid in room and pillar with- out extraction of pillars, The Trans. of the Usb. Branch of the USSR Academy of Sciences,Tashkent, 1980.

Skosobtsov B.S., Donzyl N.F., Filatov N.A. Calculation of stress-strain condition of multilayer stope back, VNIMI Trans., Lenin- grad, Vol. 91, p.p. 165-172,1980.

Filatov N.A., Belyakov V.D., Mevlev G.A. Photoelasticity in rock mechanics, Nedra, Moscow, p. 184.

Fisenko G.L. Characteristics of stability in solid, Ugletech - izdat, Leningrad, in the book Rock Mechanics and Mine Survey- ing, p.p. 91-100, 1959.

EINIGE ERGEBNISSE AUS LABORVERSUCHEN ZUM MECHANISCHEN VERHALTEN VON STEINSALZ UND IHRE BEDEUTUNG FÜR DEN THEORETISCHEN ENTWURF VON SPEICHERKAVERNEN

Some laboratory test results on the mechanical behaviour of halite and their significance for the theoretical design of salt cavities

Quelques résultats des essais de laboratoire sur le comportement mécanique du sel gemme et leur signification pour la conception théorique des cavernes de stockage

K.H.LUX & R.B.ROKAHR
Universität Hannover, Bundesrepublik Deutschland

ZUSAMMENFASSUNG:

Der vorliegende Beitrag befaßt sich mit einigen Aspekten zu Laborversuchen mit Steinsalz und zur Dimensionierung von Salzkavernen. Dazu wird zunächst ein genereller Überblick über die im Rahmen gebirgsmechanischer Untersuchungen für den Entwurf und die Ausführung von Kavernenanlagen im Salzgebirge durchzuführenden Arbeiten gegeben. Anschließend werden aufbauend auf den Ergebnissen einaxialer Kriechversuche einige Probleme diskutiert, die mit der Formulierung viskoser Stoffgesetze und den mit ihnen erhaltenen Aussagen zum Kriechverhalten verbunden sind. Insbesondere wird eine vergleichende Untersuchung zur Extrapolation von Laborzeiträumen, die im Bereich von Wochen und wenigen Monaten liegen, auf für Kavernenanlagen relevante Zeiträume von Jahren durchgeführt.

SUMMARY:

First of all a dimensioning concept is presented, which covers the general procedure of cavern design from a rock mechanical viewpoint. After presentation of some representative creep laws suggested for rock salt and their parameters which were determined by one set of uniaxial creep tests, the results of a comparative study are discussed. This study shows some interesting aspects connected with the extrapolation of the creep behaviour predicted with different creep laws.

RESUME:

Tout d'abord il se presente un concept du dimensionnement, qui traîte le procédé général du projet de cavernes d'un point de vue mécanique de rocher. Après la présentation de quelque lois de convergence recommandées pour le sel gemme et le paramètres déterminés par une série des essais uniaxial de convergence les résultats d'un étude comparatif sont discutés. Cet étude un indique quelques aspects liés avec extrapolation du comportement convergence prédite par les lois différentes.

1. KAVERNENBAU IM SALZGEBIRGE

Der Hohlraumbau im Salzgebirge ist in den vergangenen Jahren zunehmend in den Blickpunkt des wissenschaftlichen Interesses gelangt. Bei diesen Hohlräumen handelt es sich einerseits um die Grubenbaue der Salz- und Kalibergwerke und andererseits um Kavernen, die entweder bei der soltechnischen Gewinnung von Steinsalz entstehen oder die zur Speicherung von flüssigen oder gasförmigen Energieträgern sowie zur Lagerung von Industrieabfällen ausgesolt werden. Eine besondere Problematik beinhaltet die Endlagerung hochradioaktiver Abfälle in Steinsalzlagerstätten, auf die jedoch nicht näher eingegangen werden soll. In der Bundesrepublik Deutschland sind insbesondere im nordwestlichen Bereich mehr als 200 Salzlagerstätten aus dem Zechstein vorhanden, die überwiegend als Salzstöcke ausgebildet sind und in denen in den letzten 15 Jahren bereits mehr als 100 Kavernenspeicher mit Volumina bis zu 500 000 m³ je Kaverne angelegt wurden. Die Kavernen dienen hauptsächlich zur Bevorratung von Rohöl und schwerem Heizöl sowie von leicht verflüssigbaren Mitteldestillaten wie Äthylen und Butan. Darüber

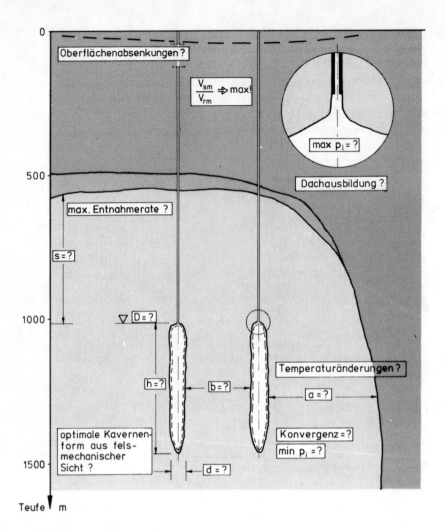

Bild 1   Fragen zum Entwurf eines Kavernenfeldes

hinaus sind neben 2 Druckluftkavernen 18 Hochdruckerdgaskavernen hergestellt und in Betrieb genommen worden.

Ein wesentlicher Forschungsschwerpunkt des Lehrgebietes für Unterirdisches Bauen (LUB) der Universität Hannover befaßt sich mit Untersuchungen zum Tragverhalten von soltechnisch hergestellten Hohlräumen im Salzgebirge. Da die nicht zugänglichen Salzkavernen im Gegensatz zu den üblichen begehbaren Tunnel- und Kavernenbauwerken im Fels keinen Ausbau zur Unterstützung der Trageigenschaften des Gebirges erhalten können, ist als Grundlage für einen sicheren und wirtschaftlichen

Kavernenentwurf einer realistischen Einschätzung des Tragverhaltens und des Tragvermögens des die Hohlräume umgebenden Gebirges die entscheidende Bedeutung zuzumessen.

Welche Anforderungen werden nun von einem Kavernenbetreiber an den auf gebirgsmechanischen Untersuchungen beruhenden Kavernenentwurf gestellt?

Bild 1 zeigt einen Schnitt durch einen Salzstock und zwei für Norddeutschland typische Speicherkavernen, die zu einem größeren Kavernenfeld gehören sollen. Das Ziel eines Kavernenentwurfs besteht nun

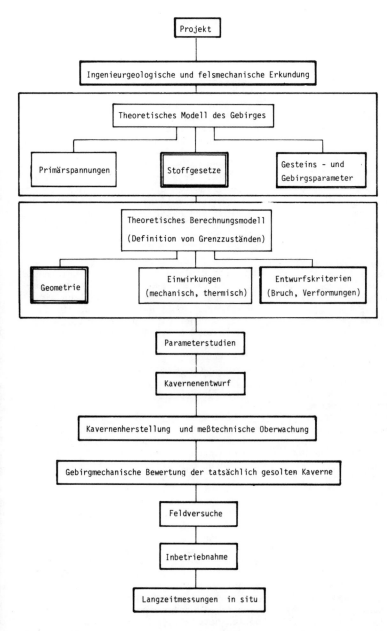

Bild 2 Vereinfachte Darstellung der Vorgehensweise bei der Planung und Ausführung von
Salzkavernen aus gebirgsmechanischer Sicht

aus volks- und betriebswirtschaftlicher
Sicht darin, ein möglichst großes Speicher-
volumen V_{sm} in einem möglichst kleinen Ge-
birgsbereich V_{rm} unterzubringen, d.h. einen
möglichst hohen Ausnutzungsgrad der nur in

begrenztem Umfang zur Verfügung stehenden
und für die Anlage von Kavernen geeigneten
Steinsalzlagerstätten zu erreichen. Für
den Entwurf folgt daraus die Forderung
nach möglichst großen und möglichst dicht

benachbarten Kavernen. Dieser Forderung entgegen stehen die begrenzte Tragfähigkeit des Gebirges, die langfristig zu erwartenden Hohlraumkonvergenzen, die aus Wirtschaftlichkeitsgründen so gering wie möglich bleiben sollen, sowie die Gebirgsverformungen und die Geländeoberflächenabsenkungen. In Bild 1 sind die von der gebirgsmechanischen Untersuchung erwarteten wesentlichen Aussagen zusammengestellt.

2. EINIGE ANMERKUNGEN ZUR GEBIRGSMECHANIK IM SALZKAVERNENBAU

Die aus gebirgsmechanischer Sicht wesentlichen Schritte bei der Planung und Ausführung eines Kavernenprojektes sind in Bild 2 in einem vereinfachten Ablaufplan dargestellt. Danach folgen auf die Festlegung der projektspezifischen wirtschaftlichen und technischen Randbedingungen wie Standort der Kavernenanlage, Art der Kavernennutzung, benötigtes Hohlraumvolumen, Betriebsbedingungen und beabsichtigte Nutzungsdauer die geologische und geotechnische Erkundung des Projektgebietes sowie die Ermittlung der mechanischen Eigenschaften des anstehenden Gesteins im Labor. Auf der Grundlage der geologischen, geophysikalischen und labortechnischen Untersuchungen ist dann ein theoretisches Modell des Gebirges zu erstellen, das die Abschätzung des Primärspannungszustandes, die Formulierung theoretischer Stoffgesetze sowie die Festlegung realistischer Gebirgskennwerte umfaßt. Anschließend ist darauf aufbauend ein theoretisches Berechnungsmodell zu erstellen, das von dem erarbeiteten Gebirgsmodell ausgeht und zusätzlich geeignete geometrische Idealisierungen eines repräsentativen Gebirgsbereiches und der Kavernenanlage sowie die Festlegung charakteristischer Beanspruchungszustände erfordert. Da die komplexen realen Verhältnisse nur näherungsweise zu erfassen sind, beruht das theoretische Berechnungsmodell auf der Definition von Grenzzuständen, die mögliche Grenzfälle im Tragverhalten der Kavernenanlage erfassen sollen. Darüber hinaus erfordert das theoretische Modell Kriterien, die eine Beurteilung der Ergebnisse im Hinblick auf das zu erwartende Tragverhalten und die Gebrauchsfähigkeit der Kavernenanlage erlauben. Mit Hilfe einer Parameterstudie, in der die Sensitivität des Modells auf die mögliche Streubreite der signifikanten Parameter untersucht wird, kann dann nach u.U. mehrfacher Variation von Kavernenform und Kavernengröße der Kavernenentwurf erfolgen.

Die Herstellung der Kaverne wird durch entsprechende Hohlraumvermessungen überwacht, um die Einhaltung der von der Gebirgsmechanik vorgegebenen Grenzabmessungen zu gewährleisten. Nach einer Endvermessung können Feldversuche durchgeführt werden, um vor Inbetriebnahme Auskunft über das tatsächliche Verhalten der Kavernen zu erhalten. Nach Auswertung dieser Feldversuche und einer darauf aufbauenden Überprüfung der geplanten Betriebsbedingungen kann die Kaverne in Betrieb genommen werden. Während der Betriebszeit sind dann schließlich Feldmessungen durchzuführen, deren Ergebnisse zu einem Vergleich zwischen der theoretischen Prognose und dem tatsächlichen Tragverhalten sowie zu einer von einer verbesserten Grundlage ausgehenden Extrapolation herangezogen werden können.

Aus Bild 2 ist zu ersehen, daß von der ersten Planung bis zur Inbetriebnahme einer Kaverne umfangreiche gebirgsmechanische Untersuchungen erforderlich sind. Im folgenden soll auf einige spezielle Bereiche näher eingegangen werden. Diese sind in Bild 2 besonders hervorgehoben und betreffen die theoretischen Stoffgesetze und die Durchführung und Auswertung von Laborversuchen.

3. LABORVERSUCHE MIT STEINSALZ

Die Grundlage für den gebirgsmechanischen Entwurf einer Kavernenanlage bildet die Ermittlung der Festigkeits- und Verformungseigenschaften des die Hohlräume umgebenden Gebirges. Detaillierte Aufschlüsse über den Gebirgsaufbau sind jedoch nur im unmittelbaren Bereich der Erkundungsbohrungen vorhanden. Das aus diesen Erkundungsbohrungen entnommene Bohrkernmaterial kann im Labor auf seine mechanischen Eigenschaften hin untersucht werden. Dabei ist zu beachten, daß die aus den Laborversuchen an Gesteinsprüfkörpern erhaltenen Ergebnisse zum Materialverhalten nicht ohne zusätzliche Überlegungen auf den großräumigen Gebirgsverband übertragen werden können. Im folgenden sollen neben einer kurzen Beschreibung der apparativen Ausstattung einige der am LUB durchgeführten Arbeiten zum Stoffverhalten von Steinsalz vorgestellt und überwiegend qualitativ diskutiert werden. Eine quantitative Auswertung bleibt weiteren Untersuchungen vorbehalten. Da die Daten weitgehend in Verbindung mit Projekten erhalten wurden, können keine detaillierten Angaben zur Lokation des jeweils untersuchten Bohrkernmaterials erfolgen.

3.1 LABORRAUMAUSSTATTUNG LUB

Die am LUB vorhandene, in zwei klimatisierten Laborräumen untergebrachte Laborausstattung kann aus Bild 3 und Bild 4 ersehen werden.

Bild 3 zeigt eine servohydraulisch gesteuerte Triaxialpresse, die für eine Vertikalkraft von 2500 kN ausgelegt ist. Mit der Hochdruckzelle kann ein Druck von maximal 50 MPa auf den Prüfkörper aufgebracht werden. Die Prüfkörper können eine Höhe von h ≤ 250 mm und einen Durchmesser von d ≤ 100 mm haben. Üblicherweise werden Prüfkörper mit den Abmessungen h/d = 180/90 mm untersucht. Der Vertikaldruck kann sowohl kraft- wie auch dehnungs- und verformungsabhängig geregelt werden. Neben einaxialen Druckversuchen (UC) können sowohl triaxiale Druckversuche (TC) wie auch triaxiale indirekte Zugversuche (TE) durchgeführt werden. Die Aufnahme der Meßwerte erfolgt über induktive Wegaufnehmer. Die Versuchsergebnisse werden in Kraft - Weg oder in Weg - Zeit - Diagrammen geplottet.

Bild 4 zeigt die vorhandenen Kriechstände, die ebenfalls servohydraulisch gesteuert werden. Dabei handelt es sich um zwei Kriechstände, in die gleichzeitig je bis zu 5 Prüfkörper eingebaut werden können, um so in relativ kurzer Zeit genügend Datenmaterial für die weitere Auswertung zu erhalten. Üblicherweise werden 3 Prüfkörper bei einer Laststufe getestet. Die Belastung wird während des Versuchs entsprechend der Prüfkörperverformung nachgeregelt, um eine konstante Spannung über die Versuchszeit zu gewährleisten. Diese Kriechversuche werden bei Raumtemperatur durchgeführt. Darüber hinaus sind zwei weitere Kriechstände vorhanden, in denen Kriechversuche bei erhöhten Temperaturen bis zu + 250° C und bei tiefen Temperaturen bis zu - 80° C durchgeführt werden können. Die Aufnahme der Meßwerte erfolgt im Temperaturbereich von etwa + 50° C bis - 80° C durch induktive Meßaufnehmer. Bei höheren Temperaturen werden die Prüfkörperverformungen mit einer speziellen Optik ermittelt. Über eine Vielstellenmeßanlage werden die Meßwerte automatisch abgelesen, ausgedruckt und auf Lochstreifen oder Magnetband für die spätere Auswertung gespeichert.

4. DISKUSSION EINIGER ANSÄTZE ZUR THEORETISCHEN ERFASSUNG DES IM LABOR BEOBACHTETEN KRIECHVERHALTENS

Zur theoretischen Beschreibung des in Laborversuchen beobachteten Kriechverhaltens von Steinsalz sind in den vergangenen Jahren zahlreiche viskose Stoffgesetze veröffentlicht worden wie zum Beispiel Odqvist [1962], Boresi/Deere [1963], Menzel/Schreiner [1976-1978], Langer [1978], LUB [1979-1981], Hunsche [1979]. Diesen Stoffgesetzen liegen unterschiedliche theoretische Ansätze zugrunde, nach denen eine Einteilung in empirische, modellrheologische und strukturrheologische Stoffgesetze erfolgen kann. Ohne auf weitere Details einzugehen, können die viskosen Stoffgesetze in der allgemeinen Form

$$\dot{\underline{\varepsilon}}^v = f\,(\underline{\sigma},\ t,\ \underline{\varepsilon},\ T,\ s) \qquad (1)$$

dargestellt werden. Die Kriechverzerrungsgeschwindigkeit $\dot{\underline{\varepsilon}}^v$ wird damit als Funktion des Spannungsvektors $\underline{\sigma}$, der Zeit t, des viskosen Verzerrungsvektors $\underline{\varepsilon}^v$, der Temperatur T sowie eines materialbedingten Strukturparameters s angesehen. Üblicherweise erfolgt eine multiplikative Verknüpfung der die Kriechgeschwindigkeit wesentlich beeinflussenden Parameter:

$$\dot{\underline{\varepsilon}}^v = f_1\,(\underline{\sigma}) \cdot f_2\,(t) \cdot f_3\,(\underline{\varepsilon}^v) \cdot \ldots \qquad (2)$$

mit

$f_i\,(\ldots)$ = nichtlineare oder lineare Funktionen des jeweiligen Parameters (....) .

Bei Stoffgesetzen, die den Kriechvorgang nach Lastwechseln in ein Übergangskriechen mit abnehmender und in ein sekundäres Kriechen mit konstanter Kriechgeschwindigkeit aufteilen, wird eine additive Überlagerung beider Kriechgeschwindigkeitsanteile vorgesehen:

$$\dot{\underline{\varepsilon}}^v = \dot{\underline{\varepsilon}}^t + \dot{\underline{\varepsilon}}^s \qquad (3)$$

mit $\dot{\underline{\varepsilon}}^t$ als übergangs- oder primärer und $\dot{\underline{\varepsilon}}^s$ als sekundärer Kriechverzerrungsgeschwindigkeit. Die einzelnen Anteile können dabei wiederum nach Gl. (2) aufgebaut sein.

Die nach den Gln. (1) bis (3) formulierten Stoffgesetze beschreiben nun von ihrem prinzipiellen Ansatz her bereits ein bestimmtes qualitatives Kriechverhalten und enthalten darüber hinaus eine gewisse Anzahl von Freiwerten, durch die entweder über einfaches 'curve fitting' oder über aufwendigere Verfahren das Stoffgesetz den gemessenen Kriechkurven mehr oder weniger gut angepaßt wird. Diese Anpassung gelingt um so schlechter, je größer der den Versuchen zugrunde gelegte Beanspruchungsbereich ist. Es ist daher grundsätzlich zweckmäßig, die Kriechversuche in dem Beanspruchungsbereich durchzuführen, der in der

Bild 3   Servohydraulisch gesteuerte Triaxialpresse des Lehrgebietes für
         Unterirdisches Bauen

Bild 4   Versuchsstände für Kriechversuche bei Raumtemperatur (links) und
         bei hohen / tiefen Temperaturen (rechts) des Lehrgebietes für
         Unterirdisches Bauen

Hohlraumumgebung erwartet wird. Bei einaxialen Versuchen sind hier von der Ver-
suchstechnik und von der unter diesen Bedingungen ertragbaren Materialbeanspruchung
enge Grenzen gesetzt.

Die in der Literatur veröffentlichten
Stoffgesetze und die jeweils angegebenen
Stoffgesetzparameter beruhen nun auf Laborversuchen, die sich sowohl im Hinblick
auf das untersuchte Steinsalzmaterial wie
auch im Hinblick auf die Versuchsbedingungen, die Meßwerterfassung und die Meß-
wertauswertung unterscheiden. Die Verwendung dieser Stoffgesetze einschließlich der
Parameter in theoretischen Berechnungen
führt dann natürlich zu entsprechend stark
voneinander abweichenden Ergebnissen. Daraus ergibt sich nun die Frage, ob sich
diese verschiedenen Stoffgesetze unter Mo-
difikation der jeweiligen Parameter auch
zufriedenstellend einer einzigen Versuchs-
serie anpassen lassen und wie sich dann
die Ergebnisse für Extrapolationen über
den Versuchszeitraum hinaus bei einem einaxialen Spannungszustand und von theoretischen Berechnungen unter mehraxialen
Spannungszuständen unterscheiden.

Für diese vergleichenden Untersuchungen sind insgesamt 5 Stoffgesetze
betrachtet worden:

Stoffgesetz nach Boresi/Deere [1963]:

$$\underline{\dot{\varepsilon}}^v(t) = m \cdot k \cdot \sigma_{ef}^{n-1} \cdot t^{m-1} \cdot \frac{3}{2} \cdot \underline{M}_2 \cdot \underline{\sigma} \quad , \qquad (4a)$$

$$k = 9,34 \cdot 10^{-19} [(\frac{kN}{m^2})^{-3,8} \cdot d^{-0,2}] ; m=0,2; n=3,8.$$
$$(4b)$$

Stoffgesetz nach Menzel/Schreiner [1976-78]

$$\underline{\dot{\varepsilon}}^v(\varepsilon_{ef}^v) = A \cdot \sigma_{ef}^{\beta-1} \cdot \varepsilon_{ef}^{v-\mu} \cdot \frac{3}{2} \cdot \underline{M}_2 \cdot \underline{\sigma} \quad , \qquad (5a)$$

$$A=1,42 \cdot 10^{-91} [(kN/m^2)^{-19} \cdot d^{-1}]; \beta=19,0; \mu=4,0 \quad .$$
$$(5b)$$

Stoffgesetz nach Hunsche [1980]/McVetty[34]

$$\underline{\dot{\varepsilon}}^v(t) = [B \cdot m \cdot e^{-m \cdot t} \cdot e^{-\frac{Q_T}{R \cdot T}} + A \cdot e^{-\frac{Q}{R \cdot T}}] \cdot \sigma_{ef}^{n-1} \cdot \frac{3}{2} \cdot \underline{M}_2 \cdot \underline{\sigma}$$
$$(6a)$$

$$A=1,7 \cdot 10^{-11} [(kN/m^2)^{-3,8} \cdot d^{-1}]; B=9,5 \cdot 10^{-11}$$

$$[(kN/m^2)^{-3,8}]; m=0,25[d^{-1}]; n=3,8;$$

$$Q=12,9[kcal/mol]; Q_T=10,7[kcal/mol] \quad . \quad (6b)$$

Stoffgesetz nach LUB [1980]/Burgers [1935]:

$$\underline{\dot{\varepsilon}}^v(t) = [\frac{1}{\overline{\eta}_M(\sigma)} + \frac{1}{\overline{\eta}_K(\sigma)} \cdot e^{-\frac{\overline{E}_K(\sigma)}{\overline{\eta}_K(\sigma)} \cdot t}] \cdot \frac{3}{2} \cdot \underline{M}_2 \cdot \underline{\sigma} \qquad (7)$$

Stoffgesetz nach Odqvist/Hult [1962]:

$$\underline{\dot{\varepsilon}}^v = k \cdot \sigma_{ef}^{n-1} \cdot \frac{3}{2} \cdot \underline{M}_2 \cdot \underline{\sigma} \qquad (8a)$$

$$\underline{\varepsilon}^v(o) = k_o \cdot \sigma_{ef}^{n_o-1} \cdot \frac{3}{2} \cdot \underline{M}_2 \cdot \underline{\sigma}$$

$$k=1,65 \cdot 10^{-20} [(kN/m^2)^{-3,8} \cdot d^{-1}]; n=3,8 \quad . \quad (8b)$$

$$k_o=1,4 \cdot 10^{-17} [(kN/m^2)^{-3,8}] \quad , \quad n_o=3,5 \quad .$$

Durch verschiedene Verfahren wurde nun ver-
sucht, die Parameter dieser Stoffgesetze so
zu bestimmen, daß die zu verschiedenen
Spannungen gehörenden 4 Kriechkurven möglichst zutreffend wiedergegeben werden. Die
für die einzelnen Stoffgesetze (4a), (5a),
(6a) und (8a) ermittelten Parameter sind in
den Gln. (4b), (5b), (6b) und (8b) angegeben. Bild 5 zeigt das Ergebnis dieser Para-
meterbestimmung. Danach können die gemesse-
en Kriechkurven im Meßzeitraum von 40 - 60
Tagen mit allen Stoffgesetzen zufriedenstellend beschrieben werden.

Bei einer Extrapolation über den Meßzeitraum hinaus führen die einzelnen Stoffgesetze jedoch zu deutlich unterschiedlichen Kriechverformungen.

Bild 6 zeigt für eine Spannung von $\sigma_1 =$
- 15,7 MPa den vom Versuchszeitraum von 60
Tagen auf einen Zeitraum von 1000 Tagen ex-
trapolierten Kriechkurvenverlauf der verschiedenen Stoffgesetze entsprechend Gl.(4)
bis Gl. (8). Die Stoffgesetze nach Gl. (4)
und Gl. (5) führen bei einaxialen Spannungszuständen zu identischen Kriechkurven.
Aus den Abbildungen ist zu ersehen, daß
diejenigen Stoffgesetze, die das Primär-
und Sekundärkriechen getrennt beschreiben,
erheblich größere Kriechverformungen pro-
gnostizieren als die Stoffgesetze, die eine Verfestigung des Materials annehmen.

Damit wird ersichtlich, daß bereits bei einaxialen Spannungszuständen eine Extrapolation über den Meßzeitraum hinaus trotz guter Übereinstimmung der mit verschiedenen
Stoffgesetzen berechneten Kriechkurven mit
den Meßkurven in diesem Zeitbereich zu größeren Unterschieden im prognostizierten
Kriechverhalten führt. Wie sieht nun die
Prognose des Kriechverhaltens bei mehraxialen Spannungszuständen aus?

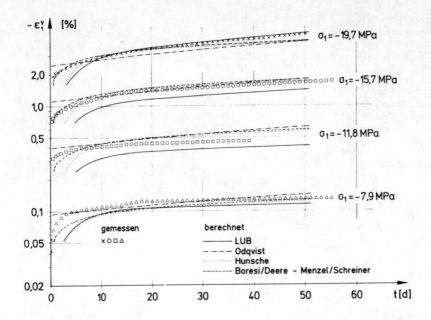

Bild 5 Gegenüberstellung von berechneten und gemessenen Kriechverzerrungen

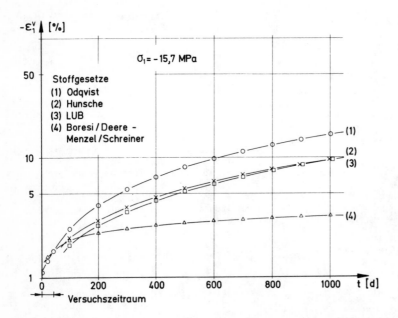

Bild 6 Extrapolation des theoretischen Kriechverhaltens für verschiedene
Kriechgesetze von 40 Tagen auf 1000 Tage ($\sigma_1 = -15,7$ MPa)

Bild 7 zeigt zunächst eine zylindrische Einzelkaverne mit einer Höhe von 300 m und einem Durchmesser von 19 m in einem Salzstock. Um den Aufwand an Computerzeit zu begrenzen, werden die Berechnungen mit einem vereinfachten geometrischen Modell durchgeführt. Dazu wird die Kaverne in ihrem mittleren Bereich durch einen zylindrischen Hohlraum idealisiert, der sich in einem unendlich ausgedehnten, homogenen Kontinuum befinden soll. Für die nachfolgenden vergleichenden Berechnungen wird ein Schnitt in 1000 m Teufe untersucht. Bei Annahme eines teufenunabhängigen Primärspannungszustandes p_o, der dem Gebirgsdruck in 1000 m Teufe entspricht, genügt es, lediglich einen Teil des zylindrischen Hohlraumes zu betrachten. Daraus ergibt sich dann als Berechnungsmodell eine kreisförmig gelochte, unendlich ausgedehnte Scheibe. Die horizontalen Ränder dieser Scheibe können als vertikal unverschieblich gelagert (plain strain) oder als nicht gelagert (plain stress) angesehen werden. Für beide Lagerungsarten wird die gleiche elastische Spannungsverteilung erhalten.

Hier soll der Fall des ebenen Verzerrungszustandes untersucht werden. Die Kaverne wird als solegefüllt mit einem Kopfdruck von p_{WH} = 0 MPa angenommen. Damit ergibt sich in der Teufe von 1000 m ein Kaverneninnendruck von p_i = 12 MPa. Der Gebirgsdruck beträgt in dieser Teufe etwa p_o = - 22 MPa. Die weiteren Gebirgskennwerte sind aus Bild 7 zu ersehen.

Für die in den Gln. (4) bis (8) angegebenen Stoffgesetze werden die zeitabhängigen Spannungen, Verzerrungen und Verschiebungen berechnet. Dazu wird das auf der Finite - Element - Methode aufbauende Programmsystem UTROEPV des Lehrgebietes für Unterirdisches Bauen herangezogen, LUB [1979]. Als Ausgangsspannungszustand zur Zeit t = o wird den viskosen Berechnungen der sich für den Lastfall 'solegefüllte Kaverne' ergebende elastische Spannungszustand zugrunde gelegt.

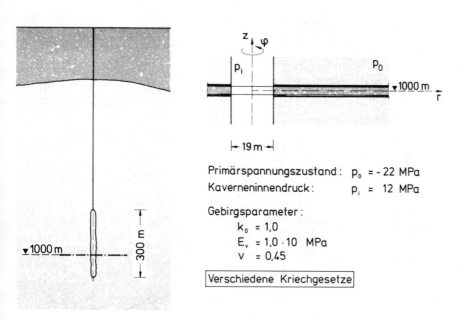

Primärspannungszustand: p_0 = - 22 MPa
Kaverneninnendruck: p_i = 12 MPa

Gebirgsparameter:
  k_0 = 1,0
  E_v = 1,0 · 10 MPa
  v = 0,45

Verschiedene Kriechgesetze

Bild 7   Kavernenanlage und vereinfachtes geometrisches Modell mit Berechnungsparametern

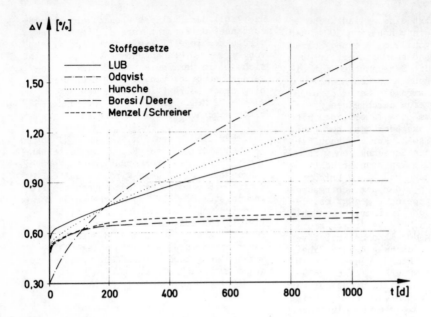

Bild 8 Vergleich der Volumenkonvergenz nach verschiedenen Kriechgesetzen

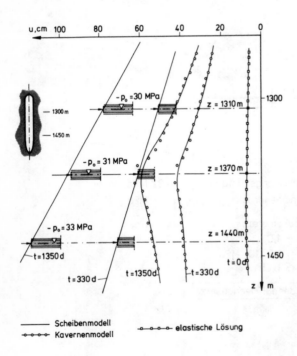

Bild 9 Vergleich der Innenrandverschiebungen nach dem Scheibenmodell und
nach dem Kavernenmodell

Die mit den verschiedenen Stoffgesetzen er- mittelte Volumenkonvergenz ΔV ist in Bild 8 für einen Zeitraum von 1000 Tagen darge- stellt. Hier zeigt sich, welchen Einfluß die Wahl des Stoffgesetzes auf die pro- gnostizierte Konvergenz haben kann. Es soll noch einmal betont werden, daß alle Stoff- gesetze entsprechend Bild 5 die Labor- kriechkurven gut wiedergeben und von daher keine Präferenz für das eine oder das an- dere Stoffgesetz gegeben ist. Die Konver- genzkurven zeigen nun für die Stoffgesetze mit Verfestigung Konvergenzen von etwa ΔV = 0,70 % nach 1000 Tagen und eine nur noch äußerst geringe Zunahme. Nach 500 Tagen be- trägt hier die Konvergenz bereits ΔV = 0,67 % und damit mehr als 95 % des Endwer- tes. Die mit den anderen Stoffgesetzen pro- gnostizierten Konvergenzen liegen zwischen ΔV = 1,13 % für das Stoffgesetz LUB und ΔV = 1,61 % für das Stoffgesetz Odqvist und zeigen eine nur wenig abnehmende Konver- genzgeschwindigkeit. Die Vergleichswerte bei 500 Tagen betragen nur ΔV = 0,93 % bzw. ΔV = 1,15 %. Daraus ist auch die für grö- ßere Zeiträume noch zu erwartende Zunahme zu ersehen.

Wenn im vorliegenden Beispiel als Be- rechnungsmodell eine kreisförmig gelochte, unendlich ausgedehnte Scheibe herangezogen wurde, so lag der Grund darin, exemplarisch für den Fall eines mehraxialen Spannungs- zustandes den Einfluß der verschiedenen Stoffgesetze auf die prognostizierte Kon- vergenz aufzuzeigen.

Die Frage ist jetzt zu stellen, ob im Rahmen einer Projektbearbeitung für die Ab- schätzung der Konvergenz das sehr computer- kostenaufwendige Modell einer Gesamtkaverne durch das wesentlich weniger aufwendige Mo- dell einer Kreisringscheibe ersetzt werden kann. Dazu sind drei Kreisringscheiben ge- wählt worden, die nach Bild 9 den zylinder- förmigen Kavernenhohlraum und das angren- zende Steinsalzgebirge in den drei Teufen $z = 1310$ m, $z = 1370$ m und $z = 1440$ m re- präsentieren. Der primäre Gebirgsdruck p_o ergibt sich dann bei Annahme einer iso- tropen Druckverteilung zu $p_o = - 30$ MPa für die Teufe 1310 m, zu $p_o = - 31$ MPa für die Teufe 1370 m und zu $p_o = - 33$ MPa für die Teufe 1440 m. Weiterhin wird für die Kreisringscheibenmodelle der ebene Verzer- rungszustand gewählt, der gegenüber dem ebenen Spannungszustand zu wirklichkeits- näheren Verschiebungsfeldern führt.

Für einen Kaverneninnendruck von $p_i = 8$ MPa sind in Bild 9 die aus exempla- rischen viskosen Berechnungen mit dem Stoff- gesetz nach Menzel/Schreiner erhaltenen

Hohlraumrandverschiebungen u für das Ka- vernenmodell und die drei Kreisringscheiben- modelle dargestellt.

Obwohl für den Zeitpunkt t = o d die radialen Verschiebungen für beide theore- tischen Modelle gleich sind, ergeben sich für Zeitpunkte von t = 330 d bzw. t = 1350 d für jedes Kreisringscheibenmodell wesentlich größere Radialverschiebungen u als in der zugehörigen Teufe im Kavernen- modell, so daß die damit verbundenen Hohl- raumkonvergenzen des Gesamtmodells durch die Kreisringscheibenmodelle sehr stark überschätzt werden. Die Ergebnisse zeigen also deutlich, daß es im Rahmen einer Pro- jektbearbeitung für eine Abschätzung der Konvergenz erforderlich ist, die zeitab- hängigen Untersuchungen am Gesamtmodell durchzuführen.

5. Ausblick

Wie die Ergebnisse zeigen, ist es allein mit Hilfe einaxialer oder triaxialer Kriechversuche, die bei konstanter Spannung durchgeführt werden, trotz einer guten Übereinstimmung zwischen gemessenem und theoretisch berechnetem Kriechverhalten im Meßzeitraum nicht möglich, die viskosen Ma- terialparameter für Steinsalz eindeutig zu

Bild 10   Gelochter und ungelochter Prüfkörper

81

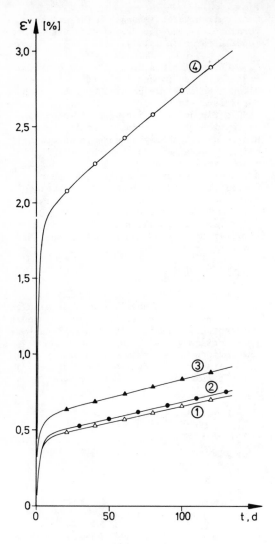

bestimmen. Hieraus ergibt sich prinzipiell die Notwendigkeit, im Anschluß an die Kavernenherstellung in situ Messungen durchzuführen. Andererseits sind derartige Feldversuche sehr kostenintensiv und können aufgrund der nicht eindeutig zu bestimmenden Primär- und Sekundärspannungszustände sowie der Temperaturänderungen in der Umgebung der Kaverne nur zum Vergleich der prognostizierten Konvergenzkurve des gesamten theoretischen Kavernenmodells, nicht aber zur Bestimmung einzelner viskoser Materialparameter herangezogen werden.

Um den Einfluß von Spannungsrelaxationen auf die Bestimmung der Materialparameter auch im Labor erfassen zu können, schlagen wir daher vor, zusätzlich zu den üblichen einaxialen und triaxialen Kriechversuchen auch Kriechversuche mit gelochten Steinsalzprüfkörpern durchzuführen. Ihr Vorteil besteht darin, daß sie nicht nur in ihrer Form und in ihren Spannungsrandbedingungen dem theoretischen Modell des dickwandigen Zylinders entsprechen, sondern auch im Gegensatz zu o.g. Kriechversuchen Spannungsumlagerungen im Prüfkörper ermöglichen.

Bild 10 zeigt einen solchen gelochten Prüfkörper. Der Innendurchmesser beträgt 30 mm bei einem Außendurchmesser von 90 mm. Im Vergleich dazu ist ein Prüfkörper mit den üblichen Abmessungen dargestellt.

Um den Unterschied zu den Ergebnissen herkömmlicher Kriechversuche aufzuzeigen, sind in Bild 11 exemplarisch für 4 verschiedene Versuchsbedingungen die theoretisch ermittelten vertikalen Kriechverformungen über einen Zeitraum von 100 Tagen dargestellt. Die Spannungsdifferenz Δσ beträgt jeweils 16 MPa.

Wie die Kurven 1 und 2 zeigen, sind bei nur vertikaler Belastung die Unterschiede im Kriechverhalten zwischen einer gelochten und nicht gelochten Probe vernachlässigbar gering. Hier liegt theoretisch der eindimensionale Fall vor. Schon bei einem zusätzlichen Manteldruck unter Beibehaltung der Spannungsdifferenz ergibt sich ein deutlicher Zuwachs der Kriechdehnungen bzw. der Kriechgeschwindigkeit. Dieser Unterschied im Kriechverhalten wird noch deutlicher, wenn die Belastung allein durch einen radialen Manteldruck von 16 MPa aufgebracht wird. Die Vertikaldehnungen nach 100 Tagen sind etwa um das 4-fache und die Kriechgeschwindigkeit etwa um das 3,6-fache größer. Es soll an dieser Stelle betont werden, daß sich die dargestellten Unterschiede in den Kriechkurven allein aus dem Einfluß des

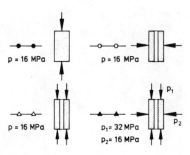

Bild 11   Berechnete Kriechdehnungen
von 4 unterschiedlichen
Prüfkörpern

mehraxialen Spannungszustandes und der anschließenden Spannungsumlagerung ergeben, da für die theoretische Ermittlung der Kriechverformungen einer einaxial oder triaxial belasteten Probe nur die Spannungsdifferenz $\Delta\sigma$ eingeht. Diese ist in den 4 untersuchten Fällen gleich.

Interessanterweise sind die berechneten Spannungsumlagerungen bereits nach 1 bis 2 Tagen abgeklungen. Hier liegt u.E. ein großer Vorteil, da dann bereits nach wenigen Wochen der entsprechende Versuch beendet werden könnte. Inwieweit diese theoretischen Voruntersuchungen mit den geplanten Laborversuchen zu korrelieren sind, ist abzuwarten.

6. Zusammenfassung

Der vorliegende Beitrag befaßt sich mit einigen Aspekten zu Laborversuchen mit Steinsalz und zur Dimensionierung von Salzkavernen. Aufbauend auf den Ergebnissen einaxialer Kriechversuche werden einige Probleme diskutiert, die mit der Formulierung viskoser Stoffgesetze und den mit ihnen erhaltenen Aussagen zum Kriechverhalten verbunden sind.

Die Ergebnisse zeigen, daß trotz einer guten Übereinstimmung zwischen gemessenem und theoretisch berechnetem Kriechverhalten im Meßzeitraum keine eindeutige Prognose des zukünftigen Verhaltens möglich ist - weder für den einaxialen Spannungszustand des Laborversuchs noch für mehraxiale Spannungszustände in der Umgebung von Kavernen, bei denen sich zusätzlich eine Spannungsrelaxation ergibt. Ohne im Anschluß an die Kavernenherstellung durchgeführte in situ Messungen zum Konvergenzverhalten scheint eine langfristige Konvergenzprognose daher nicht möglich. Abschließend wird eine Möglichkeit vorgestellt, wirklichkeitsnäher als bisher die viskosen Materialparameter von Steinsalz im Labor zu bestimmen.

LITERATURVERZEICHNIS

Boresi, A.P. u. Deere, D.U. [1963]: 'Creep Closure of a Spherical Cavity in an Infinite Medium', Report for Holmes, Narver , Inc., Las Vegas.

Burgers, I.M. [1935]: 'Mechanical Considerations, Model Systems, Phenomenological Theories', First Report on Viscosity and Plasticity, Amsterdam, 21 - 33.

Hunsche, U. [1979]: 'Das Fließverhalten von Steinsalz', 2. Zwischenbericht zum forschungsvorhaben SR 138, Bundesanstalt für Geowissenschaften u. Rohstoffe.

Langer, M. [1979]: 'Rheologisches Verhalten von Gesteinen u. Fels', Generalbericht zum Thema 1, 4. Int. Kongress für Felsmechanik, Montreux.

LUB - Lehrgebiet für Unterirdisches Bauen [1979 - 1981]: 'Entwicklung mathematisch-mechanischer Modelle zur Beschreibung des Stoffverhaltens von Salzgestein auf der Grundlage von Laborversuchen', Jahresberichte zum Forschungsauftrag ET 2011 A/ KFA Jülich.

Menzel, W. u. Schreiner, W. [1976 - 1978]: 'Zum geomechanischen Verhalten von Steinsalz verschiedener Lagerstätten der DDR', Neue Bergbautechnik, 442 - 446 [1976], 565 - 571 [1977], 143 - 148 [1978].

Mc Vetty, P.G. [1934]: 'Working Stresses for High Temperature Service', Mech. Eng. 56.

Odqvist, F.K.G. u. Hult, J. [1962]: 'Kriechfestigkeit metallischer Werkstoffe', Springer Verlag.

THE SHEAR STRENGTH OF ROCK JOINTS WITH REFERENCE TO CAUTIOUS BLASTING

Die Scherfestigkeit von Klüften in Verbindung mit schonenden Sprengverfahren

La résistance au cisaillement des diaclases d'une roche par rapport au sautage ménagé

K.MÄKI & R.HOLMBERG
Swedish Detonic Research Foundation, Stockholm

SUMMARY:

The influence of blasting on the remaining rock has been a subject for research during several years at the Swedish Detonic Research Foundation. As a result of this a model has been established which predicts the extent of the zone of damage in the remaining rock for various charge concentrations per meter borehole and various blasting situations. Since the shear strength of unfavourably oriented planes of weakness has a major influence on the rock mass stability, research was initiated to investigate the shear strength of joints after movements in the joints have occurred.

These investigations were made in laboratory scale with a specially designed direct shear apparatus which allows movements to be created in existing and potential joints before the shearing of the joints takes place. Surface profile measurements on the used geological structures were also performed. The shear tests were carried out at low normal loads corresponding to the vertical stresses in an open pit bench.

ZUSAMMENFASSUNG:

Die Einwirkung der Sprengung auf das umgebende Gestein ist seit mehreren Jahren ein Forschungsgegenstand der Stiftung der Schwedischen Detonikforschung. Als Resultat dieser Forschung ist ein Modell festgelegt worden woraus sich die Ausbreitung der Beschädigung des rückständigen Gesteines bei Verwendung verschiedener Ladungskonzentrationen per Meter Bohrloch und bei verschiedener Sprengungsverhältnissen im voraus feststellen lässt.

Da die Scherfestigkeit ungünstig orientierter Schwächeflächen auf die Stabilität des Gebirges entscheidend einwirkt, ist die Forschungsarbeit auf die Feststellung der scherfestigkeit der Klüfte nach Bewegung derselben eingerichtet worden.

Diese Untersuchungen wurden im Laboratoriummasstab mit einem für direkte Scherversuche speziellen Apparat durchgeführt, der das Zustandebringen von Bewegungen in pre-existierenden und potenziellen Klüften zulässt, ehe der Scherversuch durchgeführt wird. Man hat auch die Profilen der Kluftflächen gemessen. Die Scherversuche geschiehen bei Belastungen, die den Normalspannungen in einem Tagebauabsatz entsprechen.

RESUME:

L'influence du sautage sur le rocher environnant a été un objet de recherche pendant plusieurs années de la Fondation Suèdoise de la Recherche Détonique. Le résultat de cette recherche fut l'établissement d'un modèle permettant de prédire l'étendue de la zone d'endommagement du rocher environnant par rapport à l'emploie de concentrations de charge variées par mètre de trou de mine et aux conditions de sautage différantes.

Comme la résistance au cisaillement des zones d'affaissement d'une orientation défavorable exèrce une influence décisive sur la stabilité de la roche le but des travaux de recherche fut d'étudier la résistance au cisaillement des joints ayant été exposés aux mouvements.

Ces études furent effectuées en échelle de laboratoire à l'aide d'un appareil de construction spéciale pour faire des essais de cisaillement direct et permettant de susciter des mouvements dans les joints préexistants et potentiels avant l'exécution de l'essai. Aussi a-t-on ensuite mesuré les profils des surfaces des plans de fracture. Les essais de cisaillement furent effectués sous l'effet de contraintes modérées correspondant aux contraintes verticales dans un gradin d'exploitation à ciel ouvert.

1. INTRODUCTION

The influence of blasting on the remaining rock has been a subject for research during several years at the Swedish Detonic Research Foundation (SveDeFo). The aim of the work is to study deformations in the remaining rock caused by the blasting and to investigate effects on the strength of the rock.

The main part of the field investigations have so far been made at bench blasting operations in open pit mines in Sweden, the practical application being the possibility of increasing the final slope angle of a pit by using cautious blasting methods. Since this problem particularly demands knowledge of the shear strength of blast damaged weakness planes in the rock shear strength investigations were initiated.

In this paper results from measurements of blast-induced rock mass deformations are presented. Models for prediction of the extent of the damaged zone at bench and tunnel blasting are described. Finally results from experimental investigations of the effects of simulated blast damages on the shear strength of rock joints are presented.

2. MEASUREMENTS OF BLAST-INDUCED ROCK MASS DEFORMATIONS AND PREDICTION OF THE EXTENT OF DAMAGE

Measurements of deformations in the rock mass behind open pit blasts have been performed using steel bars anchored in holes at different depths below the surface. Figure 1 after Holmberg & Mäki (1981) shows the positions of the bars behind the last row of blast holes at a blast in the Leveä-niemi open pit mine. The bars were anchored at the depths 6 and 16 m below the surface and at the surface. Three sets of bars were placed at the distances 8, 12 and 16 m behind the last row of blastholes.

Figure 2 shows the measured extensions of the rock mass between the 0-16, 0-6 and 6-16 meter levels. The extensions are indicated to decrease with the depth below the surface and also with the distance from

the blast. The rock mass extensions at this particular blast were several times larger than the extensions obtained at other similar measurements. Holmberg and Persson (1978) report measurements behind a row of inclined boreholes with a diameter of 171 mm in the Aitik open pit mine. Three extensometers were mounted in 25 meter deep inclined boreholes at the perpendicular distances 8.0 m, 13.2 m and 25.7 m from the nearest 171 mm borehole. The measured extensions over the 25 m measuring lengths were 37.8 mm, 15.4 mm and 2.6 mm respectively. Recent measurements in the Leveä-niemi mine indicate extensions of the same order of magnitude as in the Aitik mine. This indicates that the large extensions in figure 2 may have been caused by unfavourable geologic conditions at this particular location. The results in figure 2

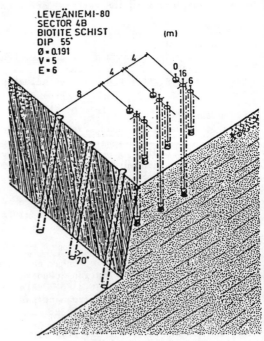

Figure 1. Positions of steel bars for extensometer tests behind an open pit blast.

and the results of the other measurements anyway show that remaining vertical extensions are introduced in the remaining rock at bench blasting.

Fractures per meter

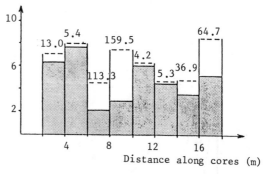

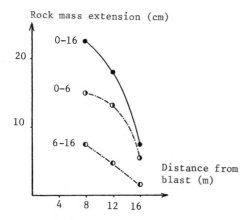

Figure 2. Rock mass extensions due to blasting.

prior
——— to blasting
- - - after

Figure 3. Dip corrected fracture frequencies prior to and after blasting. Increase of fracture frequency is given (unit percent).

At the blast in the Leveäniemi mine parallel rock cores were drilled out prior to and after blasting. The cores were drilled from a point 20 m behind the last row of blastholes towards the blast with a dip of 45°. The horizontal distance between the cores at the surface was approximately 0.6 m. As the cores intersected the main geologic structure at the location (schistosity) it was possible to evaluate the number of open fractures parallel to the schistosity prior to and after blasting. The results given i figure 3, after Holmberg and Mäki (1981), indicate that the number of fractures in the rock mass had increased due to the blasting.

The comparison of the cores was made with a correction for the dip of the schistosity which gave a better result than was obtained when the cores were compared at equal distances from the surface. The latter way of analyzing resulted in a decreased number of fractures due to blasting at two intervals along the cores.

Studies of rock cores drilled out prior to and after bench blasting in Aitik and crater blasting in the Malmberget under-

ground mine have also been performed (Holmberg and Krauland 1977, Mäki and Holmberg 1980). The results of these investigations are similar to those in figure 3. Thus the investigations of rock cores indicate that blasting creates fractures in the rock that prior to blasting would be classified as intact.

Models for calculation of the extent of the damaged zone in the surrounding rock at bench and tunnel blasting have been proposed by Persson et al (1977) and Holmberg and Persson (1979). The fundamental conception is that damage is created by strains in the rock mass which in turn is a result of wave propagation. Since the strain, for an idealized case with a sine-wave propagating through linearly elastic material, is proportional to the particle velocity it is assumed that the particle velocity can be used as a criterion for damage. The peak particle velocity is also frequently used as a criterion for damage to buildings. The results of calculations of the peak particle velocity as a function of the charge concentration and the distance from a charge hole in bench blasting are given in figure 4 b. Figure 4 a gives the results of similar calculations for the case of a small-diameter charge hole in tunnel blasting. Field measurements of peak particle velocities have been performed at different blasting operations. Results agreeing with

87

the ones predicted by the models have been obtained. By calculating fracture frequencies in cores drilled out prior to and after blasting the peak particle velocity at which damage starts to occur has been estimated to 700-1000 mm/sec.

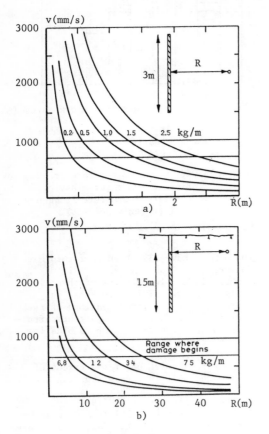

a)

b)

Figure 4 a-b. Calculated peak particle velocity as a function of distance for different linear charge densities, given in kg ANFO per meter borehole length.

a) Distance range typical of small-diameter hole tunnelblasting.

b) Distance range typical of large-diameter hole blasting.

3. THE SHEAR STRENGTH OF ROCK JOINTS WITH SIMULATED BLAST DAMAGES

From the previous discussion it may be concluded that blast damages can be regarded as a result of movements in the remaining rock which involves both movements in pre-existing joints and fracturing and movements in potential planes of weakness.

A study of the shear strength of joints subjected to movements can be made either by using field shear tests or laboratory tests. Because it was considered easier to control the degree of joint movement in the laboratory, small scale laboratory direct shear tests were performed.

3.1 Experimental equipment and testing procedures.

The equipment for the direct shear tests is shown in figures 5 and 6.

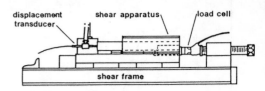

Figure 5. Equipment for direct shear tests.

Figure 6. The shear apparatus containing three mounted samples.

The equipment basically consists of an apparatus made of two steel plates, a frame, weights for normal load application and devices for shear force and displacement measurements. Three samples having a diameter of 30 mm, are fastened into through-going holes in the plates with a resin of high strength. The movement of the upper plate is guided by steel bars welded onto the lower plate.

The equipment is still at a stage of development, so far the shearing has been made manually at an approximately constant displacement rate of 0.4 mm/min. Manual recording of the peak and residual shear forces and shear displacements were made during the first stage of the testing when a dial gauge was used for displacement measurements. The final stage of the testing

88

was made using a displacement transducer and an X-Y recorder.

Because of the simplicity of the shear force application and the recordings an investigation of the errors introduced at the measuring of the shear force was made. The two main error sources were a frictional resistance of the apparatus and the manual application of the shear force. The average frictional resistance was corrected for in the evaluation of the results and variations of the shear rate were not indicated to have had any influence. Investigations made by Schneider (1978) also indicate a small influence of the shearing rate on the shear strength at the normal loads used in the tests presented here. Thus the errors added together indicated a maximum variation of the shear force of ± 0.035 kN which was found to be sufficiently less than the natural variation of the results.

A comparison of the used method with the method for determining shear strength recommended by the ISRM (1974) has been reported by Mäki (1981a).

The apparatus has facilities for creating movements in existing joints and for fracturing potential planes of weakness in intact samples before the shearing is made. Intact rock samples containing geologic structures such as schistosity can be mounted into the holes in such a way that the structures will have an orientation parallel to the axis of the applied shear force. A vertical movement of the upper plate, created by wedging, causes structural planes to be fractured in each sample. During the wedging the two plates are also clamped by a central through bolt which prevents uncontrolled fracturing of the samples. The movement of the upper plate is measured and controlled by dial gauges. When the desired vertical displacement of the upper plate has been reached the wedges are removed and the position of the upper plate is measured without and with an applied external normal load. The shearing may then proceed. Samples containing existing joints are carefully kept together and mounted into the holes. Steel balls and strips of hardened steel bands inserted between the plates may be used to keep the plates at a constant distance from each other. This arrangement gives the joints an aperture when the shearing starts which simulates a remaining aperture in an in-situ joint.

The drilling of the rock cores had to be

made very carefully so as to ensure that the orientation of the structures was to be perpendicular to the core axis. An investigation of the deviation from parallelism between the orientation of the shear surface in the shear direction and the axis of the applied shear force was made for each surface in every test. For the successful tests 79% of the surfaces had deviations less than 3°. When steel balls were used to introduce a remaining aperture at the start of shearing the samples had to be mounted so that an increasing shear displacement would tend to raise the upper plate. This in order to prevent contact between the upper plate and the steel balls when the peak and residual shear forces were measured. When the nominal shear and normal stresses were calculated a correction was made for the average deviation from parallelism in the particular test.

To establish reference data about the intact rock double shear tests and uniaxial compressive strength tests were performed. The double shear test is performed as shown in figure 7. The shear strength is given by the equation

$$\tau_s = \frac{F}{2A} \qquad (1)$$

where F is the failure load and A is the cross-sectional area of the specimen. Double shear tests on different rock materials have been reported by Lundborg (1968).

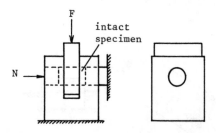

Figure 7. Apparatus for double shear tests.

As a reference one direct shear test on intact samples was made with the direct shear equipment previously described. The fracturing of the samples was guided by notches cut parallel to the structure and to the shearing direction. The notches were cut by a 2.5 mm thick diamond cutting wheel and they covered approximately 80% of the cross-sectional area of the samples.

In order to investigate the surface geometry

of the geologic structures, profile measurements were made on a number of randomly chosen sample surfaces. The principle was to manually move a sample lying on a flat surface while letting a dial gauge follow the surface of the sample. The dial gauge had an accuracy of 0.01 mm and readings were taken in steps of 1 mm.

The rock material used in the experiments was taken from two biotite schist blocks from the Leveäniemi mine. The blocks contained intact planes of schistosity. One of the blocks also contained two joints belonging to a major structure in the mine.

Data from all the experiments are reported by Mäki (1981a). A review of shear strength models presented in the rock mechanics literature is given by Mäki (1981b). Data from initial experiments are reported by Mäki, Nord and Persson (1979).

3.2 The shear strength of joints with mated surfaces.

Before studying the influence of joint movements on the shear strength it was considered necessary to investigate the shear strength of existing joints with surfaces in optimum contact. Strength models for such joints have been presented for instance by Barton (1976) and Ladanyi and Archambault (1970), an effort was however made to evaluate the experimental results in terms of the bilinear model, figure 8, originating from work done by Patton (1966).

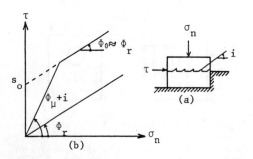

Figure 8. The bilinear model for the shear strength of rock joints with regularly inclined asperities.

According to the bilinear model the peak shear strength at low normal loads is a result of asperities sliding on each other, the peak angle of friction having a component given by the angle of inclination, i,

of the asperities. At high normal loads the failure mechanism is characterized by shearing of the asperities. In this case the peak shear strength is described in terms of the Coulomb law. The basic angle of friction, $\emptyset_\mu$, is the angle of friction for a fictive flat surface of the material.

The angles of inclination for the three types of surfaces (surfaces from intact parts of the two blocks and major joint surfaces) were evaluated from the profile measurements as shown in figure 9. For each profile the largest asperity was investigated.

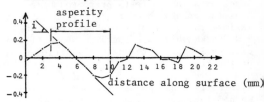

Figure 9. Determination of the angle of inclination from a major joint surface profile.

The value of $\emptyset_\mu$ was estimated from the experimental results using the relations

$$\emptyset_\mu = (\emptyset_\mu + i)_{max} - i_{max} \qquad (2)$$

and

$$\emptyset_\mu = (\emptyset_\mu + i)_{min} - i_{min} \qquad (3)$$

where $(\emptyset_\mu + i)_{max}$ and $(\emptyset_\mu + i)_{min}$ are given by the experimentally determined peak angles of friction and i_{max} and i_{min} are the largest and the smallest angle of inclination evaluated from the surface profiles. It is assumed that the largest and the smallest peak angles of friction are related to the largest and the smallest of the investigated asperities respectively. The surfaces used for the profile measurements were not always the same as the ones that were tested but they are supposed to give an estimate of the distribution of the angles of inclination of the largest asperities. The calculated $\emptyset_\mu$-values were compared with the experimentally determined residual angles of friction.

Figure 10 shows the results for the major joints. The $\emptyset_\mu$-values were calculated using i_{max}- and i_{min}-values from profile measurements on nine sample surfaces. The calculated $\emptyset_\mu$-values agree with the lowest of the

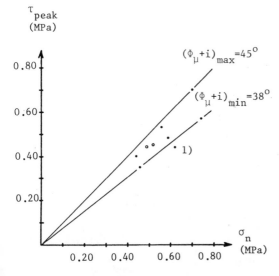

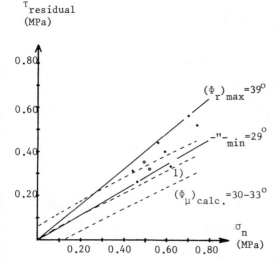

Figure 10. Angles of friction for major
joints. Dotted lines show results after
Pincock, Allen and Holt Inc. (1979).
1) Larger values were obtained in a previous test on the same set of surfaces
performed with a remaining aperture at
the start of shearing.
• Previously un-sheared surfaces.
• Previously sheared surfaces.

residual values obtained and also acceptab-
ly well with the results from large scale
direct shear tests on similar surfaces
with a nominal area of 231 cm^2 performed
by Pincock, Allen and Holt Inc. (1979).

On the basis of the results in figure 10
and the results for the other types of
surfaces it was concluded that the bilinear
model to a, for the purpose of these investigations, acceptable degree describes
the shear strength of existing joints with
mated surfaces.

The residual shear force was measured after
approximately 5 mm shear displacement. Since
about half of the investigated asperities
had a distance from valley to peak exceeding 5 mm the residual force was in several
cases probably measured while the upper
surfaces were still climbing which explains
the larger $\emptyset_r$-values compared with the $\emptyset_\mu$-
values. The main part of the results in
figure 10 were obtained on surfaces that
had been used for previous tests with a
remaining aperture at the start of shearing.
This testing procedure was not obviously
indicated to have influenced the peak
strength. The residual strength was however
indicated to increase due to repeated
shearings.

3.3 The shear strength of joints created
    by controlled fracturing of intact
    samples.

The fracturing of intact samples was created
by wedges carefully tapped in between the
steel plates. During the wedging the plates
were clamped by a central through bolt.
Notches had been made in the samples to
guide the initiation of the fractures. The
wedging had to be made very carefully so
as to avoid bending of the samples. Care-
less wedging inevitably caused the fractures to appear close to or partly inside
the holes of the plates.

Figure 11 shows the gradual fracturing of
a sample. In most samples fractures became
visible after a movement of the upper plate
of between 0.05 and 0.1 mm. Further movements of the upper plate resulted in growth
of the area of fracture.

Temporary aperture:

≈ 0.07 mm

≈ 0.15 mm

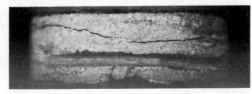

≈ 0.30 mm

≈ 0.50 mm

Remaining aperture after a normal load of
686.7 N has been applied:
≈ 0.01 mm

Figure 11. The gradual fracturing of a
          sample. Joint aperture was esti-
          mated as being equal to the ver-
          tical movement of the upper plate.

Figure 12 shows the remaining aperture as
a function of the temporary aperture for
a normal load given by the weight of the
upper plate only and a normal load with
additional weights. The remaining aperture is indicated to be a function of both
the introduced temporary aperture and the
normal load.

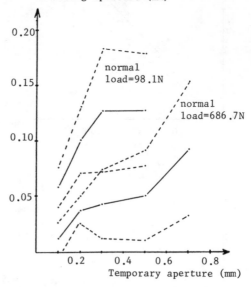

Figure 12. Mean and standard deviation
           curves for the remaining aper-
           ture as a function of the tem-
           porary aperture for two normal
           loads.

Figur 13 shows the peak shear strength as
a function of the temporary aperture for
samples from the two blocks. According to
the figure increased peak shear strength
was obtained if the initially introduced
temporary aperture was limited to small
values.

The residual strength was not found to
depend on the temporary aperture.

The relation between the temporary aperture
and the peak shear strength can be explained
by difference in joint continuity, i.e.
the relation between the area of fracture
and the total area of the failure plane.
The effect of joint continuity on the peak
shear strength was studied theoretically
using equations presented by Lajtai
(1969 a,b).

92

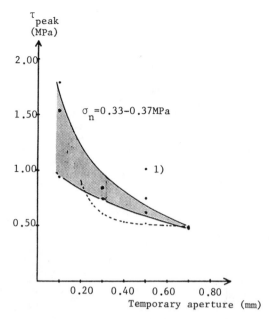

Figure 13. The peak shear strength as a
function of the temporary
aperture for block No. 2.
Dotted curve for samples from
block No. 1.
1) Irregularity of feldspar
covered a part of the surface
of one sample.

According to Lajtai intact rock subjected
to shear and low normal stresses in a
direct shear test may fail in local tension
followed by the development of the shear
plane. The failure shear stress is given
by the equation

$$\tau_{peak} = \left[T_s (T_s - \sigma_n) \right]^{\frac{1}{2}} \qquad (4)$$

where T_s is the tensile strength of the
intact rock material.

For the case of a discontinuous joint
subjected to low normal stresses the failure shear stress may be calculated from
the equation

$$\tau_{peak} = C\kappa\sigma_n \tan\emptyset_p + (1-\kappa) \left[T_s (T_s - \sigma_n) \right]^{\frac{1}{2}} \qquad (5)$$

where C = 1 if maximum fracture friction
is mobilized and $\emptyset_p$ is the angle of fracture friction.

The factor κ defines the continuity of the
potential failure plane and is given by
the equation

$$\kappa = \frac{A_p}{A_p + A_s} \qquad (6)$$

where A_p is the area of fractured shear
surface and A_s is the area of unfractured
shear surface, figure 14.

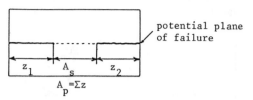

Figure 14. Definition of parameters for
calculation of the continuity.

The validity of equation (4) was studied
by comparing the results from the double
shear tests with the result of the direct
shear test on intact samples. The double
shear tests may be regarded as giving a
value of the kohesion, s_o, of the intact
rock according to the Coulomb criterion
of failure. Due to the confinement of the
double shear test the extent of tensile
fracturing along the shear planes is likely
to be limited. According to McGlintock and
Walsh theory (Lajtai 1969b, Lundborg 1968)
the tensile strength of intact rock is
given by the equation

$$T_s = \frac{s_o}{2} \qquad (7)$$

The double shear test results for block
No 2(17.8,19.2 and 18.7MPa for σ_n=0.32MPa)
and equations (4) and (7) thus predict
direct shear strength values between 8.7
and 9.4 MPa which well agree with the
measured direct shear strength of 9.9 MPa
for σ_n = 0.23 MPa.

Unfortunately only one direct shear test
on intact rock was performed. With a support
by the agreement however the equation (5)
was used for back calculations of the joint
continuity. For C = 1 and $\emptyset_u = (\emptyset_u + i)_{mean}$
= 42° for block No 2 the continuity was
calculated. The results indicate that joints
from block No 2 that had a temporary aperture of 0.1 mm still contained intact rock
bridges covering 7-16% of the area of the
failure plane. After a temporary aperture
of 0.5 mm this area had decreased to between 3 and 5%.

3.4 The shear strength of existing joints
with simulated blast damages.

Blast damages in existing joints were simulated by giving the joints in the samples
an aperture at the start of shearing which
models a remaining aperture in an in-situ
joint.

93

A theoretical investigation of the effect of remaining apertures on the shear strength can be performed if the bilinear model is modified with respect to the shape of the asperities, figure 15.

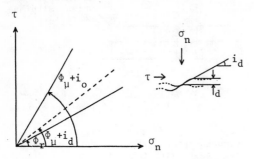

Figure 15. The bilinear model modified to describe the shape of natural asperities.

According to the bilinear model the peak shear strength for low normal loads is given by the equation

$$\tau = \sigma_n \tan(\emptyset_\mu + i) \qquad (8)$$

where $\emptyset_\mu$ is the basic angle of friction and i is the angle of inclination of the asperities.

If a remaining aperture influences the peak shear strength of the joint it has to be a result of a changed angle of inclination since $\emptyset_\mu$ is regarded as a constant for the material.

Predictions of the peak angle of friction as a function of the remaining aperture were performed using the basic angle of friction and angles of inclination evaluated from the surface profiles. The approach was to fit a cubic equation to the asperity profiles, figure 9, and calculate the decreased angles of inclination as remaining apertures were introduced. The calculations are described in detail by Mäki (1981a). The results from the calculations and the experiments for the major joints are given in figure 16.

The upper two dotted curves show the calculated peak angles of friction based on two of the largest of the investigated asperities and the lower dotted curve shows the calculated angle of friction based on one of the smallest of the investigated asperities. Two sets of experiments were performed. The upper experimental curve shows results that were obtained with remaining apertures from 0.6 mm to zero. The

tests were performed on the same set of samples with decreased remaining aperture at the start of every new test. A strength drop was obtained at an aperture of 0.2 mm. The lower experimental curve consists only of two results performed at 0.1 mm and zero remaining aperture. The previous tests were not possible to evaluate due to contact between the steel balls and the upper steel plate at shearing. The results show that remaining apertures caused a decreased peak angle of friction which could be predicted by the change of the angle of inclination on the largest of the investigated asperities.

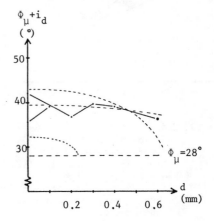

Figure 16. The peak angle of friction as a function of the remaining aperture at the start of shearing

The calculations of the peak angle of friction were performed using $\emptyset_\mu = 28°$ which is in accordance with the results of the large scale shear tests made by Pincock, Allen and Holt Inc. (1979). Use of the $\emptyset_\mu$-values that were back calculated from the results obtained for mated surfaces ($\emptyset_\mu = 30°-33°$) would merely have raised the dotted line and the dotted curves slightly.

4. DISCUSSION

The direct shear tests provide an insight into the mechanism of tensile fracture in rock and insight into the mechanisms of shear failure. The use of cautious blasting methods is encouraged by the results that show that strength decrease can be avoided if movements in joints are limited. Provided that scale effects are taken into consideration strength calculations can be made using the investigated models.

Measurements of deformations in the rock

mass at blasting provide information which can be used for strength calculations. The shear strength investigations provide, apart from basic information on the strength of rock joints, information on which parameters need to be quantified for rock slope stability calculations. The joint continuity can be regarded as such a parameter being largely effected by the blasting. It also has a main influence on the strength of the remaining rock.

5. ACKNOWLEDGEMENT

This work has been performed as a part of the rock blasting and rock mechanics programme of the Swedish Detonic Research Foundation, supported by Swedish industry in cooperation with the Swedish Board for Technical Development (STU).

6. REFERENCES

Barton, N. 1976, The shear strength of rock and rock joints, Int.J.Rock Mech. Min Sci & Geomech.Abstr. 13:255-279.

Holmberg, R. & Krauland, N. 1977, Examination of fracture frequencies prior to and after blasting of a 250 mm hole in Aitik, SveDeFo, Stockholm, Report 1977:12 (in Swedish).

Holmberg, R. & Mäki, K. 1981, Case examples of blasting damage and its influence on slope stability, Proc. 3rd Int.Conf. on Stability in Surface Mining arr.by SME of AIME, Vancouver.

Holmberg, R. & Persson, P.A. 1978, The Swedish approach to contour blasting, Proc. 4th Conf. on Explosives and Blasting Technique arr.by the Soc.of Explosives Engineers, New Orleans, pp 113-127.

Holmberg, R. & Persson, P.A. 1979, Design of tunnel perimeter blasthole patterns to prevent rock damage, Proc. Tunnelling '79, editor Jones M.J., Inst.of Mining and Metallurgy, London, March 12-16, pp 280-283.

International Society for Rock Mechanics-Commission on standardization of laboratory and field tests 1974, Suggested methods for determining shear strength, Committee on field tests, Document No.1.

Ladanyi, B. & Archambault, G. 1970, Simulation of shear behaviour of a jointed rock mass, Proc.11th Symp. on Rock Mech., California, pp 105-125.

Lajtai, E.Z. 1969a, Shear strength of weakness planes in rock, Int.J.Rock Mech.Min. Sci., 6:499-515.

Lajtai, E.Z. 1969b, Strength of discontinuous rocks in direct shear, Géotechnique 19, No.2 pp 218-233.

Lundborg, N. 1968, Strength of rock-like materials, Int.J.Rock Mech.Min.Sci., 5:427-454.

Mäki, K. 1981a, The shear strength of planes of weakness in biotite schist with simulated blast damages, SveDeFo, Stockholm, Report DS 1981:4.

Mäki, K. 1981b, The shear strength of rock joints and slope stability, SveDeFo, Stockholm, Report DS 1981:17 (in Swedish).

Mäki, K. & Holmberg, R. 1980, Rock damage from crater blasting of a raise, SveDeFo, Stockholm, Report DS 1980:8 (in Swedish).

Mäki, K., Nord, G. & Persson, P.A. 1979, The influence of blast damages on the shear strength of biotite schist, SveDeFo, Stockholm, Report DS 1979:11 (in Swedish).

Patton, F.D. 1966, Multiple modes of shear failure in rock, Proc. 1st Int. Congr. of ISRM, Lisbon, 1:509-513.

Persson, P.A., Holmberg, R. & Persson, G. 1977, Careful blasting of slopes in open pit mines, SveDeFo, Stockholm, Report DS 1977:4 (in Swedish).

Pincock, Allen & Holt Inc. 1979, Slope design study for the Leveäniemi open pit, authors Visca, P.J., Jones, S.M. and Call, R.D., Tucson, (confidential).

Schneider, H.J. 1978, The laboratory direct shear test - an analysis and geotechnical evaluation, Bull. of the IAEG, No.18 pp 121-126.

GEOMECHANIC CLASSIFICATION FOR ASSESSING ROCK MASS IN JAPAN
Geomechanische Klassifizierung von Gebirgskörpern in Japan
Classification géomécanique pour l'estimation d'une masse rocheuse au Japon

KENJI NAKAO, SHIGERU IIHOSHI & SATORU KOYAMA
Technical Institute of Taisei Corp., Yokohama, Japan
KUNIASU RYOKE
Nagamine Tunnel Project, Wakayama, Japan

SUMMARY:
A statistical reconsideration on the parameters for geomechanics classification of rock mass has been carried out to apply in the Japanese
geological conditions.
Procedures to produce the parameters and a form of data base are dis-
cribed herein on the investigation of geomechanical rock conditions and
tunnelling techniques.
A comparison of produced parameters and the results with the presented
methods by WICHAM G.E., BIENIAWSKI Z.P. and BARTON N. are being
analized at present.
An analized example of parameter is shown in conjunction with the
magnitude of tunnel deformation.

ZUSAMMENFASSUNG:
Eine statistische Neubetrachtung der Parameter für die geomechanische
Klassifizierung von Gebirgskörpern wurde durchgeführt, um eine Anwendung
für die geologischen Gegebenheiten in Japan zu ermöglichen.
Die Verfahren zur Erstellung der Parameter und zur Bildung einer Daten-
bank werden hierin im Zusammenhang mit der Untersuchung von geomechani-
schen Gesteinsverhältnissen und Tunnelbautechniken beschrieben.
Ein Vergleich der ermittelten Parameter mit den Ergebnissen der Metho-
den von WICHAM G.E., BIENIAWSKI Z.P. und BARTON N. wird zur Zeit
analysiert.
Ein analysiertes Beispiel für Parameter wird im Zusammenhang mit dem
Ausmaß der Tunnelverformung gezeigt.

RESUME:
Un examen statistique des paramètres pour la classification géomécanique
de la masse rocheuse a été exécuté à nouveau pour application aux
conditions géologiques japonaises.
Les procédés d'obtention des paramètres ainsi que la forme de la base
des données, sont décrits ici concernant les recherches des conditions
de roche géomécanique et les techniques de percement de tunnels.
Une comparaison entre les paramètres obtenus et les résultats suivant
les méthodes de WICHAM G.E., BIENIAWSKI Z.P. et BARTON N., est
actuellement en cours d'examen.
Un exemple de paramètre est donné concurremment avec l'importance de
la déformation du tunnel.

1 INTRODUCTION

In recent years, much importance has been attached to new engineering classification of rock masses related to rock excavation such as tunnelling, stabilization of rock slopes, rock foundations, cavern excavation etc. as a method of assessment related to the works. As old examples of rock mass classification related to tunnelling works, there are some ideas proposed by Terzaghi (1946), Lauffer (1958) and Deer (1964). In Japan also, rock classifications made by respective authorities from their standpoint are being used. These are mainly utilized in the planning stage of the works and used as criteria to determine the method of excavation, support system, and thickness of lining suitable for the rock. Though quantitative arrangement such as seismic wave velocity, interval of cracks, core recovery rate etc. is made partially, the most part is assessed qualitatively and the data relating to the behaviour of rock masses after excavation are not provided. From about 1972, methods of assessment that analyse parameters controlling behaviour of rocks after tunnel excavation from past construction data and quantify it after weighting the factors have been developed in relation with the modern tunnelling techniques. As examples, there are those developed by Wickham and others (1972), Bieniawski (1973) and Barton and others (1974). These assessment techniques were applied to actual tunnel excavation by Houghton (1976) and Rutledge and others (1978) for verification and comparative studies were made by them. From the results of the above, some problems in application of above-mentioned classification were pointed out. These are summarized in this paper. These classifications of rocks have been developed especially for the structurally stable hard rocks in America, South Africa, and Scandinavia. In Japan, contrarily, geological structure is complicated and underground structures are usually constructed in soft and crashed rocks. Therefore, it is considered improper to apply above-mentioned classifications to excavation works in Japan. Accordingly, with the purpose of making classification of rock masses that suit the geology of Japan and at the same time, possible to correlate with the above-mentioned three methods of classification, the authors unified the items of observation and descriptive records of the tunnels, and started to collect data of tunnelling as well as measured data of behaviour of rock masses after excavation. The intention of these works was to classify rocks quantitatively using the measured data as criteria and especially to select parameters for standard of classification. For these purposes, the above-mentioned data were stored in a computer to enable retrieval and statistic processing as the data base. This paper describes the object and method of data collection which is being conducted at present together with future lines of investigation.

2 CURRENT QUANTITATIVE GEOMECHANICAL ALASSIFICATION

The ultimate object of rock mass classification used in tunnelling is to preestimate the magnitude and the mode of acting earth pressure generating in the ground through which a tunnel is excavated, and to determine safe, effective and economical method of excavation, support system and thickness of lining. For this purpose, geomechanics classification have to be equipped with quantitative parameters which are weighted according to the degree of influence to the behaviour of rock mass. The parameters that control behaviour of rocks can be classified into those related to geology and those related to excavation methods.

As geological factors, there are:
1. Condition of rocks, stratification (rock types, anisotropy)
2. Mechanical properties of rocks
3. Discontinuity of rock mass (Location of strike, dip on the surface, frequency of discontinuity, cohesion on the surface of discontinuity, nature of filling materials, etc.)
4. Geologic structure (fault, folding, fracture zone, etc.)
5. Initial stress of the ground
6. Conditions of groundwater and inflow of water into the tunnel

As factors related to excavation method, there are:
1. Dimensions and shape of the tunnel
2. Direction of the tunnel in relation to the geological structure (discontinuity, anisotropy, etc.) of the ground
3. Method of excavation (techniques of blasting, systems of excavation by machines, order and speed of excavation, etc.)
4. Type of support system, timing of support work, etc.

These factors are interrelated mutually. Therefore, if classification is made on the basis of one parameter only, properties of the classified rock mass is assessed with a large aberration. When assessment is made by combining some of these factors, it becomes possible to fractionize properties of the ground from mechanical and engineering aspects. Since it is very difficult to design support system and lining of the tunnels on the basis of design calculation properly modelling the complicated ground, the method that determines the design empirically and corrects it according to the condition of geology is considered to be most reasonable at present. Studies on the methods of quantitative classification of rock masses basing on the accumulated data of excavation and geology were made energetically by Wickham, Bieniawski, Barton and others in recent years. Such conceptions were already presented as RSR (rock structure rating) by Wickham, as RSR (rock mass rating) by Bieniawski and as Q value by Barton, and these were used experimentally in a part of tunnels in Japan

Comparative studies were made mutually on each of the three conceptions by those who applied them. The studies can be summarized as below:

Barton compared the Q system with geomechanics classification and described the difference qualitatively. He pointed out that the stress condition seen in the Q system was not considered in the parameter taken up in RMR. On the other hand, for the criticism that parameters of interval and direction of joints which were taken in RMR were omitted in the Q system, Barton said that this causes no problem as coarseness (Jr) and degree of alteration (Ja) were determined by selecting joint or surface of discontinuity which was likely to collapse first.

Bieniawski compared RMR and Q value on 111 examples of caverns and obtained the following relation.

$$RMR = 9 \log_e Q + 44$$

Houghton also used these three classifications at the Kielder tunnel and pointed out the following from the results.

1. Coincidence and discordance in estimation of necessary scale of supporting according to each method of classification reflect difference in parameters used by respective author rather than difference in interpretation of behaviour of rocks.

2. When applying the method of classification in the field, geomechanics classification by Bieniawski is easier to apply compared with Barton's Q system.

3. Bieniawski's classification is more adequately applicable to jointed rocks in South Africa while Barton's classification was developed for massive rocks in the Scandinavian shield. A unified system that enable assessment of rocks in the whole world is necessary.

On the other hand, Rutledge et al. used the three methods of classification in

New Zealand correlated them mutually. They obtained following formula as mutual relation.

$$RSR = 0.77 \ RMR + 12.4$$
$$RSR = 13.3 \ \log Q + 46.5$$
$$RMR = 13.5 \ \log Q + 43.0$$

Further, they measured the axial force of supports by using a strain gauge in three tunnels and compared the values with the overburden estimated by Barton and Wickham. Fig. 1 indicates that estimation values obtained by Barton's expression a widely and much greater than actually measured values. Estimation values obtained by Wickham's expression are nearer to the measured values compared with those obtained by Barton's expression. Especially, more approximation is shown when 55% of the estimation value is used.
Rutledge also pointed out that in classification methods of Barton and Wickham, only mechanical excavation and blasting method were taken into consideration with regard to construction methods that exert influences on the ground load or earth pressure and these were not considered with quantitative methods such as used for other part of the study.

According to Rutledge's study, the most important parameter is the work method

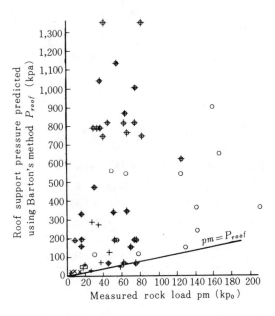

Fig. 1 Correlation between measured values and estimated ground load according to Barton (After Rutledge et al.)

Table 1. Data sheet (Form-1)

① Name of tunnel		② Excavated date		year	month	day

③ Distance from entrance	k	m	Tunnel dimension ④ Width m ⑤ Height m ⑥ Section m²

Condition of joints and cracks

⑦ Rock type ( )	1 Plutonics	2 Metamorphics	3 Sedimentaries	4 Volcanics	5 Others
⑧ Hardness of rock (kgf/cm²)	1 Hard (800 <)	2 Medium hard (200 ~ 800)	3 Soft (80 ~ 200)	4 Resudials, Clay, Sand, etc.	

Joint interval d (cm)

⑨ Horizontal direction on face	1 $100 \leq d$	2 $50 \leq d < 100$	3 $20 \leq d \leq 50$	4 $5 \leq d < 20$	5 $0 \leq d < 5$
⑩ Vertical direction on face	1 $100 \leq d$	2 $50 \leq d < 100$	3 $20 \leq d < 50$	4 $5 \leq d < 20$	5 $0 \leq d < 5$
⑪ Axial direction of tunnel	1 $100 \leq d$	2 $50 \leq d < 100$	3 $20 \leq d < 50$	4 $5 \leq d < 20$	5 $0 \leq d < 5$
⑫ Dip of major joint	1	2	3		
⑬ Condition of opening	1 No separation, unweathered.	2 Slightly separated and weathered.	3 Partly separated and weathered.	4 Separated and weathered.	
⑭ Water inflow from face	1 None, completely dry	2 Wet condition on surface	3 Partial seepage from joint	4 Seepage from whole joint	5 Partial gushing out from joint

⑮ Quantity of water inflow (at the entrance)	ℓ/min	6 Gushing out from whole joint	7 Special case, flood

⑯ Tunnel orientation to the strike of stratum	1 Nearly parallel	2 Nearly right angle	3 Oblique

⑰ Velocity of P-wave in surrounding rock mass	m/sec	⑱ Velocity of P-wave in rock specimen	m/sec	⑲ Uni-axial strength	kgf/cm²
⑳ Weight	tf/m³	㉑ Overburden	m	㉒ Ratio of uni-axial strength to the overburden	

㉓ Co-efficient of joint		㉔ Place of observation

㉔ Place of observation: 1 full face 2 arch portion 3 central drift 4 right drift 5 left drift

㉕ Remarks	1 Yes 0 No

㉖ Supporting method	1 Bolts and shotcrete	2 Steel support

㉗ Excavation technique	1 Blasting	2 Mechanical, T.B.M.	3 Hand breaker	㉘ Quantity of explosive	kg/m³

㉙ Excavation method	1 Full face	2 Heading	3 Two step bench	4 Three step bench	5 Central drift

㉚ Advance	m	㉛ Excavating cycle	times	6 Side-drift	7 Others

㉜ Support pattern

1 Shotcrete only	2 Spot bolting only	3 System bolting only	4 Shotcrete and spot bolting
5 Shotcrete and system bolting	6 Shotcrete and bolting (1)	7 Shotcrete and bolting (2)	8 Shotcrete and bolting (3)

㉝ Thickness of linning	cm	㉞ Spray times of shotcrete	times	㉟ Iron mesh	1 Yes	0 No

㊱ Types of rock bolt	1 Moltal	2 Resin	3 Others ( )

㊲ Total numbers of rock bolt	㊳ Total length of rock bolt in tunnel meter	m	㊴ Rock bolt length	m	㊵ Rock bolt pitch (transversal)	m	㊶ Rock bolt bitch (longitudinal)	m

㊷ Time difference between excavation and shotcreting	hrs	㊸ Time difference between excavation and rock bolting	hrs	㊹ Time difference between excavation and full closed section	day

㊸ Distance from face to shotcreting section	m	㊺ Distance from face to rock bolting section	m	㊼ Distance from face to full closed section	m

㊽ Steel support	1 Yes 0 No	㊾ Type of H-beam	㊿ Type of U-beam	51 Pitch of election	m

52 Linning concrete	1 Yes 0 No	53 Lagging	1 Pararell	2 Oblique	3 Wedge

Supplementaries

54	1 Yes	55 Oblique rock bolt	1 Yes 0 No	56 Length of oblique rock bolt	m	57 Number		58 Angle of bolting	°
	0 No	59 Strengthened rock bolt	1 Yes 0 No	60 Length of rock bolt	m	61 Number		62 Driving of pipe or others	1 Yes 0 No
		63 Shotcreting on face	1 Yes 0 No	64 Grouting	1 Yes 0 No	65 De-watering	1 Yes 0 No	66 Miscellaneous	

Deformation of support

67	1 Yes	68 Additional rock bolting	1 Yes 0 No	69 Additional shotcreting	1 Yes 0 No	70 Additional steel support		71 Base concrete	1 Yes 0 No
	0 No	72 Invert strut	1 Yes 0 No	73 Others					

including technique of excavation adopted, kind of supports, time from the excavation to installation of supports, etc. Further, he stated that when using geomechanics classifications, all usable ones should be utilized instead of depending on one classification. He stated that in designing steel supports for a tunnel of 8 m in width, it would be effective to use a value equivalent to 75% of the quantity of supports estimated by Wickham's system, and, for greater caverns, that supports design and excavation methods should be corrected through monitoring by experimentation, stress analysis and measuring during excavation work since rock classification alone would not provide sufficient reliability.

Maeyens compared predictions according to Barton's classification and Bieniawski's classification with the condition of tunnel rocks after excavation. As the results, he found that Barton's classification showed a tendency to give lower assessment of rock mass by about 1 rank compared with that of Bieniawski, consequently requiring greater supports. The same tendency was also observed in Barton's Q system experimentally used in Japan and the result obtained was quite different from existing geomechanics classification standard in Japan. However, Maeyens concluded that the two classifications could provide realistic assessment to geotechnologists and results of higher reliability for various grounds could be obtained by using the both together.

3 RECONSIDERATION OF PARAMETER FOR GEOME-
  CHANICAL ASSESSMENT

As mentioned above, rock classifications that assess the grounds quantitatively are being used in actual excavation of tunnels. However, there still remain some problems and reconsideration for weighting parameters seems to be necessary. Further, there are problematic points in applicability of these classifications to geology of Japan. These problems can be summarized as follows:
  1. In above-mentioned methods in foreign countries, parameters must be judged by an engineer who has much of experience on rock survey. Especially, difficulty occurs in determining parameters relating to joints that can cause diversity of ultimate judging values (Q value, RMR, RSR).
  2. Barton's classification was developed on the basis of excavation data in Scandinavian shield. Bieniawski's classification was developed in and around South Africa of stable geological structure but rich in

joints. Wickham's classification was based on tunnelling data in North America. On the other hand, in Japan, geologic structure is complicated and rock condition vary widely from hard to soft. Thus, geologic data in Japan belong to a category of poor, and it highly correspond to the uncertain part in above mentioned three classification.
  3. The scale of supports can be predicted by rock classification. Conversely, the magnitude of earth pressure that acts finally to the tunnel and stability change depending on the kind of supports. Since supports using rock bolts and shot concrete are supposed to increase in future, it is necessary to collect such data anew.
  4. Reconsideration of weighting for various parameters in regard to problems mentioned in 2. and 3. is needed. Though influences of work data (method of excavation, speed of excavation, type of support, speed of installation of support, etc.) are important, studies on this domain appear to be insufficient in aforementioned classifications. Collection of new data is necessary to conduct such investigations.
  5. When excavated in the scale of supports estimated by geomechanics classification, assessment of the results (stability condition etc.) are not made quantitatively.

Taking the above problems into consideration, the authors are collecting data of underground geology and methods of tunnelling which are under construction in Japan at present. The objects are to create a method of classification that is suitable to the geology of Japan and enables quantitative assessment, and further to find out correlation with aforementioned three classifications to make it possible to position relatively the geology of Japan from foreign countries. The following points are fundamentally taken into consideration in preparing the data sheet.
  1. Items used for observation record of underground geology are such that even a nonspecialist in geology can make correct description after training for two to three days, and can generate significant differences as parameters.
  2. Considering of importance to correlation between geological data and that of work methods, the data of excavation are to be recorded in detail. Especially, the records are to be made to enable analyses of influences exerted by excavation speed (speed of advance of the face and time of installation of support), type of support, auxiliary working method, etc. on the behaviour of rock masses after tunnel excavation.

3. Quantitative assessment is to be made for confirmation of stabilization of the ground and for deformation of support after tunnel excavation. For this purpose, convergence measurement is to be made without fail on the section for which geological data are recorded. The standard measurement to be made is for deformation of tunnel section, rock bolts, shotcrete and rock mass.

The measured values represent the behaviour of rock mass after tunnel excavation and are created by combination of rock classification and work methods. Those values are used to judge the quality of adopted excavation techniques.

4. The form should be such that allows retrieval easily as data base.

The form for data collection is shown in Table-1. For tunnels in swelling rocks and those in earth and sand, the sheets of the same form using exclusive parameters are in preparation separately.

Collected data are stored in a magnetic tape. After input, the data is used as data base for retrieval following the flowchart shown in Fig. 2, and, at the same time, it is possible to perform examination of attribution and factor from statistic processing. From this result, appropriateness of geologic parameters used at present is judged and investigation is to be made whether more effective parameters which give significant differences is necessary or not. Statistic processing to select each parameter is as given below. A factor that appears to give influences to any item of method is selected from the data sheets (refer to table-1). The distribution of each factor and category is examined by performing data analysis (simple tabulation and cross tabulation), and thus, an outline of the collected data can be known intuitively. Supposing that it is represented by a linear equation of the quantity of each category of each factor for a sample i

$$\alpha_i = \sum_{jk}\sum \delta_i(jk)\, X_{jk}$$

where

$$\delta_i(jk) = \begin{cases} 1: & \text{When the sample i reacts to factor j, category k} \\ 0: & \text{When the sample i does not react to factor j, category k} \end{cases}$$

X_{jk}: The quantity given to category k by factor j.

Here, when classification into some groups is made, X_{jk} that makes internal variance small and external variance large is to be found.
That is, X_{jk} that makes the correlation ratio $\eta^2 = \sigma_b^2/\sigma^2$ maximum is to be found.

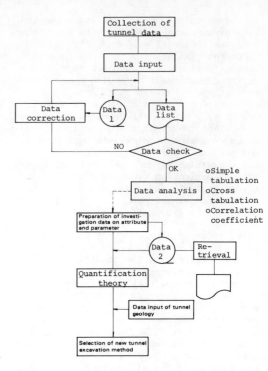

Fig. 2 Flowchart of data processing and analysis

where
total variance

$$\sigma^2 = \frac{1}{n}\sum_i^n \alpha_i^2 - \bar{\alpha}^2$$

external variance

$$\sigma_b^2 = \sum_t^T \frac{n_t}{n}(\bar{\alpha}_t - \bar{\alpha})^2$$

$$N_{jk}(t) = \sum_{i(t)=1}^{n_t} \delta_{i(t)}(jk)$$

$$\alpha_t = \frac{1}{n_t}\sum_{i(t)=1}^{n_t} \alpha_{i(t)} = \frac{1}{n_t}\sum_{jk}\sum N_{jk}(t)\, X_{jk}$$

t: Group number
T: Total number of groups
$N_{jk}(t)$: Number that reacts to factor j, category k in group t
n: Total number of samples

The result of analysis of deformation factor of a hard rock is given below as an example of analysis by statistic processing.

The convergence displacement (final quantity) of external criterion is classified into 4 groups as shown below in Fig. 3.

1: Below 1 mm
2: 1 ∿ 10 mm
3: 10 ∿ 50 mm
4: Above 50 mm
"Hardness", "Interval of joints and cracks in the horizontal direction of the face, in the vertical direction of the face, in the axial direction of the tunnel", "Dip of major joints", "Condition of opening", "Water inflow from the face" and "Support pattern" are taken up as parameters that exert influences on the convergence.

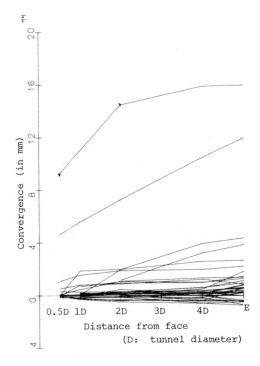

Fig. 3 An example of deformation curve (Najio Tunnel, Japan)

The simple correlation coefficients between external criterion and each factor were calculated as below:

Hardness of rock	0.8079
Joint interval (horizontal direction on face)	0.6675
Joint interval (vertical direction on face)	0.4949
Joint interval (axial direction of tunnel)	0.4464
Condition of opening	0.4447
Water inflow from face	0.2864
Support pattern	0.3588

However, since internal correlation of each factor is high mutually, analysis by com-bining the factors did not give higher correlation ratio.

By this analysis it was shown that the hardness of rocks is more dominant as deformation factor of this tunnel than crack interval and leakage of water. It is intended to make weighting of each parameter and perform calculation for quantification after establishing parameters. Further, to improve accuracy of the method of classification, new tunnel data are being added as data base.

4 FINAL COMMENTS

In this report, investigations so far made concerning geomechanics classification that assesses the rock mass quantitatively were introduced, and the method of data collection for the classification conducted at present by the authors was described.

At present, the authors are performing collection of data according to the above-mentioned system and analysis of the data. Utilization of data retrieval using the data base has already been made possible. The authors are intending to report in the near future, on positioning of the new geomechanics classification basing upon the results of analysis of data, and correlation of the classification and other classifications, and the results of application of this classification to actual tunnel excavation.

5 REFERENCES

Barton, N. 1976, Recent experiences with the Q System of tunnel support design. Proceedings of the Symposium on Exploration for Rock Engineering. Johannesburg.

Barton, N., Lien, R., Lunde, J. (1975), Estimation of support requirements for underground excavations. Design Methods in Rock Mechanics, Proc. 16th. Symp. on Rock Mech., Univ. of Minnesota.

Bieniawski, Z.T. 1979, The geomechanics classification in rock engineering applications. I.S.R.M, Montreux.

Houghton, D.A. 1976, The role of rock quality indices in the assessment of rock masses. Proceedings of the Symposium on Exploration for Rock Engineering, Johannesburg.

Maeyens, A. 1978, A comparison between the rock mass conditions as predicted and measured after tunnelling. International Association of Engineering Geology III International Congress, Spain.

Rutledge, J.C., Preston, R.L. 1978, New
   Zealand experience with engineering clas-
   sifications of rock for the prediction
   of tunnel support. International Tunnel
   Symposium, Tokyo.
Wickham, G.E., Tiedemann, H.R., Skinner,
   E.H. 1972, Support determinations based
   on geologic predictions. North American
   Rapid Excavation and Tunnelling Confer-
   ence.

INVESTIGATIONS FOR THE DRAKENSBERG POWER STATION COMPLEX IN WEAK SEDIMENTARY ROCK

Untersuchungen für den Drakensberg Kraftwerkkomplex in schwachem sedimentärem Fels

Études d'une roche sédimentaire faible pour le complexe électrique de Drakensberg

T.W.MELLORS
Golder Associates, Maidenhead, UK

J.C.SHARP
Rock Engineering Consultant, Jersey, UK

SUMMARY:
Geological and geotechnical investigations for the Power Station Complex of the Drakensberg Pumped Storage Scheme, which is sited in an essentially horizontally inter-bedded sequence of sandstones, siltstones and mudstones, are described. Investigations included surface mapping, diamond drilling and surface and downhole geophysics with additional mapping and drilling in exploratory underground works. Laboratory testing of cores was conducted for indexing of the various rock types and to investigate the deterioration characteristics of the rocks for long term stability considerations of the various excavations. Rock mass design parameters were determined using large scale in situ testing methods comprising principally a monitored test excavation of the machine hall and a series of 500 ton capacity plate bearing tests on the major rock units. In situ stress measurements were also carried out from the exploratory headings. The core logging system which was developed to permit detailed geological interpretations to be made and also geotechnical zoning of the sedimentary succession for design purposes is described.

ZUSAMMENFASSUNG:
Der Bericht beschreibt die geologischen und geotechnischen Untersuchungen fur den Kraftwerkkomplex des Drakensberg Bewässerung-und Energiespeicherungsprojektes, das sich in einem hauptsächlich horizontalen, wechselgelagerten Schichtgestein mit Sand-, Ton- und Sedimentgestein befindet. Die Forschungsarbeiten umfaßten u.a. Kartographie der Geländeoberfläche, Diamantbohrungen sowie geophysikalische Untersuchungen von Oberfläche und Schacht mit zusätzlicher Kartierung und Bohrungen in Sondierstollen. Die Kerne wurden im Labor ausgewertet, wo die verschiedenen Gesteinsarten registriert und die Verfallseigenschaften der Gesteine in Bezug auf langzeitige Widerstandsfähigkeit der verschiedenen Ausschachtungen ermittelt wurden. Die Parameter der Gesteinsmasse wurden durch umfangreiche Versuchsmethoden an Ort und Stelle bestimmt. Die Tests bestanden hauptsächlich aus der überwachten Versuchsausschachtung einer Maschinenhalle und einer Serie von Plattenlagerungsversuchen mit 500 t Trägfahigkeit an den wichtigsten Gesteinseinheiten. Außerdem wurden von den Versuchsstollen aus Belastung-smessungen an Ort und Stelle durchgeführt. Eine Beschreibung des Kernregistriersystems folgt, das entwickelt wurde, um detaillierte geologische Auswertungen zu ermöglichen und zusätzlich die geotechnischen Begrenzungen der sedimentären Schichten für Konstruktionszwecke zu ermitteln.

RESUME:
Une description est donnée des investigations géologiques et géotechniques effectuées pour le Complexe de Centrale électrique du Projet de réservoir d'eau pompée de Drakensberg, situé en terrain consistant essentiellement d'une séquence de grès, de roches de vase et de boue durcies interstratifiés horizontalement. Les investigations ont compris la cartographie de surface, des perforations de sondage au diamant et des études géophysiques en surface et sous terre, avec cartographie et perforation additionnelles en travaux souterrains d'exploration. Des essais de carottes furent conduits en Laboratoire en vue du classement des divers types de roches et pour

rechercher les caractéristiques de dégradation des roches, pour considération de la stabilité à long terme des diverses excavations. Les paramètres d'étude de la masse rocheuse furent déterminés par l'emploi à grande échelle de méthodes de test sur place comprenant principalement un essai d'excavation surveillée de la salle des machines et des essais de capacité du support de nappe à 500 tonnes et une série de mesures des charges fut aussi effectuée à partir des avancements d'exploration. Le système d'enregistrement des carottes, développé pour permettre une interprétation géologique détaillée et aussi la répartition en zones géotechniques de la succession sédimentaire, est décrit.

1 INTRODUCTION

The Drakensberg Pumped Storage Scheme is a dual purpose scheme designed for both energy storage and water supply purposes. The scheme is located in South Africa close to the headwaters of the Tugela River (Figure 1) and operates between two principal reservoirs separated by the Drakensberg escarpment. The scheme has an installed capacity of 1000 MW and an operating head in excess of 500 m.

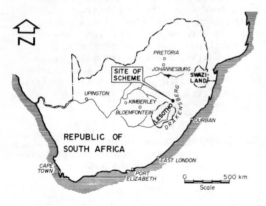

FIGURE 1 - LOCATION PLAN

The principal engineering elements of the scheme are indicated on Figure 2 and comprise (for the generating mode):
. Headworks - including intake channel, portals and headrace tunnels
. Pressure tunnels and shafts - including surge shafts, pressure shafts, pressure tunnels and penstocks
. Power Station Complex - including valve hall, machine hall, transformer hall, control block, surge chambers and associated access tunnels.
. Tailworks - including tailrace tunnel, portal and outfall excavation.
The general arrangement of the Power Station Complex is shown in plan and section on Figure 2. The Machine Hall,

which is the largest excavation, is 196 m long, 16.5 m wide and 49 m high (from vault to the bottom of the machine pits) and contains four reversible pump-turbines and 250 MW motor-generators.

The paper describes the investigations and evaluations for the scheme with particular reference to the Power Station Complex. Particular emphasis has been given to the description of geological properties in a form commensurate with the engineering design requirements. The design aspects of the Power Station excavations have been described elsewhere (Sharp 1979, 1982).

2 REGIONAL GEOLOGY OF THE SCHEME

The scheme has been constructed in rocks of the Beaufort Series of the Karroo System which consists of an interbedded sequence of sandstones, siltstones and mudstones intruded by dolerite dykes and sills. As the scheme traverses the Escarpment, altitude decreases from about 1750 m in the headworks region to about 1220 m in the vicinity of the Tailrace Portal. The escarpment topography clearly reflects the rock types with steep cliffs and associated benches occurring at each of the major sandstone outcrops together with shallower intermediate slopes in the more argillaceous rocks. Whilst distinct major sandstone horizons can be recognized and traced across the site, lateral facies variations are common and the horizontal continuity of individual minor lithological units is not always readily apparent.

The rocks have been found to be continuously graded from fine-grained mudstones to medium and coarse-grained sandstones. Thus, whilst sandstones, siltstones and mudstones occur per se, their admixtures are common i.e. silty sandstones, silty mudstones, etc.

A distinct division of rock types between the Upper and Middle Beaufort series occurs below a prominent sandstone marker horizon which outcrops on the

106

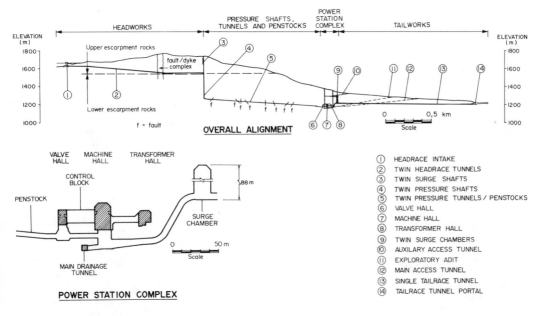

FIGURE 2 - LONGITUDINAL SECTION THROUGH THE SCHEME

escarpment at approximately elevation 1550 m (Figure 2).

Above the marker the rocks consist mainly of interbedded sandstones, siltstones and mudstones of the Upper Beaufort Series, the mudstones and siltstones of which have respectively a distinctive reddish-brown and greyish-green colouration. The rocks below the marker horizon in which the Power Station Complex is sited are primarily sandstones, siltstones and mudstones from the Middle and Lower Beaufort Series. Siltstones and muddy siltstones from these horizons vary in colour from greenish or bluish grey to dark grey. Occasional thin carbonaceous seams also occur below the marker horizon. The seams are usually thin, poorly developed fossil leaf remains within dark mudstones. Petrographic analysis of some of the rocks in the vicinity of the Power Station Complex has indicated they contain material derived from plutonic or metamorphic rocks and possibly material of volcanic origin.

The dykes within the region are typically near-vertical, from one to three metres thick, and often bounded by slickensided, serpentinized shear zones. A major sill having an upper elevation of 1133 m and over 70 m thick exists beneath the Power Station Complex.

Major faults, frequently associated with dolerite dykes exist within the region although displacements generally are limited to a few metres. The locations of significant fault structures are shown on Figure 2.

3 GEOLOGY IN THE VICINITY OF THE POWER STATION COMPLEX

3.1 Scope of Investigations

Geological and geotechnical studies of the Power Station Complex Area were carried out as part of the general investigations of the overall alignment. The nature of the proposed works of the Power Station Complex necessitated more detailed studies than other elements of the Scheme, bearing in mind that large, permanent excavations were to be formed in relatively weak sedimentary rocks.

Detailed investigations commenced in 1975 and comprised both borehole investigations and an exploratory adit and shaft with interconnecting headings in the Power Station Complex (see Figure 3). Specific test excavations were also constructed to simulate the Machine Hall and Pressure Tunnels.

Aerial photographs and satellite mosaics were examined to ascertain structural, geomorphological and other geological

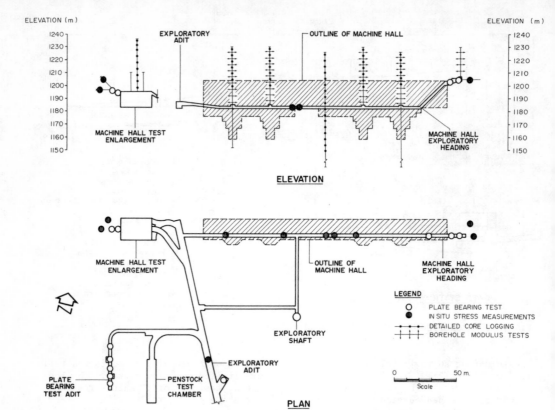

ELEVATION (m)

ELEVATION (m)

ELEVATION

PLAN

LEGEND

○   PLATE BEARING TEST
●   IN SITU STRESS MEASUREMENTS
•—•—•   DETAILED CORE LOGGING
┼┼┼   BOREHOLE MODULUS TESTS

0   50 m.
Scale

FIGURE 3 - LAYOUT OF EXPLORATORY WORKS IN POWER STATION COMPLEX AREA SHOWING TEST
          LOCATIONS

information. Surface geological mapping
was carried out at a scale of 1:2000 over
the entire alignment of the Scheme using
plane-table and alidade techniques.

Exploratory drilling was carried out
initially from surface (12 holes) and
later from the underground exploratory
headings (45 holes). All holes were of
NX size with the exception of two surface
holes which were 141 mm in diameter.
Many of the holes drilled from underground
were primarily for instrument installations or in situ tests but were cored over
their full lengths to provide supplementary
data.

Care was taken to maintain core samples
in as near in situ condition as possible
to inhibit moisture loss and deterioration
(disaggregation) of the rocks prior to
detailed logging and laboratory testing.
This was achieved by wrapping the core in
aluminium foil and then sealing with
paraffin wax.

A programme of geophysical surveying was
carried out consisting of surface seismic

refraction, cross-hole shooting with shots
fired at various depths in adjacent boreholes and sonic seismic work in some boreholes. In addition, magnetometer surveying was carried out to supplement surface
mapping of dolerite dykes.

Mapping of all underground headings was
carried out concurrently with their development and plotted at a scale of 1:100.

The mineralogy of the various rock types
was investigated by petrological analyses
of thin sections of the arenaceous rocks
and by X-Ray diffraction techniques on
the argillaceous rocks.

3.2 Groundwater Studies

The groundwater characteristics of the
rocks at the site of the scheme were
obtained from water-acceptance tests in
boreholes during their advancement using
a single mechanical packer arrangement.
Standing water levels in boreholes were
recorded during and after drilling and
pneumatic piezometers were installed in

108

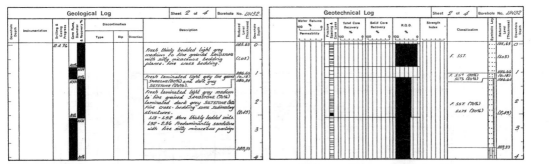

FIGURE 4 - EXAMPLES OF TYPICAL GEOLOGICAL AND GEOTECHNICAL LOGS

selected boreholes to monitor groundwater conditions at depth.

Observations of any seepage into the underground headings were recorded and samples of groundwater were collected and analysed to determine whether they would have any adverse effect on the proposed engineering structures.

3.3 Lithological Classification

A core logging system to reliably and realistically describe the rocks encountered was developed bearing in mind the interbedded nature of the succession and the requirement of geotechnical zoning for design purposes.

Examination of core obtained during a preliminary investigation by the Department of Water Affairs indicated that individual lithological beds could vary from less than 5 mm thick to in excess of 2 m thick and bedding plane spacing could vary from less than 5 mm to of the order of 0,5 m. Although the thicker lithological units (say in excess of 1 m thick) could be adequately described, engineering description of those rocks which consisted of a very closely interbedded sequence of, say, sandstone and siltstone where the individual beds could be as little as 5 mm thick was more problematic. Since apparently minor scale weak seams could have a major influence on the overall excavation behaviour, it was recognized that the description adopted would require special provision for such features.

The system that was eventually implemented was based on identifying distinct rock units within which the proportions of constituent lithological components were relatively consistent. The proportions of constituent components were estimated on the basis of visual inspection and were qualified with descriptions

of respective bedding plane spacings. To facilitate ease of presentation of the information, separate geological and geotechnical logs were produced, examples of which are given in Figure 4.

In addition every single horizon that could constitute a major plane of weakness (termed 'primary plane of parting') was identified for later use in the design studies.

The continuity of major sandstone horizons was established from the borehole information and the down-hole geophysics work and these horizons were used as the basis for the overall interpretation. It was readily apparent that, except in the case of the major sandstone horizons, lateral facies changes were common in the other rock types, particularly the close interbedded units of sandstone and siltstone – an interbedded sequence in which say, siltstone predominated could grade laterally into a sequence in which sandstone predominated.

To permit interpretation of the borehole data and underground mapping, a grouping was derived based on the premise that the characteristics of individual beds would be influenced by the relative proportions of lithological constituents. The grouping is summarized on Table 1 and described below.

Group I – Sandstones per se and interbedded sandstones and siltstones in which siltstones comprised less than 25% of the rock unit.

Group II – interbedded sandstones and siltstones in which sandstones did not exceed 75% of the rock unit and siltstone did not exceed 75% of the rock unit.

Group III – Siltstones per se and interbedded sandstones and silt-

109

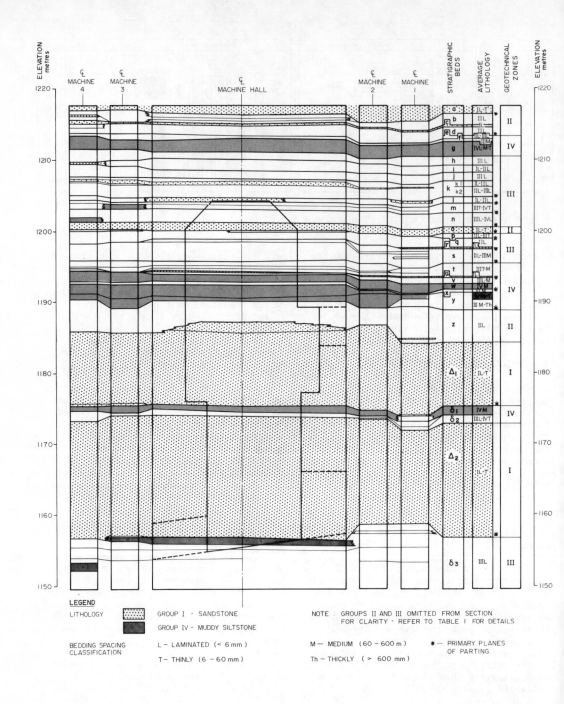

FIGURE 5 - COMPOSITE CROSS SECTION OF MACHINE HALL SHOWING GEOLOGICAL CLASSIFICATION

stones comprised less than 25% of the rock unit.

Group IV - interbedded siltstones and mudstones (not common) and muddy siltstones.

Group V - mudstones per se (including carbonaceous mudstones) and silty mudstones.

Using this sytem, 31 individual "beds" with a characteristics minimum thickness of 1 m were identified in the Power Station Complex Area extending from approximately 15 m above the proposed machine hall vault to below the base of the machine pits as shown on Figure 5 together with predicted primary planes of parting.

LITHOLOGY	CONSTITUENTS		LITHOLOGICAL GROUP
SANDSTONES	SST 100%		I
INTERBEDDED SANDSTONE AND SILTSTONE	SST 75 %	SLST 25%	II
	SST 74 %	SLST 26%	
	SST 26%	SLST 74%	
	SST 25%	SLST 75%	
SILTSTONES	SLST 100 %		III
INTERBEDDED SILTSTONE AND MUDSTONE AND MUDDY SILTSTONE			IV
MUDSTONES AND SILTY MUDSTONE			V

TABLE 1 - SUMMARY OF DERIVED LITHOLOGICAL GROUPS

For design purposes, further grouping of the rocks was carried out to produce "geotechnical zones" which formed the basis of the numerical analyses. The geotechnical zones were based primarily on lithology but also took into account the proposed geometries of the various excavations.

In general, the zones encompassed beds of similar overall ithology. Thus, for example, siltstones (Group III rocks) and interbedded sandstones and siltstones (Group II rocks) were grouped together if siltstones predominated in the interbedded unit. Discrete but relatively thin beds of potentially more competent material less than about 1 m thick, (e.g. sandstone within a succession of potentially less competent material) were disregarded. The lithological group of the potentially least competent member within a zone was assigned to the zone. If within any of the beds a facies change to a more argillaceous rock occurred, this latter rock group was assigned to the whole extent of the particular bed over the Power Station Complex Area. Thus the grouping that was carried out for design purposes can be considered as averaged worst-case lithological zoning in terms of the potential competency of the various

rock types. The resulting geotechnical zones for the Machine Hall are illustrated on Figure 5. Similar zoning was carried out for the Valve Hall and Transformer Hall.

3.4 Summary Findings

The strata within the Power Station area are essentially horizontal and bedding forms the dominant structural feature. Bedding plane spacing has been found to vary from less than 5 mm up to 500 mm. Frequently cross bedding and other sedimentary structures occur within the lithological units.

Based on the geotechnical zoning the geology of the main halls can be summarized as shown on Table 2.

GROUP	DESCRIPTION	VALVE HALL	MACHINE HALL	TRANSFORMER HALL	CONTROL BLOCK
III	SILTSTONE		ROOF AND HAUNCHES		
II/I	INTERBEDDED SANDSTONE / SILTSTONE		BASE OF HAUNCHES		
III	SILTSTONE	ROOF AND UPPER SIDEWALLS	UPPER SIDEWALLS	ROOF AND UPPER HAUNCHES	ROOF
IV	MUDDY SILTSTONE	MID SIDEWALLS	MID SIDEWALLS	HAUNCHES	UPPER SIDEWALLS
II	INTERBEDDED SANDSTONE / SILTSTONE	LOWER SIDEWALLS	MID SIDEWALLS	SIDEWALLS	LOWER SIDEWALLS
I	SANDSTONE	UPPER PITS	LOWER SIDEWALLS	BASE	BASE
IV	MUDDY SILTSTONE	MID PITS	BASE OF HALL		
I	SANDSTONE	LOWER PITS	MACHINE PITS		

TABLE 2 - SUMMARY LITHOLOGY IN RELATION TO EXCAVATIONS

Primary planes of parting are illustrated on Figure 5. Those that were particularly significant to the excavation design are given on Table 3.

TYPICAL ELEVATION (m)	DESCRIPTION	LITHOLOGY OF ADJACENT BEDS	EXCAVATION INFLUENCE
1204	PLANAR SMOOTH, MICACEOUS COATINGS	II/III	MACHINE HALL, ROOF
1201,5-1202	PLANAR, SMOOTH, SOME MICA	III/III	MACHINE HALL, MID HAUNCH
1197,5-1198	PLANAR SMOOTH	I/II	
1195,8-1196,5	PLANAR, SMOOTH, MICACEOUS, SOME RIPPLE MARKS	III/III	TRANSFORMER HALL, ROOF
1193,5-1194,2	PLANAR, SMOOTH	I/III-IV	MACHINE HALL TEST ENLARGEMENT HAUNCH
1192,5-1192,8	PLANAR, SMOOTH	III/IV	CONTROL BLOCK UPPER SIDEWALL, TRANSFORMER HALL HAUNCH
1175-1175,5	PLANAR, SMOOTH	I/IV	MACHINE HALL, FLOOR

TABLE 3 - PRIMARY PLANES OF PARTING IN RELATION TO EXCAVATIONS

Jointing within the Power Station Complex was found to be relatively limited. Three near-vertical sets were observed striking at approximately 110°, 170° and 210° (with respect to magnetic North which is about 19° west of grid north). Within the more massive muddy siltstone units notably the Group IV horizon forming the mid sidewall region of the Machine Hall, slickensided discontinuities were observed and were attributed to compaction effects within the more deformable strata. Such features dip typically at 40-60 degrees in varying directions and were significant to both the stability and deformability of the excavation profile.

No other structural features of engineering significance were encountered in the Power Station Complex Area during the excavations. Full details of the geology encountered are given in Mellors and Carter 1982.

4 ROCK MASS CHARACTERISTICS

The characteristics of the rock mass in the vicinity of the Power Station Complex were determined by in situ and laboratory testing as well as by observations of the behaviour of full scale test openings. The testing can be broadly divided into three groups as follows on the basis of scale.

. Core sample and borehole testing : determination of intact rock properties and index values for general classification purposes.
. Large scale in situ testing : provision of definitive design data for the major underground openings.
. Full scale test openings : monitoring and evaluation of the performance of full scale test openings.

The layout of the major underground tests are indicated on Figure 3. Other tests were also performed to examine specific aspects of rock behaviour such as deterioration.

Preliminary planning of the testing programme was discussed by Bowcock et al, 1976. Summary results and observations are presented below.

4.1 Core Sample and Borehole Testing

Bulk Density and Moisture Content. These parameters are of significance particularly for the argillaceous rocks and were used to determine the natural in situ state of the rock prior to any deterioration.

Uniaxial Compressive Strength/Modulus Testing. Tests on core were used as a fundamental indication of the intact characteristics of the various rock types encountered. Careful studies of the effects of modulus anisotropy, arising from the bedded nature of the rocks, were conducted. The tests were also used for control purposes on samples subjected to wetting and drying processes.

Point Load Index Testing. This test was used to classify the strength of 'intact' bedding planes in core and was useful as a basic property for determining roof stability conditions in tunnels subjected to continually varying rock conditions.

Shear Strength of Bedding Planes. Direct shear tests were carried out on small and medium scale samples (200 x 200 mm) to determine the shear strength of critical parting planes (see Table 3). Particular attention was paid to the effects of confining (normal) stress on the strength characteristics.

Borehole Modulus Testing. Testing of strata within boreholes using the Goodman Jack was carried out. The objective of the test was to determine, over a fairly large area, relative moduli between lithologies and compare measurements in horizontal and vertical directions in similar strata. The results showed significant scatter probably as a result of 'bedding-in' of the platens especially on the weaker rock units and meaningful correlations could not be made.

4.2 In Situ Testing

In Situ Stress Measurements. Borehole overcore testing using triaxial strain cells was used as the basis for measuring in situ stresses. The choice of the method was largely dictated by the weak, bedded nature of the rock. The tests were conducted in boreholes drilled from the exploratory headings as indicated on Figure 3. Conventional testing and data reduction techniques were initially applied (Leeman 1973).

Considerable difficulties were experienced with measurements in the bedded rock due to both practical problems of obtaining intact overcore and also as a result of the non-elastic, anisotropic unloading response of the material. To allow realistic evaluations of in situ stresses to be made, comprehensive calibration of each overcore was necessary to determine stress/strain conversion factors and the

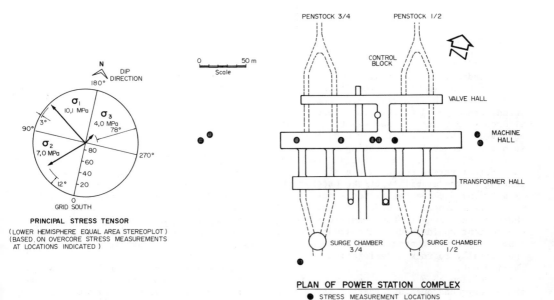

FIGURE 6 - POWER STATION COMPLEX - IN SITU STRESS FIELD

unloading response for each gauge (Gonano et al 1982).

The resultant stress field in the vicinity of the Power Station Complex is shown on Figure 6. The effect of the refined testing and evaluation procedures was to produce a significantly lower value of K than that predicted by conventional elastic solutions using standard intact moduli.

In situ Deformability Measurements. Rock mass moduli in the vicinity of the Power Station Complex were determined by means of large scale horizontal and vertical plate bearing tests at the locations indicated on Figure 3. The locations chosen reflected both variable geological conditions and relevant components of the excavation profile, such as roof strata.

A 500 tonne capacity rig was used to load circular flat jacks of areas 1,00 m^2 and 0,50 m^2 to produce bearing pressures of 4,5 MPa and 9.0 MPa respectively. Flat jacks were used below the loading plate to provide an essentially uniform bearing pressure. Displacements in the rock were measured by means of three-point mechanical extensometers with the anchors located at various depths along a borehole coaxial with the direction of loading. Maximum applied pressure was generally achieved after 5 cycles of increasing magnitude. A short term creep test was carried out at the maximum loading.

Moduli normal and parallel to bedding of 18 GPa and 24 GPa were determined and at the test scale used little variation between lithology was detected. It was concluded that the deformabilities of the siltstones and sandstones were similar and that the more deformable muddy siltstones were insufficient in extent to influence mass moduli significantly.

4.3 Full Scale Test Openings

A full scale test opening to the proposed cross-section of the Machine Hall was excavated as part of the exploratory works. The main purpose of the excavation was to establish the feasibility of developing permanent caverns in the horizontally bedded, sedimentary rock conditions using a staged excavation/rock reinforcement technique with reinforced shotcrete as the final lining. The observed behaviour of the trial excavation which was used as the basis for the main cavern design has been described by Sharp et al 1979.

A test chamber to determine the behaviour of concrete linings in the bedded rock was also constructed as part of the exploratory works. Deformability criteria determined from the chamber were in good agreement with the large scale plate bearing tests. Full details of the chamber tests are given in Sharp and Gonano, 1982.

113

4.4 Rock Deterioration Investigations

Deterioration, in the form of disaggregation, of some of the rock at the site was recognized at an early stage of the exploratory studies. Disaggregation was observed to occur predominantly in the finer-grained rocks (i.e. with an argillaceous component) which were exposed to the atmosphere and allowed to dry out. Disaggregation was also observed to be exacerbated by subjecting such rocks to cycles of wetting and drying.

It was clear that the extent and rate of such deterioration could have a direct bearing on the stability of the underground excavations and the requirements for permanent linings. In order to determine whether conditions in the underground environment would produce the same effects, laboratory testing programmes relating specifically to rock deterioration were carried out.

In addition observations were made in the underground openings (particularly the Machine Hall Test Enlargement) of the apparent susceptibility of the various rock types to deterioration. The observations were based mainly on the use of a borehole petroscope to monitor the extent and degree of fracturing arising from moisture losses with time. High resolution measurements were also carried out over an extended time scale using specially developed vibrating wire extensometers.

The scope of the laboratory testing programme can be summarized as:

. determination of moisture content variation with time for the various rock types.
. slake durability testing of the various rock types
. determination of shrinkage characteristics of the various rock types
. determination of the free-swelling characteristics of the various rock types
. determination of the swelling pressures generated in the various rock types when restrained.

In conjunction with this testing programme specific observations of the microfabric of the various rock types were made using a petrological microscope with thin sections and a scanning electron microscope.

Tests were also carried out on samples of the various rock types to determine their swelling characteristics when subjected to pressurized water in staged increments and decrements in connection with the pressure tunnels (Sharp and Gonano, 1982). Susceptibility to erosion was also investigated.

Of significance to the long-term stability of the Power Station Complex excavations the observations and test results indicated that the argillaceous rocks showed the greatest propensity for disaggregation especially when wetted periodically during the drying process. When allowed to dry out gradually under relatively constant conditions of temperature and humidity, however, even the argillaceous rocks showed no visible signs of deterioration.

It was concluded from the studies that whilst disaggregation of the more argillaceous rocks would occur as a result of excavation and support activities, the depth of disaggregation would be limited essentially to the extent of the blast damaged zone around the openings (carefully controlled blasting procedures were used in all the excavations of the Power Station Complex)

Furthermore, it was concluded that the extent of disaggregation would not increase with time and that equilibrium conditions once attained would be maintained because of the controlled temperature and humidity environment in the station under operating conditions. Adequate support to the near surface disaggregated zone was provided by means of reinforced shotcrete linings integrated with the rock reinforcement.

5 DESIGN PARAMETERS

The geological and rock mass property studies were used to provide design parameters for stability and deformation analyses of the Power Station Complex. The properties were assigned in accordance with the summary geotechnical zones shown on Figure 5.

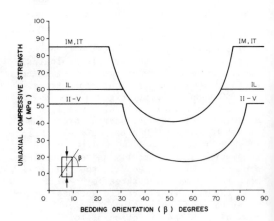

FIGURE 7 - UNIAXIAL COMPRESSIVE STRENGTH OF CORE AS A FUNCTION OF BEDDING ORIENTATION

The compressive strength characteristics of the rock were evaluated relative to the bedding orientation and are shown on Figure 7 for the various lithological groups.

To determine the potential for bedding plane slip and thus overstressing around the proposed excavations, shear strength parameters were derived from the test results for each lithological group and are given on Table 4.

GEOTECHNICAL ZONE	ASSUMED STRENGTH PARAMETERS	
	EFFECTIVE COHESION (MPa)	ANGLE OF SHEARING RESISTENCE (DEGREES)
I	16 MPa	13°
II – V	6 MPa	24°

NOTE : IN ACTUAL ANALYSES, THE ABOVE PARAMETERS WERE USED ONLY WITHIN REPRESENTATIVE STRESS STATES.

TABLE 4 – SUMMARY SHEAR STRENGTH CHARAC-
TERISTICS FOR BEDDING PLANES
ADJACENT TO UNDERGROUND OPENINGS

The influence of other structural features (jointing, slickensided features, specific planes of parting) was assessed separately in the analysis of excavation stability.

6 CONCLUSION

The scope of the investigations at the Drakensberg Scheme permitted detailed geological interpretations to be carried out for the Power Station Complex Area which formed the basis of the design studies. The scope of the investigation in terms of the locations of the exploratory boreholes and the summary interpreted geology are illustrated on Figure 8. The nature of the rocks necessitated the development of special core logging systems. Geological mapping during excavation and monitoring of excavation behaviour confirmed the predictions made.

ACKNOWLEDGEMENTS

The authors wish to thank the Electricity Supply Commission of South Africa for permission to publish this paper and Gibb Hawkins & Partners and Golder Associates for the material which has been used in its preparation. They also wish to acknowledge the extensive contribution of their many colleagues whose work is reported here.

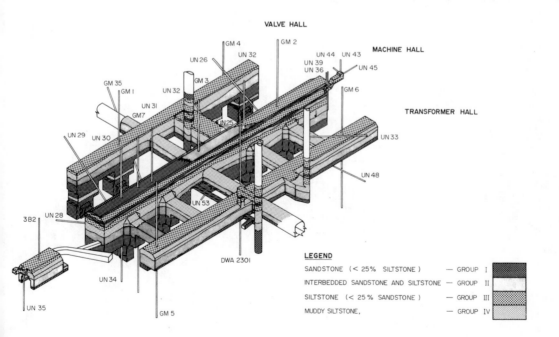

LEGEND

SANDSTONE (< 25% SILTSTONE)	— GROUP I
INTERBEDDED SANDSTONE AND SILTSTONE	— GROUP II
SILTSTONE (< 25% SANDSTONE)	— GROUP III
MUDDY SILTSTONE,	— GROUP IV

FIGURE 8 – POWER STATION COMPLEX ISOMETRIC SHOWING SUMMARY GEOLOGY

REFERENCES

Bowcock, J.B., J.M. Boyd, E. Hoek & J.C.
Sharp 1976, Drakensberg Pump Storage
Scheme - Rock Engineering Aspects, in
Proc. Symposium on Exploration for Rock
Engineering, Johannesburg.
Gonano, L.P., R.J. Pine & J.C. Sharp 1982,
Measurement of In Situ Stress in a Weak,
Bedded Rock Mass (in press).
Leeman, E.R. 1973, Instruction Manual for
the Use of the CSIR Triaxial Rock Stress
Measurement Equipment, CSIR Publication,
Pretoria, South Africa.
Mellors, T.W. & T.G. Carter 1982, Enginee-
ring Geological Studies for the Drakens-
berg Scheme (in press).
Sharp, J.C. 1979, Rock Engineering Aspects
of the Drakensberg Scheme, Tunnels &
Tunnelling, June
Sharp, J.C. 1982, in press.
Sharp, J.C., R.J. Pine, D. Moy & R.J.
Byrne 1979, The Use of a Trial Enlarge-
ment for the Underground Cavern Design
of the Drakensberg Pumped Storage
Scheme, 4th Congress of Int. Soc. for
Rock Mechanics, Montreux.
Sharp, J.C. & L.P. Gonano 1982, Rock
Engineering Aspects of the Concrete
Lined Pressure Tunnels of the Drakens-
berg Pumped Storage Scheme, ISRM Sym-
posium on Rock Mechanics related to
Caverns and Pressure Shafts, Aachen.

KONTROLLIERTE STANDSICHERHEIT GROSSER FELSHOHLRÄUME
Control of the stability of large caverns in rock
Stabilité contrôlée des grandes cavernes rocheuses

A.PAHL & W.GLÖGGLER
Bundesanstalt für Geowissenschaften und Rohstoffe, Hannover, Bundesrepublik Deutschland

SUMMARY:
Control measurements are used not only in working mines but also as a
practical method of assessing the stability of rock caverns. The assumption
upon which stability calculations are based can be checked using the
results of these measurements. It is explained with the aid of diagrams
how the stability of large rock caverns can be monitored. The results of
evaluation of control measurements carried out over a period of ten years
in the underground machine hall of the Waldeck II pumped storage station
are described, as well as the monitoring of secondary stresses in rock
pillars in a disused gypsum mine. An evaluation of the results was undertaken to assess the overall stability and to determine the need for
additional rock reinforcement.

ZUSAMMENFASSUNG:
Kontrollmessungen dienen dem Zweck wirtschaftlich zu bauen und den praktischen Nachweis der Standsicherheit zu erbringen. Die Berechnungsan-
nahmen der Standsicherheitsberechnungen können mit den Meßergebnissen überprüft werden. An Beispielen wird erläutert, wie die Standsicherheit großer
Felshohlräume durch Überwachungsmeßmethoden kontrollierbar ist. Insbesondere werden die Ergebnisse mehr als 10-jähriger Kontrollmessungen an
der Maschinenkaverne des Pumpspeicherwerks Waldeck II und spezielle Kontrollen der Sekundärspannungen in Felspfeilern einer Lagerkammer in einem
ehemaligen Gipsbergwerk dargestellt. Eine Wertung der Ergebnisse erfolgt
im Hinblick auf die Standsicherheit und ggf. erforderlicher Verstärkungen
des Ausbaus.

RESUME:
Les mesures de contrôle servent à construire économiquement et à apporter
la preuve pratique de la stabilité. Les suppositions du calcul de ceux de
la stabilité peut étre contrôlées par les résultats des mesures. Il est
expliqué par des exemples que la stabilité de grandes cavernes rocheuses
est contrôlable par des programmes de mesure de surveillance. En particulier, on y exposé les resultats de mesure de contrôle de plus d'une
décennie à la caverne centrale de pompage Waldeck II, aussi que des con-
trôles spéciaux de la tension sécondaire dans des pilliers de roche d'une
chambre d'entrepôt dans une ancienne mine de gypse. Une évaluation des
résultats a lieu en vue de la stabilité et, au cas échéant, de renforcement de soutènement qui s'avèreraient nécessaires.

1 EINLEITUNG

Im Felsbau sollen Bauwerk und Gebirge ein System bilden, das statisch zu untersuchen und zu berechnen ist. Vom Arbeitskreis 18 der
Deutschen Gesellschaft für Erd- und
Grundbau wurde ein Sicherheitskon-
zept entwickelt (DGEG 1980, Empfehlungen für den Tunnelbau unter Tage)

das alle die Sicherheit beeinflussenden Parameter enthält. Danach sind Sicherheitsaussagen für folgende Versagensfälle zu machen:
- Minderung der Gebrauchsfähigkeit. z.B. Wasserundichtigkeit
- Begrenzung der Verformungen
- örtliches Versagen des Gebirges oder einzelner Ausbauteile, z.B. Versagen von Felsankern
- Gesamtversagen, d.h. Zusammenbruch infolge Festigkeitsüberschreitungen.

Diesen Sicherheitsaussagen sind Kriterien zuzuordnen, wie Gebirgsspannungen, Verformungen und Druckfestigkeit des Gebirges, Festigkeit von Ausbauten und Tragfähigkeit von Felsankern, die realitätsnah anzunehmen, bzw. durch Untersuchungen zu bestimmen sind.

Der geologische, meist inhomogene und anisotrope Aufbau des Gebirges, mögliche Restspannungen früherer Beanspruchungen und mitunter unregelmäßige Gestaltung von Felshohlräumen haben nicht immer genau bestimmbare Größen und bringen Unsicherheit in die Berechnungen. Deshalb nehmen die meßtechnische Überwachung und Langzeitmessungen einen festen Platz im Entwurfkonzept für untertägige Felsbauten ein. Langjährige Kontrollmessungen dienen somit dem Zweck, möglichst wirtschaftlich zu bauen und den praktischen Nachweis der Standsicherheit zu erbringen. Außerdem kann mit den Meßergebnissen der rechnerische Nachweis überprüft werden.

Von den an der Planung und Bauausführung beteiligten Fachleuten sind im Einzelfall die durch Messungen zu untersuchenden Sicherheitskriterien auszuwählen. Auf der Grundlage von Erfahrungen, ingenieurgeologisch-felsmechanischen Überlegungen und Berechnungen können Grenzwerte vereinbart werden, bei deren Erreichen Maßnahmen einzuleiten sind, z.B. zusätzliche Messungen, Ausbauverstärkungen, Drainagen. Im folgenden wird an zwei Beispielen erläutert, wie und mit welchen Ergebnissen die Standsicherheit großer Felshohlräume kontrollierbar ist.

2 LANGZEITÜBERWACHUNG DER MASCHINENKAVERNE WALDECK II

In den Jahren 1970/71 wurden die großen Felshohlräume für das Pumpspeicherwerk (PSW) Waldeck II aufgefahren. Über die ingenieurgeologischen und felsmechanischen Untersuchungen für dieses Projekt haben die beteiligten Fachleute in einer Anzahl von Veröffentlichungen, u.a. HEITFELD (1972), ABRAHAM, St. BARTH, BRÄUTIGAM, HERETH, L. MÜLLER, PAHL & RESCHER (1974) und ABRAHAM & PAHL (1976) speziell über die "Bauwerksbeobachtung der großen Untertageräume des Pumpspeicherwerks Waldeck II" berichtet. Deshalb wird hier nur ein kurzer Überblick über die eingesetzten Meßgeräte gegeben, dafür aber ausführlicher über die mehr als 10-jährigen Meßerfahrungen und Ergebnisse berichtet. Betreiber des bei Waldeck am Edersee gelegenen Werkes ist die Preußenelektra Wasserkraftanlagen GmbH. Planung und Bauleitung lagen in Händen der Siemens AG. Das Oberbecken befindet sich in rund 500 m Höhe und das Unterbecken im Edertal bei etwa 200 m. Die Maschinenkaverne steht in Schiefertonen und Grauwacken des Kulm, bei etwa 260 m Überdeckung. Die größten Abmessungen der Maschinenkaverne betragen 33,5 m Breite, etwa 50 m Höhe und 106 m Länge. Der Ausbau besteht aus Felsankern (Ausbauwiderstand 0,16 MN/m^2) und bewehrtem Spritzbeton von 18-24 cm Stärke.

Das Langzeitkontrollsystem besteht aus Messungen der Verschiebungen der Kavernenwandung und von Meßpunkten im umgebenden Gebirge, Messungen der Vorspannkräfte an ausgewählten Ankern und der Beobachtung des Ausbaus, wozu die Kartierung von Haarrissen im Spritzbeton in der Firste der Kaverne gehört.

Abb. 1 gibt einen Überblick der Anordnung der Meßstellen.

Die Meßstellen sind in 4 Querschnitten angeordnet, und zwar jeweils Verschiebungsmessungen an Extensometern und Kraftmessungen an Ankern in zwei Ebenen, die aus technischen Gründen etwa 1,5 m von einander entfernt parallel zueinander liegen.

Mit Einfachextensometern von etwa 35 m Länge werden die Verschiebungen der Kavernenwandung und mit Mehrfachextensometern von ca.

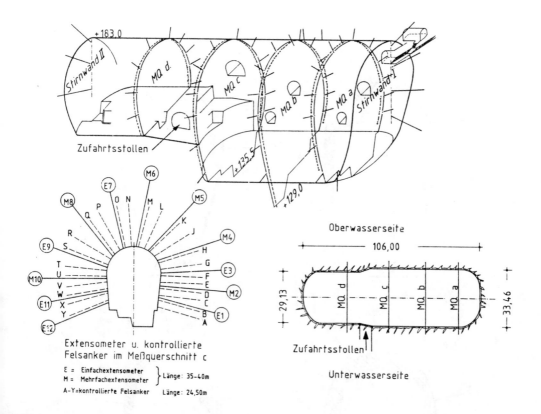

Abb. 1.: Maschinenkaverne PSW Waldeck II, Anordnung der Kontrollmessungen

40 m Länge zusätzlich die Verschiebungen von Meßpunkten im Gebirge in 25, 10, 5 und 1 m Teufe erfaßt. Dabei wird vorausgesetzt, daß in 35 bis 40 m Tiefe ab Kavernenwandung keine Verschiebungen des Gebirges mehr stattfinden. Bereits während der Auffahrung fand diese Annahme Bestätigung durch Ergebnisse der Verschiebungsmessungen mit den Mehrfachextensometern, da an den 25 m tiefen Meßpunkten nur äußerst geringfügige Verschiebungen aufgetreten waren.

Abb. 2 zeigt die Verschiebungen der Kavernenwandung, die während und nach der Bauzeit, aber vor Inbetriebnahme des Werkes bis 1975 eingetreten waren und im Vergleich dazu die Veränderungen bis Ende 1981.

Die Darstellung macht deutlich, daß seit Inbetriebnahme des Werkes nur relativ kleine Verschiebungen langzeitig eingetreten sind im Vergleich zu denjenigen, die insbesondere während des Ausbruchs in der Bauzeit erfolgten. Während d.Bauzeit

wurde die größte Verschiebung mit 37 mm in dem First gemessen, während seit 1975 die größte Verschiebung bei 2,17 mm liegt.

Aus den Zeit- Verschiebungskurven der Extensometer-Meßpunkte geht hervor, daß während der Bauzeit die größten Verschiebungen im Bereich bis etwa 5 m ab Kavernenwandung eintraten. Nach der Inbetriebnahme sind die Veränderungen vergleichsweise sehr gering, treten aber nicht nur in dem hohlraumnahen Bereich auf. Während der Bauzeit waren die Verschiebungen in den Hohlraum gerichtet, bedingt durch die Entspannung und Auflockerung des umgebenden Gebirges, insbesondere in dem 5 m - Bereich. Nach den Ausbrucharbeiten sind die Verschiebungen an den meisten Meßpunkten sehr schnell abgeklungen, lediglich im südöstlichen First-Kämpferbereich traten anhaltend geringe Verschiebungen auf. Deshalb wurde vor der Inbetriebnahme

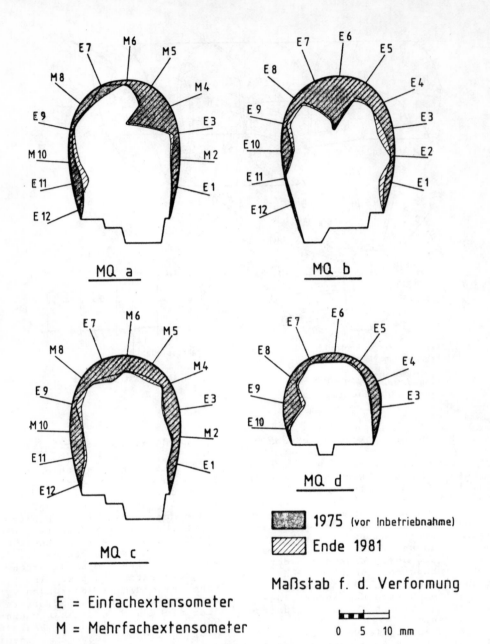

Abb. 2: Konvergenz der Kavernenwandung (Maßstab der Verschiebung stark
überhöht)

in diesem Bereich eine Ausbauver-
stärkung durch 21 zusätzliche Felsanker vorgenommen. In der Folge-
zeit kamen die Verschiebungen annähernd zum Stillstand, an einigen
Meßpunkten wurden sogar in das Ge-

birge gerichtete Veränderungen
beobachtet, die zu einer Abnahme
der vorher hohlraumseitigen Verschiebungen führten.
   In Abb. 3 sind die Verschiebungen der Meßpunkte eines Mehrfach-

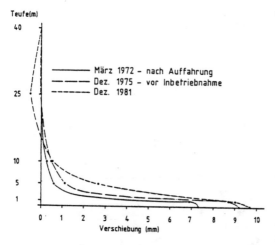

Abb. 3: Verschiebungen der Meßpunkte des Mehrfachextensometers aM4

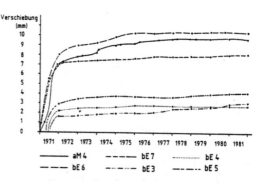

Abb. 4: Zeit-Verschiebungskurven einiger typischer Meßpunkte

extensometers dargestellt. Aus den drei Zeit-Verformungskurven, 1972, 1975 und 1981 geht hervor, daß bis 1972 die größten Verschiebungen, annähernd 7 mm, in dem Bereich bis 5 m Tiefe eingetreten sind. Danach hat sich hier noch eine weitere Verschiebung bis zur Inbetriebnahme des Werkes von fast 2 mm eingestellt. In den 6 Jahren nach Inbetriebnahme treten Deformationen auf, die in der Summe zwar klein, aber in anderen Tiefenbereichen liegen. So verändert sich der 5 m-Meßpunkt um ca. 1,5 mm kavernenseitig und der 25 m - Meßpunkt um ca. 0,5 mm gebirgsseitig. Diese langzeitigen Verschiebungen werden vor allem auf Veränderungen der Wasserführung im Gebirge zurückgeführt. Einflüsse aus dem Maschinenbetrieb der Kaverne sind dabei nicht auszuschließen.

Als Beispiel sind in der Abb. 4 die Zeit- Verschiebungskurven einiger typischer Meßpunkte der Kavernenwandung dargestellt. Die Extensometer aM4, bE6 und 7 liegen im Bereich der Zusatzankerung. Die Verschiebungen wären hier relativ groß, kamen aber nach der Zusatzankerung ab 1975 annähernd zum Stillstand. Die Extensometer bE3, 4 und 5 sind typisch für eine Anzahl von Meßpunkten, die sehr kleine Verschiebungen aufweisen und auch nach der Inbetriebnahme wenig Veränderungen zeigen.

Außer den Verformungswegmessungen werden Kontrollen der Ankervorspannkräfte durchgeführt. Nach Durchführung der Zusatzankerung sind seit 1975 die Änderungen sehr gering, d.h. sie liegen im allgemeinen im Bereich der Meßgenauigkeit von $\pm$ 2%. Die Ankerkraftkontrollen werden mit hydraulischen Ringmeßdosen (vgl. DIETRICH, H. 1982) vorgenommen, die wegen der geringen Meßgenauigkeit die Tendenzen von Veränderungen nicht so frühzeitig erfassen können wie die Extensometermessungen mit induktiven Weggebern.

Die Firste der Maschinenkaverne ist der ständigen Beobachtung zugänglich. Deshalb wird ergänzend zu den Verschiebungs- und Ankerkaftmessungen eine Ausbaukontrolle durch Aufnahme feinster Risse im Spritzbeton durchgeführt. Dabei handelt es sich überwiegend um Haarrisse. Die Öffnungweiten sind nur selten größer als 1 mm. Als Ursachen für diese Risse kommen Schwinden des Spritzbetons, Austrocknung durch Klimatisierung und Temperaturschwankungen infrage. Risse, die eindeutig auf Überbeanspruchung des Gebirges zurückzuführen sind, wurden nicht beobachtet. Allerdings deutet die Anordnung einiger Risse auf einen Zusammenhang mit der Krafteinleitung durch die Vorspannanker hin. So verlaufen einige Risse etwa mittig zwischen den Ankerwiderlagern überwiegend senkrecht zur Kavernenlängserstreckung. Abb. 5 zeigt einen Ausschnitt aus der Rißkartierung der Firste. Durch die jährliche Fortsetzung dieser intensiven Beobachtung von feinen Rissen soll sichergestellt werden, daß Veränderungen zwischen Meßprofilen frühzeitig erkannt werden. Abb. 6 vermittelt

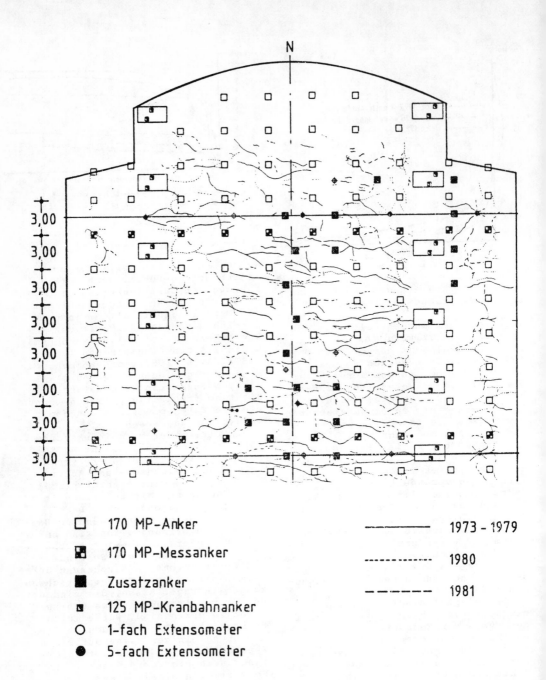

N

3,00
3,00
3,00
3,00
3,00
3,00
3,00
3,00

□	170 MP-Anker	———————— 1973 - 1979
▦	170 MP-Messanker	------------- 1980
■	Zusatzanker	— — — — — 1981
▪	125 MP-Kranbahnanker	
○	1-fach Extensometer	
●	5-fach Extensometer	

Abb. 5: Darstellung feiner Risse in der Firste der Kaverne (Ausschnitt)

einen Gesamteindruck von der Maschinenkaverne und der gut sichtbaren
Firste.

Auf der Grundlage der Verformungs-
kontrollen und der zusätzlichen
Beobachtungen kann die Standsicherheit beurteilt werden. Bei Erreichen
bestimmter Grenzwerte beziehungs-
weise stetiger Verschiebungen sind
Maßnahmen zu treffen, die eine
Klärung der Ursachen, Vorschläge
für Verbesserungen und ggf. auch
Ausbauverstärkungen beinhalten sollen.
    Die eingebauten Meßsysteme werden
turnusmäßig gewartet und überprüft,
um die Standsicherheitskontrollen

in der Maschinenkaverne auf Dauer
sicherzustellen.

3 KURZZEITIGE STANDSICHERHEITSKON-
TROLLE EINER LAGERKAMMER IN EINEM
EHEMALIGEN GIPSABBAU

In einer Lagerkammer am Rand eines
ehemaligen untertägigen Gipsabbaues
wurden Ausbauschäden festgestellt,
die eine Überbeanspruchung von Ab-
baupfeilern vermuten ließen. Deshalb sollten die Gebirgsspannungen
in den Pfeilern untersucht und mit
Gebirgsspannungen außerhalb des Ab-
baufeldes verglichen werden.
    Diese Untersuchungen wurden nach
zwei Methoden ausgeführt, und zwar

Abb. 6: Maschinenkaverne des PSW Waldeck II nach der Inbetriebnahme

nach der Kompensationsmethode mit Schlitzentlastung und Druckkissenbelastung sowie der Überbohrmethode.

Der Schlitzentlastungs-Druckkissenbelastungsversuch wurde an einem intakten Gebirgspfeiler vorgenommen. Die Untersuchungstiefe betrug etwa 1,5 m im Stoß. Die Sägeschlitze waren horizontal angeordnet, um die Vertikalspannung im Pfeiler zu erfassen. Während der Schlitzsägearbeit konnten die Entspannungswege in Bohrungen unter den Sägeschlitzen mit induktiven Weggebern gemessen werden. In Abb. 7 sind die Meßergebnisse zusammengestellt. Die linke Hälfte der Abbildung zeigt die Entlastungswege, die sich während des Schlitzsägens einstellten. In der rechten Abbildungshälfte ist die Kompensationsbelastung dargestellt, die eine Rückverformung bewirkt. Die vertikalen Spannungen ließen sich in diesem Fall mit 3,4 und 4,2 MN/m² kompensieren, die horizontale Entspannung konnte mit den horizontal eingebauten Druckkissen nicht kompensiert werden. Das Ergebnis hat nachgewiesen, daß dieser Pfeiler

entsprechend der Überlagerung, der Festigkeit und unter Annahme einer gleichmäßigen Spannungsverteilung nicht überbelastet war.

Mit Überbohrversuchen konnte die Spannungsverteilung in einem überbelasteten und einem intakten Gebirgspfeiler ermittelt werden. Die Messungen wurden durch Überbohren induktiver Weggeber (System BGR) ausgeführt mit kontinuierlicher Registrierung während des Überbohrens. Die Auswertung erfolgte unter der Annahme eines linear elastischen und isotropen Kontinuums. Für die praktische Auswertung war dies ausreichend, weil die Entlastungszeiten und Belastungszeiten in den Versuchen einander angepaßt wurden.

Die Versuchsergebnisse sind in Abb. 8 zusammengestellt. In dem überbeanspruchten Gebirgspfeiler waren die ermittelten horizontalen und vertikalen Spannungen annähernd gleich hoch, und zwar am Pfeilerrand zur Lagerkammer bis 30 MN/m² und am Pfeilerrand zum ehemaligen Abbaufeld und zu einem Verbruch abfallend bis auf etwa 10 MN/m². Vergleichsweise sind

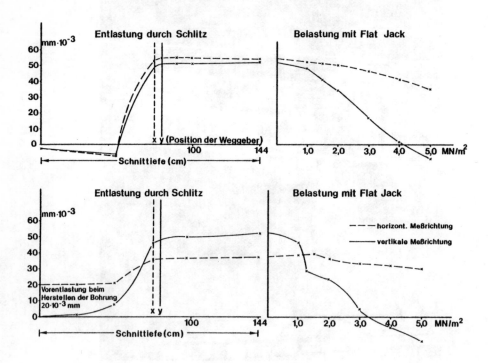

Abb. 7: Schlitzentlastung und Kompensation durch Druckkissenbelastung

die Ergebnisse von Überbohrversuchen
in einem intakten Pfeiler aufgetra-
gen. In diesem Pfeiler liegt die
Horizontalspannung wesentlich unter
der Vertikalspannung. Die Spannungen
sind zwischen 1 m und 6 m Pfeiler-
tiefe (Pfeilermitte) annähernd
gleichmäßig verteilt, um 13 MN/m²
Vertikalspannung und um 5 MN/m² Horizontalspannung.

Auf der Grundlage der Spannungs-
meßergebnisse konnten Berechnungen
und Ausbaumaßnahmen durchgeführt
werden.

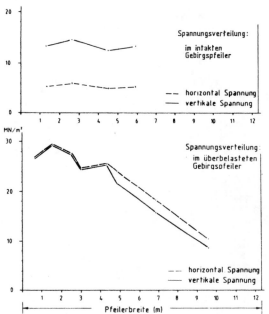

Abb. 8: Ergebnisse von Überbohrversuchen

4 AUSBLICK

Die seit mehr als 10 Jahren durchgeführten Kontrollmessungen in einer
Großkaverne im Fels haben nachgewiesen, daß diese Messungen, insbesondere die Verschiebungsmessungen
mit tiefen Einfach- und Mehrfachextensometern, eine gute Methode
sind, um die Standsicherheit zu
überwachen und nachzuweisen.

Für die Überprüfung plötzlich
auftretender Standsicherheitspro-
bleme hat sich der Einsatz von
Spannungsmeßmethoden, insbesondere
des Überbohrens, als nützlich erwiesen. Diese Untersuchungen sind
jedoch mit einigem Aufwand, bedingt
durch die Bohrungen bzw. das

Schlitzsägen, verbunden.
Grundsätzlich ist jedoch den Langzeitmessungen der Vorzug zu geben,
weil nur durch sie eine kontinuierliche Überwachung des Bauwerks
möglich ist.

5 LITERATUR

Abraham, K.H., Barth, St., Bräuti-
gam, F., Hereth, A., Müller, L.,
Pahl, A. & O.J. Rescher 1974,
Vergleich von Statik, Spannungs-
optik und Messungen beim Bau
der Maschinenkaverne Waldeck II.
Rock Mechanics Supplementum 3.
Abraham, K.H. & A. Pahl 1976,
Bauwerksbeobachtung der großen
Untertageräume des Pumpspeicher-
werks Waldeck II. Die Bautechnik
53. Jg. H. 5.
Arbeitskreis 18 der DGEG 1980,
Empfehlungen für den Felsbau
unter Tage (Fassung 1979), Tunnel-
bau 1980, Essen
Barth, St. 1972, Felsmechanische
Probleme beim Entwurf der Kaver-
ne des Pumpspeicherwerks Waldeck
II. Die Bautechnik 49, H. 3,
S. 73-83.
Dietrich, H. 1982, Langzeit-Kraft-
messungen an vorgespannten Fels-
ankern, Int. Symp. Mai 1982,
Aachen.
Glöggler, W. & K.H. Sprado 1980,
Ermittlung von Gebirgsspannungen
mit Schlitzsägeapparatur und
Druckkissen, Z. Bergbau 9/80
Heitfeld, K.-H. 1972, Engineering
geological contribution to the
construction of underground
structures for pumped storage
schemes. Symp. on Hydro Electric
storage schemes, Athen.
Müller, D. 1981, Ermittlung von Gebirgsspannungen nach dem Prinzip
des Überbohrverfahrens mit induktiven Weggebern, Z. Bergbau
9/81.
Pahl, A., Sprado, K.-H. & W.
Glöggler 1978, Kontrollierte
Standsicherheit einer Großkaverne im Fels, Z. Bergbau 9/78.

APPLICATION DE L'ÉMISSION ACOUSTIQUE POUR LE CONTRÔLE EN GÉNIE CIVIL

Application of acoustic emission for supervision in civil engineering

Anwendung der Schallemission für die Überwachung im Bauwesen

M.C.REYMOND
CNRS, Paris, France

D.JEANJEAN & J.PERDEREAU
Laboratoire National d'Essais, Paris, France

R.DE MOL
CGR, Issy les Moulineaux, France

SUMMARY:
Observational data of phenomena, termed precursores that precede mine
failures and the damaged work of art in civil engineering suggest that
an accurate prediction od impending failure may be possible. This paper
presents results of investigations aimed at establishing a mechanism of
brittle fracture in tunnel and possibilities to extrapolate data in o-
thers public works constructions provided that specific parameters of concrete or rocks were considered.

ZUSAMMENFASSUNG:

Die Beobbachtung der Phänomene als Vorzeichen eines Gebirgsschlages in
Bergwerken oder eines Einsturzes eines Baues einflüsst dass ein drohend-
Bruch vorauszesehen werdenkömt.Dieser Artihel gibt die Ergbnisse eines
Bruchmechanisms in eines Gervölbe und die Mögliehkeiten ihre Anwendung
für andere Baukoustruktione, aber unter der Bedigung dass einige Eigens
chaften eigentümliche des Stoffes berucksichtigt werden.

RESUME:
L'observation de phénomènes en termes de signes précurseurs qui précè-
dent un coup de toit dans une mine ou l'effondrement d'une structure en
génie civil suggère qu'une prédiction d'une rupture imminente est possible.
Ce papier présente les résultats d'un mécanisme de rupture dans une voûte, ainsi que les possibilités d'extrapolation dans d'autres structures
à condition toutefois de prendre en considération certains paramètres
spécifiques à la nature du matériau.

I INTRODUCTION

En Génie civil un des problèmes qui
se pose est de déterminer les caractéristiques d'un ouvrage souterrain.
Dans ce domaine, la technique du béton projeté en tant que renforcement
de voûte est une méthode d'application récente.

Le C.E.B.T.P., le C.E.T.U., la RATP
et la SNCF ont entrepris à partir de
1977 un programme d'essais sur des
maquettes de grandes dimensions afin
de tester l'efficacité de ce mode
de remise en état des ouvrages an-
ciens dont la plupart date du siècle dernier. Il s'agit d'observer
le comportement de structures en

maçonnerie ou en béton soumises à des charges croissantes.

Au-delà d'un certain niveau de contrainte, le comportement d'un matériau n'est plus linéaire et sa déformation est irréversible. le problème est de déterminer ce niveau de contrainte appelé critère par le procédé d'émission acoustique, dans le but de mettre au point un dispositif de surveillance des structures.

2 LOIS PHYSIQUES ELEMENTAIRES

On désigne par émission acoustique toute manifestation d'une onde de déplacement dont la source se trouve au sein d'un matériau subissant des modifications de structure ou de texture d'origine diverse. Chaque fois qu'un dégagement irréversible d'énergie se produit à l'intérieur d'un matériau, une part de cette énergie très faible peut-être libérée sous forme d'une onde dite de contrainte ou de déplacement.

Lorsqu'un échantillon est déformé plastiquement, deux types de signaux acoustiques sont observés:

I. un signal quasi-stationnaire qu'on désigne par émission acoustique continue (Fig. I-I)

2. des signaux brefs à caractères impulsionnels qu'on désigne par "burst" (Fig.I-II)

On distingue nettement l'instant d'arrivée de l'onde de chaque burst. On observe également que l'intervalle de temps qui sépare deux signaux est imprévisible et que l'amplitude peut être variable d'un burst à l'autre.

Les émissions de type burst sont dues à des mécanismes de déformation qui dégagent une énergie importante pendant une durée brève.

Les signaux d'émission acoustique continue ont une amplitude bien plus faible que celle des burst; elle se situe très souvent à la limite des possibilités de mesure des appareillages classiques. L'émission acoustique continue se manifeste par une augmentation apparente du bruit de l'appareillage,au-delà de la limite élastique macroscopique du matériau. Le début et la fin du signal ne peuvent plus être distingués et ses propriétés semblent indépendantes de l'instant d'observation.

Lorqu'un échantillon est soumis à une charge progressive, tant que la pression est inférieure à la limite d'élasticité du matériau, l'émission acoustique est négligeable. Par contre dès que la pression dépasse la limite d'élasticité du matériau,celui-ci se déforme plastiquement,et l'émission acoustique est très importante.

Ces observations démontrent l'interêt de l'utilisation de l'émission acoustique comme technique de contrôle et de surveillance : une structure qui ne subit aucun endommagement sous forme d'une plastification locale par exemple, ne doit pas émettre de signaux acoustiques.

3 PRESENTATION DE LA VOUTE

Le modèle se présente sous la forme d'une voûte en maçonnerie de grandes dimensions dont la base des pièdroits repose sur des blocs en béton.(Fig.2)

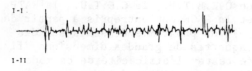

I-I

I-II

Fig.1   I-I Signal d'émission acoustique de type "burst"
         I-2 Signal d'émission acoustique continue

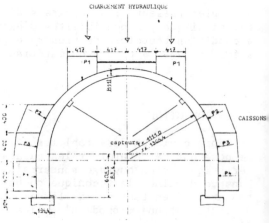

Fig.2   Schéma de la voute en maconnerie

Le chargement est réparti unifor-
mément sur la calotte de la voûte
par l'intermédiaire de vérins.Le terrain servant de butée au modèle a
été représenté à l'aide de systèmes
pneumatiques divisés en trois com-
partiments qui exercent une pression
à partir des reins et le long des
piedroits.

En résumé le modèle est soumis aux
pressions latérales des terres et
une pression s'applique au sommet
de la voûte.

4 PROCEDES DE MESURE

Un équipement fleximètrique et ex-
tensométrique très important a été
mis en place sur le modèle en vue
de mesurer les déformations en tout
point de la structure.

4.I Equipement fleximètrique

Il s'agit de réaliser des mesures
de convergence permettant de suivre
le comportement global de la structure.
    Les voûtes ont étééquipées suivant
cinq plans de mesure disposés perpendiculairement à l'axe de la voûte et régulièrement espacés entre
eux.

4.2 Equipement extensométrique

L'équipement est constitué de défor-
mètres à billes et d'extensomètres
à cordes vibrantes.Les mesures permettent de connaître les déformations
ponctuelles et après étalonnage préalable d'en déduire les contraintes.

4.3 Chaine d'enregistrement d'émis-
sion acoustique

Le détecteur est un accélèromètre de
sensibilité 60 mV/g. Selon les types d'expériences les capteurs ont
été implantés en clé de voûte au
milieu de l'intrados ou aux abouts.

L'analyse des signaux délivrés par
le capteur puis adaptés au point de
vue impédance se fait par l'appareil
de contrôle d'émission acoustique.
    Dans cet appareil,après amplifi-
cation et filtrage, les signaux dépassant un certain seuil préréglé
sont transformés en impulsions.Les
impulsions sont comptées par un
compteur numérique.Le résultat du
compteur est fourni sous forme analogique à intervalles de temps ré-
guliers fixés à l'avance.
    A la sortie de l'appareil de comp-
tage est branché un magnétophone
dont la bande de fréquences est comprise entre 20 Hz et 20kHz

5 CONDUITE DE L'ESSAI

Cinq voûtes ont été testées, quatre
en maçonnerie et une en béton.La
conduite de l'essai s'est effectuée
en deux étapes:
    I.Dans un premier temps,plusieurs
cycles de charge-décharge ont été
appliqués jusqu'à apparition des
fissures.
    2.Dans un second temps,la voûte
a été renforcée à l'aide de béton
projeté;28 jours après,plusieurs cycles de charge-décharge ont été appliqués à nouveau jusqu'à la rupture
de la structure.

6 ANALYSE DES DONNEES ACOUSTIQUES

6.I Seuils critiques de fissuration

D'après les courbes obtenues à partir de la relation taux de comptage
émission acoustique -contraintes,
trois phases essentielles du comportement des voûtes renforcées ont été
mises en évidence lors des essais
jusqu'à rupture, corroborées par l'é-
volution des mesures extensométriques et la courbe de convergence
(tableau I)
    I. début de microdéformation
    2. apparition de fissures
    3. prérupture
    Au cours de la phase de microdé-
formation, l'énergie libérée par le

matériau en cours de sollicitation
est nettement plus importante(ordre
de grandeur 10^2 à 10^3) entre 34 et
38% de la contrainte de la rupture.
A ce stade on suppose un endommagement interne de la voûte (Fig.3)

A partir de la connaissance de ce
premier seuil critique de fissuration,on peut approximer l'apparition
des premieres fissures à 10 % près.

Au cours de la phase de prérupture,un phénomène assez remarquable
de par son ampleur se manifeste qui
se traduit par:

I. une augmentation très importante de l'activité acoustique excédant
le taux moyen d'émission.

2. suivie par une diminution non
négligeable du taux d'émission acoustique d'environ 100 fois la valeur
moyenne considérée; la rupture se
produit dans une période de calme
acoustique.

Le temps qui s'écoule entre le phénomène de prérupture proprement dit
et la rupture est égal approximativement à deux heures d'après la figure 4.Un pronostic de rupture peut
être établi de la façon suivante:
soit T_d le temps pendant lequel le
matériau émet un nombre de coups
élevé qui correspond à la prérupture.

Soit T le temps qui sépare la prérupture de la rupture proprement di-
te.Connaissant   et la valeur du

OBSERVATIONS	NUMEROS DES VOÛTES MACONNERIE		
	II	IV	V
non renforcée			
microdéformations	70 KN	dès la mise en charge	dès la mise en charge
apparition fissures	90 KN	60 KN	40 KN
charge maximum	100 KN	70 KN	
Prérupture			150 KN
Charge de rupture			190 KN
renforcée			
microdéformation	110-150 KN	110 KN	
apparitions fissures	230 KN	130 KN	
Prérupture	340 KN	240 KN	
RUPTURE	400 KN	320 KN	

Tableau n° 1 - Les niveaux de contraintes correspondent aux différentes étapes de dégradation des voûtes,
mises en évidence simultanèment par
l'émission acoustique,les mesures
locales extensomètriques et la courbe de convergence.

rapport T/T_d on peut approximer la
rupture proprement dite à 10% près.

Ce second critère de fissuration
se situe dans une fourchette entre
75% et 86% de la contrainte de rupture du matériau. Ces données acoustiques peuvent être extrapolées à
d'autres structures à condition que
la vitesse de mise en charge soit

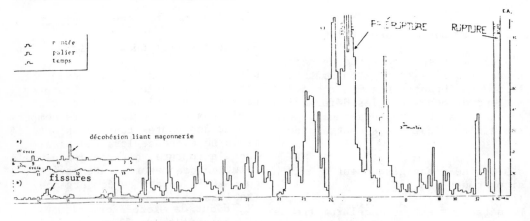

Fig. 3   Histogramme du taux de comptage des impulsions en fonction de
la charge.Une vingtaine de minutes s'écoulententre chaque palier
de charge afin de permettre le relevé des mesures extensométriques
et fléximétriques.
On distingue trois phases: a) début de microdéformation (avant
initiation des fissures) b) apparition des fissures et propagation
c) prérupture. (voute IV)

130

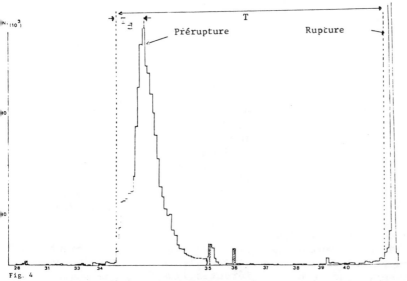

Fig. 4

Phéno:ène .n prérupture d'une durée d'une dizaine de minutes suivie par ur diminution notable de l'émission acoustique jusqu'à
la rupture qui intervient deux heures après le début du phénomène
Le rapport $\frac{T}{T_d}$ permet d'établir un pronostic de rupture sur d'autres voutes à 10 % près . (voute II)

effectuée lentement et que le modèle
de voûte soit identique.

L'observation d'un phénomène simi-
laire a permis à BRADY(1977)d'évacuer
le personnel d'une mine une heure a-
vant un coup de toit aux U.S.A.

Les critères de fissuration déterminés par la méthode acoustique correspondent à des niveaux de contrainte identiques à ceux obtenus à partir des méthodes extensométriques et
fleximètriques (Fig.5)

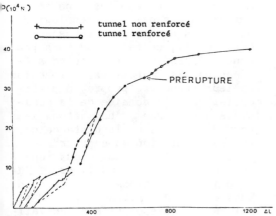

Fig.5 Courbe de convergence obtenue
dans une zone très localisée du
tunnel (voûte II)

6.2 Analyse des spectres de fré-
quences

L'évolution des spectres de fréquences a été enregistrée en fonction
des niveaux de contrainte.

Lorsque la contrainte appliquée
est inférieure à $0,3\sigma_R$, σ_R étant
la contrainte de rupture, les composantes basses fréquences prédo-
minent (Fig.6)

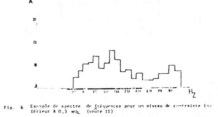

Fig. 6 Exemple de spectre de fréquences pour un niveau de contrainte inférieur à 0.3 σ_R (voûte II)

Dès que la contrainte appliquée
est supérieure à $0,5\sigma_R$ des fissures
apparaissent et se développent; les
spectres s'enrichissent en hautes
fréquences (Fig. 7)

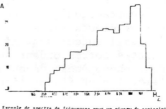

Fig. 7 Exemple de spectre de fréquences pour un niveau de contrainte
supérieur à 0.5 σ_R (voûte II)

131

Au-delà de 0,8 σ_R une diminution importante des fréquences élevées est très nette Fig. 8.

Fig. 8 Exemple de spectre de fréquences pour un niveau de contrainte supérieur à 0,8 σ_R (voûte 11)

A partir de ces observations, des hypothèses relatives au mécanisme de fissuration des voûtes peuvent être avancées qui serviront de base à la conception d'un modèle, à savoir:

I. La prédominance des basses fréquences semble caractériser les décohésions du liant avec les pierres calcaires.

2. Lorsque les fissures se propagent, les spectres s'enrichissent en hautes fréquences.

3. La chute spectaculaire des hautes fréquences est caractéristique d'un endommagement total de la voûte, la déformée telle qu'elle a été calculée par MARCHANDISE(1980) excède 10% par rapport à son contour initial.

6.3 Discussion

Des travaux scientifiques dans différents domaines attestent deux types de fréquences.

HARDY(1968) explicite l'existence de fréquences spécifiques au type de matériau étudié.

TERRIEN(1980) a montré lors d'une étude du comportement d'un béton sollicité en traction que l'on peut distinguer plusieurs types de spectres. D'après l'auteur deux limites en contraintes correspondent au début de deux phénomènes: décohésion granulat-mortier et fissuration intergranulat.

FISHER(1978) explicite les différences spectrales entre les déformations plastiques et l'initiation de fissures dans les aciers de la façon suivante: les mécanismes d'émission au cours de la phase d'initiation de la fissure sont dus à des décohésions de microdéfauts, la durée des évènements est plus importante que les mouvements de dislocations au cours de la phase plastique. De telles différences entre les spectres d'émission acoustique ont été observées également dans les aciers par GRAHAM et ALERS (1974).

Bien que les essais ne soient pas comparables et les structures différentes, il existe une analogie très intéressante qui peut permettre une extrapolation des données.

7 CONCLUSIONS

Le pronostic d'un coup de toit dans les mines est plus difficile à déterminer en raison de l'évolution mal contrôlée de la répartition des contraintes et de leur redistribution après tirs de mines dans le temps et dans l'espace alors que ces paramètres sont plus aisément contrôlables dans les structures en Génie Civil.

A l'échelle des applications des surveillances des sites géologiques et miniers et des structures en Génie Civil, certains facteurs peuvent influer sur les fréquences émises par les matériaux en fonction de leur structure propre en particulier dans le domaine de la mécanique des roches et des bétons le taux d'humidité et la distance de source d'émission au capteur.

Néanmoins la méthode acoustique présente un très grand intérêt. Sur le plan international notamment en Russie, aux U.S.A., au Japon et en Pologne des dispositifs de surveillance acoustique sont mis en oeuvre dans les exploitations minières.

REFERENCES

Brady, BT (1977) An investigation of the scale invariant property of failure. Int. J. Rock Mec.Min.Sci. et geomech. Abst. Vol.I4 p.121-126.

Fischer, T., Seifert, K., Kunze, H.D. and Wolitz,K.(1978) "Acoustic emission analysis for evaluation of critical faults in welded structures of an austenitic Nuclear Pressure Vessel Steel", paper 4-2, The fourth acoustic emission Symposium, High Pressure Institute of Japan. Tokyo.

Graham,L.J. and Alers, G. (1974) "Spectrum analysis of acoustic emission in A 533-B steel"Materials evaluation 32,2 p.31-37.

Hardy, H., Chugh, Y.P. and Stefanko, R. (1968). An investigation of the frequency spectra of microseismic activity in rock under tension. Tenth Symposium on rock mechanics, The University of Texas at Austin.

Marchandise, J.P. (1980) Etude du confortement des tunnels en maçonnerie par coques de béton projeté. Thèse CNAM Génie Civil.

Terrien, M. (1980) Emission acoustique et "comportement mécanique postcritique d'un béton sollicité en traction" Bull. Liaison Labo. P. et Ch.

DER IN-SITU DURCHLÄSSIGKEITSVERSUCH IN GEKLÜFTETEM FELS PROBLEME UND INTERPRETATION

The in-situ permeability test in jointed rock – Problems and interpretation

L'essai de perméabilité in situ dans des roches fissurées – Problèmes et interprétation

H.J.SCHNEIDER

Bundesanstalt für Geowissenschaften und Rohstoffe, Hannover, Bundesrepublik Deutschland

SUMMARY:

The pumping-in test has been in common use in engineering geology for decades for the in-situ determination of rock permeability. The conventional LUGEON method is prone to systematic errors due to loosely defined initial conditions. This can lead to wrong interpretation of the test results. By modifying the test somewhat, the reliability of the results can be improved. The interpretation of the test results are discussed for both the continuous and discontinuous model of permeability in jointed rock, and ways of operating the test as a one-hole or multiple-hole set up are suggested.

ZUSAMMENFASSUNG:

Der Wasserabpreßversuch gehört seit Jahrzehnten zu den gebräuchlichsten Verfahren der Ingenieurgeologie für Durchlässigkeitsuntersuchungen in-situ. In seiner herkömmlichen Anordnung nach LUGEON bestehen aufgrund unklar definierter Ausgangsbedingungen systematische Fehler, die bei der Durchlässigkeitsbestimmung zu Fehlinterpretationen führen. Durch eine Veränderung des Versuchskonzeptes kann der Aussagewert des Wasserabpreßversuches verbessert werden. Interpretations- und Auswerteverfahren des Wasserabpreßversuches werden für das kontinuierliche und diskontinuierliche Durchlässigkeitsmodell von geklüftetem Fels diskutiert und Vorschläge zur Versuchsdurchführung nach der Einbohrloch- und Mehrbohrlochmethode unterbreitet.

RESUME:

L'essai de LUGEON est une des méthodes les plus communes dans le domaine de la geologie de l'ingenieur. Elle est appliquée depuis des dizaine d'années pour déterminer la perméabilité des roches fissurées. La méthode conventionelle possède par des conditions initiales pas clairement définies quelques défauts systématiques, qui provoquent une fausse interprétation des resultats de l'éssai. La certitude des resultats de l'éssai se laisse améliorer par un changement de l'arrangement de l'éssai. Des méthodes d'interpretation sont discutées. Des propositions concernant le mode d'exécution de l'éssai d'injection dans un ou plusieurs forages sont présentées.

1. Einführung

In jüngerer Zeit hat die experimentelle Felshydraulik durch die Entwicklung zahlreicher neuer Untersuchungsverfahren zur Durchlässigkeitsbestimmung einen raschen Aufschwung erfahren. Dies hat seine Ursache in den zahlreichen neuen Aufgaben, die der Felshydraulik erwachsen sind, z.B. bei der Anlage von Sondermülldeponien unter Tage, der untertägigen Speicherung von Energieträgern, der Nutzung geothermischer Wärme und anderem. Weiterhin ist mit der Entwicklung numerischer Rechenverfahren (Wittke 197o), mit denen erstmals eine Berechnung der äußerst komplexen Strömungsvorgänge im Gebirge möglich ist, ein Bedarf an Untersuchungsverfahren entstanden, welche eine exakte Kennwertermittlung ermöglichen.

Die Komplexität der Strömungsvorgänge in geklüftetem Fels verursacht größte Probleme, repräsentative Durchlässigkeitskennwerte für größere Gebirgsbereiche zu ermitteln, da die Daten des Kluftgefüges als Hauptwasserwege sich nur unzureichend bestimmen lassen. Zum anderen liegen analytische Lösungsmöglichkeiten für Strömungsvorgänge nur für stark vereinfachte Fälle vor (Wittke & Louis

1969). In der Geotechnik sind zur Durchlässigkeitsprüfung von Fels der Drainageversuch, der Pumpversuch, der Wasserabpreßversuch, der Auffüllversuch, der Puls-Test und der Slug-Test gebräuchlich. Zur Durchlässigkeitsprüfung größerer Gebirgsbereiche, wie sie bei Fragen der Wasserhaltung und Entwässerung oder zur Abschätzung von Sikkerwasserverlusten erforderlich ist, eignen sich der Drainageversuch und der Pumpversuch. Die Versuche erstrecken sich über längere Zeiträume. Kleinmaßstäbliche Untersuchungen vor allem in gering durchlässigem Gebirge zur Prüfung der Durchlässigkeit von Einzelklüften werden mit dem Puls- oder Slug-Test durchgeführt. Bei den kurzen Versuchszeiten dieser Verfahren können nur Erkenntnisse über die unmittelbare Umgebung der Untersuchungsbohrung gewonnen werden. Der Wasserabpreßversuch (WD-Versuch) - der im folgenden eingehender behandelt wird - stellt hinsichtlich Reichweite und Versuchszeit ein Bindeglied zwischen großmaßstäblichen und kleinmaßstäblichen Untersuchungsverfahren dar.

2. Standard WD-Versuch

Der WD-Versuch wurde von Lugeon (1933) ursprünglich als Kriterium zur Prüfung von Dichtungsmaßnahmen bei Talsperren konzipiert. Nach diesem Versuchskonzept wird in einem definierten Bohrlochabschnitt Wasser unter konstantem Druck verpreßt. Die Wasseraufnahme des Gebirges wird bezogen auf 1 m Bohrlochsegment bei einem Preßdruck von 1o bar, in Lugeon-Einheiten angegeben. Diese Maßeinheit stellt keine hydrologisch eindeutige Kenngröße der Durchlässigkeit dar, sondern kann nur als Richtwert betrachtet werden. Heitfeld (1965), Ewert (1977) und Nonveiller (197o) leiten empirisch die Durchlässigkeitsbeiwerte K_f aus Lugeon-Einheiten ab. Berechnungsverfahren, die auf der Brunnenformel nach Thiem (19o6) basieren, liegen unter Annahme stationärer Strömungsbedingungen für poröse, isotrope und homogene Wasserleiter vor (Earth Manual 1963, ISRM 1977). Das Versuchskonzept des Standard WD-Versuchs ist einfach und erfordert wenig apparativen Aufwand. Zur Abdichtung des Verpreßsegmentes in der Untersuchungsbohrung ist eine Einfach- bzw. eine Doppelpackeranordnung erforderlich. Der Verpreßdruck wird am Manometer der Pumpe und die Durchflußmenge mittels Wasseruhr bestimmt. Die Verpressung erfolgt in einzelnen Stufen in ansteigender und absteigender Reihenfolge. Pro Stufe wird nach einer gewissen Vorlaufzeit der Druck über zehn Minuten konstant gehalten. Dieses Versuchskonzept weist eine Reihe von systematischen Fehlern auf, wie Heitfeld (1965),

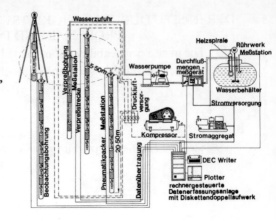

Abb.1: Versuchsanordnung für felshydraulische Mehrfachbohrlochuntersuchungen

Ewert (1977) und Rißler (1977) nachgewiesen haben. Neuere Versuchsverfahren sehen die Messung des Verpreßdruckes mittels Luftwaage im Verpreßsegment vor (Schetelig et al. 1978). Als Einbohrlochversuch erlaubt diese Standardanordnung nur eine Betrachtung der Vorgänge im Verpreßsegment, woraus Fehlinterpretationen bei der Durchlässigkeitsermittlung resultieren können.

3. Erweitertes Konzept des WD-Versuches

Da die Vorgänge im Verpreßsegment beim WD-Versuch nur bedingt Auskunft über die Durchlässigkeitseigenschaften des Gebirges erlauben, wurde ein Versuchsverfahren für Mehrbohrlochuntersuchungen zur Beobachtung der Strömungsvorgänge im Gebirge entwickelt (Abb.1). Die Versuchsanlage arbeitet nach einem kombinierten Prinzip von Tracer- und WD-Versuch. Die Verpressung eines Tracers (NaCl-Lösung) erfolgt analog zum WD-Versuch in einem zentralen Bohrloch, das durch eine Mehrfachpackeranordnung abschnittsweise abgedichtet wird. Der Verpreßdruck wird mittels Druckaufnehmer elektronisch im Verpreßsegment gemessen. Diese Meßanordnung wurde inzwischen von der Baupraxis für serienmäßige Durchlässigkeitsuntersuchungen übernommen. Die durch die Verpressung hervorgerufene Bergwasserströmung wird in peripher angeordneten Bohrungen beobachtet. Die Beobachtungsbohrungen sind durch Packer wiederum in einzelne Segmente unterteilt, in denen jeweils eine Meßsonde zur Messung des Bergwasserdruckes, der Wassertemperatur und der spezifischen, elektrischen Leitfähigkeit (Tracer-Messung) installiert ist (Schneider 1979).

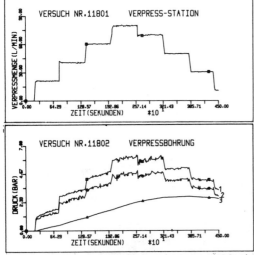

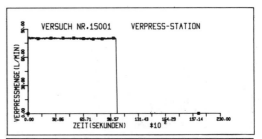

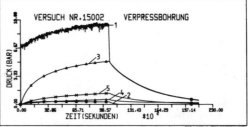

Abb.2: Verpreßmengen-Zeit Diagramm (11801)
Druck-Zeit Diagramm (11802)
Verpreßdruck-Pumpe (1),Verpreßdruck-Verpreßsegment (2),Bergwasserdruck in einer
10 m entfernten Beobachtungsbohrung,Mehrstufenversuch mit konstanter Verpreßung
Geologie: Buntsandstein

Abb.3: Verpreßmengen-Zeit Diagramm (15001)
eines Einstufenversuches mit konstanter
Verpreßmenge
Druck-Zeit Diagramm (15002),Verpreßdruck
Verpreßsegment (1),Bergwasserdruck:Beobachtungsbohrung I(2) 20 m von der Verpreßstelle,
Beobachtungsbohrung II(3) 10 m,Beobachtungsbohrung III(4) 15 m,Beobachtungsbohrung IV
(5) 5 m - Geologie: Buntsandstein

4. Zur Durchführung des WD-Versuches

4.1 Mengen- oder Druckregelung des WD-Versuches

Nach Lugeon wird der herkömmliche WD-Versuch über einen konstanten Pumpendruck gesteuert. Eine Druckdifferenz zwischen Pumpe und Verpreßsegment ergibt sich durch den hydrostatischen Höhenunterschied, durch Energieverluste aufgrund von Umlenkungen, von Reibungsverlusten und Querschnittsveränderungen im Leitungssystem. Diese Druckdifferenzen zwischen Verpreßsegment und Verpreßbohrung stellen eine systematische Fehlerquelle bei der Versuchsauswertung dar (Abb.2) und müssen für jede Versuchsanordnung individuell bestimmt werden. Diese Fehlerquelle läßt sich einfach durch direkte Messung des Druckes im Verpreßsegment umgehen. Der Druckverlauf im Verpreßsegment wird sowohl von der Pumpe als auch von den hydraulischen Materialeigenschaften des Gebirges bestimmt. Um einen konstanten Druck im Verpreßsegment zu erhalten, wäre ein enormer Versuchsaufwand bei der Pumpensteuerung, vergleichbar mit einer servogesteuerten Prüfmaschine, erforderlich. Dies kann in Standardversuchen nicht bewerkstelligt werden. Da der Druck im Verpreßsegment nicht immer analog zum Bergwasserdruck verläuft, wäre außerdem noch keine Druckkonstanz im Gebirge erzielt. Es ist daher zweckmäßig, die Verpreß-

menge als konstante Größe im WD-Versuch vorzugeben. Eine konstante Fördermenge läßt sich technisch mit einer Kolbenpumpe ohne großen Aufwand erzielen. Es ergibt sich außerdem eine Parallelität zum Pumpversuch, die, wie noch gezeigt wird, bei der Auswertung erhebliche Vorteile bietet.

4.2 Druckverlauf im Verpreßsegment

Der Druckverlauf im Verpreßsegment ist zu Beginn des WD-Versuches durch einen steilen Anstieg charakterisiert (Abb.3). Dieser unmittelbar einsetzende Druckanstieg ist auf die Überwindung der Einlaufverluste an den Eintrittsöffnungen der Klüfte im Verpreßsegment, sowie auf die Überwindung der Trägheit des unbewegten Grundwassers zurückzuführen. Im weiteren Verlauf ergibt sich bei Vorgabe einer konstanten Verpreßmenge ein langsamer und stetiger Druckanstieg analog zum Bergwasserdruck in den Beobachtungsbohrungen. Wird am Versuchsende der Pumpenzulauf über einen Schieber plötzlich geschlossen, so daß der Druckabbau nur zum Gebirge stattfinden kann, so ist im Verpreßsegment wieder ein plötzlicher Druckabfall zu beobachten, der anschließend in ein asymptotisches Abklingen übergeht (Abb.3). In den Beobachtungsbohrungen ergibt sich

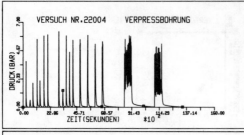

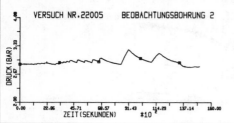

Abb. 4: Druck-Zeit Diagramme von kurzzeitigen Druckpulsen. Verpreßsegment (22oo4) Beobachtungsbohrung II (22oo5) 1o m Entfernung. Geologie: Buntsandstein

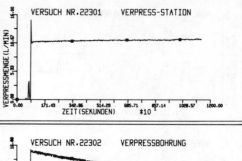

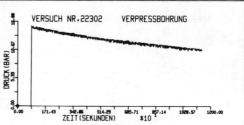

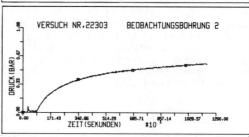

Abb. 5: Verpreßmengen-Zeit Diagramm (223o1) eines Einstufenversuches.
Verpreßdruck - Zeit Diagramm (223o2) (Verpreßsegment).
Bergwasserdruck in Beobachtungsbohrung II in 1o m Entfernung von der Injektionsbohrung. Geologie: Buntsandstein

hingegen ein langsamer stetiger Druckabfall. Der Betrag von Druckanstieg und Druckabfall im Verpreßsegment ist nicht identisch, da die zu überwindenden Trägheitskräfte am Versuchsende wesentlich kleiner sind als zu Versuchsbeginn, und außerdem die Klüfte während des Versuches durch den Verpreßdruck eine Aufweitung erfahren haben, was eine Abminderung der Einlaufverluste zur Folge hat. Wird das Gebirge nur mit kurzzeitigen Verpreßpulsen von wenigen Sekunden beaufschlagt, so sind Druckanstieg und Druckabfall im Verpreßsegment nahezu identisch, da die geringen Verpreßmengen nicht zu einer Erhöhung des Bergwasserdruckes und somit zu keiner Aufweitung der Kluft ausreichen (Abb.4).

Der Druckverlauf im Verpreßsegment während einer längeren Injektionsperiode zeigt zwei Charakteristiken. Im ersten Fall steigt der Druck bei konstanter Verpreßmenge zu Beginn des Versuches stetig an, um in der Endphase einem Endwert zuzustreben (Abb.3). Im zweiten Fall, wiederum bei konstanter Verpreßmenge, fällt der Druck nach Erreichen des Maximums in der ersten Versuchsphase stetig ab, um in der zweiten Phase wiederum einem Endwert zuzustreben (Abb.5). Der Bergwasserdruck steigt wie in Fall 1 stetig an. Der Kurvenverlauf von Fall 1 wird durch ein kontinuierliches Öffnen der Kluft und eine völlige Sättigung des umgebenden Gebirges gekennzeichnet. Liegen zu Beginn des Versuches instationäre Strömungsverhältnisse vor, so stellt sich nach Erreichen eines Gleichgewichtes von Strömungsdruck und Gebirgsspannungen sowie

einer völligen Sättigung des Gebirges mit Bergwasser ein stationärer Strömungszustand ein. Der Kurvenverlauf von Fall 2 zeigt dieselbe Charakteristik wie sie bei hydraulisch induzierten Bruchvorgängen zu beobachten ist. Der Druckanstieg im Verpreßsegment führt zu einer plötzlichen Aufweitung der Kluft, bzw. zu einer Kluftneubildung. Der Druck im Verpreßsegment fällt solange kontinuierlich ab, bis sich ein Gleichgewicht zwischen Kluftwasserdruck und Gebirgsspannung einstellt, was beim hydraulic fracturing-Verfahren dem pumping pressure entspricht. Der Druckverlauf im Verpreßsegment wird einmal durch die Einlaufverluste des Verpreßgutes ins Gebirge und zum anderen von der Durchlässigkeit des Gebirges bestimmt. Beide Faktoren kann man klar trennen. Die Einlaufverluste lassen sich eindeutig am Versuchsbeginn bzw. Versuchsende beobachten, während die Durchlässigkeitseigenschaften des Gebirges aus

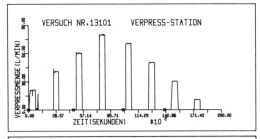

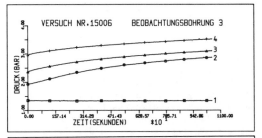

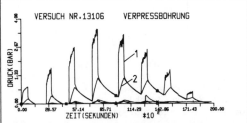

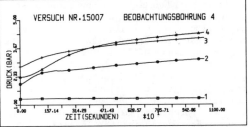

Abb. 6: Mehrstufenversuch mit 1o minütiger Verpreßzeit pro Stufe und 3o minütiger Pause zwischen den Stufen. Verpreßmengen-Zeit Diagramm (13lo1), Druck-Zeit Diagramm (13lo6), Verpreßsegment (1), Beobachtungsbohrung II (2), Beobachtungsbohrung I, III, IV. Geologie: Buntsandstein

Abb. 7: Bergwasserdruck-Zeit Diagramme Beobachtungsbohrung III (15 m Entfernung zur Injektionsbohrung. Beobachtungsbohrung IV (5 m Entfernung), Unterteilung der Beobachtungsbohrungen in 4 Segmente (Kurven 1-4) (vgl.Abb.3). Geologie: Buntsandstein

der zeitlichen Druckänderung ermittelt werden können (Abb. 3, 4, 5, 6).

Der Lugeon-Versuch sollte aufgrund der Phänomene im Verpreßsegment deshalb nicht mehr in seine ursprüngliche Form mit einer kontinuierlichen stufenweisen Steigerung des Verpreßdruckes oder einer stufenweisen Steigerung der Verpreßmenge durchgeführt werden (Abb.2). In diesem Falle gehen wertvolle Informationen über die Energieverluste im Verpreßsegment, über den von Stufe zu Stufe sich ändernden hydrostatischen Ausgangszustand verloren. Es empfiehlt sich stattdessen, zwischen den einzelnen Verpreßstufen Pausen einzulegen, die mindestens der Länge der Verpreßzeit entsprechen (Abb.6).

Mit dieser Versuchsanordnung erhält man beim WD-Versuch nicht nur umfangreichere Informationen, es werden hierdurch auch Möglichkeiten für andere Durchlässigkeitsberechnungsverfahren geschaffen (vgl.Kap.5).

Der Verlauf des Bergwasserdruckes in den Bohrungen ist in der Regel durch einen stetigen Anstieg gekennzeichnet, der sich asymptotisch mit Erreichen stationärer Fließbedingungen einem Maximalwert annähert. Die Druckausbreitung im Gebirge ist völlig inhomogen. Es ist nicht nur zwischen den einzelnen Beobachtungen ein völlig unterschiedlicher Druckverlauf zu beobachten, auch innerhalb derselben Bohrung variiert der

Bergwasserdruck von Segment zu Segment (Abb. 3 u. 7)

Einzelne Beobachtungssegmente zeigen keinerlei Druckänderung, andere nur ein Ansteigen des Bergwasserspiegels. Nur bei direkter, hydraulischer Verbindung zwischen Verpreßsegment und Beobachtungssegment ist im Gebirge ein äquivalenter Druckverlauf festzustellen. Die relative Druckänderung im Gebirge ist jedoch im Vergleich zum Verpreßsegment wesentlich kleiner infolge von Energieverlusten durch den Einlauf des Verpreßgutes ins Gebirge, durch turbulente Strömungen in der Nachbarschaft des Verpreßabschnittes sowie durch Reibungsverluste in den Klüften. Der Betrag der Druckänderung im Gebirge wird sowohl von der Größe des Verpreßdruckes im Verpreßsegment als auch von der Verpreßdauer bestimmt. Kurze Verpreßzeiten bewirken nur geringfügige Veränderungen des Bergwasserdruckes. Die Fließbedingungen in diesen Kurzzeitversuchen sind in der Regel instationär. Stationäre Strömungsbedingungen werden erst in Langzeitversuchen von mehreren Stunden erzielt. Die druckabhängigen Durchlässigkeitseigenschaften des Gebirges bzw. die Veränderung des Hohlraumvolumens infolge von Kluftaufweitung kann nur in diesen Langzeitversuchen bestimmt werden. Die Reichweite des WD-Versuches kann durch

Verlängerung der Versuchszeiten vergrößert werden.

5. Durchlässigkeitsermittlung

Angaben zur Durchlässigkeit haben in den in der Hydrologie verwendeten Einheiten des Durchlässigkeitsbeiwertes $K(K_f)$, der spezifischen Permeabilität k oder der Transmissivität T zu erfolgen. Die in der Ingenieurgeologie gebräuchliche Lugeon-Einheit stellt keine eindeutige physikalische Größe dar und sollte daher nur als grober Richtwert zur Abschätzung der Durchlässigkeit des Gebirges in Ausnahmefällen verwendet werden. Die Verwendung der einzelnen Kennwerte hat sich am Zweck der Untersuchung zu orientieren. Bei Fragen der Wasserhaltung oder der Drainage ist eine Angabe der Durchlässigkeit als Durchlässigkeitsbeiwert oder Transmissivität zweckmäßig; für Injektionsmaßnahmen sollte die Angabe als spezifische Permeabilität erfolgen. Da die Kennwerte für denselben Versuch, je nachdem welches Durchlässigkeitsmodell (kontinuierliches bzw. diskontinuierliches Durchlässigkeitsmodell) bzw. welches Berechnungsverfahren zugrunde gelegt wird, differieren, sind zusätzliche Angaben über die Kennwertermittlung unbedingt erforderlich.

Die meisten herkömmlichen Verfahren zur Berechnung der Durchlässigkeit basieren auf den Brunnenformeln nach Dupuit (1863) und Thiem (19o6). Diese Verfahren sind nur bei stationären und laminaren Fließbedingungen gültig und setzen eine radialsymmetrische Geometrie des Aquifers, eine isotrope und homogene Beschaffenheit des Gebirges voraus. Grundlage der Durchlässigkeitsbestimmung ist die Verpreßdruck-/Verpreßmengenrelation. In WD-Versuchen, die in derselben Verpreßteufe durchgeführt wurden, ergeben sich je nach Versuchsanordnung unterschiedliche Verpreßdruck-/Verpreßmengendiagramme. Im herkömmlichen Mehrstufenversuch nach Lugeon ohne Pausen zwischen den Verpreßstufen steigt der relative Verpreßdruck linear mit der Verpreßmenge an (Abb.8). Bei abnehmender Stufenfolge ergeben sich generell höhere Verpreßdrucke, da die relative Druckänderung fälschlich auf die Ausgangssituation zu Beginn des Versuches bezogen ist. Werden zwischen den Stufen Pausen eingelegt, so gleichen sich die Verpreßmengen-/Verpreßdruckrelationen von ansteigendem und absteigendem Kurvenast an (Abb.9). Wird die Verpreßzeit auf drei Stunden pro Stufe verlängert, verdoppelt sich die relative Druckänderung gegenüber den Mehrstufenversuchen bei zehnminütiger Verpreßzeit (Abb.1o).

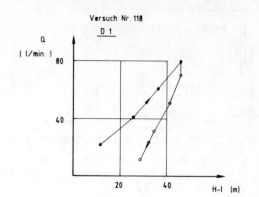

Abb.8: Verpreßdruck-Verpreßmengen Diagramm (vgl.Abb.2), Mehrstufenversuch ohne Pausen 1o min Verpreßzeit pro Stufe, durchschnittlicher Verpreßdruck.
Geologie: Buntsandstein

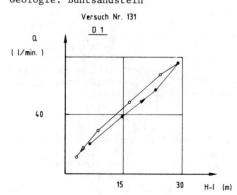

Abb.9: Verpreßdruck-Verpreßmengen Diagramm (vgl.Abb.6). Die Verpreßstufen und geologischen Bedingungen von Versuch 118 u. 131 sind identisch. Mehrstufenversuch: 1o min Verpreßzeit pro Stufe, 3o min Pause

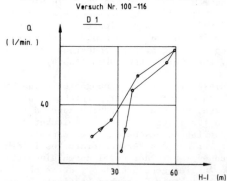

Abb.1o: Langzeitversuch mit 3 stündiger Verpreßzeit pro Stufe und 3 stündiger Pause zwischen den Stufen (vgl.Abb.17).
Geologie und Verpreßstufe wie Versuch 118 und 131

Auch in diesen Langzeitversuchen wurden zwischen den einzelnen Versuchen Pausen von mindestens drei Stunden eingeschaltet. Bei der Berechnung der Durchlässigkeitsbeiwerte nach der Einbohrlochformel unter Zugrundelegung eines Kontinuums (ISRM 1977) differieren die Durchlässigkeitsunterschiede beim herkömmlichen Lugeon-Versuch zwischen ansteigendem und absteigendem Kurvenast in der Größenordnung von 1 : 3 (Abb.11)

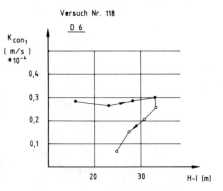

Abb. 11: Durchlässigkeitsbeiwerte eines Mehrstufenversuches (vgl.Abb.8)

Die Durchlässigkeitsbeiwerte der Mehrstufenversuche mit Pausen liegen unabhängig vom Verpreßdruck bzw. der Verpreßmenge in derselben Größenordnung (Abb.12).

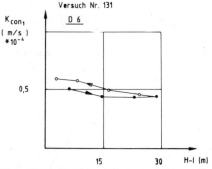

Abb. 12: Durchlässigkeitsbeiwerte eines Mehrstufenversuches mit Pausen (vgl. Abb.9)

Die Durchlässigkeit ist in den Langzeitversuchen halb so groß wie in den Kurzzeitversuchen (Abb.13). Stationäre Strömungsbedingungen, eine Voraussetzung dieses Auswerteverfahrens, werden annähernd nur in den Langzeitversuchen erreicht. Die Energieverluste im Verpreßsystem, die in den Kurzzeitversuchen zwischen 4o bis 6o % des Verpreßdruckes ausmachen, bleiben hierbei unberücksichtigt (Abb.14).

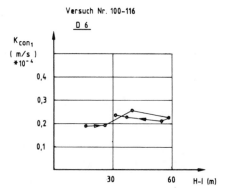

Abb. 13: Durchlässigkeitsbeiwerte von Langzeitversuchen (vgl. Abb.1o)

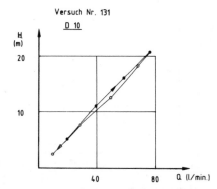

Abb. 14: Energiehöhenverluste im Verpreßsegment in Abhängigkeit von der Verpreßmenge (vgl.Abb.6)

Wird die relative Druckänderung im Verpreßsegment um diese Einlaufverluste reduziert, so erhöht sich die Durchlässigkeit um das Doppelte (Abb.15). Liegt eine Kluft im Verpreßsegment vor, so kann aus den Einlaufverlusten nach Rißler (1977) die Kluftöffnungsweite bestimmt werden. Die Kluftöffnungsweite ist keine konstante Größe, sondern deutlich vom Verpreßdruck bzw. der Verpreßmenge abhängig (Abb.16).
Da die Fließvorgänge im WD-Versuch überwiegend instationär sind, sollte die Durchlässigkeitsbestimmung mit anderen geeigneten Verfahren vorgenommen werden. Das Auswerteverfahren nach Cooper & Jacob (1946) berechnet die Durchlässigkeit bei konstanter Verpreßmenge aufgrund der zeitlichen Änderung des Bergwasserdruckes (Abb.17). Es bietet gegenüber den herkömmlichen Verfahren den Vorteil, daß Energieverluste beim Einlauf in die Klüfte oder bei turbulenten Strömungen in der Nähe des Verpreßsegmentes nicht mehr berücksichtigt zu werden brauchen. Nach diesem Verfahren kann die Durchlässigkeit sowohl für das

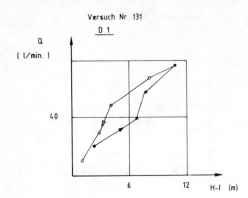

Versuch Nr. 131

D 1

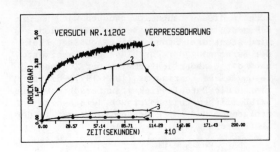

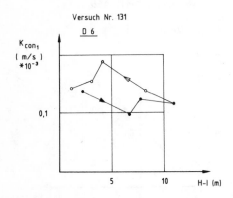

Versuch Nr. 131

D 6

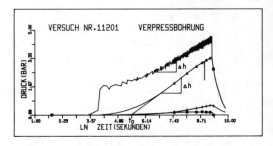

Abb. 15: Verpreßdruck-Verpreßmengen Diagramm
unter Berücksichtigung der Energieverluste
im Verpreßsegment.
Durchlässigkeitsbeiwerte (vgl.Abb.6,9,12)

Abb. 17: Druck-Zeit-Diagramme (11202) von
Langzeitversuchen mit konstanter Verpreß-
menge (50 1/min). Verpreßsegment (4)
Beobachtungsbohrung I (1) 20 m
Beobachtungsbohrung II(2) 10 m
Beobachtungsbohrung III (3) 15 m
Druck-Zeit-Diagramm mit logarithmischer
Zeitachse (11201)

Verpreßsegment, wie für den Bergwasserdruck in den Beobachtungsbohrungen errechnet werden (Abb.18).

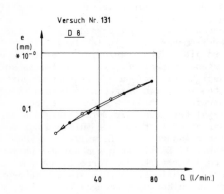

Versuch Nr. 131

D 8

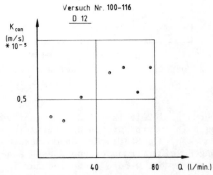

Versuch Nr. 100-116

D 12

Abb. 18: Durchlässigkeitsbeiwerte nach
Cooper & Jacob (1946) (vgl.Abb.13)

Abb. 16: Kluftöffnungsweite in Abhängigkeit
von der Verpreßmenge (vgl.Abb.6,14)

Die Durchlässigkeit, der wiederum ein Kontinuum zugrunde gelegt ist, ist um eine
Zehnerpotenz kleiner gegenüber den Durch-

lässigkeitskoeffizienten bei stationären Strömungsannahmen. Aus der Druckänderung in den Beobachtungsbohrungen kann außerdem der Speicherkoeffizient des Gebirges analog zum Pumpversuch ermittelt werden (Abb.19).

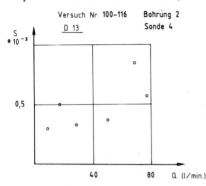

Abb. 19: Speicherkoeffizient nach Copper & Jacob (1946)

Eine weitere Möglichkeit der Durchlässigkeitsbestimmung ergibt sich bei der Beobachtung des Druckabfalles am Versuchsende, analog zum Wiederanstiegsverfahren nach Theis (1935) (Abb.2o).

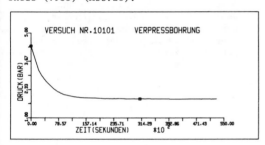

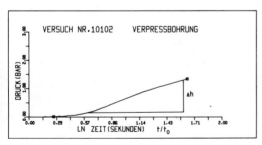

Abb. 2o: Druckverlauf im Verpreßsegment in einer Versuchspause nach vorausgegangener Injektion (1o1o1)
Auswertung nach Theis (1935)

Durchlässigkeitskoeffizienten, die nach den Jacob- und Theis-Verfahren errechnet wurden, liegen in derselben Größenordnung (Abb.21). Liegen im Versuch mehrere Beobach-

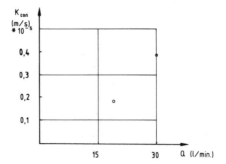

Abb. 21: Durchlässigkeitsbeiwerte nach Theis (1935) (vgl.Abb. 13,18)

tungspegel um die Verpreßbohrung vor, so kann die anisotrope Durchlässigkeit nach den Verfahren von Hantush & Thomas (1966), Schneebeli (1966 und Maini (1971) ermittelt werden. Die Durchlässigkeit der Einzelkluft ergibt sich nach Louis (1974) aus der Öffnungsweite und der relativen Rauhigkeit, die sich aus dem Mehrstufenversuch nach dem Verfahren von Rißler (1977) näherungsweise bestimmen lassen.

Die Durchlässigkeit der Einzelkluft ist mit $3 - 4 \times 10^{-2}$ (m/s) zwei bis drei Zehnerpotenzen größer gegenüber dem Durchschnittswert des Gebirges (ISRM 1977).

6. Empfehlungen zur Durchführung von WD-Versuchen

Art und Durchführung des WD-Versuches haben sich am Zweck der Untersuchungen zu orientieren. Durch eine Variation der Länge des Verpreßabschnittes, der Verpreßdauer und der Verpreßmenge bzw. des Verpreßdruckes lassen sich sowohl Aussagen über die Durchlässigkeit größerer Gebirgsbereiche als auch über Einzelklüfte gewinnen. Zur Durchlässigkeitsprüfung von Einzelklüften bzw. kleinster Gebirgsbereiche reichen Mehrstufenversuche mit Verpreßzeiten von 1o Minuten pro Stufe aus. Wie in den Langzeitversuchen sollte auch in den Kurzzeitversuchen die Verpreßmenge konstant gehalten werden. Zwischen den einzelnen Stufen sind Pausen einzulegen, die mindestens der Verpreßzeit entsprechen. Die Durchlässigkeit oder Transmissivität sollte in den Kurzzeitversuchen nach Auswerteverfahren für instationäre Strömung berechnet werden. Die Bohrungen sind so anzusetzen, daß jeweils eine Kluftschar normal zur Bohrlochachse verläuft. Durch ein geeignetes Bohrraster besteht außerdem die Möglichkeit durch zusätzliche Beobachtungssonden den Verlauf des Berg-

wasserdruckes im Gebirge zu untersuchen.
Aussagen über großräumige Durchlässigkeiten
können nur aus Wasserabpreßversuchen über
mehrere Stunden erzielt werden. Aus dem
Druckverlauf der einzelnen mehrstündigen
Verpreßstufen lassen sich geologisch bedingte Durchlässigkeitsänderungen, wie das
Freispülen von Klüften u.ä. erkennen. Mit
dieser Versuchsanordnung ist es möglich,
großräumige Durchlässigkeitsuntersuchungen
in Gebirgsbereichen über dem Grundwasser-
spiegel vorzunehmen, wo Pumpversuche nicht
möglich sind. Analog zum Pumpversuch sollten zusätzliche Beobachtungspegel in der
Umgebung der Verpreßstelle in einem Radius
von 5-2o m installiert werden. Die Achse
der unverrohrten Beobachtungsbohrungen ist
wie die Verpreßbohrung entsprechend dem
Kluftgefüge zu orientieren. Die Auswertung
dieser Langzeitversuche kann nach den Verfahren des Pumpversuches zur Berechnung
der Durchlässigkeit und Speicherkapazität
erfolgen.

7. Literatur

Cooper, H.H. & Jacob, C.E.1946, A generalized graphical method for evaluating
formation constants and summarizing
well-field history. Trans.Am.Geophys.
Union,Nr.27,S.526-534,Richmond

Dupuit,J.1863, Etudes théoriques et
pratiques sur le mouvement des eaux dans
les canaux decouverts et à travers les
terrains permeables. 3o4 S.,Dunod,Paris

Ewert, F.K. 1977, Zur Ermittlung eines
k_f-Wertes für Fels und Kriterien zur
Abdichtung des Untergrundes von Talsperren. Ber. 1.Nat.Tagung Ing.Geol.,S.393-
4o8,Paderborn

Hantush, M.S. & Jacob, C.E. 1955, Non-
steady radial flow in an infinite leaky
aquifer. Am.Geophys.Union Trans.,Vol.36,
S.95-1oo

Heitfeld, K.H. 1965, Hydro- und baugeolo-
gische Untersuchungen über die Durchlässigkeit des Untergrundes an Talsperren
des Sauerlandes. Geol.Mitt.,5,Nr.1/2,
S.1-21o,Aachen

Louis, C. 1974, Introduction à l'hydrau-
lique des roches. Bull.BRGM,2ième série
Section III,Nr.4,S.283-356,Editions
B.R.G.M.,Paris

Lugeon, M. 1933, Barrages et Geologie.
138 S., Dunod,Paris

Maini, Y.N.T. 1971, In situ hydraulic
parameters in jointed rock - their measurement and interpretation. Ph.D.Thesis
Imperial College,32o S.,London

Nonveiller, E. 197o, Permeability, uplift
pressure, seepage discharges. Int.Symp.
on Rock Mech.,Madrid,Oct.1968,p.369-377

Rißler, P. 1977, Bestimmung der Wasser-
durchlässigkeit von klüftigem Fels.
Veröffentl. Inst.f.Grundbau,Bodenmecha-
nik,Felsmechanik und Verkehrswasserbau
der RWTH Aachen,H.5,144 S.,Aachen

Schetelig, K. Schenk, V. & Heyberger,W.
1973, Neues Meßverfahren für die Durchführung von Wasserabpreßversuchen. Veröffentl. 3.Nat.Tag.Felsmechanik,S.29-45,
Aachen

Schneebeli, G. 1966, Hydraulique souterraine. 662 S.,Eyrolles,Paris

Schneider, H.J. 1979, Neue Versuchsappara-
tur zur Bestimmung der Durchströmungs-
eigenschaften von Fels. Ber. 2.Nat.Ta-
gung f.Ing.Geol.,S.75-83,Fellbach

Theis, C.V. 1935, The relation between the
lowering of the piezometric surface and
the rate and duration of discharge of a
well using groundwater storage. Am.Geo-
phys.Union Trans.,Nr.16,S.519-524,Rich-
mond

Thiem, G. 19o6, Hydrologische Methoden.
56 S., J.M.Gebhardt's Verlag,Leipzig

Wittke, W. & Louis, C. 1969, Anströmung
von Hohlräumen im Fels. Proc.Int.Symp.
on Large Permanent Underground Openings,
S.291-3o3,Oslo

Wittke, W. 197o, Rechnerische und elektro-
analoge Lösung dreidimensionaler Aufgaben der Durchströmung von klüftigem Fels.
Proc. 2nd Int.Congr.Rock.Mech. ISPM,Bd.3,
p.6-18,Belgrad

REDUCTION OF STRENGTH OF ROCKS SURROUNDING MINE WORKINGS
Festigkeitsabminderung des Gebirges um den Abbauhohlraum herum
Abaissement de la résistance des roches autour des vides d'exploitation

V.V.SMIRNYAKOV
Leningrad Mining Institute, USSR

SUMMARY:
The report proved the necessity of taking into consideration the solid
rocks strength reduction in the area around mine workings.
For this purpose it is recommended to investigate physicalmechanical
properties of rocks using both samples taken from the face of the working to be driven or cores of exploratory workings and the rock samples
selected in the roof, sides and floor of the mine working not long after
its driving.
A method and results of investigations are given to show the variability
of the physical-mechanical properties of rocks surrounding mine workings
at the mines of the Donbas and Karagande basins.

ZUSAMMENFASSUNG:
Im Referat wird die Notwendigkeit der Festigkeitsminderung der Felsenge-
steine um die Abbaue begründet. Es wird vorgeschlagen, die physikalisch-
mechanischen Eigenschaften der Gesteine nicht nur nach Proben aus dem
Ort oder nach Kernproben der Schürfbohrungen zu untersuchen, sondern
auch nach Proben, die den Ober- und Seitenstößen wie auch dem Liegenden
einige Zeit nach dem Auffahren entnommen werden.
Es werden die Methodik und die Untersuchungsangaben der Veränderung der
physikalisch-mechanischen Eigenschaften der Gesteine um die Abbaue in
den Gruben der Donezker und Karagandaer Reviere angegeben.

RESUME:
Dans le présent rapport on prouve avec évidence la nécessité de tenir
compte de l'abaissement de résistance des roches avoisinantes autor des
ouvrages miniers en exploitation. Dans ce but, on propose d'effectuer
un examen des propriétés physico-chimiques des roches non seulement
d'après les échantillons prélevés dans le front de taille de l'ouvrage
que l'on creuse, ou selon des carottes des sondages, mais aussi suivant
les échantillons pris dans le toit, les épontes et le sol de l'ouvrage
quelque temps après son creusement.
On présente la méthode et le résultats de l'examen de changement des
propriétés physico-chimiques des roches avoisinantes autour des ouvrages
miniers dans les mines des bassins de Donetzk et de Karaganda.

Observations on rock behaviour on
contour of workings show changes
of rock strength in the course of
time. Thus, we observed the cases
when at first a working was driven
in strong rocks, but later the rocks
on contour turned into clayey mass
which can be easily separated from
rock mass by hand. As a rule,
increased rock pressure and
deformation of supports occured in
such workings. While widening work-

ings the lowest rock strength was observed on their contour. Rock strenght increased, with the distance from the contour being increased. To choose the type of support and to solve some other problems it is impotant to know changes of rock properties in time their stability. In this connection we investigated the changes of rock properties in mine workings of Karagande and Donetz basins. In the first stage as the size of rock zone around the working in the limit of which the properties of rocks were changing was unknown the samples were taken by drilling cores 45 mm in diameter at the distance of 2 m from the contour of working. Later studies showed that changes of rock properties took place at the distance of not more than 1 m from the contour of working section. In this case driving with pneumatic hammer appeared to be the simplest way of coring. Before coring the working section contour surface was thoroughly examined, planes of bedding determined and then cores were taken on the working contour and at different distances from it. Coring was done by gradual winning of rock seam with pneumatic hammer to the rise and to the dip. For each type of rocks cores were taken in the centre of each seam every 10 cm at the distance of not less than 1 m beginning from the working contour. The time when this section of working was driven was determined at the site of coring according to mine surveying data. Drilled cores were dilivered to the surface and properties of rocks were determined in the laboratory. Rock strenght limit on compression was determined on cores of irregular form according to technique elaborated by the Mining Institute named after A.A.Skochinsky /I/. Validity of the application of this method was proved at every basin by comperative tests of all existing rocks on drilled cores of both regular and irregular forms. Angle of internal friction and rock cohesion coefficient were also determined on drilled cores of irregular form according to our method /5/. Investigations of changes of rock properties under the conditions of Karaganda and Donetz basins showed that strength parameters of rocks surrounding workings decreases in the process of its development. Reduction of strength of rock and the distance to which it occurs are greatly influenced by the type of rocks and the mode of working driving. Reduction of strength of rock in the process of its development must be also influenced by some other factors (support pressure, distance from the surface, the shape of working cross section, type of support, composition of mine atmosphere etc.). Their role, however, has not yet been determined. In haulage levels of Karaganda basin sandstone strength decrease 6 months after driving takes place in the depth up to 20-30 cm, with rock strength decreasing to 1.5-2 on the working contour. The zone of strenght decrease in clay shales is about 50 cm, with rock strenght limit on compression decreasing to 2.5-3 on section contour. As to strenght sand shales are in the intermidiate position between sandstones and clay shales. While driving first floors in air levels of Karaganda basin mines stability of uniform rocks is considerably lower than in those of haulage levels. Thus, strenght of clay shales on working section contour 6 months after its driving decreases to 3-5, the depth of the strenght decrease zone is 1 m. Rock strenght decrease of air levels at shallow depth (60-80 m) near the exposure of main rock under the overburden can be explained by their smaller strenght and the higher degree of weathering. More deatiled investigations of changes of rock properties under conditions of Karaganda basin were carried out in a field air level at the Churubai-Nurinsk mine 13. The heading was driven partly by drilling and shooting 5 cores were taken in one layer of clay shales in the wall side of working 2, 21, 32, 60 and 193 days after the driving. Tests on rock compression and determination of moisture content in rocks were carried out during each coring Besides, angles of internal friction and cohesion coefficient were determined at different distances from heading section contour by the last coring (193 days after the

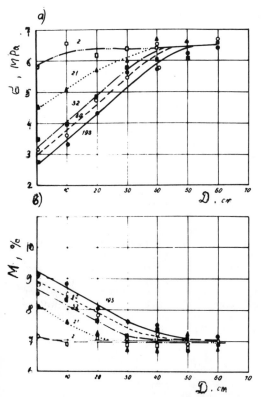

Fig.1. Changes of strenght (a)
and moisture (b) in clay
shales.

er than rock strength in driving.
At the heading section driven
with pneumatic hammers the depth
of rock strength variation during
185 days was about 30 cm, with
strenght in the section contour
decreasing to 1.9 as compared
with rock strenght while driving.
Hence, strenght change of surrounding rocks is greatly influenced by
the mode of driving a working. High
degree of rock strength decrease
around the working results in a
higher rate of shifting of rock
contour which, in its turn, influenced greatly the conditions of
its maintenance. To get quantitative indexes of heading section
contour shifting depending on the
mode of driving a working at
sections driven by drilling and
shooting and with pneumatic
hammers sizes of their cross
section, and it was supported by
the circular lining of special
profile with the same ring pitch,
with rock strenght limit on
compression being approximately the
same. The results of measurements
of changes in the sizes of heading
section in the clear driven by
both methods are given in Fig.2.

drilling). While driving a working
185 days later rock strenght limits
on compression of clay shales were
determined from one layer at the
section of heading driven with
pneumatic hammers. The results of
investigations of changes of rock
strength ε and rock moisture M
content depends on distance $\mathcal{D}$ to
heading section contour and the
time of its operation at the heading section driven by drilling and
shooting are shown in Fig.I.
Numbers on curves of rock strenght
and moisture content changes
correspond to number of days N
after driving a working. As is well
seen from the results of investigations strenght and moisture
content of rocks surrounding the
working underwent most intensive
changes during the first month
after its driving. The depth of
rock strenght variation during
193 days after driving was about
50 cm. Rock strenght in the contour
during that time was 2.4 times low-

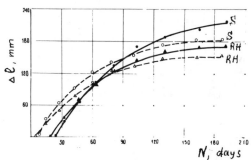

Fig.2. Convergence of contour of
heading section driven by
drilling and shooting and
with pneumatic hammers.

Line on the plot corresponds to
the changes of heading sizes in
the clear driven by drilling and
shooting, dot-lines correspond to
those driven with pneumatic hammers
In both methods of driving curves
S and RH represent dependence
of convergence $\Delta \ell$ of sides and
roof - heading bottom accordingly.

147

From the given data it is seen that shifting of heading section contour in the clear driven with pneumatic hammers began in a shorter period of time after driving a working than those driven by drilling and shooting. Rate of shifting in the first case, however, was 30-35% smaller than in the second one; so after 3-4 months of working development common values of convergence were approximately the same and 6 months later decrease in sizes of working cross section in the clear (due to yielding of support) driven by drilling and shooting were about 15% larger than those driven with pneumatic hammer. Delayed manifestations of working section contour shifting in the clear driven by drilling and shooting can be explained by bad contact between the working contour and support due to large clearance in lined area and its unconsolidated backing. This causes considerable delay in the interaction of support with rock mass. In spite of this, the total value of shifting of rock working cross section driven by drilling and shooting was considerably higher than this of working driven with pneumatic hammers. Thus, the convergence of side walls measured on contour rock rippers 6 months after driving the working by drilling and shooting were 320 mm, and that of with pneumatic hammers – 205 mm. Changes in the angle of internal friction φ and cohesion coefficient of rocks C at different distances from heading cross section contour 193 days after driving it by drilling and shooting are as follows:

D cm	0	10	20	30	40	50	60
φ degr	12	10	13	15	17	17	16
C MPa	0	0.3	0.8	1.2	1.8	1.8	1.6

From these data it is seen that cohesion coefficient of rocks near working cross section contour decreases greatly, that is confirmed by previous investigations. Our investigations, at the same time, do not confirm the accepted ideas that angles of internal friction of all kinds of rocks surrounding the working are constant. It seems to be true only for the rocks moisture content of which changes neg-

ligibly near working cross section contour in the process of its development. Changes of rock properties in time were also studied at the mine "Cherkasskaya Severnaya" (Donbas) in the working situated at the depth of 460 m from the surface in the rocks with dip angle 35 - 40'. The results of the investigation showed that the strength of rocks surrounding the working also decreases, particularly of clay shales. Thus, their rock strength limit on compression on the working contour 6-9 months after driving decreases to 1.4-1.8 as compared with the distance of 50-60 cm from the contour. Strength of sand shales and sandstones of the working section contour decreased during the same time to 1.3 and 1.2 accordingly as compared with the distance of 60 cm from the contour. The maximum moisture content of rocks was on the working contour and with distance from it the moisture content decreased; the rock moisture content remained

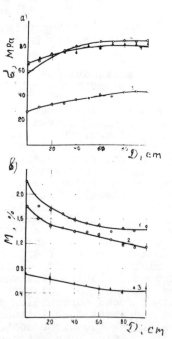

Fig.3. Changes of strength (a) and moisture content (b) of rocks: 1 – of shales, 2 – of sandstones, 3 – of limestones.

constant at the distance of more
than 50-60 cm. Three kinds of rocks
extracted from the field haulage
levels of steeply inclined seams
at the depth of 680 and 800 m
(Fig.3) were tested on strength at
the XXII congress of CPSU mine in
Donbas.

Strength limit of clay shales on
working cross section contour 9.2
months after driving decreased to
1.7. The zone of strength changes
spread into the rock mass to the
distance of 80-90 cm. Changes in
moisture content of rocks depending
on distance to the working cross
section contour were contrary in
character to changes in strength,
Strength of sandstones of heading
cross section contour during 50
months of its development decreased
to 1.5, and moisture content increased to 1.6 as compared with the
same values of rocks at the depth
of 1 m from the working cross section contour (Fig.3, curve2).
Changes of strength and moisture
content of limestones 38.5 months
after driving the working were investigated at the same time.Strenght
limit on cross section contour was
66 MPa, at the distance of 1 m from
contour 83 MPa, i.e. 1.26 times
more. Moisture content of limestones was rather small in the
whole interval of investigated
depth. Even here its decrease though
negligible was, however, observed
as the working was driven into the
depth of rock mass. Studies carried
out in different minegeological
conditions of mines show that
strength properties of rocks surrounding the working decrease in
all cases in the course of time.
Not only compression strength
seems to change in rock mass surrounding the working, but also
other strength and theology parameters of rocks; latter being
determined it will be possible
to choose supports with good reason,
to work out recomendations on working stability, to evaluate stability
of unsupported workings depending
on the time of its development,
choice of methods of driving the
working etc. Studying these problems is one of the most urgent
tasks of workings maintenance.

REFERENCES

Baron, L.I.,1962, Determination of
rock properties,Moscow.
Liberman, J.M., 1969, Support pressure in permanent workings,
Moscow.
Panov, A.N., Ruppeneit, K.V., Liberman, J.M., 1969, Rock pressure
in stopes and development workings, Moscow.
Ruppeneit, K.V., 1954, Some aspects
of rock mechanics, Moscow.
Smirnyakov, V.V., Mirzaev, G.G.,
Chutashvili, A.G., 1972, Some
observations on rock pressure
manifestation in mines, Georgian
polytechnical institute, Tbilisy.

ROCK-STRESS VARIATIONS CONTROL METHODS
Eine Kontrollmethode für Gesteinsspannungsänderungen
Méthodes de contrôle des variations des tensions dans les roches

G.SOBOLEV & M.SHPORKEN
Shmidt's Institute of the Physics of the Earth, Moscow, USSR

SUMMARY:

The authors of the paper have developed a method and equipment for
monitoring stress variations in the ground in order to forecast seismic
phenomena. The basis of the recording consists of the formation
of a measuring slot in the rock into which sensitive element, i.e. a
stress sensor, is installed. During tests which were carried out in an
operational mine alterations of stresses as a result of mining work were
ascertained. Stress monitoring measurements that were taken in the vicinity of the dam at the Ingouri underground hydro-electric power station
during construction indicated alterations in the form of a "bay". The
alterations are identical to those that preceded the failure of the
laboratory samples.

ZUSAMMENFASSUNG:

Die Autoren dieser Arbeit haben eine Methodik und eine Apparatur ausgearbeitet für die Kontrolle der Spannungsvariationen in Erdboden, welche für
die Prognose der seismischen Erscheinungen bestimmt sind. Das Registrier-
prinzip besteht in der Fertigung einer Mess-Spalte im Erdgestein, in die
ein empfindliches Element, nämlich ein Spannungsgeber hineingestellt wird.
Während der Versuche, die in einem im Betrieb befindlichen Bergwerk durchgeführt wurden, wurden Spannungsänderungen infolge der Bergwerksarbeiten
festgestellt. Die Spannungskontrollmessungen, die im Bereich des im Bau
befindlichen Dammes, des in den Bergen gelegenen Wasserkraftwerkes Ingouri,
durchgeführt werden zeigten Veränderungen in Form einer "Bucht". Diese Änderungen sind identisch mit denen, die dem Bruch der Laborproben voran-
gingen.

RESUME:

Les auteurs de cette étude out élaboré une méthode théorique et expéri-
mentale de l'euregistrement des variations de tensions dans le massif de
roches. Le complexe d'enregistrement se compose des elements tensometrique
et compensateur. La sensibilité de la méthode est déterminee par le coefficient de transformation entre le transfigurateur de déformations et
la membrane de l'enregistreur.
Pendant les essais réalisés dans une mimère fonctionnante ont été enregistrées les variations de tensions provoquées par facteurs tectoniques.
Les essais de contrôle de tensions effectués dans la zone de construction
de la digue de la station hydroélectrique à Ingouri, située dans les mon-
tagnes, ont enregistrés des variations du type "de baie". Ces variations
sont identiques aux variations précédantes la destruction des spécimes au
laboratoire.

The analysis of existing methods and means of seismic phenomena forecashing show that hitherto there are no reliable solutions of the earthquake and seismic shock problem. The forecashing of the mentioned phenomena is based on obtaining and analysing the data that indirectly define the Earth8s stresses. It may be supposed that recording of stressed and deformed state variations will allow to improve the prognostic investigations. The heterogeneity and discretness of mechanical rock properties on different scale levals /1,2/ require a simultaneous observation of the stress variations in many points.

The available results of earthquake precursor observations testify to anomalous deformation variations from 10^{-7} to 10^{-8} /3,4/. Such a sensitivity must be also inherent to the apparatus for stress variation recording. In addition, the apparatus being developed must be cheap, simple in building and operating.

The authors of the present work have developed techniques and devices for Earth's stress variations control with the object of forecashing the seismic phenomena. The registration principle consists in formation of a measuring slot in the rock with a consequent installing into it of a sensitive element, i.e. of a stress sensor.

1.1 Control techniques and apparatus

Let the large edges of the measuring slot be normal to the controlled component of the external stress tensor δ_{ii} . The rock around slot considered to be elastic and isotropic, its temperature being invariable.

If the slot depth and length are much greater then the distance between its edges according to /5/, we have

$$dP \simeq d\delta_{ii}$$

It means that using a maesuring slot with a pressurized liguid it is possible to register the stress variations in rocks.

The sensitive element /the stress sensor/ installed into the measuring slot represents an elastic-isotropic, hermetic shell filled with a liquid /for instance with water/ under pressure of 10^5 to 10^6 n/m^2, which ensure a good contact of rocks with sensitive membranes of the pick-up sensor. The stress variations in the rock mas-

size result in a slot-wall deformation and naturally in a displacement of the sensor membrances, which is accompanied with supplanting the liquid in its cavity, the liquid being transfered along the connecting channel to the registering apparatus in the form of a differential manometer.

The sensitivity may be increased by means of using a transformation factor between the sensitive element membranes and the registor. The transformation factor is

$$K = \frac{D^2}{d^2}$$

where D -is the sensitive element membrane diameter,
d -the register membrane diameter.

Already with the sensitive element membrane diameter of ;300mm. and the registor membrane diameter of 10mm we obtain a transformation factor of 900. In other words, using mechanical means an increase of the sensitivity by three orders of magnitude may be provided.

The measuring slot was made by drilling a series of boreholes with a consequent destruction of bridges between them. The roughness on the inner slot surface were excluded by means of condensing concrete. This ensures a contact surface without visible defects. Between the contacting concrete surfaces a strain sensor was installed which was fixed on a given plane. Then the assembly was filled with a pressurized liquid As the sensitive element we used a specially developed rock-strain sensor without any structure hysteresis /6/.

If necessary the temperature errors may be eliminated by using a compensating branch analogous to the operating one. But the compensating element is included between two rigid, elastically connected plates, which makes it possible to fix in the compensating brench the liquid volume equal to the volume of the6 operating branch /7/.

For calibrating of the system a rock sample was used with dimensions of 500 x 200 x 200mm. A 100 x 60 x 35mm. slot was made in the sample center. The stress sensor membrane diameter was 60mm. The sample with the sensitive element installed in it was placed between plates of a press. The slot plane was oriented normally to the direction of a single-axis load. The sample loading was

cyclic. After the load corresponded
to 100 tonn the unloading operation
was performrd. Then the load was
increased up to 200 tonn with a subsequent unloading, and so on till
the slot formation process. According
to the obtaine calibration results
the sensitivity was 1 bar. The stress
sensor diameter being 60mm.

1.2 Test results.
The field test were carried out in
condition of an operated mine and
in the base of high-altitude dam.
   The mine tests were conducted with
the purpose of registering the stress variations due to technogenous
factors, the approach of the mining-
work front to the measuring apparatus, site zone.The large slot edges
were oriented normally to the work
front. The sensitivity of a 300mm
diameter stress sensor was $1,7 \times 10^4$ M/m². At the time when the investigation were set out/the distance
between the measuring slot and controlled massif was about 80m.
The observed results are given in
Fig. 1. In february 4979 the distance between the measuring slot
and the work front decreased by 30m
and come to 50 meters. At the end
of the same month the work front
shifted on other horizonts, and this
was reflected in the stress variations character. A slowing down of
the strain growth with its subsequent fall /in March and April/.
The variation picture shows that a
moving away of mining works results
in decrease of stress in the massif.
The process of stress growth in May
1979 is correlated with the renewal
of works on nearly horizonts situated at a distance of 150m from the
measuring slot. The constant stress
level in June and July corresponds
to the period of work conducted at
a distance of 250÷300m from the measuring slot. In September 1979 landslides were registared that possibly
might lead to appreciable variations
Stress reduction during October and
Novemberis apparently connected with
a removal of mining work front from
the measuring apparatus.
   An other test cycle was carried
aut in the construction zone of
Inguri hydroelectric station. There the projected dam height is
271,5m. The reservoir volume is
1100 millions of cubic meters /8/.
The presence of multiple tectonic
disturbations aggravates the danger
of dam destruction.The construction

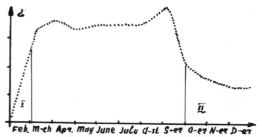

Fig.1. Stress variation in
a working mine.
$\overline{I}$ - the stage of approaching of
the work front to the stress
registor.
$\overline{II}$ - the stage of moving avay of the
work front from the stress re-
gistor site.

zone is located near a tectonic
fracture. The dam body is situated
in the zone of junction between the
folded system on the southern slope
of the Great Caucasus and the Georgian block. The high level of seismicity /the eight-ball zone/ testi-
fies to now continning deformation
processes in the construction zone.
   The registering apparatus is installed on the right bank of Inguri river, in the tail water. The registering device was placed on hydraulic cushions of a Yugoslav company. The sensitive element diameter
was 2000mm. The effective sensiti -
vity was $3 \cdot 10^2$ n/m².
   Fig. 2 shows the stress variations
during the period from December 21,
1980 to January 8, 1981. Since the
first day of registration a visible
growth of stress is noted. In order
to control the apparatus a calibration was made at December 24,1980.
In december 1980, on a background
of total stress growth a sharpgrowth
was fixed at December 31,1980. A
sharp stress fall was noted of January 2, 1981, after which there were
no stress variations during the three
subsequent days. Further stress
falls on 5-th and 6-th of january
1981. Some variations analogeuos to
the earth tides were observed. The
stress leap of january 2,1981 does
not explained by the known anomaleus.
processes of technogenous or seismic
nature.
   The coil-type changes of stress
during the period from december 29,
1980 to january 3, 1981 are identified in their shapes with the laboratory experiments results for rock

sample demolition /9/. The stress
growth of the period from December
28, 1980 to December 31, 1980 is
probably due to a massif compression
or to a crack accumulation and the
subsequent stress drop depends on
a partial destruction. After the
stress drop some variations of earth-
tide field were registered.

1.3 Conclusions
The developed apparatus and techniques for registering of earth -
stress variations of long-term con
trol of massif in a stress-defor-
med in order to reveal the prognos
tic signs of earthquake, rocky
shicks, landslides and rock shooting, as well as to estimate the
stability of large industrial structures being erected and functioning in seismically dangerous
regions of the Earth.

Acknowledgement.
Authors express their thanks to
the workers from the Mining Institute of the Soviet Academy of
Sciences, namely to senior scientific workers A.Kozyrev and
A.Lovchikov, as well as doctor
A.Savich from the Hydroproject,
for their valuable assistance in
realization of the calibrating
and field experiments.

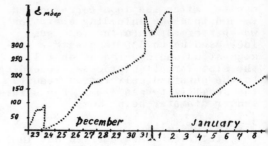

Fig. 2. Stress variations in the
base of the Inguri dam

7. Shporkin M."A device for measuring of rock deformations".
Author sertificate no.638909,
Published at 25.12.78. Bulletin
no.47.
8. Mastitski A, Dgigauri G, Kerese-
lidze C. "Engineering and geological peculiarities of arn bases
of Inguri dam". Hydrotechnical
construction, no.6, 1974.
9. Sobolev G. "Shift-type precursor
formation studies in laboratory
conditions". "Nauka" edition, Moscow, 1980, 86-99.

2. REFERENCES

1. Sadovski M., "Natural block struc
ture of rocks". Academy of Science
/USSR/ Reports, v.247, no.4, 1979
829-831.
2. Semerchan A, Sobolev G, Salov B
"Investigations on precursors of
mechanical demolishions in large
specimens". Academy of Science
/USSR/ Reports, v.260, no.3, 1981,
p.616
3. Rikitake T. "Earthquake prediction". "Mir" edition, Moscow,
1979, p.388.
4. Latynina L, Karmaleeva R."Defor-
mographic measurements". "Nauka"
edition, Moscow, 1978, 154pp.
5. Swolf H, Brechtel C, Pratt H,
Brace W. "Stress-monitoring system for earthquake prediction".
Terra tek, Inc. University research park, 1974.
6. Shporkin M, Sobolev G, Luft G.
"A device for measuring of rock
deformations". Author sertificate
no.779580. Published at 15.11.80
Bulletin no. 42.

* 2 *

UNDERGROUND CAVERNS WITH LARGE SPAN
Untertägige Hohlräume mit grosser Spannweite
Cavités souterraines de grandes portées

THE DETERMINING ROLE OF DISCONTINUITIES IN FAILURE
OF GREAT-SECTION UNDERGROUND OPENINGS

Der massgebliche Einfluss der Klüftigkeit beim Versagen von unterirdischen Hohlräumen
mit grossem Querschnitt

Le rôle déterminant des discontinuités dans la rupture des cavités souterraines
de grandes dimensions

Cs. ASSZONYI
Central Institute of Mining Research, Budapest, Hungary

M. GÁLOS & P. KERTÉSZ
Technical University, Budapest, Hungary

SUMMARY:

Failures occuring with underground openings of large section without locking depend on stress field, its orientation, the physical characteristics of the rocky environment of openings, the geometry of openings and the character of discontinuity. In this case the quantity, orientation and quality of discontinuity is meant by the character of discontinuity.

Rheological properties of rocks and discontinuity are mainly responsible for failures. Consequently, stress field, deformation field and displacement field after driving the opening should be determined by considering the rheological properties of rocks. As next step the assessed system of discontinuity should be drawn around the opening and rock bloks tending to move off potentially should be subjected to stability investigation.

It is made possible by test results that by considering the character of the surfaces of discontinuity and its frequency the sections of openings requiring locking can be indicated.

ZUSAMMENFASSUNG:

Die bei den Untergrundhöhlen mit grossem Profil ohne Sicherung eintretenden Einbrüche hängen vom primären Spannungsfeld, von dessen Orientierung, von den physikalischen Eigenschaften der Gesteinsumgebung der Anlage, der Geometrie der Höhle sowie vom Character der Klüftigkeit ab. Beim Eintreten der Einbrüche spielen rheologischen Eigenschaften des Gesteinkörpers und die Klüftigkeit die Hauptrolle.

Dementsprechend muss das Spannungs- Deformations- und Verschiebungsfeld nach Strecken abbau mit Berücksichtigung der rheologischen Eigenschaften des Gesteins bestimmt werden.

Es ist der folgende Schritt, das bemessene Klüftigkeitssystem um die Höhle zu zeichnen und diejenigen Gesteinblöcke, die potentiell zur Verschiebung geneigt sind, einer Stabilitätsuntersuchung zu unterwerfen. Als Ergebnis der Untersuchung können mit Berücksichtigung des Charakters und des Häufigkeitswerts der Klüftigkeitsflächen diejenigen Strecken angesetzt werden, an denen Versicherungsanlagen gebaut werden müssen.

RÉSUMÉ:

Les ruptures de toit des cavités souterraines de grande dimensions dépendent du champ de contraint primaire et de son orientation, des propriétés de l' environnement rocheux, de la géométrie de la cavité ainsi que de la présence des discontinuités. La discontinuité doit être exprimée par les mesures, l' orientation et la qualité.

Ce sont le comportement rhéologique et la discontinuité qui jouent le rôle plus important au cours des ruptures. Les champs de contraint et de mouvement doivent être déterminés en tenant compte des propriétés rhéologiques des roches. Le pas suivant doit être de projeter le système de discontinuité mesuré autours de la cavité, et exécuter une analyse de stabilité des blocs potenciellement prêts aux movements.

Les sections, où un soutènement doit être assuré peuvent être déterminées à l' aide de caractère et de fréquence des discontinuités comme le résultat de notre considération.

1. STRESS FIELD IN THE ROCKY ENVIRONMENT OF OPENINGS

The choice of safety system in case of underground openings, caves of large section is made possible by knowing

the primary state of stress,

the rock-physical characteristics, and

the regularity of mechanical processes due to geological effects. In favourable conditions it is not necessary to ensure the safety of openings by the means of special built—in mechanism, because the developing state of stress does not cause any failure in the environment of the opening. Even in such cases local failure may occur in some sections.

The driving of openings is accompanied by failures expanded in time. This phenomenon can be explained by discontinuity dividing rock bodies into bloks, consequently mechanical regularities due to geological effects should be investigated.

2. PRIMARY STATE

Rocky environment before starting building activity is inactive and this state of stress is called primary state of stress (if rocky environment is disturbed e. g. by other mining caverns, then the state of stress before starting building is considered as quasi-primary state). This state at depth H is represented by stress tensor $F_p(H)$ having as a rule general orientation instead of horizontalvertical one:

$$F_p = \begin{Vmatrix} p_x & t_{xy} & t_{xz} \\ t_{yx} & p_y & t_{yz} \\ t_{zx} & t_{zy} & p_z \end{Vmatrix} = F_p\langle x, y, z\rangle.$$

Three perpendicular to one another orientations can always be found in space in which the matrix of primary state of stress becomes diagonal

$$F_p = \begin{Vmatrix} p_1 & 0 & 0 \\ 0 & p_2 & 0 \\ 0 & 0 & p_3 \end{Vmatrix} = \begin{Vmatrix} p & 0 & 0 \\ 0 & \dfrac{p}{k_2-1} & 0 \\ 0 & 0 & \dfrac{p}{k_3-1} \end{Vmatrix} = F_p\langle 1, 2, 3\rangle,$$

where k_2 and k_3 are the so called quasi-Poisson's ratio in the value of which the effect of the dead weight in the rocky environment and the resultant of geological and tectonic force effects are expressed.

It is not easy to determine the characteristics of the primary state of stress. It can be stated in general that the determination of primary principal stresses by calculation using the dead load and Poisson's ratio may involve errors of an order of magnitude. Asszonyi (1970) and Asszonyi–Kapolyi (1976) carried out about 100 in-situ measurements in the Eocene basin at Tatabánya (Hungary) at a depth of 180–320 m from the ground surface. The trends orientations of principal stresses always deviated considerably from the vertical—horizontal ones, and from the $\rho g H$ values and the components calculable by the means of Poisson's ratio.

For determining primary stress fields there is a possibility for laboratory and in-situ measurements with the common features that

measurements should be carried out at least in three directions of the space situated in more than one plane

measurements can be carried out in an indirect way, that is some kind of disturbance (e. g. bore hole) is set up the effect of which on the state of stress is known and the original state of stress can be determined by applying the values of displacement and deformation obtained by measurements.

The widespread use of acoustical emission measurements has been made possible by the recognition of Kaiser's effect and due to it the primary state of stress can be determined from the sample taken out of the drill core.

Similar measurements are carried out in our country at the Central Institute for Mining Researches by Huszár and his collaborators on the basis of Kapolyi's intention and at the Technical University of Budapest by Czoboly and his collaborators.

Primary stress tensor can be determined on the basis of at least 6 samples taken from drill cores. The example in figure 1 represents the case when specimens are formed for uniaxial compression tests in a way that their axes lie in the direction of datum lines and in datum planes and that axes constitute an angle of 45°.

The primary stress tensor can be determined on the basis of the six compression tests from the compressive stress values:

$$\sigma_x; \sigma_y; \sigma_z; \sigma_\xi; \sigma_\eta; \sigma_\zeta$$

at which stress exceeded the values obtained before in the direction in question and so another sound emission takes place.

From the measured values follows that

$$\tau_{xy} = \sigma_\xi - \frac{1}{2}(\sigma_x + \sigma_y)$$

$$\tau_{yz} = \sigma_\eta - \frac{1}{2}(\sigma_y + \sigma_z)$$

$$\tau_{zx} = \sigma_\xi - \frac{1}{2}(\sigma_z + \sigma_x)$$

and so the tensor of the primary state of stress is

$$\mathbf{F}_p = \begin{Vmatrix} \sigma_x & \sigma_\xi - \frac{1}{2}(\sigma_x + \sigma_y) & \sigma_\xi - \frac{1}{2}(\sigma_z + \sigma_x) \\ \sigma_\xi - \frac{1}{2}(\sigma_x + \sigma_y) & \sigma_y & \sigma_\eta - \frac{1}{2}(\sigma_y + \sigma_z) \\ \sigma_\xi - \frac{1}{2}(\sigma_z + \sigma_x) & \sigma_\eta - \frac{1}{2}(\sigma_y + \sigma_z) & \sigma_z \end{Vmatrix}$$

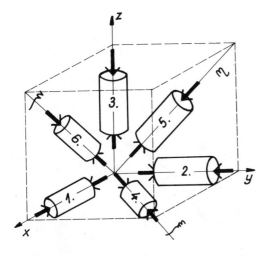

Fig. 1 Forming of specimens for determining primary state of stress

Due to starting driving a secondary stress field characterized by an $\mathbf{F}_s$ tensor developes in the primary stress field. The secondary stress field depends on the primary stress field, the geometric dimensions and shape of the opening. Due to the removal of rock blocks confined with surface „S" some motions take place with time. So

$$\mathbf{F}_s\,(\mathbf{F}_p, S, t).$$

The difference between primary and secondary stress tensors can be expressed by the means of complementary stress tensor $\mathbf{F}_k$

$$\mathbf{F}_k = \mathbf{F}_s - \mathbf{F}_p \qquad \mathbf{F}_s = \mathbf{F}_p + \mathbf{F}_k.$$

Starting from the simple assumption that in primary states deformations took place during the different eras of the Earth history ($\mathbf{D}_p = 0;\ \mathbf{u}_s = 0$) the tensor of deformations occuring after starting driving is

$$\mathbf{D}_s\,(\mathbf{F}_k)$$

and the vector of displacements is

$$\mathbf{u}_s(\mathbf{F}_k)$$

The secondary field of deformation and displacement with complementary stress tensor $\mathbf{F}_k$ can be calculated by the means of the constitutive equation chosen in accordance with rock characteristics.

When chosing the material model representing the mechanical behaviour of rock block two opposing requirements have to be reconciled
the model should represent the mechanical characteristics of the real rock as adequately as possible (it should also satisfy theoretical — thermodynamical — laws and demands set up by practical experience)
it should be applicable easily for the simplest practical calculations in its mathematical form.

When reconciling the two opposing requirements an optimum should be realized with which the most significant mechanical characteristics can be expressed by the means of simple mathematical apparatus and the approximation can be considered as satisfactory.

In case of isotropic rock blocks the constitutive law for the block should be found among isotropic rheological bodies. Investigations (Asszonyi, 1980.) show that for describing elastic state behaviour the Poynting–Thomson rheological body can be applied which fully realizes the above mentioned compromise and at the same time it is suitable for lineat solution of elastic deformation, creep and relaxation.

The mechanical model of the standard body can be found in fig. 2.

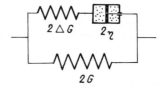

Fig. 2 Mechanical model of the Poynting–Thomson standard body

The determination of material characteristics in laboratories or in-situ is given by Asszonyi and Kapolyı (1976).

The tensor equation of standard bodies expressing constitutive law is

$$\mathbf{T} = 2G\mathbf{E} + 2\eta'(1 + \frac{G}{\Delta G})\,\dot{\mathbf{E}} - \frac{\eta}{\Delta G}\,\dot{\mathbf{T}}$$

159

$$\mathbf{T_0} = 3K\mathbf{E_0} \qquad \dot{\mathbf{T}}_0 = 3K\dot{\mathbf{E}}_0,$$

where

$\mathbf{T}$ stress deviator tensor
$\dot{\mathbf{T}}$ stress velocity tensor
$\mathbf{T_0}$ stress sphere tensor
$\dot{\mathbf{T}}_0$ velocity of the stress sphere tensor
$\mathbf{E}$ deviator tensor of deformation
$\dot{\mathbf{E}}$ velocity tensor of deformation
$\mathbf{E_0}$ sphere tensor of deformation
$\dot{\mathbf{E}}_0$ velocity of the sphere tensor of deformation

η viscosity coefficient:

$$2\eta'(1 + \frac{G}{\Delta G})$$

τ relaxation time

$$\frac{\eta'}{\Delta G}$$

G shear modulus of elasticity
K modulus of compressibility

The solution of tensor equation for uniaxial stress state:

$$\sigma = E\epsilon + \lambda\dot{\epsilon} - \vartheta\dot{\sigma}$$

where

E modulus of elasticity
λ linear viscosity coefficient
ϑ relaxation constant.

3. FAILURES IN THE ROCKY ENVIRONMENT OF OPENINGS

Work carried out in a material system increases the energy level of the system. One part of the introduced energy (U), i. e. the elastic potencial energy (Φ), is stored, the other part of it ($\mathcal{L}$) dissipates.

$$U = \Phi + \mathcal{L}$$

Failure in the material takes place when the change of energy reaches the level where rocky environment can not dissipate the excess of energy: it „throws" it out. Fracture conditions of rocks depend therefore not on the state of stress, but on energy dissipation.

It follows from the theorem of conservation of impulse that stress rearrangement takes place simultaneously with driving openings. Motions and deformations pertaining to modified state of stress are set up extended in time and in scale depending on the character of rocks. (fig. 3.).

The field of deformation and displacement of round openings can be determined in closed form if idealized conditions are supposed to be present.

The deformation field

$$\epsilon_r = -\frac{p}{2G}(\frac{R}{r})^2(1 - e^{-\beta t})$$

$$\epsilon_\varphi = \frac{p}{2G}(\frac{R}{r})^2(1 - e^{-\beta t})$$

The dislacement field

$$u = \frac{p \cdot R}{2G}(\frac{R}{r})(1 - e^{-\beta t})$$

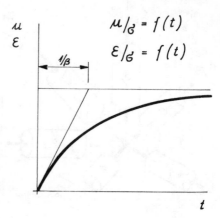

Fig. 3 Schematic curve of creep

Rheological characteristics can be properly determined on the basis of Poynting–Thomson assumption by the means of uniaxial compression tests supplementes with creep tests.

The creep curves for permian sandstone and for eocene andesite can be seen in figures 4. and 5. Investigations showed that creep curve for futher dimensioning work can be determined by the function

$$\epsilon_\infty = \epsilon_0 + r \ln(1 + t)$$

where

ϵ_∞ deformation setting up at time taken as infinite
ϵ_0 deformation set up at $t = 0$
r rheological constant

Rheological constant r can be determined by the method of minimum squares applying measuring values.

Results of tests and material constants calculated from them can be found in table I.

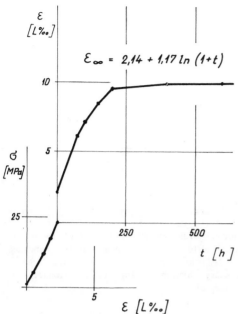

Fig. 4 Creep curve of Permian sandstone

Mohr's envelopes are presented in figures 6 and 7, where equation is given by the parabola lying on the great circle of tensile and compressive strengths. Results obtained with triaxial tests show very clearly that this kind of approximation increases safety.

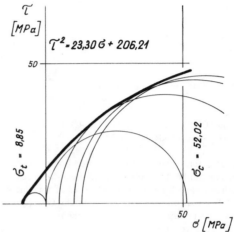

Fig. 6 Mohr's envelope of Permian sandstone

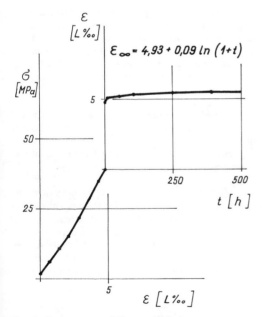

Fig. 5 Creep curve of Eocene andesite

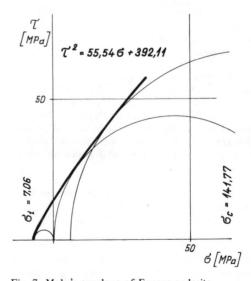

Fig. 7 Mohr's envelope of Eocene andesite

161

			Permian sandstone	Eocene andesite
compressive strength	σ_c	MPa	52,02	89,74
tensile strength	σ_t	MPa	8,85	7,06
Brinke's number	B		5,88	12,71
shear strength	τ	MPa	14,36	19,80
deformation	ϵ_0	$L‰$	2,14	4,93
deformation	$\epsilon_\infty = \epsilon_{6360}$	$L‰$	12,39	5,69
coefficient of linear viscosity	λ	GPah	256	5176
constant of relaxation	ϑ	h	69	750
Young's modulus	E	MPa	1870	6890

Table I. Rock physical properties

4. DISCONTINUITY IN THE ROCKY ENVIRONMENT OF OPENINGS

Structural characteristics of rock bodies around openings can be determined by the means of rock-physical and rockmechanical test series of specimens taken from discontinuity-free rock blocks. Consequently when determining the stability of openings only small size discontinuities smaller than the geometrical dimensions of specimens can be taken fully into consideration. It is desirable to take discontinuities greater than the dimensions of specimens i. e. discontinuity, in accordance with their actual location.

Determination of discontinuity involves operations of various kinds. The quantity, orientation and quality of discontinuity ahould be determined. Determination of quantity and orientation requires geometrical measurements which can be carried out during driving of openings by measuring the lines of intersection of the opening wall and the surfaces of discontinuity.

Determination of the quality of the surfaces of discontinuity requires more consideration as regards rock-physics and rock-mechanics. By the quality of the surfaces of discontinuity we mean the subsequent effect of the development of the surfaces of discontinuity, their thickness, filling and the mechanical characteristics of the surfaces of discontinuity along surfaces.

Surfaces of discontinuity in the environment of openings are of geological and technological origin or they are formed during failure processes (table II.).

Discontinuity surfaces of geological origin may be found on the boundary surfaces of the formation rock when the interruption or change of geological formation processes constitute quality limit. These voids of discontinuity are generally closed, but having generally no structural relationship.

In case of homogeneous petrogenesis boundary surfaces are the surfaces along which structural relationship could not develop because of the interruption of formation processes. Very thin bands as e. g. clay folms can often be found on the layer boundary which may change surface characteristics considerably.

Volume contraction due to cooling or drying results in fissures and joints. Voids of discontinuity disconnect originally connected rock units, that is why they are generally rough. Voids have open or opening character, they become closed only due to special stress state. These surfaces are generally filled with their own alteration products only.

Lithoclases developed due to tectonic reasons are considered to be tensile or shear cracks, hence they have open and rough or closed and sheared surfaces. They are often filled with strengthening materials (e. g. calcite) ensuring structural binding as well or with clayey skin (rotted rock) facilitating displacement.

Lithoclases transformed into faults lose a part of their roughness depending on the character of motion slickenside can develop, too. They may be considerably large they are generally filled with detritus, sometimes in great quantity.

Discontinuity originated by technology depends on the breaking methods used for forming the opening (e.g. shooting on the tree) and on stress rearrangement accompanying the driving of opening immediately. These voids of discontinuity have an orientation depending on location, their proceed may deviate from the plane considerably, the surfaces are rough and have shear character.

Energy dissipation has an extreme value along surfaces of discontinuity which depends first of all on the quality of the surface of discontinuity. For the

162

Table II. Summary of the characterization of discontinuity

origin and characteristics of discontinuity			structure in space	gap-characteristics	filling out	character of surface	
geologic	connected with petrogenesis	bedding boundary	generally regular	closed	frequent (e.g. calyey), with smoothing character	smooth	
		rock boundary	generally irregular	closed	infrequent (alteration product)	rough	
	epigenetio	joint of contraction	generally regular	open or in opening	infrequent (alteration product))	rough	
	tectonic	fissure	framelike	in opening or closing	infrequent with strengthening or smoothing character	smooth-rough	
		fault	connected with one or several main directions	open	frequent (detritus or alteration product)	smooth	
technologic		cracks and fractures due to blasting or driving	irregular	open	–	rough	
connected with failure processes		cracks and fractures due to mouvements in the rock	to determine	in opening	–	rough	

moment it is not possible yet to introduse some of the measurable characteristics into dimensioning formulas, consequently, discontinuity as determinant should be analysed separately in every case.

During driving openings rocky environments of engineering structures become well known so that they having chosen the right idealization they can be divided into rock bodies comprising both rock blocks and discontinuity separating rock bloks.

Rock properties of rock blocks can be determined by laboratory measurements and by the help of them the fields of stress, deformation and displacements around the opening can be defined as well. In case of circular openings they can be given in the form of closed mathematical formulas. Measured discontinuity, however, can not be taken into consideration in a simple way like that.

5.   DETERMINATION OF FAILURES

A great number of papers are concerned with the phenomenon of failures of openings. Earlier investigations are based on observing actual breaks stating that they may threaten life and property as well as the stability of engineering structures due to abrupt structural rearrangement.

Mosztkov (1978) has analysed 45 breaks and stated that 65% of failures occured 10–15 days after driving the opening. The depth of failures was 1,2–4,2 m what coincides with that experienced by us. It means at the same time that rock bolt locking (in case of short rock bolts) and rock blocks fail simultaneously.

Mosztkov does not give ani explanation based on rheological structural characteristics. He considers geometrical characteristics of openings first of all as standard.

Discontinuity developing after driving the opening in stable rock without locking may join discontinuity developed just after driving the opening or may lead to disjunction of rock block(s) even without it. Disjunction takes place where and when convective momentum control takes over the function of conductive control.

163

Original surfaces of discontinuity are suitable for convective control by themselves. The character of convective control depends also on energy transmission between the walls of the voids of discontinuity. The smaller the resistance to friction the more energy is absorbed and the greater is the possibility for rock blocks in critical situation to fall. The interruption of the structural connection of rock blocks with their environment is also required for falling. This phenomenon depends on time. The final time for the possibility of changes can be determined by the means of the rheological characteristics of rocks. After this time if no other changes occur falls are not to be supposed to occur.

Failures can be determined in advance and the way of protection can be predicted if the development of deformation and displacement fields around openings is considered as processes developing in time according to the rheological characteristics of rocks and if the given discontinuity system is supposed to be a place where failures can occur.

In order to investigate failures the measured discontinuity system characteristic for the given rock body should be drawn over the roof of the opening and after it the behaviour of rock blocks should be analysed taking into consideration the displacement field developing in time (fig. 8.).

Investigation should be started with the standard rock block units of the rock body separated into rock blocks and it should be continued until rock block(s) considered to be moved off make other rock blocks unstable.

The development of failures can be determined by the rheological properties of rocks. The variety of rheological properties is well illustrated by sandstones from the Permian epoch and andesite from the Eocene epoch shown in figures 4. and 5.

In both rocks track entries of large section were formed without locking or to be more exact rock bolts were applied at short intervals to ensure homogeneity of rocky environment.

Creep curves representing rheological variety adequately prove that development of displacements in sandstone is in fact a process requiring much more time to proceed. While failures in andesite proceed in the first days after driving those with sandstone take 20—40 days.

By assessing the density of the surfaces of discontinuity it becomes possible to determine the sections of openings which should be protected against failures.

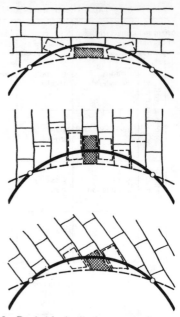

Fig. 8. Rock block displacements due to roof displacement between calculated zero points in case of surfaces of discontinuity with different orientation

6. REFERENCES

ASSZONYI, CS. – RICHTER, R. : Rheologische Untersuchung von mechanischen Feldern in der Umgebung der Strecken. *Bergbauwissenschaften,* (1969) Vol. 16. No 9. pp 326—333.

ASSZONYI, Cs. : Determination by in situ measurements of the characteristic parameters of the field of primary stresses and deformations. *Publ. of the Techn. University for Heavy Industry* (1970), 31. pp 39—60.

ASSZONYI, Cs. – GÁLOS, M. – KERTÉSZ, P. – RICHTER, R. : A kőzetmechanika anyagszerkezeti és reológiai alapjai (Material structural and rheological fundamental principles of rock mechanics), (1980), VEAB, Veszprém.

ASSZONYI, Cs. – KAPOLYI, L. : Kőzetek mechanikai jellemzőinek laboratóriumi meghatározása (Determination of the mechanical characteristics of rock), (1976), VEAB, Veszprém.

MOSZTKOV, V. M. : Nagyszelvényű föld alatti üregek (Underground openings of great surface), (1978), Műszaki Könyvkiadó, Budapest.

SZÉCHY, K. : The art of tunnelling, Akadémiai Kiadó, (1973), Budapest.

ORIENTATION IN MASSIF, ANALYSIS AND MONITORING
OF STATE OF LARGE UNDERGROUND CAVERNS

Die Anordnung im Massiv, Berechnung und Überwachung von grossen unterirdischen Kavernen

Emplacement dans le massif, calcul et contrôle de l'état des grandes cavernes souterraines

G.M.BABAYANTZ
Ministry of Ferrous Metal Industry, Moscow, USSR

J.M.KAZIKAEV & G.G.SOURZHIN
VIOGEM Institute, Belgorod, USSR

SUMMARY:

The report covers three aspects of hard rock mass mechanics with respect to large caverns, namely: orientation of cavern axes applying to massif parameters; evaluation of cavern mechanical system and their supporting elements; cavern wall state monitoring by means of measurement devices. Orientation of cavern axes with respect to direction of natural stress vectors and axes of folding and fracture discontinuities is of great importance for underground cavern stability. Tectonic stresses having been measured in-situ are considerably higher than gravitational ones and more often oriented in horizontal direction. Monitoring of rock, roof and wall exposure state is of great importance for construction and mainte--nance of large caverns. The eleborate procedure and laser tacheometer for surveying inaccessible rock exposures in caverns are very efficient means for determining cavern attitude with relative error not more than 1/300 at 100-150m distance.

ZUSAMMENFASSUNG:

Im Vortrag betrachtet man drei Aspekte der Mechanik des Felsmassivs im Zusammenhang mit grossen Hohlräumen: die Orientierung der Hohlraumachsen in Bezug auf die Massivparameter; die Abrechnung des mechanischen Systems der Hohlräume und ihrer Stützelemente; die messtechnische Kontrolle des Wändezustandes des Hohlraums. Die grosse Bedeutung für die Stabilität der Untertagehohlräume hat die Orientierung ihrer Achsen in Bezug auf die Richtung der Vektorwirkung der Naturspannungen und die Achsen der plikativen und zerreissenden Massivstörungen. Mit Hilfe der direkten Messungen im Felsmassiv wurden die tektonischen Spannungen, die die Grössen der Gravitations- und Orientierungsspannungen in der Horizontalrichtung bedeutend überschreiben, bestimmt. Bei dem Abbau der grossen Hohlräume hat die Kontrolle des Zustandes der Freilegung der Gebirge im Dach und in den Wänden die grosse Bedeutung. Die ausgearbeitete Methodik und der Lasertacheometer sind effektiv für die markscheiderische Aufnahme der unzugänglichen Freilegungen der Gebirge in den Hohlräumen, die ihre Lage im Raum mit dem relativen Fehler nicht mehr 1/300 in der Entfernung 100-150 m bestimmen lassen.

RESUME:

Les trois aspects de la mécanique des massifs rocheux sont envisagés dans le rapport en liaison avec des excavations de grande ouverture: l'orientation des axes des excavations de grande ouverture relative des paramètres du massif; le calcul du système mécanique des excavations et de leurs éléments de base; le contrôle de l'état des parois des excavations à l'aide des instruments de mesure. L'orientation des axes rélative des directions d'actions des vecteurs de contraintes naturelles et rélative des axes des discontinuités du massif plissées a une grande importance pour la stabilité des excavations souterraines. Les contraintes tectoniques, établies par des mesures directes dans le massif, sont plus grandes que des valeurs des contraintes gravitationnelles et orientées le plus souvent horizontalement. Au cours de creusement des excavations de grande ouverture le contrôle d'état des affleurements de roches dans le toit et des parois des excavations est d'une grande importance. La méthode et le tachéomètre à laser élaborés pour le levé des affleurements non-admissibles des roches dans les excations sont bien effectifs pour cela et permettent d'établir leur emplacement dans l'espace avec une erreur rélative pas plus 1/300 à distance 100-150 m.

Room mining is widely spread when thick mineral deposits characterized by hard ores and enclosing rocks are developed. In some cases such deposit mining is made without overlying rock caving when for instance it is necessary to preserve earth surface and to prevent underground water breaking through out of overlying rocks. Mining efficiency in this case depends on grounded solutions of some geomechanical aspects and in the first place on rational (for this given conditions) room and pillar dimensions. The authors will consider some aspects of rock massif mechanics while formation of large cavern (rooms) ordered systems and respective system of their supporting pillars according to the example of one of the USSR iron ore deposits. Mining system is schematically shown in figure 1.

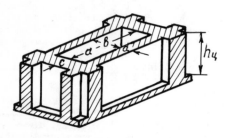

Fig. 1. Mining diagrammatic representation (cap pillar is not conditionally shown)
a - roof length; b - roof width; c, d - pillar width (thickness); $h_ц$ - pillar (roof) height.

Similar problems are also met in other cases of large underground cavern usage. In the present report some aspects of isolated cavern stability are not to be covered.

Chosen from the wide range of geomechanical problems connected with evaluation of parameters both of caverns themselves and their supporting pillars three aspects of this problem are under discussion, namely: cavern axes orientation relatively to massif natural parameters; evaluation of effective stress and strain in such system elements analytically; instrumentation monitoring of underground cavern (room) wall position. While

these problem solving the authors proceeded from a number of premises arisen from mainly the objective conditions of cavern formation in rock massif.

Firstly, in this given case the hard rock massif with mechanical characteristics allowing for large underground cavern (rooms) formation is under consideration. As a rule these are rocks characterized by high strength and small fracturing and rheological processes in such rocks does not practically change rock stress state so history processes are negligible. The theory of elasticity with many of its aspects is applied to such rocks.

Secondly, in mine area there is no traces of contemporary geological processes affecting rock massif characteristics and state, i.e. geological history may be neglected.

Thirdly, the statements being practically exercised which are governing ones when room shape choosing, room orientation and their relative position in massif from the geomechanical point of view are not obligatory the best ones. There fore the researches while these problem solving were guided mainly by the possibility of such cavern formation together with the existing mining technique.

One of the geomechanical factors though being underestimated in the process of large underground cavern formation is the original (natural) stress state of the massif being mined.

Meanwhile as a result of many stress-state in-situ measurements made both in the USSR and abroad stated that stress distribution differs considerably from the gravitational ones, i.e. the stress caused by gravitational force action. These stresses are called tectonic ones. Effective stress in-situ measurements were made up at sites outside the mining work effects area, i.e. in massif with natural stress state and in separate elements of underground structures themselves. The main result of this work is the conclusion that tectonic stresses occur not only in comparatively young folded system characterized by contemporary tectonic processes but in structures of the platform type where according to modern concept any tectonic activity had been finished long ago.

As this work is not a subject of these stresses nature detalization the authors present only main results of their studies:

- the stresses in massif are of compressive character and the absolute major maximum ones (σ_3) are oriented in a plane next to horizontal one; but the minimal major stresses (σ_1) are oriented approximately vertically;

- horizontal stresses (σ_2 and σ_3) are 2,5-3 times as much than vertical ones (σ_1);

- major stress orientation in horizontal plane reveals evident connection with bedding elements of geological features; σ_3, greater in absolute value, is oriented along the strike; σ_2, minor one, is oriented normal to the strike, respectively;

- horizontal stresses σ_2 and σ_3 differ slightly in absolute value (within 20-30%);

- with adopted geometrical parameters of room and pillar system magnitudes of horizontal stresses in cap and support pillars correspond to their values in nature massif, i.e. considerable stress concentration in this part of massif does not occur;

- vertical stresses in support pillar system distribute proportional to rigidity of this system separate elements;

- within single room a cap pillar does not suffer any considerable deformations due to deflexions, i.e. it may be regarded as rigid plate.

At the mine being discussed more than 200 rooms with total amount of 20 million m³ had been mined out. As a rule room dimensions were 55 x 30m in plane with height 55m.

Visual studies and periodic surveys of a great number of rooms (more than 100) at a decade period revealed some peculiarities concerning large exposure behavior. For the whole period of monitoring no cap caving had been occurred and authors explained this fact by roof outward pressure caused by horizontal stresses, considerable in magnitude (250kg/cm² or 25 MPa). This was explained as well by the absence of sloping fractures in roof rocks. Strong fractures the strike of which coincides with the longitudinal room axis are the most unfavourable for roof rock stability. The theoretical statement analysis shows that in order to increase large room roof stability the roof is to be oriented by longitudinal axis parallel to major compressive stress action. These statements were confirmed by cavern (rooms) stability simulation on the models of the corresponding materials.

The case is somewhat different with intervening pillar stability. Pillar revealed disturbances are connected mainly with availability of tectonic zones in pillar body or tectonic disturbances. Pillar failure is explained mainly by tectonic disturbances which intersect pillar in longitudinal direction and fracture planes go out to open space of the rooms, i.e. there is an opportunity for the part of the pillar to slide over the weakness plane. The fractures which intersect long chain pillars perpendicularly decrease their stability. Monitoring and experiment analysis indicate that in the field of the natural stresses long chain pillars are more stable than if they are oriented normal to the direction of the maximum compressive stress action.

Meeting of these requirements simultaneously for the rectangular room-pillar system is rather difficult or simply impossible and necessiates to solve this problem with account for the specific mining and geological conditions. The other way of ensuring of room and pillar stability followed with the high degree of mineral extraction is the original decision of this question concerning the shape and relative position of the caverns themselves which resulted in creation of room and pillar mining system variant. This variant means that rooms of cylindrical shape are positioned on equilateral triangles grid. This room pattern had passed commercial tests and demonstrated obvious advantages in everything what concerns stability, economy and complete ore extraction. This system is the most effective in the fields of tectonic stresses. The analytical determination of stresses and displacements for the systems being considered present interest as well. In many cases the previously considered systems of large cavities in massif should not be regarded as plane problem because of the high error. Therefore the authors made an evaluation of stress-strain behavior of the system elements (cap and intervening pillars) on the basis of some three-dimensional problems of elasticity theory. As pattern of stress and displacement magnitude calculations the authors accepted a pattern of calculation for bending of thin rectangular slab (in this case slabs with relationship between thickness and the least dimension may be regarded as thin slabs), bearing freely upon the contour, resting on the elastic base and being acted upon by lateral uniform load. There assumed that the behavior of elements of the system being considered corresponds to elasticity theory equations but as concerns natural rock massif it is replaced by the model of uniform elastic medium. The results of experimental field and laboratory studies are taken as a basis for idealization accepted.

The following premises are taken as initial data for calculation pattern choice and problem solving on stress and displacements in the system "roof caps-pillars":

1. before excavating in future cap pillar there occur some vertical stresses $\sigma_z = \gamma H$; and axisymmetrical compressive stresses due to lateral stresses and tectonic forces $\sigma_x^T = \sigma_y^T$;

2. in the process of development bending stresses caused by overlying rock mass pressure contribute considerably to the original rock stress state. Vertical load "q" on cap pillar is assumed to be equally distributed across the whole area;

3. bending stresses are arithmetically summarized with original stresses acting across the whole cap pillar thickness;

4. elastic base yieldability (support pillar system) is assumed to be in linear dependence on room height, and reaction in foundation base - linear function of cap pillar vertical deflexions. These conditions are met with elastic

base model developed by Winkler the calculation pattern of which is worked out in details and solutions are acceptable from the engineering point of view.

According to this theory for each point of the elastic base there is an equality

$$p = k \cdot W \; ;$$

$$(1)$$

where p - pressure equal to its reaction in a point on the base; W - base settlement in that same point; K - base stiffness modulus (bed factor)

Base stiffness modulus "K" is regarded as magnitude characterizing base rebound and expressed as relationship between pressure on the given site and settlement caused by the same pressure at that given site. In conformity with system of pillars which form elastic base base stiffness modulus magnitude may be found through the concept of reduced stiffness of pillar system under axial compression. This approach being exercised the real structural and orthotropic base is replaced by solid base with reduced stiffness equivalent to the original one. Omitting intermediate calculations the final expression for factor "K" may be writen as

$$k = \frac{E \cdot \lambda}{h_4 (1 - \mu^2)} \; ; \qquad (2)$$

where E - modulus of massif elasticity;
μ - Poisson ratio;
h_4 - pillar height;
λ - ore portion left in pillars;

$$\lambda = 1 - \frac{a \cdot b}{(a+c)(b+d)} \; ;$$

a - room length;
b - room width;
c,d - pillar thickness

As boundary conditions on outside contour of the site being calculated the conditions of the free bearing upon are accepted. Practically an intermeadiate condition between the free bearing upon and rigid restraint will be occurred. According to the authors' opinion the free bearing pattern approaches to practice as ceiling rigid restraint at shallow depths is hardly probable. Error which is possible with the accepted conditions of free bearing upon contributes to stability margin.

The general differential equation for bending of rectangular plate on the elastic base is written as

$$\nabla^2\nabla^2 W = \frac{q}{D} - \frac{K \cdot W}{D} \; ,$$

(3)

where $\nabla^2 = \frac{\partial^2}{\partial x} - \frac{\partial^2}{\partial y}$ Laplace operator;

q - uniform lateral load;

$D = \frac{E \cdot h_n^3}{12(1-\mu^2)}$ - bending stiffness of cap pillar;

K - elastic base factor.

It is comfortable to present solution of the equation (3) by means of the double trigonometric series in a form proposed by Navie:

$$W = \frac{16q}{\pi^2}\sum_m^\infty\sum_n^\infty \frac{Sin\frac{m\pi x}{A} \cdot Sin\frac{n\pi y}{B}}{mn\left[\pi^4 D\left(\frac{m^2}{A^2}+\frac{n^2}{B^2}\right)^2 + K\right]} ;$$

(4)

where A and B are typical ceiling dimensions;

M and N - 1,3,5...

X and Y are orthogonal coordinates (fig.2)

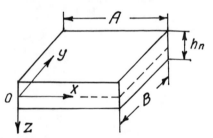

Fig.2. Diagram for cap pillar calculation

If we introduce notations:

$$f = \frac{K}{\pi^4 D} = \frac{12}{\pi^4 h_n^3 h_4} \; ;$$

(5)

then the necessary for calculation formula will be written as:

$$W = \frac{16q}{\pi^6 D}\sum_m^\infty\sum_n^\infty \frac{Sin\frac{m\pi x}{A} \cdot Sin\frac{n\pi y}{B}}{mn\left[\left(\frac{m^2}{A^2}+\frac{n^2}{B^2}\right)^2 + f\right]} ;$$

(6)

Now the maximum stress $\sigma_{x, y max}$ is easy to find from the relationships between stresses, bending

moments and deflexion for the case of the pure plate bending:

$$\sigma_{x max} = \frac{6M_x}{h_n^2} = -\frac{6D}{h_n^2}\left(\frac{\partial^2 w}{\partial x^2}+M\frac{\partial^2 w}{\partial y^2}\right);$$

$$\sigma_{y max} = \frac{6M_y}{h_n^2} = -\frac{6D}{h_n^2}\left(\frac{\partial^2 w}{\partial y^2}+M\frac{\partial^2 w}{\partial x^2}\right);$$

(7)

and we get the final solution substituting values of W from equation (6):

$$\sigma_{x max} = \frac{96q}{\pi^4 h_n^2}\sum_m^\infty\sum_n^\infty \frac{\left(\frac{m}{nA^2}+M\frac{n}{mB^2}\right)}{\left(\frac{m^2}{A^2}+\frac{n^2}{B^2}\right)^2 + f} \cdot Sin\frac{m\pi x}{A} \times$$

$$\times Sin\frac{n\pi y}{B} ;$$

$$\sigma_{y max} = \frac{96q}{\pi^4 h_n^2}\sum_m^\infty\sum_n^\infty \frac{\left(\frac{n}{mB^2}+M\frac{m}{nA^2}\right)}{\left(\frac{m^2}{A^2}+\frac{n^2}{B^2}\right)+f} \times$$

$$\times Sin\frac{m\pi x}{A} \cdot Sin\frac{n\pi y}{B} ;$$

(8)

These stresses will be occurred in cap pillars in its top and bottom margins.

The maximum deflexion will be observed in the centre of the calculated rectangular site when

$$X = \frac{A}{2}; \quad Y = \frac{B}{2};$$

$$W = \frac{16q}{\pi^6 D}\sum_m^\infty\sum_n^\infty \frac{(-1)^{\frac{m+n}{2}-1}}{mn\left[\left(\frac{m^2}{A^2}+\frac{n^2}{B^2}\right)^2+f\right]} ;$$

(9)

and pressure corresponding to this deflexion and acting on elastic base will be as follows (in accordance with previously adopted Winkler model):

$$P_{max} = K \cdot W_{max} = \gamma H ;$$

(10)

Displacements in any point of the cap pillar plane may be found from equations:

$$U = Z \cdot \frac{\partial W}{\partial X}; \quad V = -Z \cdot \frac{\partial W}{\partial y} ;$$

(11)

The adopted calculation procedure has, in authors's opinion, a number of advantages the most important of which are the following ones:

- practical calculation are fairly simple from the engineering point of view;
- there appears the opportunity to evaluate the part of cap pillar

separately and to ground a necessity of leaving support pillars in order to ensure the whole system performance;

- is it not difficult to answer the question what stiffness reserves the pillar system has got and what changes are to be introduced further on;

- there are all system parameters in their evident form in design formulas and their effect on the stress-strain behavior of the whole system can be evaluated as well;

- it is not diffucult to observe magnitudes of vertical loads on pillars in the process of development;

- there can be determined the working-out zone dimensions when the conditions of complete excavation are realized, i.e. that equilibrium condition when the cap pillar at least its central part does not transmit loads on support contour and the whole weight of overlying rocks is taken by the pillars.

One of the problems concerning large underground caverns is the control of their state and in the first place, their surveying. A number of tacheometer of the light-projecting type, with gas laser as light source, are developed for large underground cavern surveying. From the geometrical point of view the device is based on the principle of measuring parallactic angle between two light beams projected on definite point with permanent base. But another variant provides for variable base on the device itself and parallactic angle between two light beams is assumed to be constant. Lasers are fed by small storage battery (mining battery may be taken as well) via transistor converter. The device is fairly light-weighted and is serviced by one man. Usage of lasers as light sources in device has a number of advantages the most important of which are: high resolution of laser beam in mine atmosphere and high accuracy of alignment of light marks projected on the inaccessible surface. The developed device prototype permits underground inaccessible objects (exposures) determining at the distance of 100-150 m with relative error not more than 1/300.

The complex of studies being completed has ensured grounded approach to roof and pillar parameter evaluation, their relative position and orientation in massif with account for structure stress state, improved observation of large exposure behavior; these all factors allow for solving a number of practically important problems and to increase efficiency of thick deposit roof and pillar system mining.

STOPPING OF GROUND SUBSIDENCES CAUSED BY CAVE-IN APPLYING ROCKBOLTS OR HYDRAULIC FILLING IN SHALLOW UNDERGROUND CAVERNS

Die Eindämmung von durch Hohlraumeinbruch verursachten Geländesenkungen durch die Anwendung von Felsnägeln und Spülverfahren in oberflächennahen Kavernen

L'endiguement des tassements du terrain provoqués par le creusement d'une cavité à l'aide de boulons d'ancrage ou de procédé d'injection dans les cavernes situées près de la surface

E.BOBOK & Zs.SOMOSVÁRI
University for Heavy Industry, Miskolc, Hungary

SUMMARY :
Ground subsidences caused by cave-in can be avoided by rockbolting or hydraulic filling of shallow underground caverns under the busy downtown of Eger. Reinforced caverns are suitable to multi-purpose utilization. Abandoned, partially collapsed caverns are filled with sand to stop or reduce further surface subsidences. The improved technology is the cheapest one, and both traffic and people's everyday life are not disturbed by the work.

ZUSAMMENFASSUNG:
Die Beseitigung von Zusammengehen des Kellers verursachten Bodensenkungen in der Innerstadt Egers ist möglich mit Ankerausbau oder mit Spülversatz. Die mit Ankerausbau verstärkte Kellern kann man für viele zwecken benutzen. Bei durch Spülversatz mit Sand gefüllten verlassenen und teilweise zusammengebrochenen Kellern sind die weitere Bodensenkungen beseitigt. Diese ausgeprobte Technologie hat sich als billigsten Verfahren erwiesen. Ein weitere Vorteil war dass die Anwendung dieser Technologie beeinflusste den Verkehr und das tägliche Leben in der Innenstadt nur minimal.

RESUMÉ :
Les affaissements du sol, provenants des écroulements des caves au centre de la ville Eger, peuvent etre éliminés par boulonnage ou remblayage hydraulique. Les caves, reinforcées de soutenement par boulons d'ancrage sont utilisables pour plusieurs de destinations. Au cas du remblayage hydraulique par gres des caves abandonnées ou partiellement rupturées, les affaissements renouvelés sont exclus. Cette technologie essayée est la plus économique, et ni la circulation ni la vie quotidienne des habitants n'étaient incommodées par les travaux.

1. INTRODUCTION

Eger is a dynamically growing town in Northern Hungary, having a historically important inner district. Under this beautiful baroque downtown an interconnected network of cellars and tunnels has developed through the 17th and 18th centuries. Even if the whole length of this network is not completely known, it is probably longer than 100 km. These underground caverns have rather different size, shape configuration and depth. Most cellars /90 %/ were excavated in rhyodacite tuffs, the rest are found in fresh-water limestones and calciferous sandstones. Cellars are partly abandoned in a ruinous condition. In the depth of 12-15 m, most abandoned caverns are flooded due to heavy rainfalls or the failures of the water supply pipelines.

The heavy traffic of the downtown and the higher and heavier buildings accelerate the cave-in of the abandoned and flooded caverns. The last ten years have brought a great number of abrupt ground subsidences over the tumbled cellars, making unsafe both the traffic and some of the historic buildings. Civic design and reconstruction is also restricted due to the uncertain underground circumstances.

It appeared that this oppressing problem had been too serious to be solved by full exploitation of local vesources. Recognizing this situation, an Inter-departmental Coordination Committee were set up to elaborate a plan to stop these dangerous circumstances.

Among these efforts a nation-wide competition was invited in 1977. The authors recommended a complex method for the reinforcement and the elimination of the underground cavern-system of Eger. Both the reinforcement and the elimination were succesfully improved. This plan won one of the three first prizes.

2. METHODS TO AVOID GROUND SUBSIDENCES CAUSED BY CAVE-IN

Occurence of cave-in induced the ground subsidences can be avoided by two different methods. One of these possibilities is the reinforcement of the cavities. The other way is the hydraulic filling with sand. Both methods are applicable for Eger cave-network. The main advantage of the supporting is that the reinforced cave-tunnels become exploitable for various purposes. On the other hand supporting is an expensive and slow process in comparison to hydraulic filling. Thus the relatively uninjured caverns came to reinforcement while the abandoned. ruined, flooded caverns were filled.

To choose the most suitable supporting method we had to consider the following important circumstaces:

- The surroundings of the caverns is mainly rhyodacite tuffs.
- The shape and size of the cross-sections of the tunnels vary along the length of the tunnel.
- The cave tunnels often intersect each other.
- There are a lot of adjacent caves close to each other with remained rock pillars between them.

In this situation rock bolting seemed as the most convenient permanent supporting method, considering sane of its advantages:

- The rhyodacite tuff has a very good drillability, and it is suitable for fastening of rockbolts as it was obtained from our pull-out tests.
- Rockbolt pattern can be adjusted to the arbitrary shape of any cave cross section.
- To support the tunnel crossings can be solved easily and the remained pillars can be sup - ported effectively.

Rock bolting hadn't had traditions in Hungary in the field of underground work, ore mining industry had some experiences only. Thus, from the point of view of design, technique of installation and behaviour, both singly and in a pattern, a comprehensive programme of investigation of rock bolting was the undertaken.

The presence of fill in a cavern can prevent large scale movements and collapse of the cavern merely by occupying the void. Fill as support can reduce subsidence on the surface and an reduce the load on pillars. And the wide-spread opinion that the strength of fill must be equal with the strength of the surrounding rock-of the cavern is needless. The function of the fill is to reduce the ground subsidences caused by cave-in keeping the displacement of wall rock within predefined acceptable limits. This requirement can be satisfied if the filling up of the cavern is satisfactory and the bulk compressibility modulus is sufficient. Thus the fill may be satisfactory without any strength, i.e without cohesion.

To predict the efficiency of the filling a mathematical model was elaborated. Using this model the surface subsidence referring to the collapse of the cavern can be computed. The sensitivity to subsidence of the buildings determines the acceptable limit of the cave-wall displacement.

A comprehensive series of laboratory investigation was made to determine the mechanical behaviour of fill first of all the bulk compressivity. It is obtained, that Egerszólát sand is an excellent filling material without any quantity of portland cement.

3. THE MAIN PARAMETERS OF ROCK BOLTING

Rockbolts anchored into the solid elastic rock beyond the zones of failed rock and tension around the caverns compose an active support which imposes deliberate loads on the rock surface. Different bolting patterns were designed for each typical cross-section of the caverns. Drilling holes having a diameter of 45 mm were made from the inside of the caves. Steel bolts with length of 1,5 m to 3,5 m were placed into the holes. The annulus between the bolt and the hole was filled with cement mortar, a washer and screw-nut closed it. The main parameters of bolting are the strength of a given type bolt P_H [kN], the number of bolts/m² q, the bolt-length l [m]. Using a safety factor ξ / $1,3 \leq \xi \leq 1,7$ / the following relationship was obtained:

$$q = \xi \frac{p_S}{P_H} ,$$

where p_S is the sufficient supporting pressure. For shallow caverns, at 2-5 m depth, the surface loading was regarded, too. Under these conditions /rock surroundings, unalloyed steel bolts, technology/ the rockbolts may be designed for strength

P_H / ξ = 50 kN. Some typical bolting pattern is shown in Fig.1. It seems that bolt the roof and the sidewalls were supported. Whenever doubts arose concerning the efficiency of supporting, pull-out tests were conducted and the rockbolt displacement was measured. The supported cave sections are stable as their behaviour until now shows.

4. HYDRAULIC FILLING OF ABANDONED CAVERNS

The presence of the fill as a ground support need not entirely prevent local failure of the wall, but should reduce the total rock movement to pre-defined specific limits. These limits are determined by the effect on the performance of mechanical structures. Both the surrounding rock component of the system and the filled cavern were modelled as continuous elastic medium. The appropriate method for this case was a stress-deformation type analysis. The fill-rock geometry was modelled using finite differences technique, the boundary conditions were the admissible ground subsidence and the deformation of the cave cross section. It was sufficient to investigate the mechanical properties of the rock and the feasible filling materials. Both laboratory and in situ tests were made. It was obtained that pure Egerszólát sand without any cement is a satisfactory and cheap filling material. Even the most shallow /2-5 m/ caves could induce inadmissible ground subsidences filling up the caves more than 90 per cent.

An effective technology was elaborated to force the consolidation of the sand. This is the key problem of the filling. The prepared slurry was delivered to the caverns by a pipeline having a diameter of 100 mm. Cyclic layered filling and draining method has lead to the effective compaction of the sand, producing a denser fill, with higher internal friction and stiffness. This method of fill placement has a

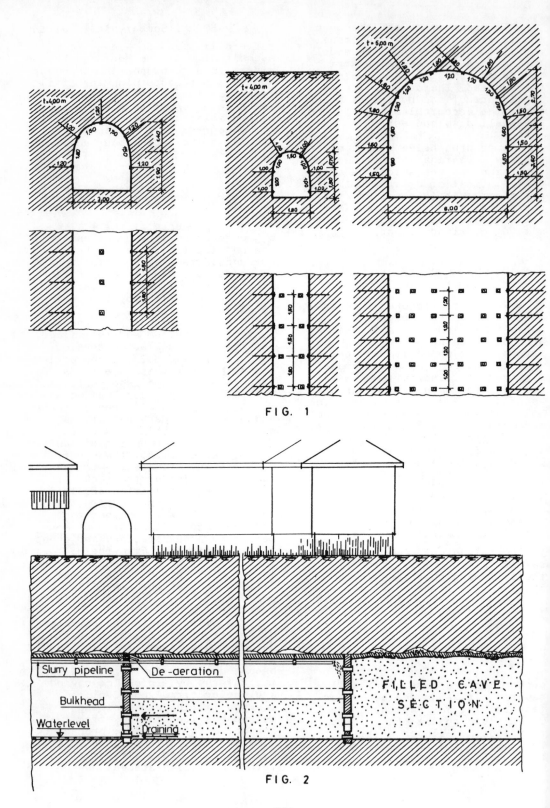

FIG. 1

FIG. 2

Slurry pipeline De-aeration

Bulkhead

Waterlevel Draining

FILLED CAVE SECTION

great effect on the overall properties of a fill mass and on the
variations within the fill. Cyclic
filling decreases the anisotrophy
of in situ density and segregation.
This filling technology was suitable to fill flooded, ruined caves.
The approach of the caverns was
possible through a simple borehole.
Pre-fabricated bulkheads were sub-
merged from the surface. Drainage
system with submersible pump was
placed to 30 m from the borehole
where slurry entraced to the cave,
as it is shown in Fig.2. One step
of this cyclic filling technique
produced a consolidated sand layer
having a thickness of 0,4 m. The
exhausted water was recirculated
to the fill preparation station.

The new filling technology
has proved satisfactory. Almost
40 000 m³ of ruined caverns have
filled. This proved to the most
economic method, since cement is
not needed at all. A further advantage is that permeability does
not decrease as it is with the
inereased cement content. Thus
filling does not affect the present hydrogeological circum -
stances. Both traffic and people's
everyday life are not distrubed
by the filling work.

REFERENCES:

ASSZONYI,Cs.-R.RICHTER /1979/
  The Continuum Theory of Rock
  Mechanics
  Transtech Publications, New York
BOBOK,E.:/1979/ New concept to
  describe flow through porous
  media
  SIAMOS, Granada Vol.II.693-708.
BOBOK,E.-Zs.SOMOSVÁRI /1979/
  Mechanical erosion in flow
  channels of rocks
  Acta Geodaetica Geophysica et
  Montanistica 14, 1-2.
ERINGEN,C.: /1962/ Nonlinear
  theory of Continuous Media
  McGraw Hill, New York
ODEN,J.T.: /1964/ Finite Elements
  of Nonlinear Continua
  McGraw Hill, New York
SOMOSVÁRI,Zs. /1972/ Theoretical
  and practical fundamental
  questions of arch pillar
  dimensioning
  Publ.of the University for Heavy
  Industry, 32, 7-23.
SOMOSVÁRI,Zs.: /1979/ Dimension-
  erung des Ankerausbaues bei
  Verwendung einbetonierter Anker.
  30.Berg- und Hüttenmännischer
  Tag, Freiberg

The details of the hydraulic
filling technology is patented.

ANALYTICAL STABILITY INVESTIGATIONS OF ROCK SURROUNDING THE WORKING FOR HYDRAULIC PUMPED-STORAGE POWER PLANTS

Standsicherheitsuntersuchung für das Gebirge um den Ausbruch
von Pumpspeicherkraftwerken herum

Étude analytique de la stabilité du massif rocheux autour des travaux de construction
des cavernes des centrales de pompage

N.S.BULYCHEV, N.N.FOTYEVA & A.K.PETRENKO
Tula Polytechnical Institute, USSR

S.A.CHESNOKOV
All-Union Institute 'Orgenergostroi', USSR

L.B.SHEINMAN
All-Union Institute 'Hydroproject', USSR

SUMMARY:
One efficient source of peak-load power in a power system is a hydraulic pumped-storage power plant. An especially promising innovation for regions with flat terrain are underground plants of this type. They are usually designed with the power house and lower reservoir arranged in a wide-span horizontal working at a substantial depth below the surface. The cross section of the lower reservoir may have a span up to 40 m and a height of 60 to 70 m if the reservoir is located in strong crystalline rock. The feasibility of designing such workings with no loadcarrying supports can be analysed on the basis of an assessment of the stability of the rock surrounding the rock exposure. This paper proposes a procedure for assessing the stability of the rock surrounding unsupported workings of large cross section, located at a considerable depth and subject to various geological engineering conditions. The procedure is based on the determination of the so-called conditional zones of nonelastic deformation. These are defined as regions surrounding the working in which the stresses, determined by solving a plane problem of elasticity theory for an opening that models the cross-section of the working in a ponderable medium, do not comply with the Coulomb-Mohr strength condition. The procedure is illustrated by examples in which the above-mentioned zones are determined for various cross sections of the working for the lower reservoir of a high-head hydraulic pumped-storage power plant constructed in strong granite gneiss.

ZUSAMMENFASSUNG:
Eine der effektivsten Quellen der Spitzenleistung der Energiesysteme sind die Pumpspeicherwerke. Für die Gebiete mit Flachgeländen sind die Kavernenspeicherwerke, die durch bedeutende Vertiefung der Grubenbaue des Maschinenraums und des Unterbeckens mit grosser Spannweite gekennzeichnet sind, sehr perspektiv. Der Querschnitt der Grubenbaue des Unterbeckens im festen kristallinen Gestein kann eine Spannweite bis 40 m und eine Höhe von 60 - 70 m haben. Die Möglichkeit, solche Grubenbaue ohne Tragausbau zu lassen, kann auf der Grundlage der Einschätzung der Gesteinsfestigkeit um den Aufschluss analysiert werden. Im Vortrag wird die Methodik der Einschatzung der Gesteinsfestigkeit um die nicht ausgebauten, grossquerschnittigen Grubenbaue dargelegt, die in bedeutender Tiefe unter der verschiedenen ingenieur-geologischen Bedingter Zonen nicht elastischer Verformungen. Darunter versteht man die Bereiche um den Grubenbau, in denen die Spannungen, die aus der Lösung der flachen Aufgabe der Elastizitätstheorie für die den Querschnitt des Grubenbaus in der wägbaren Umgebung modellierte Öffnung gefunden wurden, die Bedingung der Coulomb-Mohr-Festigkeit nicht befriedigen. Die Methodik wird an Beispielen der Bestimmung angegebener Zonen für verschiedene Querschnitte der Grubenbaue des Unterbackens eines Hochdruckpumpspeicherkraftwerkes, das in festen Granitgneisen liegt, illustriert.

RESUME:
Une des sources efficaces de la puissance de pointe des systèmes énergétiques sont les centrales de pompage. Pour les régions à relief de plaine, d'une bonne perspective sont les centrales hydroélectriques de pompage en caverne qui se caractérisent par une implantation de profondeur considérable de cavernes de grandes travées, destinées à la salle des machines et au bassin inférieur. La section transversale des cavernes du bassin inférieur peut avoir une travée de 40 m et une hauteur de 60 à 70 m à condition de leur im-

plantation dans des roches dures cristallines. La possibilité de la réalisation de telles cavernes sans soutènement portant peut être analysée compte tenu de l'estimation de la stabilité des roches le long des parois. Dans le rapport est exposée la méthode de l'estimation de la stabilité des roches autour des cavernes de grandes sections sans soutènements, implantées à une profondeur considérable dans les différentes conditions géologiques. Cette méthode est basée sur la détermination des soi-disantes zones conventionnelles des déformations non élastiques par lesquelles on entend les zones autour de la caverne où les contraintes trouvées par la solution du problème plan de la théorie de l'élasticité pour une ouverture simulant la section transversale de la caverne, dans un milieu pondérable, ne satisfont pas à la condition de la résistance de Coulomb-Mohr. La méthode est illustrée par des exemples de la définition des zones indiquées pour les différentes sections transversales de la caverne pour le bassin inférieur de la centrale de pompage à haute chute implantée dans des granites-gneiss durs.

Technical and economic calculations demonstrated that the effective depth of location of pumped storage power plants with the underground lower reservoir and the powerhouse is about 1200 m (under condition that the existing caverns are not used). Power plants with such location of the lower reservoir are competitive to the pumped storage power plants with the surface location of the lower reservoir utilizing a head of some 100 m (Sheinman, Chesnokov 1976). The volume of the underground lower reservoir is a function of the power plant capacity, daily hours of its turbine operation and the developed head and it may reach 5-6 mill. m³.

Design studies show that the cost of construction of the lower reservoir is not less than 30% of the total cost of the pumped storage power plant. Consequently the problems of the optimum layout of the lower reservoir caverns, studies of their stability and selection of efficient methods of work execution are the most important factors of realization of the underground pumped storage power plant.

The present paper deals with the results of stability studies of the lower reservoir and the power-house caverns of one of the pumped storage power plants under design with a head of 1200 m. From the drilled prospecting holes core samples were taken at a depth down to 740 m which were studied in the laboratory. Taking into account a homogeneous character of the rock mass of the crystalline shield and absence of deeper bore holes it has been proposed that the properties of rocks in the depth range varying from 740 to 1200 m do not suffer substantial changes.

The rock mass is composed of Archean granites and Paleozoic gneissose granites. Triaxial compression tests were used to study the samples in the Karman's type apparatus. 72 samples 30x30x30mm in size were tested showing the following averaged results: bulk density γ = 2.7 t/m³, ultimate compression strength 143.3 MPa, ultimate tensile strength 14 MPa; determined by Mohr circles angle of internal friction φ = 52.5°, coefficient of rock cohesion K - from 15 to 31 MPa. The rock mass is characterized by homogeneity and poorly defined systems of joints of subvertical and subhorizontal directions with a pitch 1-3 and 3-6 m accordingly. The design coefficient of permeability at a depth H= =1200 m does not exceed 2x10⁻⁶cm/ sec. The natural stressed state of the rock mass at a depth of 1200 m was assumed as follows: the vertical component is equal to the weight of overlying rocks σ_v =γH= =32.4 MPa, the horizontal component σ_h = $\lambda\gamma$H, where λ - coefficient of lateral pressure taking the values 0.5; 1.0 and 2.0.

The lower reservoir is proposed to be constructed in the form of several congruent tori of a circular or elliptical shape in plan inside which the cavern of the powerhouse is located. The outline of the tori is determined by the relation between horizontal components of natural stresses at a depth of 1200 m: in case of the equality of the components the tori are of a circular outline; in case of unequal components the tori are of an elliptical outline with a big axis stretched towards great stresses. The cross-section of the torus is taken on the basis of its stability and conveniences of tunnelling work at a large depth and at places of poor knowledge of geological engineering conditions. The cross-section of caverns of the lower reservoir with an arched upper section, vertical walls and conical lower section was adopted to be studied. Since the geological conditions on the route of the torus may change, different cross-sections of caverns of 25, 30, 35 and 40 m span have been analysed. The height of cavern varied with the span because in the conical section designed for outlet of the rock after the blast at an angle of 55° its height also increased.

Evaluation of stability of excavated caverns was made by the sizes of conditional zones of nonelastic deformations (Bulychev, Fotyeva 1977). By these zones are meant the areas of rocks around the cavern where stresses found from the solution of a plane problem of elasticity theory of concentration of stresses around the opening in linear-deformable homogeneous isotropic medium do not comply with the conditions of strength. For the rocks of inconsiderable natural disturbance which the rocks of location of the pumped storage power plant are related to the most preferable are the Coulomb-Mohr strength conditions in the form of: $(\sigma_\rho - \sigma_\theta)^2 + 4\tau_{\rho\theta}^2 = \sin^2\varphi\,(\sigma_\rho + \sigma_\theta + 2K\cdot\mathrm{Ctg}\,\varphi)^2$, where σ_ρ, σ_θ and $\tau_{\rho\theta}$ - components of stress tensor; K - coefficient of rock cohesion; φ - angle of internal friction.

Though these zones cannot be identified with the zones of nonelastic deformations for location of which the solution of the elastic-plastic problem would have been required (with the adopted approximate approach strength conditions are not satisfied for the whole area but only on its boundary, because of which they are called conditional), but nevertheless the sizes of these zones allow the dangerous zones around the excavated cavern and the level of its stability to be evaluated approximately.

It might be well to point out particular features of stability evaluation of the caverns of the lower reservoir as an underground structure. The caverns filled with water

are not pressurized, i.e. there is always a free air space. Water velocity in caverns is about 1 m/sec which demands no trimming of the working excavated outline after blastings. The demands of absolute unchangeability are not raised to the working outline, i.e. separate rock cavings which do not result in loss of stability and pressurizing of the cavern (taking into account the coefficient of rock loosening) are allowed. The presence of water in the excavated caverns does not exercise a considerable effect on a stressed state of the rock around the cavern. On the basis of experience of construction of large-span caverns and their operation taking into account specific operation conditions of the lower reservoir caverns it may be supposed that for these excavated caverns the conditional zones of nonelastic deformations in the outline of the cavern with a maximum size along the normal to the outline of the cross-section of not more than 1/3 of the cavern span are allowed. It should be noted that the presence of these zones does not mean that all rock will cave-in in these zones. Small rock failures within the limits of these zones will cause redistribution of stresses towards their decrease which will not result in the loss of total stability of the excavated cavern. On the basis of these considerations stability of caverns of different spans was analysed.

For calculations the angle of internal friction of rocks was taken constant and equalling 45° which is by 7.5° lesser than the angle defined by the results of laboratory tests. Taking into consideration a homogeneous structure of the rock mass and considerable natural stresses inside the coefficient of cohesion in the rock mass was adopted as equal to the least value obtained by the results of sample testing, i.e. 15 MPa. Taking into account that blasting operations and concentration of stresses near the cavern slacken a monolithic structure of rocks a case of layer-by-layer change of the coefficient of cohesion around the cavern was analysed. In the first layer of 5m in thickness the coefficient of rock cohesion was taken as 5 MPa; in the second layer of 5-10 m in thickness it was 10 MPa and in the third layer a value of 15 MPa was taken.

The algorithm and the program of construction of conditional zones of nonelastic deformations for the computer of the EC family were elaborated at the Tula Polytechnical Institute (Bulychev, Fotyeva 1977) and modification of the program for the layer-by-layer change of strength characteristics of rocks was worked out by Eng. A.S.Sammal.

For each cross-section of the cavern conditional zones of nonelastic deformations at three values of the coefficient of lateral pressure λ were constructed. For cases where the coefficient of lateral pressure is uncertain the envelopes of conditional zones of nonelastic deformations for three values of were determined. In Fig. 1 solid lines show boundaries of conditional zones at layer-by-layer change of the coefficient of rock cohesion and dash lines demonstrate a homogeneous rock mass with the coefficient of rock cohesion of K= = 15 MPa. As it is seen from Fig.1 the difference in sizes of zones

does not exceed 10-15% which points to the fact that the change in the coefficient of rock cohesion for the given outline of excavated cavern and the analysed stress field does not exert a pronounced effect on the configuration and the value of conditional zones of nonelastic deformations.

The analysis of the shape and sizes of conditional zones of nonelastic deformations allows the following main conclusions to be drawn:

1. For all cavern spans at coefficients of lateral pressure λ =0.5 and 1 the conditional zones of nonelastic deformations cover the whole outline of excavated caverns with maximum sizes measured about the centre line of the vertical wall and in the lower section at the centre of generatrix of the conical part. In the arch portion of the cavern the maximum size of zones is half as much as in the wall.

2. For all cavern spans with the coefficient of lateral pressure λ = = 2 two areas of size increase are observed in the conditional zones of nonelastic deformations, i.e. in the foundation of the arched section

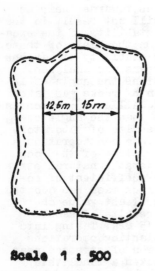

12,5m 15m

Scale 1 : 500

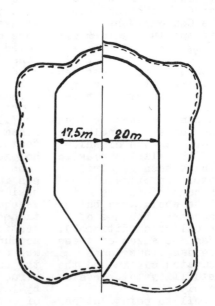

17.5m 20m

Fig. 1. Envelopes of conditional zones of nonelastic deformations around excavated caverns of the lower reservoir of span 25, 30, 35 and 40 m for three values of coefficient of lateral pressure λ = 0.5; 1 and 2.

of the outline and at the centre of
the generating line of a conical
portion. In this case the lower area
is by 73% less than the upper one.
In all cases during calculations of
a homogeneous (relative to the coefficient of rock cohesion) mass an
area free from nonelastic stresses
appears on a vertical wall. For the
layer-by-layer change in the coefficient of rock cohesion in excavated
caverns of 30-40 m span the jointing
of conditional zones of nonelastic
deformations took place. In excavated caverns of 25 and 35 m span no
jointing was found.

3. There are no conditional zones
of nonelastic deformations in the
lower portion of the excavated caverns in question.

4. For all spans of caverns the
increase of the coefficient of the
lateral pressure from 0.5 to 1 results in a decrease of conditional
zones of nonelastic deformation
(down to 24%). A further increase
of the coefficient of the lateral
pressure from 1 to 2 entails the increase in sizes of the zones (up to
52% compared with the zones at $\lambda =$
= 1).

5. Regularities of changes in the
sizes of conditional zones of nonelastic deformations due to the increase of the cavern span are not
observed. With the increase of the
span from 25 to 30 m at $\lambda = 0.5$
the decrease in sizes of the zones
by 19% is observed. In case the
span grows up from 30 to 35m at the
same λ the sizes of the zone will
be increased by 63%. With a further
increase of the span the sizes of
the zone are reduced by 2%. The similar situation is observed at
other values of the coefficient of
the rock lateral pressure as well.
This may be explained by the dependence of sizes of zones on the form
of the cross-section of the cavern
but not only on its span.

6. The analysis of outlines of
the envelopes of the conditional
zones of nonelastic deformations
demonstrates that all of them are
of about the same configuration characterized by inconsiderable sizes
in an arch section of the cavern,
presence of an enlarged size in the
foundation of an arched section and
then by reduction of the size near
the vertical wall and a sharp increase at the center of the gene-

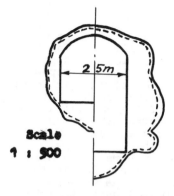

Fig. 2. Envelopes of conditional
zones of nonelastic deformations
around excavated cavern of the machine hall at its stage-by-stage
opening for three values of coefficient of lateral pressure $\lambda =$
=0.5; 1 and 2.

rating line of a conical portion.

7. By evaluation of stability of
the lower storage cavern as a whole
it may be noted that at $\lambda = 0.5$
and 1 the maximum size of conditional zones of nonelastic deformations does not exceed 1/3 of the
cavern span, i.e. according to the
above mentioned criterion the excavated caverns located in such field
of natural stresses and having a
span of 25-40 m are stable enough
for their utilization as a lower
reservoir. At the coefficient of lateral pressure $\lambda = 2$ the size of
conditional zones of nonelastic deformations reaches 1/2 of the span
and stability of the excavated cavern as a whole may appear insufficient.

Under similar geological engineering conditions stability of the machine hall cavern of 25 m in span
and 40 m in height was studied. The
cavern is driven at three stages -
first the arch section is driven,
then the 1st bench is excavated
(height of the working is 24 m),
and the 2nd bend (height of the
working is 40 m) is driven. The occurrence of conditional zones of
nonelastic deformations around the
working opened up to 24 and 40 m
was analysed. Taking into account
that inside the cavern of the machine hall the operating personnel

and the expensive equipment will be located, the obtained values of conditional zones of nonelastic deformations are the criterion for the preliminary selection of supporting.

The analysis of the envelopes of conditional zones of nonelastic deformations (Fig. 2) shows that the arch portion of the excavated cavern shall be strengthened by spray concrete and conventional anchors of 4 m in length.

Prestressed anchors of 15 m in length shall be installed in the middle section of the wall and anchors of 12 m in length shall be installed in other sections of the wall.

REFERENCES

Bulychev, N.S & N.N.Fotyeva 1977, Otsenka ustoichivosty porod, okruzhajushchikh gornie virabotki, Shakhtnoye stroitel'stvo, N° 3, pp. 14-17.
Sheinman, L.B. & S.A.Chesnokov 1976, Podzemnie gidroakkumulirujushchie elektrostantsii. Obzor "Informenergo", p.61.

RECONSTITUTION DES CONTRAINTES NATURELLES DANS LE MASSIF ROCHEUX ET DE LA TECHNOLOGIE DE CONSTRUCTION LORS DU CALCUL DES CAVERNES PAR LA MÉTHODE DES ÉLÉMENTS FINIS

Reproduction of naturel stresses in the rock massif and the building technology by finite element method calculations

Wiedergabe der natürlichen Spannungen im Gebirge und der Bauzustände durch Berechnungen mit der Methode der finiten Elemente

TODOR N.CHRISTOV

Institut des problèmes des eaux, Sofia, Bulgarie

SUMMARY:

The state of stresses, both in the rock massif, surrounding a cavern and in the elements of a consolidating construction largely depends on the natural stresses, which have existed before the excavations, on the technology and the sequence of construction as well. It is suggested that the natural stresses should be calculated in advance by the finite element method in a separate calculation, treating the intact rock massif and considering all the information about the complex geological and topographic formation of the rock massif with its inherent physical and mechanical properties, obtained from the engineering and geological survey. The new state of stresses and deformations, due to changes of the static system (excavations, anchorage, and consequtive involving of consolidating structure elements, etc.) is directly obtained, the calculation being carried out by steps, corresponding to the technology, sequence of construction and anulating the deformations, resulting from the previous step. To that purpose either the method of initial strains or the method of initial stresses can be used, the advantages of the latter being indicated. The boundary conditions of the rock block, containing the calculated structure are considered into 3 principal groups and estimated from viewpoint of the influence of the eliminated part of the rock massif. A numerical model illustration is produces by the calculation results of a variant solution of an underground hydro-electric station.

ZUSAMMENFASSUNG:

Der gespannte Zustand im Steinmassiv um einer Kaverne und in den Elementen des Stutzwerkes hängt in hohem Grade von den natürlichen Spannungen, die in dem Massiv vor den Grabungen existiert haben und von der Technologie und der Reihenfolge des Augbaus der Konstruktion. Im Vortrag wird vorgeschlagen, das die natürlichen Spannungen vorzeitig bemessen werden nach der Methode der finiten Elemente in einer speziellen Aufgabe über den com Graben ungerührten Steinmassiv, indem Kontrolle der ganzen Information gefordert wird, über der Topographie, der Geologie und den physikalisch-mechanischen Parameter des Massivs, aus den geologischen Forschungen übermittelt. Auf der Theorie der Methode der finiten Elemente als eine Deformationsmethode fussend, sind die natürlichen Spannungen, die auf dieser Weise gewonnen sind, von hier an in der Berechnung sind dem Steinmassiv auf solcher Weise angeschrieben, die die ihnen entsprechenden Deformationen ausschliesst. Der neuer Zustand der Spannungen und Deformationen, die aus Veränderungen im statischen System hervorkommen: Grabungen, Ankerien, reihenforgeweise Anschliessen vom Stützwerkelemente u.a. folgt unmitelbar, indem die Berechnung in Etappen durchgeführt wird, die der Technologie und der Reihenfolge des Aufbaus entsprechen, und es werden anulliert die Deformationen, die aus der vorigen Etappe stammen. Zu diesem Zweck kann wie die Methode der Einsatzdeformationen, als auch die Methode der Einsatzspannungen benutzt werden, indem die Vorteile der Letzten unterstrichen werden. Die Grenzbedingungen des Steinblocks, der die bemessene Anlage einschliesst, die in drei Hauptgruppen verteilt sind, sind besprochen und abgeschätzt in Sachen Einluss des bei der Bemessungen eliminierte Teils vom Steinmassiv. Das numerische Modell ist illustriert durch die Resultate von der Berechnung einer Variantelösung für die Kaverne der Wasserkraftanlage.

RESUME.

L'état des contraintes dans le massif rocheux aux environs d'une caverne et dans les élé-

ments de la construction de soutenement dépend au plus haut point des contraintes naturelles, existantes dans le massif avant les fouilles, de la technologie et de la consécution des travaux de construction. On propose dans l'exposé de calculer les contraintes
naturelles par la méthode des éléments finis dans un calcul préalable du massif rocheux
intact, tenant compte de toute l'information de la topographie, la géologie et les pro-
priétes physiques et mécaniques du massif rocheux, donnée par les réconnaissances géologiques. Sortant de la théorie de la méthode des éléments finis en qualité de méthode de
déformations, les contraintes naturelles reçues de cette façon, sont appropriées au massif rocheux à partir de ce moment de calcul, d'une manière abrogeante les déformations
correspondantes. On reçoit directement l'état nouveau des contraintes et les déformations
dues aux changement du système statique: fouilles, ancrages, inclusions successives des
éléments de soutenement etc, en calculant par étapes conformés à la technologie et à la
consécution des travaux de construction, toujours en réspectant l'abrogation des déformations, reçues dans l'étape précédente. Dans ce but on peut appliquer soit la méthode
des déformations initiales, soit la méthode des contraintes initiales. Certaines avantage
de la méthode des contraintes initiales sont présentées au point de vue l'influence de la
partie éliminée du massif rocheux dans le calcul. Une illustration du modèle de calcal
est présentée par les résultats du calcul de la caverne d'une usine hydraulique.

1 INTRODUCTION

Il est bien connu que les contraintes et les déformations dans un
ouvrage souterrain et dans le massif rocheux qui l'entoure sont
étroitement liées aux contraintes
naturelles éxistantes dans le massif avant les fouilles. La sollicitation des éléments de la construction souterraine provient de la redistribution de ces contraintes naturelles et les déformations subséquentes dans le massif rocheux pendant les fouilles. D'autre part la
redistribution des contraintes est
étroitement liée à la consécution
des travaux de construction.
Cette question nous l'avons déjà
discutée (Christov, Iliev 1977).
A part le rappel des points de départ de base, on présente dans cet
exposé certains détails, qui aura-
ient été utiles dans le calcul des
problèmes des ouvrages souterrains
par la méthode des éléments finis.
On présente également en qualité
d'exemple les résultats du calcul
d'une caverne une usine hydraulique en projet.

2 INFORMATION GEOLOGIQUE ET SA MISE
EN OEUVRE DANS LE CALCUL DES
CONTRAINTES NATURELLES

Malgré la grande importance des contraintes naturelles pour le calcul
des ouvrages souterrains normalement
on n'en connaît pas grand' chose.
Au mieux on connaît les valeurs des
contraintes dans quelques points du
massif rocheux, obtenues par des
essais in situ. Et ces résultats

se caractérisent d'un grand éven-
tail de dispersion, dépendant de la
méthode de recherche.
La majeure partie de l'informatio
procurée par les ingénieurs géolo-
gues concerne les facteurs et les
conditions qui déterminent ces contraintes: le poids propre, les phénomènes de filtration, les phénomènes thermiques, les propriétés
physiques et mécaniques de la roche
la topographie, les particularités
géologiques du massif rocheux etc.
Heureusement la méthode des éléments finis, étant une méthode de
déformation, admet plus facilement
l'introduction d'un certain état
des contraintes par les sollicita-
tions et les conditions qui le déterminent, que par l'appropriation
de ces contraintes au système
directe de ces contraintes au système calculé.
se trouve dans une étape peu avan-
cée, ou on n'a que peu de ressour-
ces financières pour les reconnaissances in situ, l'information géologique comprend quelques renseigne
ments concernant les propriétés phy
siques et mécaniques de la roche et
une description du massif rocheux
non pas détaillée. Dans ce cas-là
la manière de reconstitution des
contraintes naturelles, présentée
sur la Fig. 1 s'avère presque
unique. On n'y tient compte que des
forces du poids propre. Les solli-
citations et les conditions aux
limites assurent des contraintes
au système, soumises à la loi géo-
statique

$$6_v = \gamma H; \quad 6_h = \frac{\nu}{1-\nu} 6_v \qquad (1)$$

où γ est le poids spécifique de la

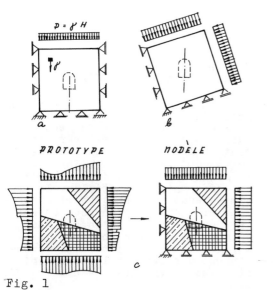

PROTOTYPE   MODÈLE

Fig. 1

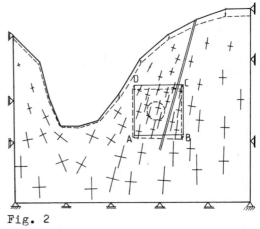

Fig. 2

roche, H la distance du point en question à la surface, ν coefficient de Poisson.

Quand l'information géologique est complétée par des données ou d'une appréciation des valeurs et des directions des contraintes principales on peut utiliser le schème présenté à la Fig. 1b

Dans tous les autres cas, quand on a une information plus détaillée de point de vue des particularités géologiques du massif rocheux, les manières, présentées à la Fig. 1 comme le dit Kovari (1972) nous amènent à une perte de précision dans le calcul.

Il est bien commode dans ce cas-là d'avoir recours au calcul particulier du problème des contraintes naturelles dans le massif rocheux. Fig. 2. Il est possible d'y introduire par cette manière presque toute l'information reçue par les reconnaissances géologiques. Ainsi les contraintes dans la région intéressée ABCD sont-elles coordonées à la structure géologique, à la topographie et aux propriétés physiques et mécaniques de la roche et correspondent dans un grand dégré à nos savoirs de l'état du massif rocheux.

Ce qu'il y a de gênant, c'est qu'il faut mettre au jeu une bonne partie du massif rocheux pour éviter l'influence des conditions aux limites sur la répartition des contraintes dans la région de l'ouvrage.

La plupart de cette partie du massif n'est pas nécessaire pour le calcul de la répartition des contraintes due aux fouilles. Cela nécessite l'élaboration d'un schème contenant un grand nombre d'éléments finis et de noeuds et le calcul consomme beaucoup de temps d'ordinateur.

On peut éviter cet inconvénient en calculant le problème de l'état des contraintes naturelles en deux étapes. On trouve tout d'abord le champ des contraintes dans le massif rocheux, contenant la région de l'ouvrage à construire ABCD (Fig.2). Les éléments peuvent être plus gros et le schème ne doit tenir compte que du contour du fragment ABCD qui jouera son rôle dans les calculs ultérieurs. Dans l'étape suivante on réproduit les contraintes naturelles, reçues par le calcul précédent, mais dans le fragment du massif seulement. Dans ce but on y applique une sollicitation comprenant l'action de la partie éliminée du massif rocheux et toutes les forces agissantes dans le volume examiné. Dorénavant le réseau des éléments finis doit être conforme à la géométrie de l'ouvrage et à la consécution des travaux.

On peut faire les calculs en suivant les schèmes décrits par n'importe quel programme, composé selon la théorie générale de la méthode des éléments finis. Mais quand il s'agit des schèmes dans lesquels on doit introduire la construction de l'ouvrage souterrain, l'utilisation de ces programmes peut nous amener à des résultats erronés. Cela se voit de l'exemple présenté à la

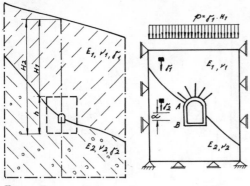

Fig. 3

Fig. 3 où l'ouvrage et le massif rocheux se mettent en jeu, selon le
schème, en même temps que la sollicitation due au poids propre. La
partie du revêtement incluse entre
les points A, B s'oppose non seulement aux déformations dues à la
concentration des contraintes autour
de l'ouverture, mais aussi aux déformations de la couche rocheuse α
dues à l'action du poids propre.
On fait en réalité les fouilles et
le renforcement de l'ouverture dans
le massif rocheux contraint et déformé par les forces de gravitation.

Cette particularité dans le comportement des ouvrages souterrains
est bien imitée dans le modèle de
calcul que nous utilisons (Christov,
Iliev 1977). Dans ce modèle les contraintes naturelles, calculées
d'après les schèmes décrits sont
mises en oeuvre sans provoquer des
déformations dans le massif rocheux
intact.

On obtient cet effet en calculant
le problème en deux étapes. On re-
soud tout d'abord le problème des
contraintes naturelles et après on
y ajoute à la sollicitation de tous
les éléments finis des déformations
intèrnes initiales, contraires à
celles reçues dans l'étape précédente

$$\{\varepsilon_o\}_2 = \{\varepsilon\}_n \qquad (2)$$

L'effet de ces déformations initiales dans le calcul s'exprime
dans l'apparition des forces nodales
contraires à celles, dues à la sollicitation de base.

Du point de vue mathématique on
reçoit un système d'équations homogène pour les déplacements des
noeuds, qui a la solution unique

zéro

$$\{\delta\}_2 = 0, \text{ respectivement } \{\varepsilon\}_2 = 0, \qquad (3)$$

tandis que

$$\{6\}_2 = [D](\{\varepsilon\}_2 - \{\varepsilon_o\}_2) = \{6\}_n \qquad (4)$$

Dans le cas où l'introduction des
déformations initiales est accompagnée d'une modification du système
physique, par exemple la reconstitution des fouilles et du renforcement de l'ouverture, on a comme résultat un manque d'équilibre entre
la sollicitation de base et celle
des déformations initiales. Le système d'équations ne sera plus homogène et sa résolution nous donnera
les déplacements des noeuds dûs
uniquement à cette modification.
Les résultats des contraintes nous
donnent directement l'image modifiée des contraintes naturelles.

3 LA TECHNOLOGIE ET LA CONSECUTION DES TRAVAUX DE CONSTRUCTION ET LEUR MISE EN OEUVRE DANS LE CALCU

La généralisation des conclusions
du paragraphe précédent nous permet
de mettre en oeuvre dans le calcul
la téchnologie et la consécution
des travaux (Christov, Iliev 1977).

On peut toujours présenter les
contraintes après une étape de calcul donnée k-1 comme un "état des
contraintes naturelles" par rapport
à l'étape suivante k par l'élimina-
tion des déformations, reçues dans
l'étape k-1, en introduisant les
déformations initiales complémen-
taires $\{\varepsilon_o\}_k = -\{\varepsilon\}_{k-1}$.

Tout changement dans le système
physique, reconstituant les fouilles
l'inclusion des nouveaux éléments
de construction, etc déséquilibre
la sollicitation de base et celle
des déformations initiales et les
résultats du calcul nous donnent
directement les contraintes redis-
tribuées et les déformations dues
à ce changement.

En reconstituant la téchnologie
et la consécution des travaux de
construction par un changement ap-
proprié du réseau des éléments finis, des propriétés physiques et
mécaniques des zones du système
physique et par l'affectation des
déformations $\{\varepsilon_o\}_k^{im}$ aux éléments i
de la zone m dans l'étape de calcul

k d'après la formule

$$\{\mathcal{E}_0\}_k^{im} = - \sum_{l=p}^{k-1} \{\mathcal{E}\}_l^{im} \qquad (5)$$

où $\{\mathcal{E}\}_l^{im}$ sont les déformations, reçues dans l'étape de calcul l dans
les éléments finis i de la zone m,
p l'étape de calcul dans laquelle
l'élément nouveau de construction
est présenté par les éléments finis
de la zone m, on peut suivre l'évolution des contraintes et des déformations pendant les travaux de construction et l'exploitation de
l'ouvrage souterrain.

La méthode des contraintes initiales a également lieu dans le calcul du problème en question. L'effet ne changera pas si au lieu des
déformations initiales $\{\mathcal{E}_0\}_2 = -\{\mathcal{E}\}_n$
on prend les contraintes initiales

$$\{\mathfrak{G}_0\}_2 = \{\mathfrak{G}\}_n \qquad (6)$$

Dans le calcul le plus générale
les contraintes initiales $\{\mathfrak{G}_0\}_k^{im}$,
affectées aux éléments i de la zone
m dans l'étape de calcul k seront

$$\{\mathfrak{G}_0\}_k^{im} = \sum_{l=p}^{k-1} [D]_l^{im} \{\mathcal{E}\}_l^{im} \qquad (7)$$

où $[D]_l^{im}$ est la matrice de l'élasticité des éléments i de la zone m
dans l'étape l.

Quoique les deux méthodes semblent
adéquates il existe une différence
essentielle dans leur application.
Il y a des cas dans la pratique
où certaines zones du système physique, par la suite des mesures de
stabilisation (injections de mortier dans le massif rocheux), des
phénomènes physiques et chimiques
dans les materiaux, de l'action des
eaux de filtration etc changent ses
propriétés mécaniques sans changer
dans le même temps l'état des contraintes dans le système. La reconstitution de cette particularité
dans le calcul n'est pas possible
par la méthode des déformations
initiales. L'application de la sollicitation fictive des déformations
initiales $\{\mathcal{E}_0\}_k^{im}$ accompagnée d'un
changement de la matrice de l'élas-
ticité $[D]_k^{im}$ ne peut pas donner des
forces nodales qui auront l'effet
de faire le système d'équations
homogène et d'annuler les déplace-

ments des étapes de calcul précédentes.

La méthode des contraintes initiales nous permet de changer les
propriétés mécaniques d'une manière
arbittraire en allant d'une étape
de calcul à l'autre sans toucher
l'équilibre entre la sollicitation
fictive et la sollicitation de base.
Cela s'explique par l'absence de la
matrice de l'élasticité $[D]_k^{im}$ dans
les formules des forces fictives
nodales lors du calcul de l'étape k.

On a un effet à la première vue
paradoxal. Si on a un système physique arbitraire, calculé deux fois,
la première sur la base des modules
de l'élasticité et des coefficients
de Poisson égales dans toute la région, et la deusième fois en y ajou-
tant la sollicitation fictive des
contraintes initiales $\{\mathfrak{G}_0\}_2^{im}$ affectées à tous les éléments, accompa-
gnée d'une modification arbitraire
des propriétés mécaniques, on re-
cevra les mêmes résultats des contraintes et les déplacements annu-
lés. Fig. 4.

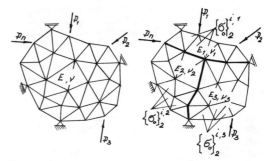

Fig. 4

Cette particularité du modèle nous
permet de faire une approximation
utile dans le schéma de calcul des
contraintes naturelles de point de
vue la facilité de calcul. Par exemple si la situation géologique est
pareille à celle-ci, montrée à la
Fig. 5, le calcul élastique nous
donnera une répartition compliquée
des contraintes naturelles, surtout
dans la région au voisinage de la
ligne de contact AB. On peut dire
néanmoins, qu'en réalité, soit à
cause des déformations plastiques,
soit à cause des phénomènes réolo-
giques et géologiques les contraintes se sont rendu dans un certain
dégré égales.

187

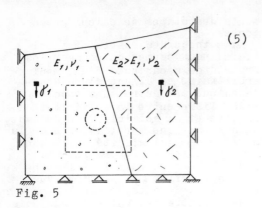

(5)

Fig. 5

Dans ce cas là au lieu d'utiliser des modèles de calcul compliqués qui tiennent compte des déformations non élastiques, on peut résoudre le problème des contraintes naturelles sur la base des propriétés mécaniques, égales pour toutes les deux zones, et dans l'étape suivante introduire les propriétés réelles.

D'après les formulations données ci-dessus le calcul d'un problème particulier d'un ouvrage souterrain dans un cas plus général comprendra les moments essentiels suivants:

a) étape préliminaire - le calcul de l'état des contraintes naturelles dans le massif rocheux et la détermination des conditions aux limites sur le contour du fragment rocheux, comprenant la région de l'ouvrage à construire.

b) étape première - réproduction de l'état des contraintes naturelles dans le fragment rocheux en imposant des forces et des déplacements données sur le contour, qui remplacent la partie éliminée du massif rocheux. Dans cette étape on détermine les déformations initiales $\{\varepsilon_.\}_2^{im} = -\{\varepsilon\}_n^{im}$

ou les contraintes initiales $\{6_.\}_2^{im} =$ $= [D]_n^{im} \{\varepsilon\}_n^{im}$ qu'on imposera en qualité de sollicitation fictive dans les étapes suivantes.

c) étapes suivantes dans lesquelles, selon la téchnologie et la consécution des travaux de construction et l'éxploitation, grâce à l'introduction de la sollicitation fictive $\{\varepsilon_.\}_k^{im}$ ou $\{6_.\}_k^{im}$ on suit les nouvelles répartitions des contraintes du commencement des fouilles jusqu' à l'éxploitation de l'ouvrage.

On réproduit l'action du massif rocheux éliminé sur le contour du fragment rocheux dans la première étape soit par les composantes des déplacements nodals données, soit par les composantes des forces nodales, toutes les deux espèces, déterminées dans l'étape précédente.

Les conditions aux limites du fragment rocheux sont d'une importance particulière. En principe elles doivent écarter la possibilité d'un déplacement de translation ou de rotation du système physique. Elles doivent réspecter aussi la règle, que nous avons établie (Christov 1977) selon laquelle à tous les noeuds du contour, qui ont eu des déplacements préscrits dans la direction de l'un ou des deux axes du système des coordonnées dans l'étape première de calcul, il faut y affecter des déplacements nuls dans les étapes suivantes. Fig. 6.

CONDITIONS AUX LIMITES

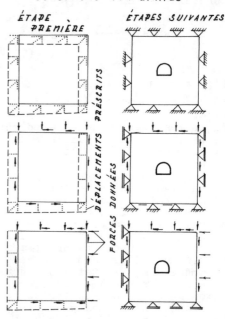

Fig. 6

L'un des schèmes possibles des conditions aux limites est dans le cas où l'action de la partie éliminée du massif rocheux est réproduite par des déplacements préscrits des noeuds du contour du bloc. Fig. 6a. Dans ce cas là la forme du contour n'a pas d'importance.

Ces conditions aux limites ne représentent que le point de départ selon lequel l'effet total d'arc du massif rocheux éliminé se met en oeuvre dès le commencement des fouilles et supporte toute la charge provenante de la répartition des contraintes dans le même massif rocheux éliminé. Evidement le calcul basé sur un schème pareil nous donnera des contraintes un peu abbaissées vis-à-vis les résultats théoriquement éxacts. L'inexactitude diminuera en élargissant les dimensions du bloc et au delà de certaines limites elle deviendra insignifiante, mais au compte d'augmentation du nombre des éléments finis et le temps de calcul d'ordinateur.

Un autre schème possible des conditions aux limites est présenté à la Fig. 6b. Il prévoit des composantes horizontales préscrites des déplacements et des composantes verticales des forces, affectées aux noeuds des contours verticaux et à l'envers - des composantes verticales préscrites des déplacements et des composantes horizontales des forces, affectées aux noeuds du contour horizontal inférieur. Les conditions aux limites sur le contour supérieur ne comprennent que des forces nodales. Ces conditions aux limites représentent l'idée de la transmission totale du poids propre de la roche superposée au bloc sans tenir compte de l'effet d'arc de cette partie du massif rocheux, éliminée. Le calcul nous donnera des contraintes au dessus des résultats théoriquement exacts.

Il y a troisième schème possible. Fig. 6c. On y supprime totalement l'effet d'arc du massif rocheux éliminé.

Le choix du schème dépend en fin de compte de l'estimation d'ingénieur à l'égard de l'influence des conditions aux limites dans le cas particulier.

4 ALGORITHME ET PROGRAMME DE CALCUL

Les idées de la mise en oeuvre des contraintes naturelles et la téchnologie et la consécution des travaux de construction dans le modèle de calcul, présentées dans les paragraphes précédents ont été réalisées dans un algorithme et un programme de calcul, la conception desquels

a été exposée par nous en I977 (Christov, Iliev). Depuis ont été réalisées certaines améliorations parmis lesquelles la plus essentielle est la mise en oeuvre de l'influence de la fissuration orientée de la roche à la base de la formulation de Zienkiewicz (I971). A cause de restriction dans le volume de cet exposé on n'y présente pas les détails.

5 CALCUL DE LA CAVERNE D'UNE USINE HYDRAULIQUE

Le calcul a été fait sur une variante de projection dans une période où on ne disposait pas d'une information détaillée sur les caractéristiques du massif rocheux et les contraintes naturelles. C'est pourquoi celles-ci étaient déterminées selon le schème simle, présenté à la Fig. 1a, en supposant le milieu rocheux homogène et isotrope. Le réseau des éléments finis, construit sur la base d'une symétrie par rapport à l'axe vertical est présenté à la Fig. 7.

Le calcul a été fait en cinq étapes sur la condition préalable de conduite élastique du milieu. Fig. 8.

Les numéros des zones qui changeaient ces propriétés physiques et mécaniques étant allées d'une étape à l'autre dans le calcul en liaison avec la consécution des travaux, sont présentés à la même figure.

Pour l'annulation des déformations on a appliqué la méthode des contraintes initiales.

Dans la première étape on a calculé les contraintes naturelles $\{6_0\}_n^{im}$, les déformations correspondantes $\{\varepsilon\}_n^{im}$ et les contraintes initiales, nécessaires à l'étape suivante $\{6_0\}_2 = [D]_n^{im}\{\varepsilon\}_n^{im}$.

On a affecté aux zones du milieu continu 1,2,3,4,5,6,14,15,16,17 et 18 des propriétés, correspondantes au massif rocheux et aux zones des éléments linéaires 7,8,9,10,11,12, 13,19 et 20 des caractéristiques nulles de manière qu'elles ont été exclues de travail à l'étape donnée. L'action du poids propre du massif rocheux au dessus du contour horizontal supérieur, d'une puissance

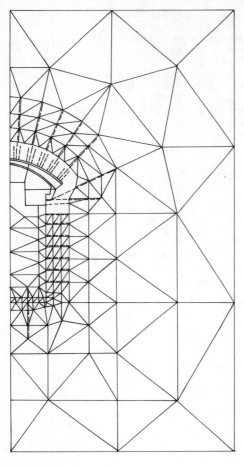

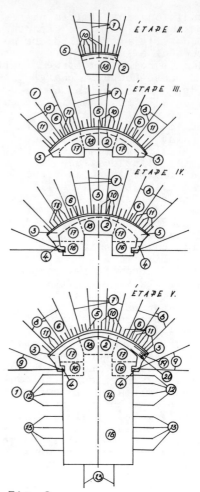

Fig. 8

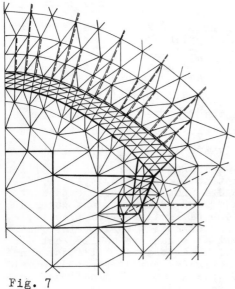

Fig. 7

de 270 m a été présentée par des forces nodales.

Dans la deuxième étape on a calculé la répartition des contraintes et des déformations dues aux fouilles des zones 2 et 18 et à l'encrage précontraint (les zones 7). L'annulation des déplacements a été réalisée par l'affectation des contraintes initiales $\{6_0\}_2^{im}$, déterminées dans l'étape précédente.

Les calculs ont été menés par une variable particulière dans le programme $BB(m)$. Quand $BB(m) = 1$ (dans le cas c'étaient pour les zones $m = 1,3,4,6,14,15,16,17$) les contraintes initiales ont été affectées aux éléments finis des zones m et quand $BB(m) = 0$ (dans le cas c'étaient les zones $m = 2,5,7,8,9,10,11,$

190

12,13,18,19) on n'y a pas affécté des contraintes initiales en les ayant annulées $\{6_0\}_1^{im} = 0$.

D'après la téchnologie et la conséqution des travaux, le béton projeté, ainsi que les ancres courts (la zone 10) ont été faits "instantanément" avec les fouilles et ils prenaient part dans la répartition des contraintes. Dans ce but on a affecté à la zone 7 les propriétés correspondantes à celles du béton projeté et à la zone 10 celles de l'acier.

L'effet de la précontrainte des ancres (la zone 7) a été introduit dans cette étape par deux forces opposées, appliquées aux noeuds aux bouts de l'ancre, égales à la force de précontrainte. Fig. 9a.

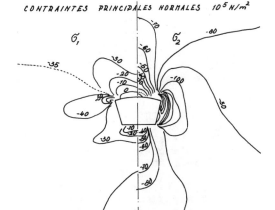

CONTRAINTES PRINCIPALES NORMALES $10^5 N/m^2$

Fig. 10

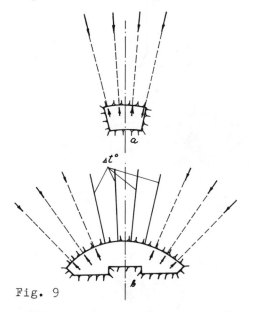

Fig. 9

L'état des contraintes dans la deuxième étape est présenté à la Fig. 10 par les courbes des valeurs égales des contraintes principales.

Etant sorti des déformations $\{\varepsilon\}_2^{im}$ on a déterminé la sollicitation fictive, nécessaire à l'étape suivante $\{6_0\}_3^{im} = \{6_0\}_2^{im} + [D]_2^{im}\{\varepsilon\}_2^{im}$.

Dans la troisième étape on a calculé la rédistribution des contraintes et les déformations dues aux fouilles dans la région des parties latérales de l'arc (les zones 3 et 17) et à la précontrainte des ancres 8. Dans ce but, pareillement à

l'étape précédente on a annulé les déplacements des étapes calculées par l'affectation de la sollicitation fictive aux zones indiquées par la variable $BB(m) = 1$ (m=1, 4, 5,10,14,15,16). Pour les zones où $BB(m) = 0$ on a mis $\{6_0\}_2^{im} = 0$.

La modification des propriétés des zones de l'étape précédente a été comme il suit: on a imposé pour les zones 6 les propriétés du béton projeté et pour les zones 11 les propriétés de l'acier. La précontrainte des ancres (les zones 8) a été réproduite par des forces opposées. Fig. 9b.

La question de la mise en oeuvre l'influence des ancres précontraints (les zones 7) est un peu compliquée. En principe ces ancres changent sa tension de précontrainte à cause des déformations subséquentes aux fouilles de l'étape.

D'après la formulation générale, présentée dans les paragraphes précédents, les résultats des déplacements, réspectivement des déformations, y inclus ceux de la précontrainte sont nuls en allant d'une étape à l'autre à condition qu'il n'y ait pas de changement de la sollicitation ou du système physique. Dans le même temps l'état des contraintes reste le même.

L'état des contraintes ne changera pas également si en annulant les déformations de l'étape on remplace les forces qui représentent la

191

précontrainte par des éléments finis linéaires, reproduisants les ancres, soumis à une sollicitation thermique Δt° de manière qu'on retient les mêmes forces de l'ancrage. Fig. 9b.

La sollicitation thermique Δt° dans ce cas sera calculé par la formule

$$\Delta t° = \frac{P}{\alpha E A}$$

où P est la force de précontrainte de l'ancre, α le coeffitient de dilatation linéaire thermique de l'acier de l'ancre, E le module d'élasticité de l'acier et A la section de l'ancre.

Dépuis là les ancres précontraints prennent part dans la répartition des contraintes dans le système calculé.

Dans le cas concret les ancres précontraints ont été introduits par l'affectation des propriétés de l'acier à la zone 7 et de la sollicitation Δt° aux éléments linéaires appartenans à cette zone. Après l'introduction des fouilles dans le calcul par les propriétés physiques et mécaniques nulles des zones 4 et 17 on a reçu la nouvelle répartition des contraintes (Fig. 11) et les déformations conséquentes.

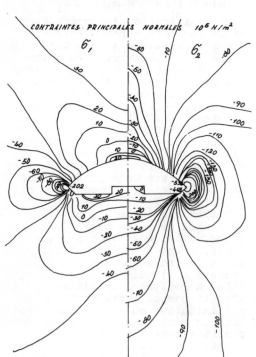

Fig. 11

La quatrième et la cinquième étapes ont été accomplies après avoir introduit des changements appropriés par les données d'entrée de ces deux étapes.

Selon la succession des travaux de construction l'arc de béton devait être soumis à une charge due aux fouilles dans la cinquième étape. En respectant cette particularité on a introduit l'arc dans le calcul ayant affecté les propriétés du béton aux zones 2,3,4 dans la même cinquième étape.

Létat des contraintes de cette étape est présenté à la Fig. 12 et celui de l'arc à la Fig. 13.

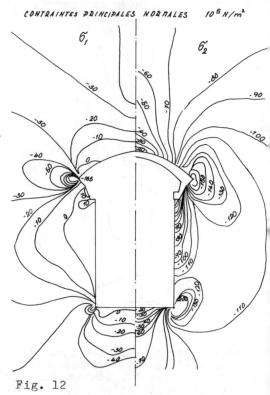

Fig. 12

Les déplacements nodals du contour de la caverne dépuis la deuxième jusqu'à la cinquième étape sont présentés à la Fig. 14.

6 CONCLUSIONS

Le modèle présenté de reconstitution dans le calcul des contraintes naturelles de la téchnologie et de la consécution des travaux de construc-

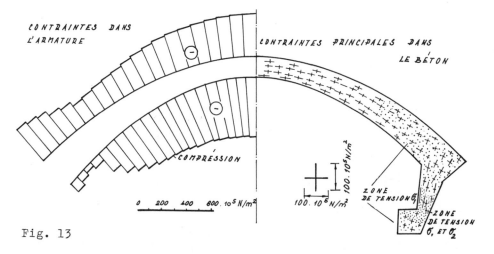

Fig. 13

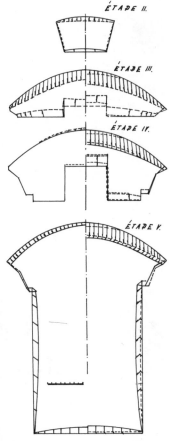

Fig. 14

tion des ouvrages souterrains s'est
bien imposé dans nos recherches
grâce à ses possibilitées d'adapta-

tion aux problèmes pratiques.

Le calcul de la caverne de l'usine
hydraulique, ainsi que d'autres
ouvrages (tunnels, barrages, etc)
nous a prouvé les avantages particu-
liers du modèle au point de vue
programation.

D'autre part il est en état de
s'adapter librement aux différentes
méthodes de reconstitution des déformations nonlinéaires grâce à la con-
formité de leurs points de départ.

On est en train de dresser un système des sousprogrammes, ayant de
bonnes possibilités dans ce domaine.
Il sera appliqué au calcul du projet
de travail de l'usine hydraulique et
les résultats de l'ordinateur seront
comparés aux essais in situ.

7 BIBLIOGRAPHIE

Christov, T. 1977, Reconstitution
    des contraintes naturelles dans le
    massif rocheux lors du calcul des
    ouvrages souterrains par MEF (en
    bulgare), J. Vodni problémi 6.
Christov, T. & S. Iliev 1977, Consi-
    deration of natural stresses in
    the rock massif and the technology
    of construction with respect to
    the calculation of underground
    opening by means of the FEM, Proc.
    Int. Symp. Field measurements in
    rock mech., Zurich: 905-918.
Kovàri, K. 1972, Methoden der Dimen-
    sionierung von Untertagbauten. Int.
    Symp. für Untertagbau, Luzern.
Zienkiewicz, O. C. 1971, The finite
    element method in engineering
    science, London, MCGRAW-HILL.

STABILITY ANALYSIS OF LARGE UNDERGROUND EXCAVATIONS USING THREE-DIMENSIONAL ANALOGY APPROACH

Stabilitätsberechnung für grosse unterirdische Hohlräume mit Hilfe des dreidimensionalen Analogieansatzes

Calcul de la stabilité des grandes cavités souterraines au moyen de la méthode d'approche analogique tridimensionnelle

B.B.DHAR, S.RATAN & K.V.SHANKAR
Department of Mining Engineering, Banaras Hindu University, Varanasi, India

P.K.BEHRA
Indian School of Mines, Dhanbad

SUMMARY:

Simulation by electrical tank analogue based on the laws of elasticity, seems to be a good tool for analysis of underground structures in three-dimensions particularly in hard rock mines. This method is a combination of analytical approach based on model study of actual underground structures. This application has been used earlier mainly for the simulation of mine-design problems. The main instrument in this technique is either an electrical tank analogue or a resistance analogue. However, electrical tank analogue has been used in this, to study the stability of large underground excavations. From the design point of view, the technique seems quite suitable particularly in hard rocks, where the rocks behave more or less under elastic conditions. It is thus believed that the technique can be very well used in the design of underground caverns that can be used for the storage of oil, gas etc.

ZUSAMMENFASSUNG:

Eine Möglichkeit zur dreidimensionalen Berechnung von unterirdischen Bauwerken, insbesondere solchen in hartem Gestein, bietet aufbauend auf den Elastizitäts gesetzen, die Elektro-analogon-Methode. Diese Methode ist eine Kombination von analytischen Näherungen, die auf Modellstudien unterirdischer Anlagen basieren. Diese Methode hat früher hauptsächlich Anwendung bei der Simulation von Untertageentwürfen gefunden. Das Hauptinstrument bei dieser Technik ist entweder ein Potentialanalogon oder ein Widerstandsanalogon. In der vorliegenden Untersuchung wurde die Elektroanalogon-Methode angewendet, um die Stabilität grosser unterirdischer Hohlräume zu untersuchen. Die beschriebene Elektroanalogon- Methode bietet insbesondere in hartem Gestein mit mehr oder weniger elastischem Verhalten eine brauchbare Entwurfsgrundlage. So wird daher angenommen, dass sich diese Methode auch für den Bau von Kavernen als Öloder Gaslager gut eignet.

RESUME:

La simulation par la méthode électro-analogique basée sur les lois de l'élasticité semble être un bon instrument de calcul tridimensionnel des structures souterraines, particulièrement dans le cas des roches dures. Cette méthode est une combinaison d'approches analytiques appuyées sur des études modèles des structures souterraines actuelles. Cette méthode a été utilisée autrefois, principalement dans la simulation des projets de constructions souterraines. L'instrument principal de cette technique est ou bien une analogie potentielle ou bien une analogie de résistance. Cependant, pour analyser la stabilité des grandes cavités souterraines, la méthode d'électro-analogie a été employée dans cette étude. Du point de vue de dimensionnement, la technique paraît être tout à fait adéquate, particulièrement dans les roches dures ayant un comportement plus ou moins élastique. Aussi est il admis que cette méthode convient très bien au dimensionnement des cavernes souterraines destinées au stockage de pétrole et de gaz.

2 INTRODUCTION

Stress in rock mass plays a significant role in the stability of underground excavations. Therefore the knowledge of the distribution and concentration of these stresses on pillars in underground and on supports which form significant parts of the mine structures is of major importance. These stress concentrations on the pillar vary with the amount of load coming on the pillar due to progressive mining. For safe and stable structure, it therefore, becomes necessary to study the strength and distribution of pillar supports.

The failure of rock pillar support in mine takes place due to increase in the average maximum stress over the pillar. This increase in pillar stress causes displacement which is a function of average stress to a large extent than that of stress concentration. It has been observed that the displacement of a pillar has a close relation with the stability of the pillar.

Simulation by electrolytic tank analogue based on the laws of elasticity, seems to be a good tool for three-dimensional analysis of underground structures, particularly in hard rock mass (Dhar 1970; Patel 1973; Behra 1977). This method is a combination of analytical approach on model study of actual underground structures and has been applied earlier mainly for the simulation of mine design problems. The main instrument in this technique is either an electrolytic tank analogue or a resistance analogue. However, in this laboratory investigation, electrolytic tank analogue has been used to study the stability of large underground excavation in a one of the lead-zinc mines of India.

3 PRINCIPLE OF ANALOGY

It has been shown that a mathematical analogy exists between the elastic laws and equations governing the steady flow of electricity. Both these systems satisfy the Laplace's equation $\Delta^2\phi = 0$. This analogy has been exploited and the experimental determination of the closure, i.e., the relative displacements of the hanging wall (roof) to the foot wall (floor) of the excavations has now become possible with the aid of electrolytic tanks.

The basic assumption before attempting an elastic solution in any live situation are: (i) that the hard rock mass involved is isotropic and homogeneous and (ii) that the hard rock mass obeys elastic laws.

In an electrolytic tank, the unmined ground surrounding the excavation is represented by top earthed electrode, which contacts the upper surface of the electrolyte. Within the working area, in the centre of top electrode, the model plate is placed whose cut out portion represents the excavation.

A voltage distribution is generated at the top surface of the electrolyte by supplying a constant voltage to the bottom electrode of the tank. In terms of analogy, this voltage distributiin is equivalent to displacement at the roof. Under the earthed electrode the voltage is zero which confirms to the actual situation, i.e. there can not be any closure in the solid unmined ground.

3.1 Calculation of displacement or closure

The ideal solution for calculating displacement at a particular point P (x_o, y_o, z_o) within the solid rock mass as a result of excavation of an elementary portion at $\Delta EA(x_1,y_1)$ is given by (Salamon 1963-64; Cook et al 1966; Ortlepp & Nicoll 1964):

$$\delta w = -\frac{S_z(x_1,y_1)\Delta EA}{8\pi(1-\mu)} \; Z_o \frac{2(2-\mu)Z_o^2 + (1-2\mu)r^2}{(r^2+Z_o^2)^{5/2}} \quad ..(1)$$

where,

$S_z(x_1,y_1)$ = relative displacement i.e. closure, at (x_1,y_1)

μ = poisson's ratio

x_o,y_o,z_o = coordinate at which the displacement is to be calculated

x_1, y_1 = coordinate of the elemental area, ΔEA

r = $(x_o-x_1)^2 + (y_o-y_1)^2$

The closure distribution $S_z(x_1,y_1)$, at Z=0 plane, i.e. at the seam level, can be calculated from the equation:

$$S_z(x_1,y_1) = \frac{4(1-\mu)\,S_o\,h\,V}{V_1\,E} \quad ...(2)$$

provided

$$V_o = \frac{V_1}{hs}\,\Omega_o \;, \text{ and } \Omega_o = \frac{E\,S_m}{4\,(1-\mu^2)\,S_o}$$

where,

$S_z(x_1,y_1)$ = closure at point (x_1,y_1),

S_o = average cover load,

h = tank depth at the origin,

s = scale factor,

V_1 = applied voltage at the bottom of the electrode,

V = measured voltage at (x_1,y_1)

E = Young's modulus of elasticity,

S_m = seam thickness, and

V_o = measured voltage corresponding to total closure of the seam.

The total displacement at P (x_o,y_o,z_o) due

to the whole excavated area can be calculated by integrating the whole excavated area, yield the required influence of mining. The total displacement would be (Dhar 1970).

$$W = \frac{h}{2\pi}\frac{(1+\mu)}{EV_1}\,S_o \iint_{E\ A} V(x_1,y_1) \; \times$$

$$Z_o \frac{2(2-\mu)Z_o^2 + (1-2\mu)\,r^2}{(r^2+Z_o^2)^{5/2}}\;dx.dy \quad ..(3)$$

where,

W = total displacement at point P (x_o,y_o,z_o) in the vertical directions.

4 CASE STUDY

The present study involves the analysis of crown pillar in one of the lead-zinc mines of India. The pillar has 1,120 sq.m. of area, length being 63.438 m. and average width being 18 m. The average thickness of the crown pillar is around 8 m.

The method of stoping practiced in this mine has resulted in the problem that the crown pillar of a particular stope had developed some horizontal cracks, possibly indicating some movement in strata, followed by some tension cracks. Subsequently these cracks were noticed to be on increase. It is believed that the cracking phenomenon resulting in downward deflection of the pillar may be due to a single cause or a number of causes together. However, the possibility of failure phenomenon due to either the side wall pressure as a result of cover load or due to its own weight of the crown pillar were examined by simulating the mine models on an electrolytic tank analogue.

197

5 EXPERIMENTAL PROCEDURE

The following assumptions were made for the laboratory investigations of the stoping area.

(i) The influence of the workings in the neighbourhood of the open stope under study have been ignored for the experimental observation.

(ii) The open area of the stope under observations was limited within the vertical pillars and the side walls only.

(iii) In the vertical plan, the area was limited by the crown and sill pillars in the upper and lower levels.

Experimental models were made on the printed copper circuit board to depict the following cases:

Case I :- An open stope surrounded by vertical pillars on the side and the walls on the remaining sides.

Case II :- The stope interposed by the middle pillar approaximately of the same size as that of vertical pillar (i.e. 9 m. thick).

Case III :- The width of the middle pillar is half of the size of the vertical pillar (i.e. 5.5 m. thick).

Case IV :- The width of the pillar is one fourth of the vertical pillar (i.e. 2.25 m).

The mine plan depicting the stope under study was scaled down to 1 mm = 2.5 m in order to accommodate in the 280 x 280 mm working area of the tank. The holes 0.25 mm were drilled at an interval of 6 mm. A small voltage of 10 V was applied to the bottom of the electrode. The voltage distribution at the surface was measured with the help of a platinum probe. These voltage values were used to determine the relative displacement components of hanging

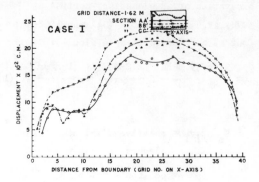

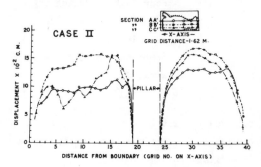

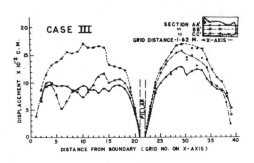

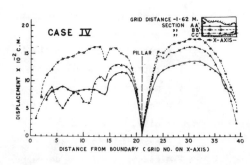

Fig.2: Effect of pillar insertion on the displacement.

(A) Case I, (B) Case II, (C) Case III and (D) Case IV.

wall and foot wall. The relative displacement components at the sections AA', BB' and CC' as shown in the Fig. 1 were determined.

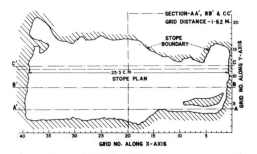

Fig.1: Isolated enlarged mine model plan of stope 503 W (with grid nos.).

In the present analysis, the closure value, i.e. the relative displacement of hanging wall and foot wall, using the equation (2), alongwith the sections AA', BB' and CC' have been calculated.

6 RESULTS AND DISCUSSIONS

The observed maximum and minimum displacement values along the sections AA', BB' and CC' for cases I, II, III and IV are shown in Figs. 2A, 2B, 2C and 2D respectively. In all parts of the model plate beyond the boundary line and on isolated solid remnants the observed voltage was zero. This phenomenon indicates that there will be no closure in the area of solid rock.

In case I (Fig. 2A), the overall trend indicates that the peak values of relative displacement are maximum at the centre of the stope and gradually decreasing as the distance from the abutments decreases. These observations seems to be in complete agreement with the theoretical concept that the maximum relative displacement are along

the largest span of the excavation lies along the middle of the section.

Referring to Fig. 2B, for case II, suggest that the introduction of a full size pillar of 9 m. thick in the middle of the stope reduces the relative displacements considerably, which seems to be in close agreement with the theory. Similarly for cases III and IV (Figs. 2C, 2D) where the middle pillar is 4.5 m. and 2.25 m. thick respectively, slight change in the relative displacement values are observed.

The maximum displacement of all the above four cases are summarized in Figure 3. The level of the maximum displacement with no central pillar is represented by the horizontal line. With the excavation the displacement has increased. It can be seen from the figure that with the insertion of the pillar the relative drop in the displacement has reduced. In case of western zone, it can be observed that with the introduction of 9 m. (full size) pillar the drop in displacement has reduced by 5.50×10^{-2} cm. When the pillar thickness has decreased by half, this drop is only

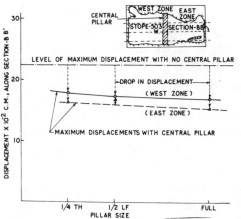

Fig.3: Graph showing the reduction in displacement values as a result of interposed single middle pillar in the mine stope.

199

5.0×10^{-2} cm and it further reduces to 4.6×10^{-2} cm for one fourth of pillar size. This suggests that from the stability point of view, the stability of the large underground excavation can be improved significantly by the insertion of the type of pillar in the excavated area. Such an analysis therefore suggests that actual design of large excavations can be well understood if such exercises are done at the planning stage itself without going into the actual working conditions. According to authors this analytical approach coupled with laboratory experiments seems to be significant tool useful for practicing rock engineers.

7 CONCLUSIONS

On comparing the results of cases I, II, III and IV, it can very well be concluded that the insertion of the pillar in the middle of the total mining span does show a considerable decrease both in maximum and minimum values of displacements. However, because of the size limitations on the model plate, the significance of the change in the size of the central pillar from 9 m. to 2.25 m. is not very well felt. But the general trend is that the values of displacements were decreased by 50% in case of minimum range and by about 30% in case of maximum.

The existing span of the stope is large enough to develop the tendancies of displacements in the walls and consequently the stress developed may tend to upset the equilibrium in the sill pillar. Hence, interposing of the middle pillar reduces the span as well as the deformations, the knowledge of which can be used as a guide to design workings of similar nature.

8 ACKNOWLEDGEMENT

The authors are thankful to the Head, Department of Mining Engineering and the Director, Institute of Technology, Banaras Hindu University, Varanasi, India for providing all the necessary help in this study.

Thanks are also due to the Management of Hindustan Zinc Ltd., Udaipur, India for their help and assistance.

9 REFERENCES

Behra, P.K. 1977, Three dimensional study of stoping problem using electrical analogue technique. M.Tech. Project Report Thesis, Department of Mining Engineering, B.H.U., Varanasi, India.

Cook, N.G.W.; E. Hoek, J.P.G. Pretorius; W.D. Ortlepp & M.D.G. Salamon 1966, Rock mechanics applied to the study of rockbursts, J.S. Afr. Inst. Min. and Met., 66:436-528.

Dhar, B.B. 1970, A three dimensional study of pillar stresses with irregular mining boundaries. Ph.D.Thesis, McGill University, Montreal, Canada.

Ortlepp, W.D. & A. Nicoll 1964, The elastic analysis of observed strata movement by means of electric analogue. J.S.Afr. Inst. Min. and Met. 65:4.

Patel, H.R. 1973, Further investigations in the simulation of mine openings using an electrolytic analogue. M.Tech.Thesis, Department of Mining Engineering, B.H.U., Varanasi, India.

Salamon, M.D.G. 1963-64, Elastic analysis of displacements and stresses induced by the mining of seam or reef deposits, Part I & II. J.S.Afr. Inst. of Mine. and Met. 60: Nov. & Jan.

HYDROTECHNISCHE TIEFBAUARBEITEN IN DER UDSSR UND WEGE ZUR WEITEREN ENTWICKLUNG

Underground hydraulic engineering in the USSR and ways of its future developments

Les constructions hydrotechniques souterraines en URSS et les voies de leurs développements futurs

N.W.DMITRIJEW
Unionsvereinigung 'Hydrospezstroj', UdSSR
J.S.BUBMAN
Institut 'Hydrospeztroj', UdSSR

SUMMARY:

In the report are given an account of the state and perspectives of underground hydraulic engineering in the USSR.
In the report are shown complications of specific underground enginee-ring, outlined ways of their future developments.

ZUSAMMENFASSUNG :

Der Vortrag führt die Hauptangaben über den Stand und die Entwicklungs-tendenzen von hydrotechnischen Tiefbauarbeiten in der UdSSR an.
Es sind die Schwierigkeiten von spezifischen Tiefbauarbeiten angegeben, sowie die Wege zu ihrer Weiterentwicklung vorgeschlagen.

RESUME :

Dans le rapport on cité les données principales de l'èta contemporain et de perspectives du développment de la construction hydrotechnique souterrainne en l'URSS.
Le rapport montre les complexités des travaux souterrainee spécifiques et les voies de leurs développement futurieur.

Geehrte Damen und Herren !
Geehrte Kollegen !

Erlauben Sie uns vor allem im Na-men der Sowjetischen Spezialisten-delegation unsere freudschaftliche Glückwünsche anläßlich des zwanzig-sten Jubiläums der Internationalen Gesellschaft für Felsmechanik zu übergeben und unsere Erfolgwünsche sowie in der Arbeit der Gesellschaft, als auch seines Jubiläumskongres-ses zu äußern, der von unseren Gastgebern – Kollegen aus der Bun-desrepublik – so exakt organisiert ist und so erfolgreich durchgefüh-rt wird.

Die Arbeit unserer Gesellschaft hat außer seiner rein technischer Auf-gabe – persönliche Kontakte und gegenseitige wissenschaftlich-tech nische Information der Spezialis-ten – auch zum Ziel eine weitere und bedeutende Aufgabe – Vereini-gung aller Menschen vom guten Wil-len im Namen und zum Wohl der Völ-ker. Darauf ist auch unsere gemein same Berufstätigkeit gerichtet, die Tätigkeit eines der edelsten Berufe auf der Erde – nähmlich der Bauleute. Und darin sehen wir die Garantie der Erfolge unserer Gesell-schaft und seines zwanzigsten Ju-biläumskongresses hier in der gastfreundlichen Stadt Aachen.

Die Tiefbauarbeiten werden in der UdSSR im großen Umfang im Interes-

se von verschiedenen Wirtschaft-
zweigen geführt, so z.B. Verkehrs-
wesen, Landwirtschaft, Bergbau,
hydrotechnischer und energetischer
Bau.

Wir betrachten weiter die Fragen
von hydrotechnischen Teifbauarbei-
ten, die eigenartin und spezifisch
sind.

Der hydrotechnische Tunnelbau wird
in der Sowjetunion schon über 50
Jahre geführt. Der Anfang war in
Armenien bei dem WKW "Dzorogatin-
skaja".

In der Zwischenzeit sind Tunnels
mit einer Gesamtlänge gegen 350
km gebaut, im Land sind 9 WKW mit
den Maschinenhallen unter Tage mit
einer Gesamtleistung von 2,5 mio
kW's im Betrieb.

Besonders ist der Umfang von den
Tiefbauarbeiten in den letzten 20-
25 Jahren gestiegen, nachdem diese
Arbeiten im Rahmen des Ministeri-
ums für Energetik und Elektrifizie
rung der UdSSR der Unionsvereinigung "Hydrospezstroj" übergeben
wurden.

Von den in dieser Zeit gebauten
und zur Zeit im Betrieb stehenden
hydrotechnischen Anlagen unter Tage könnte man folgende besonders
erwähnen:
- der Tunnel "Arpa-Sewan" mit einer Länge von 48 km zur Wasserumleitung vom Fluß Arpa in den sei-
cht werdenden Bergsee Sewan;
- WKW "Nurekskaja" mit einem Tief-
baukomplex von 2,7 mio m^3, WKW
"Unguri" - gegen 2,2 mio m^3,
WKW "Shirkejskaja" - gegen 0,7 mio
m^3, WKW "Sharwakskaja" - gegen
0,5 mio m^3, WKW "Toktogulskaja" -
gegen 0,4 mio m^3, WKW "Chantaj-
skaja"- gegen 0,3 mio m^3, WKW "Wi-
lujskaja" - gegen 0,3 mio m^3 und
andere.

Nur in den letzten Jahren sind unter Tage gegen 10 mio m^3 Felsboden
ausgehoben, in die Konstruktionen
unter Tage gegen 3 mio m^3 von Beton und Stahlbeton eingebaut, gegen 150 km von Tunneln, Kammern
und Maschinenhallen unter Tage gebaut. Die Tiefbauarbeiten unter
Tage wurden vorwiegend in den
Felsböden mit einer breiten Palet-
te von technisch-geologischen Verhältnissen und in verschiedenen
Landesregionen geführt.

So wurde, z.B. der Bau eines eigen
artigen 48-km-langen Tunnels zur
Wasserumleitung aus dem Fluß Arpa
in den Sewan-See in sehr komplizierten hydrogeologischen Verhältnissen geführt: mit großem
Wasserzulauf(bis 1200 m^3/h), mit
hohen Fels- und Lufttemperaturen
(bis +40^{3}C), mit großem Gas-(bis
300000 m^3) und Gesteinausbruch(
bis   m^3) und mit Bergschlägen.

Die Allunionsberatung in Moskau
(Oktober 1981) stellte fest, daß
zur Zeit im hydrotechnischen Bau
eine stabile Tendenz zum volumet-
rischen Ansteigen von Tiefbauarbeiten zu verfolgen ist, was sich
aus dem komplexen Charakter der
Ausnutzung von Wasservorräten der
Flüsse ergibt, die im Gebirge und
in den Gebieten mit einer komplizierten Geländegestaltung fließen.

Zu den zukünftigen Anlagen mit
den Tiefbauarbeiten mußte man vor
allem die Wasserkraftwerke "Rogunskaja", "Kolymskaja", "Irganajska-
ja", "Zaramagskaja", "Burejskaja",
sowie den Südukrainischen Energie-
komplex und andere Objekte zählen.

Zu den Hauptanlagen des größten
WKW "Rogunskaja" am Fluß Wachsch
mit einer installierten Leistung
3600 MW(6x600) gehört außer einem
Staudamm, der zu den größten in
der Welt gehört(Höhe 335 m, Umfang 72,5 mio m^3), auch ein einmali-
ger Baukomplex unter Tage, zu dem
294 Untertagebauten mit einer Gesamtlänge 64 km, 5100000 m^{3}Felsab-
bau, sowie 1600000 m^{3}Beton und
Stahlbetoneinbau unter Tage zählen
Die komplizierten Naturverhältnis-
se am Bauort, großer Arbeitsumfang
und kurze Bautermine, der Zusammen
hang und große Unterschiede von
Untertagebauten(von den waagerech-
ten bis zu senkrechten, von den en
gen Stollen mit dem Querschnitt 16
-18 m^2 bis zu Großmaschinenhallen
mit einer Höhe von 68 m und einer
Feldesbreite 27-33 m, sowie 232 m
lang).

Das alles bestimmt die Einmaligke-
it dieses unterirdischen Komplexes.

Die Tendenz zum Umfangswachstum
von den Tiefbauarbeiten stellt vor
die Bauleute auch die Aufgabe der
Beschleunigung ihrer Ausführung,
denn z.B. der mittlere Jahresum-
fang von Felsabbau über 1,1 mio m^3

betragen wird, was beinahe um das 1,5-fache höher ist, als die zur Zeit erreichten Jahresumfangsquoten.

Die Sicherung des vorgesehenen Arbeitsumfanges erfordert, daß eine Reihe von bevorstehenden Fragen und Aufgaben gelöst wird, darunter solche wie:
- Vervollkommnung der Aufbau- und anordnungslösungen,
- Vervollkommnung der Technologie der Tiefbauarbeiten,
- Komplexe Mechanisierung der Tiefbauarbeiten,
- Einsatz von leistungsfähigen Maschinen und Anlagen aus eigener Produktion und aus den Exporten.

Eine erfolgreiche Lösung der angegebenen und der weiteren Aufgaben ist erst auf der Basis von Grundforschungen und wissenschaftlich-technischen Entwicklungen möglich. Wissenschaftlich-technische Entwicklungen im Rahmen des hydrotechnischen Tiefbaues führen in der UdSSR mehrere Organisationen durch, einige von diesen Organisationen haben Vorträge ihrer Mitarbeiter bei diesem Kongress vorgelegt.

Die modernen wissenschaftlich-technischen Entwicklungen betrachten die Fragen der Vervollkommnung von Arbeitmethoden und Ausführungsarten, der Ausarbeitung und des Einsatzes von neuen Baustoffen mit neuen Betriebseigenschaften, z.B. Latex-Beton und Faser-Beton; der Entwicklung von neuen Maschinen und Vorrichtungen, der Anwendung der Rechenmaschinen für die automatische Produktionssteuerung.

Auf der Grundlage der durchgeführten wissenschaftlichen Forschungsarbeiten werden Richtlinien ausgearbeitet, die dann in die normative Dokumentation aufgenommen werden, die für alle Bau-, Projektierungs-, Forschungs- und wissenschaftliche Organisationen verbindlich ist.

Solch ein grundlegendes Dokument ist in der UdSSR "Baunormen und Bauregeln", welches vom Staatskomite für Bauwesen beim Ministerrat der UdSSR(Gosstroj UdSSR) bestätigt und umgearbeitet wird.

Die "Baunormen und Bauregeln" für alle Arten von Bauarbeiten enthalten vier Teile:

Teil I - Allgemeine Festlegungen
Teil II - Projektierungsnormen
Teil III - Arbeitsausführungs- und Abnahmeregeln
Teil IV - Kostenanschlagnormen.

Jeder Teil besteht aus Unterteilen und Kapiteln für einzelne Bauarten

So ein deutliches System sichert ein einheitliches Niveau der technischen Anforderungen, was von besonderer Bedeutung beim so großen Umfang und so großen Entfernungen ist, wie es in der Praxis in der UdSSR vorkommt.

Eine der Hauptrichtungen in der Vervollkommnung des hydrotechnischen Tiefbaues ist verbunden und wird bestimmt von der Neuheit und dem Wirkungsgrad der Aufbau- und Anordnungslösungen.

Im Ramen der Aufbau- und Anordnungslösungen sollte man solche Anordnung der unterirdischen WKW-Bauten vorsehen, die auch vom Standpunkt der Arbeitsorganisation optimal ist und die vorhandenen hydrotechnischen Strecken für die weiteren Bauarbeiten maximal auszunutzen läßt.

Beim Projektieren und beim Bau von hydrotechnischen Anlagen unter Tage wird eine sehr große Bedeutung der Auswahl von ständigen Verkleidungen beigemessen. Zur Zeit werden in der Baupraxis vorwiegend Massivverkleidungen aus Beton und Stahlbeton angewendet, die sich durch hohe Masse, Arbeitsaufwand und Kosten auszeichnen. In den letzten Jahren kommt im hydrotechnischen Tiefbau auch eine kombinierte Verkleidung aus vorgefertigten Stahlbetonelementen mit einem inneren Stahlbetonring zum Einsatz.

Die Anwendung von montierbaren Verkleidungen garantirt Sicherheit beim Tunnelbau, einen hohen Grad der Arbeitmechanisierung bei der Verkleidungsmontage und senkt bedeutend den Arbeitsaufwand.

Zur Zeit werden Arbeiten durchgeführt, die eine weitere Vervollkommnung der Verkleidungskonstruktion beim hydrotechnischen Tiefbau vom Standpunkt der Arbeitaufwandsenkung und gleichzeitig der weiteren Steigerung der Betriebssiherheit zum Ziel haben. Dazu gehören die Verkleidungen aus Pressbeton und die dünnwändigen Verkleidungen, die auf dem Prinzip basieren, nach dem die Belastungen in die umgebenden Gesteinsmassen über geleitet werden. Falls die umgebenden Gesteinsmassen Risse haben und nicht stabil sind, so muß man ihre Befestigung durch die Zementation oder Verankerung, oder beides gleich, vorsehen.

Eine breite Anwendung finden ständige Verkleidungen als Leichtbaukonstruktionen aus Ankerbolzen (auch vorgespannt) und Spritzbeton, Verkleidungen aus gepresstem Gußbeton oder Tiefmodulbeton, die durch die Zementation abgepresst sind. Eine breite Anwendung von solchen Verkleidungstypen wird begünstigt durch die Aufgaben zur

Terminverkürzung, zur Bauaufwandsenkung und zur Arbeitskostenersparung beim Tiefbau.

So wurde im Bautunnel des WKW "Kurpsajskaja" die Verkleidung aus dem Spritzbeton zusammen mit den Stahlbetonankern ausgeführt. Nach einem 3-jährigen Betrieb unter sich wechselnden Bedingungen zeigte eine Besichtigung, daß die Verkleidung sich im guten Zustand befindet. So wurde noch mals praktisch nachgewiesen, daß in den hydrotechnischen Tunnelen eine Verkleidung aus dem Spritzbeton möglich ist.

Gleichzeitig werden immer breiter Spritzbeton-Verkleidungen beim Bau von Transporttunneln für den Dauer- und Kurzbetrieb eingesetzt(WKW "Toktogulskaja", "Kurpsajskaja", "Sajano-Schuschenskaja", "Nurekskaja" ua.m.). An einer Baustelle wurden tiefe vorgespannte Ankerbolzen(Spannkraft bis 40 tp) zusammen mit Spritzbeton verwendet.

Die weiteren Anwendungsbereiche für den Spritzbeton eröffnen sich mit dem Einsatz von den vorgespannten Ankerbolzen mit einer Spannkraft von 100-200 tp, von einer

dispersen Armierung und der richtigen geometrischen Formgebung für Reibungsverminderung.

Neben der Verkommnung der konstruktiven Lösungen mußte man, um die gestellten Aufgaben zu erfül-

len, auch die Arbeitsorganisation und die Technologie beim Tiefbau überprüfen und die Betriebsmittel verbessern, damit die Arbeiten voll mechanisiert werden.

Die fertigungstechnische Verbesserung des Tunnelbaues mit großen Durchmessern an den Abschnitten mit geringerer Gesteinsfestigkeit ist mit dem Eisatz von vorauseilenden Verkleidungen verbunden, z.B. mit den vorgespannten Ankern und Bindelösungen, wie es im Technischen Entwurf für den Bau unter Tage des Komplexes WKW "Rogunskaja" am Fluß Wachsch vorgesehen ist.

Am meisten sind verbreitet beim Sprengvortrieb mit "Glattsprengen" für die größeren Nennweiten die beiden Verfahren – strebenweise beim Querschnitt bis 60-100 m^2 und strossenweise beim Tunnelquerschnitt über 100 m^2. Dabei wird die obere Stufe als Regel mit Spurlochladungen strebenweise, und der untere Absatz stufenweise mit Bohrlochladungen und vorläufiger Rissbildung an der vorgesehenen Wandfläche gesprengt.

Das schafft reelle Voraussetzungen für die Senkung der Nebenkosten, die im Zusammenhang mit einer unprofilierten Gesteinsabnahme(Hölungen) entstehen und eine spätere Auffüllung mit teueren Konstruktionswerkstoffen z.B. Beton erfordern.

Es ist wichtig, zu unterstreichen, daß durch die Versuche festgestellt und durch die Praxis bestätigt ist, daß es eine bestimmte Abhängigkeit gibt, die mathematisch durch eine Normalverteilungskurve beschrieben wird, die den Zusammenhang des Wertes und die Wahrscheinlichkeit von Höhlungen mit einer Reihe von Einflußgrößen charakterisiert, und vor allem mit der Aufgabegenauigkeit und der Beibehaltung der vorgegebenen Spurloch- und Bohrlochrichtung.

Im Rahmen der Komplexmechanisierung der Tiefbauarbeiten und des Einsatzes von modernen Maschinen und ausrüstungen gewinnen eine besondere Bedeutung die Arbeitsmittel für Spurloch- und Bohrlochvorbereitung.

In den letzten Jahren finden in der Praxis des Tiefbaues breite Verwendung Bohrmaschinen mit einem hydraulischen Arbeitsorgan, deren Leistung um das 1,5-2-fache höher ist, als bei den pneumatischen Bohrmaschinen. In unserem Lande befassen sich mit der Entwicklung von hydraulischen Bohrmaschinen mehrere Konstruktionsbüreau, darunter auch das Institut für Bergbaumechanisierung bei der Kirgisischen Filiale der Akademie der Wissenschaften der UdSSR

Eine Vervollkommnung der Betonarbeiten unter Tage muß geführt werden vor allem in der Richtung der Mechanisation von Gleitschalungen beim Bau von Beton- und Pressbetonverkleidungen, sowie von Hochdruck-Betonpumpen mit einer Leistung von 10, 20 und 40 m³/h, die imstande sind Betonmischungen jeder Konsistenz zu fördern. Gleichzeitig müssen die Arbeiten zur Vervollkommnung der Druckluftsysteme zum Transport von Beton fortgesetzt werden, sowie zum schalungslosen Betonieren.

Zum Zweck der weiteren bedeutenden Bauterminabkürzung müssen neue mechanisierte Vortriebsverfahren mit den Vortriebsschildern und -kombinen eingeführt werden. Die Erfahrungen zeigen, daß die Gesamtgeschwindigkeit beim Tunnelvortrieb mit den mechanischen Verfahren um das 2-4-fache höher ist, als beim Bergverfahren. Man kann vermerken, daß von dem bis zum Jahr 1990 vorgeplanten Tiefbauumfang im hydrotechnischen Bau sich nach den geologischen Verhältnissen gegen 40% aller Tunnele mechanisiert bauen lassen.

Zur Zeit wird bei den Betriebsverhältnissen beim Vortrieb eines Umleitungstunnels Chussa-Marucha des WKW "Selenshukskaja" eine Vortriebkombine 4ПП-5 überprüft. Bei demselben WKW am Wasserzuführ-Drucktunnel wird zur Inbetriebnahme ein Vortriebsschild KT-1-5,6 vorbereitet. An der Baustelle des WKW "Saramagskaja" steht in der Vorbereitung zum Prüfeinsatz im Umleittunnel bei den Betriebsverhältnissen eine Vortriebkombine АФП-I , die für einen Zweiphasenvortrieb im Felsboden mit einer Festigkeitsgrenze bis 1200 kp/cm² beim Tunnel-

durchmesser 5,3 m ausgelegt ist. In der Vorbereitung ist die Kombine ГТК-16.

Die komplexe Mechanisierung der Tiefbauarbeiten hilft die Aufgaben erfolgvoll zu lösen, die vor der Hydroenergetik in den XI und XII Fünfjahrplänen gestellt sind.

Bessere Konstruktion von hydrotechnischen Tiefbauobjekten, Entwicklung wirkungsvoller Organisation und Verfahren zur Durchführung von Tiefbauarbeiten, Auswahl von optimalen mechanisierten Baumaschinenkomplexe gehören zu den dringenden und alltäglichen Aufgaben für den Bau und die Projektierung, die auf Terminverkürzung, Steigerung der Arbeitsproduktivität und Baukostensenkung gerichtet sind.

Bei der Lösung der gestellten Aufgaben spielt eine große Rolle die wissenschaftlich-technische Zusammenarbeit der Sowjetunion mit den Firmen in verschiedenen Ländern, insbesondere im Rahmen des Internationalen Gesellschaft für Felsmechanik, die vom Sowjetischen Ausschuß der ISRM durchgeführt wird.

Es erscheint zweckmäßig zu sein, daß diese Zusammenarbeit in verschiedenen Richtungen verstärkt und erweitert wird:
- Entwicklung und Lieferung von neuen Maschinen und Anlagen,
- Entwicklung und Teilnahme an der Verwirklichung von gemeinsamen Projekten,
- Austausch der wissenschaftlich-technischen Information.

Das alles wird nicht nur zur Erweiterung von der wissenschaftlich-technischen und der wirtschaftlichen Seiten der Beziehungen zwischen unseren Ländern beitragen, sondern gibt eine sichere Gewähr zur Annäherung und Verständnis zwischen der UdSSR und den anderen ISRM-Ländern in ihrer edelsten und verantwortungsvollen Mission vor den Menschen des guten Willens - in der Sicherung und Erhaltung des Friedens in der ganzen Welt.

Danke !

FEM-ANALYSIS OF AN UNDERGROUND CAVERN WITH LARGE SPAN
Statische Berechnung eines unterirdischen Hohlraums mit grosser Spannweite
mit der Finite-Element-Methode
Calcul d'une caverne souterraine à grandes portées par la méthode des éléments finis

M.DOLEŽALOVÁ
Hydroprojekt, Prague, Czechoslovakia
R.HEJDA & F.LEITNER
Hydroprojekt, Brno, Czechoslovakia

SUMMARY:
The paper deals with the FEM - analysis of a large underground cavern which is the main object of a pumped storage power plant under construction in northern Moravia. The FEM program was modified by taking into account all important geological (geostatic stress state, anisotropy, nonlinearity, joints) and technological (excavation, anchoring, concreting) features of the problem under consideration. The results of the analysis proved the feasibility of the design, the correct orientation of the caverns and a favourable influence of the subhorizontal orientation of bedding planes on the stability of the high side walls of the power station cavern. Along with these results some short - comings (overstressing of the joints and some loosened zones, underestimating of the anchoring effect, neglecting of the time effect) were found out. The paper discusses these problems and outlines the further stage of the FEM - analysis where all these factors including excavation face influence and the new geological findings will be taken into account.

ZUSAMMENFASSUNG:
Dieser Beitrag beschreibt statische Lösung eines unterirdischen Hohlraums mit ausserordentlich grossen Abmessungen (Spannweite 26,5 - 33,0 m. Höhe 51,5 m, Länge 120 m), der das Hauptobjekt eines Pumpspeicherwerkes klassischen Typs mit Dreimaschinensätzen in Nordmähren bildet. Das Programm der FEM wurde modifiziert um die hauptsächlichen geologischen (den primären Spannungszustand, die Nichtlinearität, die Diskontinuitäten) und technologischen (den Ausbruch, die Verankerung, die Betonierung) Faktoren zu berücksichtigen. Die Berechnungsergebnisse haben die Durchführbarkeit des Projekts, die richtige Orientierung des Haupthohlraums und einen günstigen Einfluss der subhorizontalen Orientierung der Felslagen auf die Standfestigkeit der hohen Seitenwände des Kraftwerkhohlraums bewiesen. Aufgrund dieser Ergebnisse wurden einige unvollkommen erfasste Faktoren (Überlastung der Klüfte und einiger aufgelockerten Zonen, Unterschätzung der Ankerwirkung, Vernachlässigung des Zeiteinflusses) gefunden. Dieser Aufsatz behandelt diese Probleme und schlägt eine weitere Etappe der FEM - Berechnung wor, wo alle diese Faktoren samt dem Einfluss der Vortriebsbrust und neuen Bestimmung geologischer Verhältnisse berücksichtigt werden sollen.

RÉSUMÉ:
Le présent rapport traite la solution d'une caverne souterraine des dimensions extraordinairement grandes (l'écartement de 26,5 à 33,0 mètres, l'hauteur 51,5 mètres, et la longueur 120 mètres) qui fait l'objet principal d'une usine d'accumulation par pompage du type classique de groupement à trois machines. L'ensemble de programme de la méthode des éléments finis fut modifié de façon que tous les facteurs principaux géologiques (l'état de tension originaire, la non-linéarité et le discontinu) et technologiques (le creusement, l'ancrage, le bétonnage) fussent respectés. Les résultats de la solution montrèrent que l'on peut réaliser la caverne des dimensions données et que son orientation dans le massif rocheux est juste. Ils montrèrent de même l'influence favorable de la concordance soushorizontale des cou-

ohes à la stabilités des murs de roche hauts. Sauf des résultats mentionnés on trouv
quelques facteurs qui ne purent être atteints en largeur pleine. Ces problèmes sont
discutés dans le présent rapport. En développant le modelage à aide de la méthode de
éléments finis, on prendra en considération tous ces facteurs, l'influence du creuse
ment de la roche et les connaissances géologiques nouvelles y compris.

1 DESCRIPTION OF THE WORK

The development of the economy in our
country requires an increasing amount of
electrical energy, particulary in the
peak period. An especially appropriate
source of energy to cover this demand
are the pumped storage power stations.
The Dlouhé Stráně Power Station - at present under construction - is one of the
largest scheme of this type built in
Czechoslovakia.

The hydropower plant is situated in
northern Moravia in the region of Hrubý
Jeseník Mountains with an altitude up to
1 500 m.

The pumped-storage power plant is a
classical type with an upper reservoir
on the top of the Dlouhé Stráně Hill, a
lower reservoir on the Desná River and
utilizing a head of 550 m. The underground power station consists of the
machine hall, the spherical branch hall
and a complicated system of tunnels and
galleries including the pressure shafts
(ϕ 3,6 m) connecting the power station
with the upper reservoir. In the machine
hall there are four vertical-shaft triple
units with an installed capacity of
4 x 150 MW (Fig. 1).

The underground power station is located in the rock massif on the left bank
of the Desná River. The dimensions of the
machine hall were determined by the necessity to place all equipment (the pump-
-turbine units, the generators, the trans
formators of 400 kV) in one hall. The
corresponding main cavern is 120 m long,
26,5 - 33,0 m wide and 51,5 m high.

The attempt to find a suitable place
for the location of this large underground cavern and the great extent of the
remaining underground works called for a
large scale geological and geotechnical
investigation. Apart from several adits,
geophysical methods were widely used and
extensive rock mechanics tests were performed.

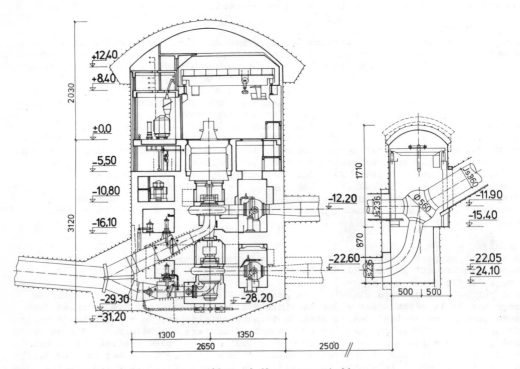

Fig. 1 Charakteristic cross section of the power station

2 GEOLOGICAL CONDITIONS

The geological and tectonic structure of the Hrubý Jeseník Mountains is very complex. The proposed site is in an area formed by **crys**talline schist represented by fine to coarse grained biotitic paragneiss, mostly slightly to medium migmatized, with locally occurring minor insertions of amphibolite, pegmatite or mica shist gneiss.

The tectonic structure of the territory as a whole is a combination of fold and block structure. The predominant tectonic lines are NW - SE and N - S.

As far as foliation is concerned the direction of inclination depends on the fold wall in which the section measured was located, the directions being NW and SE.

The tectonic lines are interrupted by reverse faults, and the entire area is thus divided into blocks with a more or less specific tectonic structure. There is no clear continuity between faults in individual blocks, nor have the faults the same character, and discontinuity was also found in cracks, fissures and dislocations.

Under such conditions it was necessary to find for the site of the cavern a block of relatively unfaulted rock. One was found lying in the so-called tectonic shade. The rock mass selected for the machine hall is sound and compact, with minor cracks and faults (up to 3 cm). In view of the geological and tectonic conditions found, the orientation of the cavern is optimal, since any faults are more or less perpendicular to the longitudinal axis of the cavern and are steep.

In order to determine the geostatic stress state, the deformations and the strength properties of the rock mass an extensive field tests programme was carried out. The geostatic stresses were found out by tensometer, flat jack and corvegence measurements. The deformation moduli perpendicular and parallel to the stratification were measured by oriented jack tests while the shear strength parameters of the joints by oriented direct shear tests. A trial cavity with a span of 7 m was excavated too, in order to measure the loosening of the rock mass in the roof. The field test results were complemented by an extent laboratory test programme carried out for the intact rock specimens.

3 SOLUTION CONCEPT

In view of the size of cavern, which is unique in Czechoslovakia, the main purpose of the solution consisted in proving the feasibility of the structure under the given geological conditions.
This required
- the assesment of the caverns stability
- the preliminary design of the temporary support and the concrete arch
- the analysis of the mutual influence of openings with regard to the construction work sequence.

Mathematical modelling by the finite element method (FEM) was selected as the best tool for the solution of these problems.

The basic factors to be taken into account in the analysis were considered to be the following:
- the geostatic stress state according to field tests
- the jointed structure of the rock mass, i.e. the explicit modelling of the discontinuities by joint elements
- the anisotropy of the deformation and strength characteristics of the rock blocks
- the non-linearity, i.e. the dependence of the deformation characteristics on the first invariant of the stress tensor (hardening by increasing the octahedral normal stress σ_{oct}) and the second invariant of the stress deviator (loosening by increasing octahedral tangential stress τ_{oct})
- the accurate stress state of the rock mass, i.e. the removal of the overstresses from the solution by the initial stress method
- the constructional sequence (excavation, anchoring, concreting) according to the design.

The formulation of the computational model required the simplification of the geological conditions of the site, the material properties, the geometrical arrangement of the structures and the construction work sequence. The assumptions and simplifications were considered, as follows:
- in view of the cavern shape and the inclination of the joints, a plane strain problem is solved - a hypotetical plane section with idealized geological conditions
- simplification of the geological conditions should be carried out so as to keep the solution on the safe side: the joints are continuous and planar and have the least favourable

inclination with regard to the main cavern (Fig. 2)
- the ratio of the horizontal (σ_x = -1.8 MPa) and the vertical components (σ_y = -4.5 MPa) of geostatic stresses K_o = 0,4, which was measured in the adit is valid for the whole section under consideration
- the biotitic paragneiss can be considered as transversally isotropic medium
- with regard to the rock type - - crystalline paragneiss - the time effect is ignored
- the immediate filling of the gap between the concrete arch and the surrounding rock, i.e. a perfect contact between them is assumed
- prestressed bolts and anchors are simulated by a pair of forces corresponding to the magnitude of prestressing and by the rock mass shear strength parameters remaining unchanged in the anchored zones.

In view of the extent of geological investigation preceding the FEM analysis, the advanced stage of the design, and the fact that the power station was already under construction, a detailed computational model was formulated.

4. ALGORITHM OF THE SOLUTION

The algorithm was based on the incremental method frequently used for the solution of the nonlinear problems (Kolář et al, 1975). It was supplemented with some procedures for the determination of factors mentioned in Chapter 3. This was necessary for the correct physical modelling of the rock mass.

4.1 Constitutive equations

The constitutive equations were approximated by the following relations:

$$E = (E_o - k\,\sigma_{oct})\,(1 - h^n), \qquad (5.1)$$

$$\mu = \mu_o + (\mu_{max} - \mu_o)\cdot h^{m_1}, \qquad (5.2)$$

where

$$h = \frac{\tau_{oct}}{{}^m\tau_{oct}},$$

$${}^m\tau_{oct} = k_1 - k_2\,\sigma_{oct}, \qquad (5.3)$$

$$k_1 = \frac{2\sqrt{2}\,c\cdot tg\delta}{2 + tg^2\delta}, \qquad (5.4)$$

$$k_2 = \frac{2\,(tg^2\delta - 1)}{2 + tg^2\delta}, \qquad (5.5)$$

$$\delta = \frac{\pi}{4} + \frac{\varphi}{2},$$

c, φ are parameters of shear strength, k, n, m_1 are constants determined experimentally. The tension is taken as positive.

During the computational process the loading and the unloading are checked using σ_{oct}. In the case of loading the stress is compared with the tensile or shear strength of the rock material. The tension is checked by its limit value σ_t. The limit values of stress are represented in the σ_1 σ_2 σ_3 space by a cone open at the base. Using this cone and the generalized Von Mieses failure hypothesis we check the shear stress by relations (5.1) - (5.5). If the stress reaches the corresponding strength the limit values of deformation modul and Poisson's ratio E_{min}, μ_{max} are used. This enables us to describe the mecha-

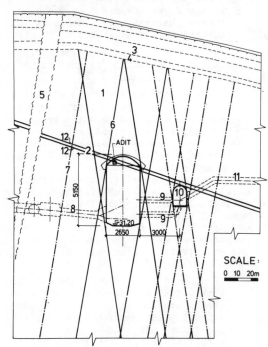

Fig.2 Schematic geological section (1, 2, ... 12 - material numbers)

SCALE:
0 10 20m

nical behaviour of the material in failure.

In the case of unloading the folowing approximations were applied:

$$E = (E_{UN} - k \, \sigma_{OCT}) \, (1 - h^n), \qquad (5.6)$$

$$\omega = \omega_{UN} + (\omega_{max} - \omega_{UN}) \, h^{m_2} . \qquad (5.7)$$

Some typical values of E_{UN}, ω_{UN} are given in TAB 1. This approximation may be taken as a crude simulation of the plastic deformation of the rock mass.

4.2 The anisotropy of deformation

The rock mass - biotitic paragneiss - has a layered structure. The deformative and strength properties of the materials were therefore modelled as transversal isotropic.

The values of the deformation moduli E_1, E_2 were determined by oriented experiments. An approximative relation was used for the determination of the generally independent value G_2 (Zolotarev, 1973):

$$G_2 = \frac{E_2}{1 + \dfrac{E_2}{E_1} + 2\,\omega_2} \qquad (5.8)$$

The results of the loading tests showed a distinct influence of the level of the stress on E_1, i.e. the modulus in the direction of foliation (this direction encloses an angle β with the positive direction of the axis x). The modulus E_2 - vertical to the direction of foliation - was nearly independent of the growth of loading. The constitutive relations (5.1) - (5.5) have therefore been applied only to the quantity E_1, ω_1, while E_2 and ω_2 have been considered constant until the stress has reached the limit state.

The fulfilment of the condition:

$$\frac{E_2}{E_1} (1 - \omega_1) - 2 \, \omega_2^2 > 0, \qquad (5.9)$$

which expresses the positivity of the deformation energy of the elastic material was also checked in the programme.

4.3 The anisotropy of strength

The shear strength of biotitic paragneiss displays distinct anisotropy. The growth of the shear strength is dependent on the direction of the maximum compression stress (taken at absolute value). For each of the triangular elements the parameters of the shear stress c, tg φ were determined as follows. If the direction of the maximum compression stress deviates from the direction of foliation by an angle $\delta < 55°$, then the strength on the foliation surfaces is applied, i.e.c $\parallel$, tg $\varphi \parallel$. For the values $55° < \delta < 90°$ the values c, tg φ are determined by linear interpolation in the intervals $< c \parallel , c \perp >$, $< tg \varphi \parallel , tg \varphi \perp >$, where c $\perp$, tg $\varphi \perp$ are the parameters of the shear strength in the vertical direction of foliation.

This approach which has been used in the algorithm is in its simplified form analogous to the analytical relation introduced in (Hibino et al, 1977).

4.4 Redistribution of overstresses

During the calculation there occurs in the model at a selected stage of the solution an exceeding of the tensile or shear strength in a certain number of elements comprising the area of the rock mass. This phenomenon reduces the accuracy of the model, since the materials used in it then have a higher strength than strenght valid for the rock mass. Thus we choose an algorithm which, in the computing step being performed, will determine the excesses of shear or tensile strength in the elements, and according to common procedures used in FEM estabilishes equivalent nodal forces to eliminate this phenomenon.

A tensile failure occurs where the following relation is fulfilled for a maximum tensile stress of σ_1 (positive designation):

$$\sigma_1 > \sigma_t ,$$

where σ_t is the tensile strength input.

The contribution of overstresses is established by the relation

$$\varkappa_1 = \frac{\sigma_1 - \sigma_t}{\sigma_1} . \qquad (5.10)$$

If

$$\sigma_2 > \sigma_t$$

is also valid for the second principal stress, then

$$\mathcal{X}_2 = \frac{\widetilde{\sigma}_2 - \widetilde{\sigma}_t}{\widetilde{\sigma}_2}, \qquad (5.11)$$

otherwise

$$\mathcal{X}_2 = 0. \qquad (5.12)$$

We assume that the increase of principal stresses $\Delta\widetilde{\sigma}_i$ (i = 1, 2, 3) encloses the same angles with positive directions of the coordinates as the principal stresses calculated in the previous step - ${}^p\widetilde{\sigma}_i$ (i = 1, 2, 3). This assumption also applies to shear failure.

Then

$$\widetilde{\sigma}_1 = {}^p\widetilde{\sigma}_1 + \Delta\widetilde{\sigma}_1, \qquad (5.13)$$
$$\widetilde{\sigma}_2 = {}^p\widetilde{\sigma}_2 + \Delta\widetilde{\sigma}_2,$$
$$\widetilde{\sigma}_3 = {}^p\widetilde{\sigma}_3 + \Delta\widetilde{\sigma}_3.$$

The stress compontents in the selected Cartesian system of coordinates for which the equivalent nodal forces are established are then:

$$\overline{\Delta\widetilde{\sigma}_x} = (\mathcal{X}_2 \cdot \widetilde{\sigma}_2 \cdot P_1 + \mathcal{X}_1 \cdot \widetilde{\sigma}_1)/(1+P_1), \quad (5.14)$$

$$\overline{\Delta\sigma_y} = (\mathcal{X}_1 \cdot \widetilde{\sigma}_1 \cdot P_1 + \mathcal{X}_2 \cdot \widetilde{\sigma}_2)/(1+P_1),$$

$$\overline{\Delta\tau_{xy}} = (\mathcal{X}_1 \cdot \widetilde{\sigma}_1 - \overline{\Delta\widetilde{\sigma}_x})/P_1,$$

where P_1 = tgα (α is the angle of stress $\widetilde{\sigma}_1$ or ${}^p\widetilde{\sigma}_1$).

With <u>shear failure</u> the situation is more complex. We define the function

$$F = {}^m\widetilde{\tau}_{oct} - \widetilde{\tau}_{oct}$$

and depict its limiting values in the simple diagram

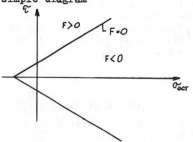

If in the previous step the relation ${}^pF \leq 0$ held for a given element stressed to (${}^p\widetilde{\sigma}_1$, ${}^p\widetilde{\sigma}_2$, ${}^p\sigma_3$), in the current computation step for the same element stressed to (${}^p\widetilde{\sigma}_1 + \Delta\widetilde{\sigma}_1$,

${}^p\widetilde{\sigma}_2 + \Delta\widetilde{\sigma}_2$, ${}^p\widetilde{\sigma}_3 + \Delta\widetilde{\sigma}_3$) the relation $F > 0$ holds, then $\mathcal{X}$ in the interval $0 < \mathcal{X} < 1$ is established from:

$$A\mathcal{X}^2 + B\mathcal{X} + C = 0, \qquad (5.15)$$

where

$$A = \frac{1}{4}\left[(\Delta\widetilde{\sigma}_1 - \Delta\widetilde{\sigma}_2)^2 + (\Delta\widetilde{\sigma}_2 - \Delta\widetilde{\sigma}_3)^2 + (\Delta\widetilde{\sigma}_3 - \Delta\widetilde{\sigma}_1)^2 - k_2^2 P^2 \right], \qquad (5.16)$$

$$B = \frac{2}{9}\left[({}^p\widetilde{\sigma}_1 - {}^p\widetilde{\sigma}_2)(\Delta\widetilde{\sigma}_1 - \Delta\widetilde{\sigma}_2) + ({}^p\widetilde{\sigma}_2 - {}^p\widetilde{\sigma}_3)(\Delta\widetilde{\sigma}_2 - \Delta\widetilde{\sigma}_3) + ({}^p\widetilde{\sigma}_3 - {}^p\widetilde{\sigma}_1)(\Delta\widetilde{\sigma}_3 - \Delta\widetilde{\sigma}_1) - k_2^2 JP + 3k_1 k_2 P \right],$$

$$C = \frac{1}{9}\left[({}^p\widetilde{\sigma}_1 - {}^p\widetilde{\sigma}_2)^2 + ({}^p\widetilde{\sigma}_2 - {}^p\widetilde{\sigma}_3)^2 + ({}^p\widetilde{\sigma}_3 - {}^p\widetilde{\sigma}_1)^2 - 9k_1^2 + 6k_1 k_2 J - k_2^2 J^2 \right],$$

$$J = {}^p\widetilde{\sigma}_1 + {}^p\widetilde{\sigma}_2 + {}^p\widetilde{\sigma}_3,$$

$$P = \Delta\widetilde{\sigma}_1 + \Delta\widetilde{\sigma}_2 + \Delta\widetilde{\sigma}_3,$$

k_1, k_2 – see the section Constitutive Equations.

The stress components for which the equivalent nodal forces are calculated as follows:

$$\overline{\Delta\widetilde{\sigma}_x} = [(1-\mathcal{X})\Delta\widetilde{\sigma}_2 \cdot P_1 + (1-\mathcal{X})\Delta\widetilde{\sigma}_1]/(1+P_1),$$

$$\overline{\Delta\sigma_y} = [(1-\mathcal{X})\Delta\widetilde{\sigma}_1 \cdot P_1 + (1-\mathcal{X})\Delta\widetilde{\sigma}_2]/(1+P_1),$$

$$\overline{\Delta\tau_{xy}} = [(1-\mathcal{X})\Delta\widetilde{\sigma}_1 - \overline{\Delta\widetilde{\sigma}_x}]/P_1 \text{ resp.}$$

$$\overline{\Delta\tau_{xy}} = [\overline{\Delta\sigma_y} - (1-\mathcal{X})\Delta\widetilde{\sigma}_2]/P_1,$$

where P_1 has the same significance as in the case of a tensile failure.

The procedures described apply to the elimination of **overstresses** (tensile and shear) in a single isolated triangular element. In order to eliminate these unwanted phenomena in a subarea containing more than one failed element, an iterative procedure must be used.

4.5 Joints

Line contact elements with branching nodes were used. Their interpolation functions are linear, which ensures the compatibility of these elements with the triangular elements used. The deformation of contact elements is determined by normal and shear stiffness (k_n or k_t).

Following a tensile failure normal stiffnes is zero, following a shear failure - according to the Mohr-Coulomb theory- - the shear stiffness falls to a residual value. The use of the joint elements has a considerable influence on the correct modelling the rock mass behaviour. Instead of calculating continuum, pseudocontinuum is calculated, where movements are realized on predisposed surfaces.

The derivation of the stiffness matrix, the calculation of normal and shear stress and the procedure for establishing equivalent nodal forces can be found in (Goodmann et al, 1968).

numbers.

The reason for the numbering of the material with numbers 8, 9, 11 is that during construction there is a weakening of the rock mass in the regions parallel to the plane of solution. The effect of weakening is modelled by a lowering of the initial stresses in the corresponding elements. We introduce the notion of "reduced materials". For each of these material we prescribe in the corresponding computational stage a coefficient of reduction - p. From the point of view of the algorithm this is an analogical strategy used in the case of the deleted elements.

	E_1 [MPa]	μ_1	k	n	γ	C‖ [MPa]	tg Ψ‖	C⊥ [MPa]	tgΨ⊥	E_0 [MPa]	E_{min} [MPa]	σ_t [MPa]	E_{UN} [MPa]	μ_{max}	μ_{UN}	m_1	m_2	COSβ	E_2 [MPa]	μ_2	μ_0
1	30000	0,26	300	2	27,6	0,90	0,582	2	1,0	30000	3000	0,90	41000	0,47	0,22	2	2	-0,956	12000	0,18	0,26
2	6500	0,27	130	1,13	27,2	0,56	0,932	1,75	1,0	6500	600	0,40	30000	0,38	0,27	0,8	2	-0,956	2000	0,27	0,27
3	4000	0,20	0	1	26,7	0,48	1,0	0,48	1,0	4000	600	0,50	5000	0,20	0,20	1	1	-0,956	4000	0,20	0,20
L	17000	0,20	0	1	26,7	0,84	1,0	0,84	1,0	17000	2500	0,70	17500	0,20	0,20	1	1	-0,956	17000	0,20	0,20
5	1000	0,32	83	1,75	26,7	0,10	0,7	0,10	0,7	1000	150	0,10	2200	0,38	0,32	0,8	2	-0,956	1000	0,32	0,32
8	30000	0,26	300	2	27,6	0,90	0,582	2	1,0	30000	3000	0,90	41000	0,47	0,22	2	2	-0,956	12000	0,18	0,26
9	30000	0,26	300	2	27,6	0,90	0,582	2	1,0	30000	3000	0,90	41000	0,47	0,22	2	2	-0,956	12000	0,18	0,26
10	30000	0,26	300	2	27,6	0,90	0,582	2	1,0	30000	3000	0,90	41000	0,47	0,22	2	2	-0,956	12000	0,18	0,26
11	30000	0,26	300	2	27,6	0,90	0,582	2	1,0	30000	3000	0,90	41000	0,47	0,22	2	2	-0,956	12000	0,18	0,26
13 ×	25000	0,15	0	1	25,0	4	0,9	4	0,9	25000	12500	2,50	25000	0,15	0,15	2	2	1	25000	0,15	0,15

× CONCRETE

Tab. 1   Material properties of the rock mass

5 DESCRIPTION OF THE COMPUTATIONAL MODEL

The region was divided into 2793 triangular and joint elements with 1655 nodes. The resulting system of linear algebraic equations was solved by the Gauss elimination method. The computation was performed on the Swedish computer DATASAAB D21 with floating point unit. This is a computer of the 2nd generation. Its programming language is ALGOLGENIUS (a combination of ALGOL 60 and COBOL). A triangular element with the linear polynomial in x, y for displacement functions u, v was used for the solution.

5.1 Input data

In the following text we restrict ourselves to an account of the input data which describe the properties of the rock mass. They are given in TAB.1 (triangular elements) and in TAB. 2 (joints). The materials are denoted in the schematic geological section (FIG.2) by corresponding

5.2 The loading stages

The main construction stages were numerically modelled. The original geological stress-state of the rock mass was considered the initial stage of the solution. This stress-state was determined by the solution of a two-dimensional elastic boundary value problem. The material was assumed to be isotropic. Constants E, μ were selected to correspond

	KN [kN/m³]	KS [kN/m³]	C [MPa]	tg Ψ	KT [kN/m³]	δ [m]	σ_T [MPa]
6	800000	657000	0	0,625	66000	-0,002	0
7	1150000	283000	0,05	1,0	28000	-0,002	0
12	800000	657000	0	0,625	66000	-0,002	0

KN - NORMAL STIFFNESS
KS - SHEAR STIFFNESS
KT - RESIDUAL SHEAR STIFFNESS
δ - JOIUT DOSURE
σ - TENSILE STRENGTH

Tab. 2   Material properties of the joints

213

to the measured stresses σ_x = 1.8 MPa, σ_y = 4.5 MPa in the adit. The second criterion for the determination of these constants was the ratio

$$K_o = \frac{\sigma_x}{\sigma_y} = 0.4$$

measured in the adit, in the upper part of the cavern.

The upper boundary of the region under consideration was loaded by nodal loads corresponding to the weight of the upper layers removed from the model. Using this approach we cannot obtain the same values of vertical stress σ_y as measured. In the rock mass the values of σ_y measured always exceed the values of the

lution.

At the end of this stage the influence of anchoring at the roof the cavern was simulated.

The second computational stage models the excavation of the full roof and the construction of the arch springers. Thirteen interative steps were performed, including the determination of the influence of anchoring. The third stage models the concreting of the arch of the cavern and the excavation of the spherical branch cavern. The reduction of materials No 8, 9, 11 used is $p_8 = p_9 = p_{11} = 0.2$. In the fourth stage the excavation of the upper part of the cavern main is modelled (11 interative steps including anchoring) and at the

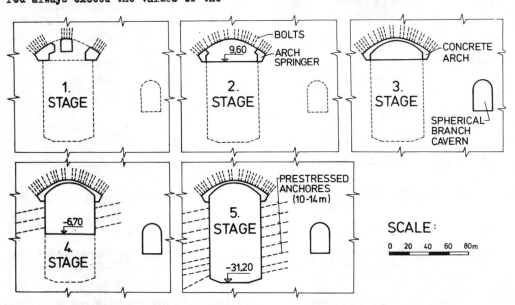

Fig. 3 Construction work sequence simulated by the computational model

overburden pressure. For this reason the upper boundary of the triangulated region was loaded by a fictive loading to obtain a better agreement between the measured and computed values of σ_y.

The further stages of the computational process, consisting of the excavation, anchoring and concreting, are schematically demonstrated in the following figure (Fig. 3).

The first computational stage models the excavation of adit in the roof region of the cavern. There were seven iterative steps in which the redistribution of stresses was performed in order to eliminate the overstresses from the so-

end the whole excavation of the main cavern is modelled (8 iterative steps including anchoring).

6 SOLUTION RESULTS

The analysis carried out provided detailed information on the strains and stresses of the rock mass and the concrete arch for all loading stages under consideration.

The displacements of the rock mass after finishing all construction work (excavation of full sections of the caverns setting and prestressing of bolts and anchors, concreting the arch) are plotted in Figs. 4 and 5. The vertical displacements are substantially larger than the horizontal ones, especially above the schisted zone of the rock. This is evidently caused by the greater loading effect and greater compressibility of the rock mass in this direction due to anisotropy. The maximum displacement - - 24 mm - arises in the part of the roof where it is crossed by the schisted layer. Approximately the same movement occurs in the roof of the smaller cavern with a much shorter span - 10 m. The unfavourable influence of the larger cavern is demonstrated, the influence zone of which is considerable ($\frac{B + H}{2}$ = 39 m

according to Hayashi at al, 1979) in comparison with the width of the pillar (25 m) between the caverns.

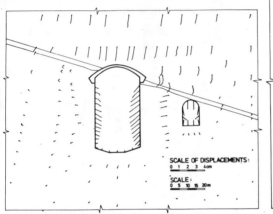

Fig. 4 Displacement vectors of the rock mass surrounding the caverns

crease in the cavern span, utilizing the rock mass bearing capacity for the temporary and permanent support) it could grow as a main factor determining the excavation work sequence.

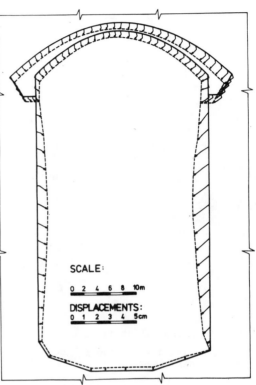

SCALE:

0 2 4 6 8 10m

DISPLACEMENTS:

0 1 2 3 4 5cm

Fig. 5 Displacement vectors along the cavern surface

Due to the favourable subhorizontal bedding of the paragneiss the relieving of the 40 m high rock walls caused comparatively small displacements. The lateral deflection of the pressure side wall is 16 mm, the buckling of the opposite wall does not reach 9 mm (Fig. 5). This favourable influence of the bedding is emphasized by other authors, too (Hayashi et al, 1979, Sharp et al, 1979), and it is proof of the suitable location and orientation of the caverns. On the other hand the solution indicates considerable horizontal displacements in the pillar, which demonstrate the mutual influence of the caverns. This influence was proved by the FEM analysis (Doležalová, 1979) and measured in situ in the underground power station Shintakasegawa (Mizukoshi, Mimaki, 1979). This is a factor which was previously neglected but now according to modern trends (in-

The stress state redistribution caused by the excavation work is demonstrated in Fig. 6. Along the cavern surface a large stress concentration occurs, especially in the tangential direction (up to three times the original values) while in the normal direction a considerable reduction stresses can be found. Extensive tensile zones arise around the cavern, 6 m in the roof and 17 and 12 m in the walls. The distribution of the principal stresses in the roof of the cavern demonstrates the effect of the large excavation span as well as the favourable effect of the reduction of this span by the arch springers constructed before the roof excavation.

The shear and tensile failure zones with the maximum extent of 6 m are plotted in Fig. 7. As regards the joints, the extent of the failure zones is even larger according to their low strength and continuity as assumed by the computational model.

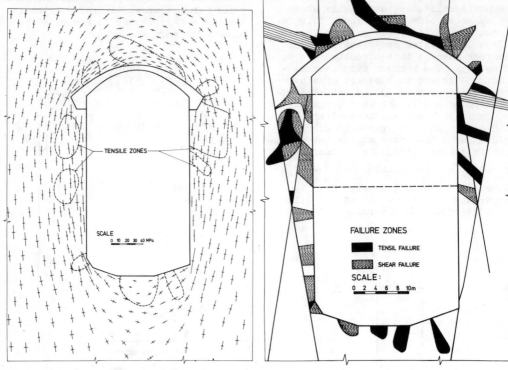

Fig. 6 Principal stresses around the cavern after the 5th computational stage

Fig. 7 Failure zones around the excavation

The strains and stresses of the concrete arch were computed assuming a perfect contact between the arch and the surrounding rock mass. This is particularly important for the springers of the arch, which are concreted in advance in order to achieve a reduction in the actual span of the roof excavation from the original 33.5 m to 26.5 m. However, the positive effect seen in Fig. 6 and 7 occurs only when the construction gap between the springer and the rock surface has been effectively eliminated.

The concrete arch is loaded by its own weight and also by movement of the rock mass on which it rests. First there is an nonuniform settlement of the springers and an increase in the span of the arch under the influence of its own weight. During the gradual excavation of the main of cavern a pronounced convergence of the walls come into play (2 mm in the case of the left wall, 6 mm in the case of the right wall), which induces a compression of the whole arch

except for the springers. The springers are under tension and the tensile strength of the concrete along the line of contact with the rock is exceeded. Thus springers of the arch must be constructed of the reinforced concrete.

7 DISCUSSION AND EVALUATION OF THE RESULTS

Before drawing any conclusions the correctness of results obtained has to be evaluated, including their completeness, from the point of view of the problems to be solved.

The computed displacements are similar to the measured ones in analogous structures as regards both their magnitude and distribution (Hibino, S. et al., 1977, Yoshida, M., Yoshimura, K. 1970, and others). The use of the joint elements has a favourable influence on the computation results as they allow the concentration of the movements on the predis-

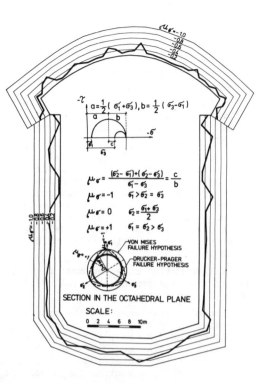

Fig. 8 Lode parameter along the cavern
outline

posed surfaces in a way corresponding to
reality. On the other hand not all
overstresses have been removed from the
solution (this concerns above all the
joints with extremely low strength and
the excavation surfaces). Accordingly
the computed displacements are rather
smaller, i.e. they do not correspond
absolutely to the extent of the computed
failure zones.

The considerable extent of failure zones corresponds to the input data selected in order to keep the solution on the
safe side. Supplementary geological investigations discovered that the asump-
tion of the continuity of the joint
systems is valid only for the system
perpendicular to the main cavern axis
and that the remaining systems are discontinuous. Hence, it follows that the
extent of the failure zone around the
cavern should be reduced in comparision
with the computed results.

Taking this into consideration, we can
attempt to answer the questions put before starting the analysis.

As regards the feasibility of the project, the answer is clear and positive.
Even for the computed extent of failure

zones the size of the temporary support
does not exceed the acceptable limits:
the length of the bolts 6.0 m, the
anchors 10 - 14 m with average value of
prestressing 0.083 MN/m^2 in the cavern
roof and 0.071 MN/m^2 along the cavern
walls.

Concerning the value of prestressing
of the bolts and anchors it has to be
noted that for the given relations between the geostatic stresses, shear
strength of the rock mass and range of
prestressing values, it is impossible to
determine the correct value of the latter by FEM computation. The reason is
the inaccuracy of the computed stresses
along the excavation surface where the
possible deviations approach the magnitude of the rock mass cohesion and bolt
prestressing. Analogous conclusions have
been drawn by other authors (Manfredini
et al., 1976). Hence it follows that in
the given conditions, characterized by
large values of geostatic stresses and
low values of the residual shear strength,
the FEM analysis performed could be useful for anchor length design, but not for
the determination of its prestressing.

As regards the concrete arch the FEM
calculation demonstrated a considerable
influence of the convergence of the arch
springers on the stress state of the
arch. The greater part of the arch is
compressed but the springers produce
tension. This type of stress state is
considerably different from the previously common static scheme: the loading of
the arch by loosened rock causing bending, possibly an increase in arch span.
The results of monitoring, however, confirm the computed type of stress state
of the arch, and thus it can be considered accurate (Hibino et al. 1977,
Yoshida, Yoshimura, 1970, Mizukoshi,
Mimaki, 1979). As a matter of fact, technical progress in excavation supporting
manifests itself, successfully limiting
the loosening of the rock mass. This
ought lead to a change in the type structure, i.e. to replacing concrete arches
by prestressed anchors and reinforced
schotcrete (Bart, 1972).

From this discussion there also follow the problems still to be solved. It
will be necessary to improve the procedure for computing the excavation surface stresses and modelling bolts and
anchors. The face influence (Wittke,
1975, 1976, Maury, 1979) including the
time effect has to be taken into account
also. The problem consists in the retardation of the stress redistribution and

the development of the deformations in
the rock mass around large caverns. This
retardation can influence the magnitude
and the distribution of displacements
considerably and it has also been registered by field measurements in crystalline rock (Mizukoshi, Mimaki, 1979).
All these factors have to be considered
in the next computational stage, which
is to be performed due to the new findings of supplementary geological investigations.

8 CONCLUSIONS AND RECOMMENDATIONS

According to the FEM-analysis performed
we can conclude that

- the orientation of the cavern in the
  rock mass is favourable and it produces acceptable conditions for the construction of a cavern of the required
  size
- the subhorizontal bedding of the biotitic paragneiss forms favourable
  conditions for ensuring the stability
  of the heigh rock walls
- the stability of the cavern roof is
  lower than stability of the walls and
  if the roof were excavated to the full
  length without permanent support the
  formation of larger displacements than
  the computed ones cannot be excluded
- the computed stress state and the
  extent of the failure zones are kept
  on the safe side with respect of some
  assumptions of the solution (low value
  of the coefficient at rest K_o for geostatic stress state and the continuity
  of the joints)
- for the underground spaces of the given size it is necessary to consider
  the successive redistribution of the
  stresses and strains in the rock mass
  with time; the corresponding values of
  the displacements could be larger than
  the computed ones
- the concrete arch is loaded above all
  by the movements of the surrounding
  rock mass during the excavation; the
  convergence and nonuniform settlement
  of the arch springers cause the formation of tension zones in the springers.

According to the FEM-analysis so far
performed the following measures are
required in order to secure the stability of the rock mass around the underground spaces:

- extending the length of the bolts to
  6 m and of anchors to 10 - 14 m, and
  increasing their prestressing in the
  selected zones of the cavern
- using reinforced concrete for the arch
  spingers
- fitting the excavation shape to the
  computed stress state of the rock mass
  (bevelling the walls and rounding the
  sharp cuts)
- the modification of the excavation
  sequence in order to minimize the
  unfavourable stress concentration; the
  stress state of the rock mass could be
  considerably improved if the excavation of the spherical branch cavern
  and the inlet and outlet tunnels was
  performed prior to the excavation of
  the cavern main.

The information obtained must be included in the measurement observation project. We recommend:

- increasing the length of the extensometers (by up to 30 - 35 m) and decreasing their number; the aim is to
  measure the time scale of the displacements in individual zones of the rocl
  mass, which is essential for a correct
  interpretation of movements of the
  excavation face
- in view of the extensive zone of influence of excavation the location of
  fixed points at greater distances
  (80 - 100 m) from the excavation face
- to pay particular attention to the
  timing of measurements, which should
  correlate closely with that of excavation work and react flexibly to changes in it.

In view of new information regarding
the tectonic conditions in the area of
the cavern further steps in the FEM calculation must be performed. The followin
problems must be solved:

- more accurate modelling of the stresses in the joint systems and on the
  excavation face
- closer simulation of the effect of
  anchorages
- modelling of the excavation face influence in connection with the effect
  of time on the stresses and strains
  of the rock mass.

ACKNOWLEDGEMENT

The authors wish to express their gratitude to Professor V. Mencl for his help-
ful suggestions during the formulation
of the computational model and the preparation of the input data.

9 REFERENCES

Barth,S. 1972, Felsmechanische Probleme
beim Entwurf der Kaverne des Pumpspeicherwerkes Waldeck II. Die Bautechnik, Heft 3.

Doležalová,M. 1979, The influence on
construction work sequence on the stability of underground openings. Proc.
of 3rd Int. Conf. on Num. Math. Methods in Geomechanics, Aachen, Germany.

Goodmann,R.E., R.L. Taylor, L.Brekke 1968,
A model for the mechanics of jointed
rock. Proc. ASCE, SN, V.

Hayashi,M. et al. 1979, Detection of
anisotropic geostresses trying by
acoustic emission and non-linear rock
mechanics on large excavating caverns.
Proc. of 4th Congress ISRM, Montreux,
Switzerland.

Hibina,S. et al. 1977, Forecast and
measurement of behaviour of rock masses during underground excavation
works. Int. Symp. of Field Measurements, Zurich.

Kolář,V., J.Kratochvíl, F.Leitner,
A.Ženíšek 1975, Berechnung von Flächen und Raumtragwerken nach der Methode der finiten Elemente. Springer
Verlag, Wien - New York.

Maury,V. 1979, Use of test and measurements in laboratory and in situ for
five projects of underground storage.
4th Int. Congress of ISRM, Montreux.

Manfredini,G., S.Martinetti, R.Ribacchi,
R.Riccioni 1976, Design criteria for
anchor cables and bolting in under-
ground openings. Proc. of Int. Conf. on
Num. Math. in Geomechanics, Blacksburg,
USA.

Mizukoshi,T., Y.Mimaki 1979, The behaviour of bedrock by the large carvern
opening and comparison with the analysis. Proc. of 4th Congress ISRM,
Montreux, Switzerland.

Poisel,R. 1981, Ein Beitrag zur Wir-
kungweise von Systemankerungen bei
tiefliegenden Gebirghohlraumbauten.
Rock Mechanics, Suppl. 11.

Sharp,J.C. et al. 1979, The use of a
trial enlargement for the underground
cavern design of the Drakensberg Pumped Storage Scheme. Proc. of the 4th
Congress ISRM, Montreux, Switzerland.

Terzaghi,K. 1946, Introduction to tunnel geology. Ohio.

Wittke,W. 1976, Stability analysis of
tunnels in jointed rock. Proc. of Int.
Conf. on Num. Math. in Geomechanics,
Blacksburg, USA.

Wittke,W. 1975, New design concept for
underground openings in rock. Int.
Symp. on Num. Meth. in Soil Mechanics
and Rock Mechanics, Karlsruhe, BRD.

Yoshia,M., K.Yoshimura 1970, Deformation
of rock mass and stres. in concrete
lining around the machine hall of
Kysenyama Underground Power Plant.
2nd Congress ISRM, Belgrade.

Zolotarev,G.S. et al. 1973, Opyt ocenki
ustojčivosti sklonov složnogo geolo-
gičeskogo strojenija metodom konečnych
elementov i experimentami na modeljach,
Moskva.

POWERHOUSE CAVERN OF THE HYDROELECTRIC COMPLEX 'RIO GRANDE NO. 1'

Kraftwerkskaverne des hydroelektrischen Komplexes 'Rio Grande No. 1'

Caverne de la centrale électrique du complexe hydroélectrique 'Rio Grande No. 1'

RICARDO DORSO, JUAN C.DEL RÍO, DANIEL DE LA TORRE & RAÚL SARRA PISTONE
Agua y Energía Eléctrica, Soc. del Estado, Córdoba, Argentina

SUMMARY:

The purpose of this paper is to describe the Powerhouse Cavern of Río Grande I as regards the following aspects: Geological explorations, theoretical studies and measurements of deformations, construction techniques and support system. Geological explorations included photogeological studies, drillings and geoelectrical and geoseismic prospections. Uniaxial and triaxial compression, tensile and shear stress tests were carried out from intact rock cores. In order to determine the mechanical property of the rock mass, plate bearing and in situ shear tests and measurements of in situ stress conditions were undertaken in special tunnel recesses during the construction of the Access Tunnel. Mathematic models of Finite Elements (FEM) and Boundary Elements (BEM) were applied to predict any deformations surrounding the cavern. Mechanical and electrical extensometers and load cells for bolts were placed to measure these deformations. Rock bolts were installed as definitive support, as a result of a detailed geological mapping of the structural features found in the excavations. Also shotcrete with mesh was applied in particular zones against the roof where the rock was badly jointed. Finally the roof was lined with a galvanized wire mesh. Once the excavations were finished, satisfactory performance of the support was proved and the monitored deformations were compared with the predicted ones.

ZUSAMMENFASSUNG:

Diese Arbeit hat den Zweck der Darstellung der Zentrale in der Kaverne mit folgenden Aussehen: Grund-forschung, Arbeits-weise, Stütz-system und Studium und Messung von Verformung. Die Grund untersuchung wurden speziell mit Fotogeologie, Bohrungen mit Entnahme der Bohrprobe. Geoelektrische und Geoseismische Schürfarbeit durchgeführt. Die Bohrproben wurden mit einfachen Druckversuch und Triaxialer Druckversuch sowie Scherwiderstand und Zugspanhung geprüft. Um die genauen mechanischen Eigenschaften des Gesteins während des Banes des Lugangs Tunnel zuerkunden wurden spezielle Nischen angelegt. In diesen Nischen wurden die Proben von Druckversuch, Scherversuch und innere Spannungsmessung. Um die Veränderung umliegend der Kaverne voranssagen zu können, wurde die mathematischemethode von Finite-Element und Bord-Element angewannt. Um diese Veränderungen zu messen wurden mechanische und elektrische Extensometer und Ankerkraftmesser angebracht. Als endgültige Stütze wurden Ankergliederung nach Grundlage einer geologischen Detailzeichnung angelegt. Man verwendete Schutzstreifen von Spritzbeton auf Stahldraht in Zonen wo Spalten am meissten auftraten und das Gewölbe wurde mit einem galvanisierten Maschendraht verkleidet. Man konnte feststellen, nach beendeter Ausschachtung, das Ergebnis der Anlage Stütze beiden Vergleich der Verschiebungen war der Gleiche wie die Messvorhersage.

RESUME:

Ce travail a pour objet la description de la Centrale en Caverne de Rio Grande par rapport à: Recherches de base, étude et mesures de déformations, méthodologie de construction et système de support. Les recherches de base ont été réalisées sur la base des études photogéologiques, perforations avec l'extraction des échantillons et prospections géoélectriet géoséismiques. Les échantillons ont été essayés à la compression simple et triaxiale, à la coupure et à la traction. Afin de préciser les caratéristiques mécaniques du massif rocheux, on a effectué pendant la construction du tunnel Carretier, dans des niches speciales des essais de charges, de coupure et des mesures de tensions naturelle. Pour prédire les déformations autour de la Caverne on a appliqué les modèles mathématiques d'Element Finit et d'Element de Bord. Pour mesurer ces déformations sont employés extensomètres mécaniques, électriques et cellules de charge pour boulons. Comme support définitif on a appliqué un boulonnage structural sur la base d'un relèvement géologique de détail. On a mis des panneaux isolés de gunite armée en zones òu le diaclassement fut plus intense et on a recouvert toute la voûte avec une maille de fils de fers galvanisés. Après avoir fini les excavations on a pu vérifier le fonctionnement du support installé et comparer les déformations mesurée et prévues.

1 INTRODUCTION

The purpose of this work is a description of the Río Grande Cavern in its principal aspects, which was totally excavated when this report was made.

The Río Grande N°1 Hydroelectric Complex is located in the Province of Córdoba, in the centre of the Argentine Republic, 700 km NW of Buenos Aires.

Agua y Energía Eléctrica, a State Enterprise, is the owner, has made the basic project and is in charge of the control of the works.

The complex will allow:

1. The installation of a pumping-storage scheme, with an underground machine hall. The output will be 750 MW, with a mean annual generation of 977 GWh, and an energy demand of 1180 GWh/year. The effective head will be 178 m and the generation flow 500 m3/sec.

2. The installation of a conventional hydroelectric powerhouse 10 MW output, and 15.5 GWh/year of mean generation at the lower reservoir, Arroyo Corto.

3. The forming of the Cerro Pelado reservoir of yearly regulation of 371 hm3 capacity, which will contain a great energy reserve in the order of 88 GWh.

4. The forming of Arroyo Corto reservoir of weekly compensation of 30.8 hm3 capacity which will permit weekend pumping.

The project has been conceived to cover the daily peak loads of the National Interconnected System, and should start functioning in 1985.

1.1 Project

The Río Grande, principal tributary of the Río Tercero, on which the Hydroelectric Complex is being constructed, has a module of 11.5 m3/sec, with two typical periods during the year, one of low water from May to September and another of high water from October to April.

In the length of the Río Grande between the main dam of Cerro Pelado and the empla-cement of Arroyo Corto dam, the river has a fall of 120 m in 12.5 km.

The total underground works involve the construction of 3,100 m of access tunnels, 6,800 m of tunnels for water conveyance and 350 m of vertical shafts. The total excavation volume is 1,533,000 m3.

The location of the Cavern was fixed on the southern hillside of Cerro Pelado, with its longitudinal axis parallel to the axis of the principal dam, and displaced 65 m downstream to this. The middle plan of the distributor is at 130 m below the river bed. Its dimensions are: 105 m long, 27 m maximum wide and 50 m high. The volume is 100,000 m3.

Another important structure of the project is the Tailrace Tunnel, whose section is 12 m wide and 18 m high with a length of 5,504 m.

2 GEOLOGICAL AND GEOTECHNICAL SURVEYS

2.1 Introduction

The geological, geophisical and rock mechanics studies to define the quality of the mass in which the Cavern for the Río Grande Powerhouse was to be constructed, may be grouped in:

1. Preconstruction studies.
2. Studies during construction.

The first were developed by the Jefatura de Estudios y Proyectos Zona Centro Cuyo de AGUA Y ENERGIA between 1970 and 1972.

The latter were developed by AGUA Y ENERGIA and the contractor in charge of civil works PANEDILE ARGENTINA S.A. through their consultants: ESTUDIO PIETRANGELI (Italy), BOLOGNESI-MORETTO, ING.CONSULTORES S.R.L. (Argentina) and GOLDER ASSOCIATES (Canada), from 1976 to 1981, when the excavation was finished.

A description of the studies undertaken follows; methods and instruments used and a synthesis made of the conclusions which contributed to the definitive project.

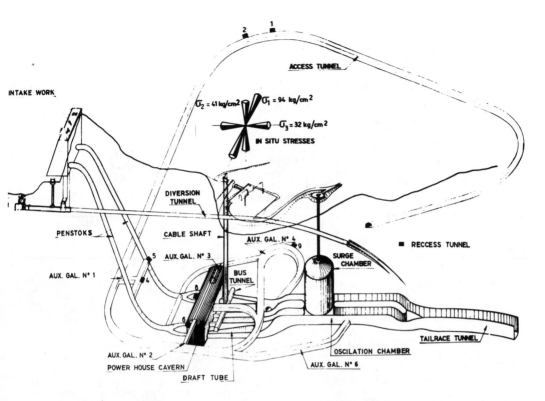

Fig. 1 Río Grande I Pumped - Storage station. Underground structures perspective view

2.2 Preconstruction studies

Photogeology: to scale 1:7,500 and 1:20,000. The main geostructural plans were decided upon. Base of the geological field studies (See fig. 2).

Surface Geology: the different lithologies and structures detected in the photointerpretation were studied in detail. Two distinct geological environments were defined: Cerro Pelado and Contraembalse. The Cavern was located in the Cerro Pelado environment whose outstanding characteristics were:

1. Lithology: Tonalitic gneiss massive and homogeneous. Paragenesis: quartz – plagioclase – biotite – garnet – cordierite (Gordillo y Lencinas, 1979).

2. Structures: Primaries, it is an homogeneous migmatite. The schistic autoliths lack significance. Secondaries, there are two principal systems of fractures; one bearing NNW and another bearing EW, both in accordance with the regional faulting scheme.

3. Geomorphology: ball-shaped outcrops and dome-shaped hills with marked spherical exfoliations.

Geophisical Studies: geoelectric and geoseismic explorations were effected.

Geoelectric: in the area of the implantation of the Powerhouse, resistivity soundings were carried out using the Schlumberger method. ..." Which commence with a mean resistivity of 1,000 Ohm/m and increase with depth until they surpase 10,000 Ohm/m for an AB/2 = 150 m. This demonstrates that we are in the presence of a compact, sound rock with elastic parameters which improve with increasing depth"(Agua y Energía, 1972).

Geoseismic: the refraction method was used. From the soundings undertaken in the Powerhouse area and pressure shafts, velocities of 5,000 m/sec. resulted, a very good quality homogeneous mass without any important geological accidents being detected.

Laboratory rock mechanics tests: samples of

223

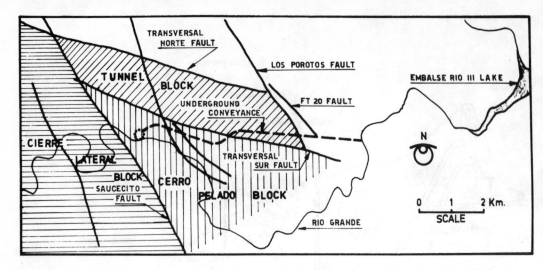

Fig. 2 Photogeology - Geostructural plan

the explorations bores were cut with a ratio of h/d=1 for testing. The values obtained were considered representative of the quality of the mass for RQD% greater than 65%.

Average values in kg/cm2: shear strength of the intact rock, 150; tensile strength, 74; young's modulus, 450,000.

Explorations drillings: perforations with extraction of samples with diamond bits Ø NX, with double core tube. Four drills were bored for the Cavern. These drills holes indicated that the rock in the neighbourhood of the Cavern was a very fresh and homogeneous gneiss with a RQD greater than 90%. The tests of water absorption undertaken in the Cavern's influence area gave very low values in the order of one litre/metre/minute, at a pressure of 30 kg/cm2 showing a mass with closed discontinuities with no erosionable fillings.

Conclusions: based on the results of the investigations carried out it was concluded that a rock mass of excellent technical qualities had been found, of a homogeneity seldom met with and scarcely affected by structural discontinuities of major importance. It was considered therefore that the site chosen for the location of the cavern was geotechnically of optimun conditions.

2.3 Geology - Synopsis

The work under construction is situated on the eastern hillside of the Comechingones range, belonging to the Sierras Pampeanas system.

Lithologically they are constituted by gneiss and plutonities of Precambriam and Eocambrian age, pertaining to a cratonic nucleus denominated Nesocraton Pampeano (Harrington, 1968). The sedimentary covering has only slight significance in the region we are dealing with.

For the Sierras Pampeanas is observed a structure of blocks limited by reverse faults of southern bearing that dip to the east giving rise to steep western slopes and gentle eastern ones (Gordillo y Lencinas, 1979). In this case, the Comechingones range is a horst. The actual morphology is due to the movements produced by the Andean Orogeny at the end of the Tertiary and the beginning of the Quaternary periods.

At the site two geological environments with well-marked lithological, structural and morphological characteristics are defined; Cerro Pelado and Contraembalse. Contact between the two environments is produced by a reverse fault.

The main structures are (fig. 2): FT20 fault, Los Porotos fault, the Saucesito fault all these with a NNW bearing coincident with the great reverse fractures that limit the mountain ranges. And also the Transversal Norte and Sur, of EW strike, fault, coincident with the regional oblique faulting. It must be emphasized that the relief of this environment is a peneplain cut in the crystalling basement and rejuvenated by the orogeny mentioned. It is not affected by any megastructure like those that limit the mountain ranges.

Therefore, three blocks limited by these faults are defined: (Fig. 2).
1. Tunnel Block
2. Cerro Pelado Block
3. Cierre Lateral Block

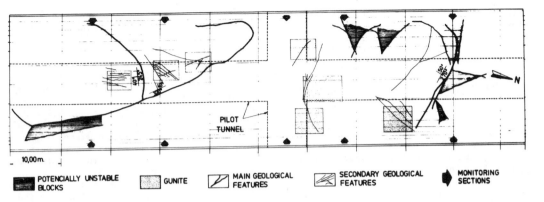

POTENCIALLY UNSTABLE BLOCKS GUNITE MAIN GEOLOGICAL FEATURES SECONDARY GEOLOGICAL FEATURES MONITORING SECTIONS

Fig. 3 Plan view of the Cavern roof

The Cavern for the Powerhouse of Río Grande was constructed on the Cerro Pelado block that is wedged towards the NW producing a monolithic hill of semispherical shape constituted by homogeneous gneiss of very good quality.

2.4 Studies during construction

At Cerro Pelado these studies were made while the Access Tunnel was being excavated, in auxiliary galleries and in the Cavern Pilot Tunnel itself, in tunnel recesses specially excavated for that purpose.
The studies carried out include:
1. Geostructural surveys
2. Microseismic
3. Rock Mechanics laboratory tests
4. Failure criterion determination
5. Rock mechanics in situ tests
6. In situ stress measurements
7. Monitoring with extensometers

Geostructural surveys. They will be effected all along the Access Tunnel and auxiliary galleries with the object of registering the type and state of the rock, the predominating sets of structures, description of the principal faults, characteristics of the joints and obtaining values of the classifications of rock masses of the NGI (Barton Et.al, 1974) and the CSIR (Bieniawski, 1976) in order to compare Río Grande with experiences of other excavation works in other parts of the world.
The aim of this work was to obtain a complete knowledge of the mass and its behaviour on being excavated in order to infer from that its characteristics in the Cavern zone.
In the Cavern Pilot Tunnel a detailed measurement was made of the notable discontinuities with the purpose of extrapolating them to the surface of the vault of the Cavern, detecting in this manner probable blocks of unstable rock formed by the intersection of joints, allowing progressive treatment as it was being excavated and furthermore, with the same criterion, the installation of monitoring devices to measure deformations and check the work of support installed there. In figure 3 a schematic plan of this topographical survey is shown, made out to scale 1:50. Modified monitoring sections in accordance with the design of the principal geological structures are also indicated.
Summary of geological records: it was possible to note a complete coincidence of the characteristics of the rock mass with those foreseen in the study of the surface. Typical Cerro Pelado environment, fresh rock, predominance of subvertical joints, closed, with strong and rough walls, without filling.Subhorizontal joints less frequent with signs of movement, of ondulating forms. Ratings of rock masses classifications obtained: CSIR 85 to 92; NGI 95 to 380.

Microseismic. The method of seismic by refraction was employed. The purpose of this study was to determine the value of the coefficient of Poisson (0.16-0.20), determine the modulus of dynamic elasticity as much for the unaltered rock by excavation (600,000 kg/cm2) as for the decompressed crown surrounding it (350,000 kg/cm2), from which the thickness was also obtained (1.00 m).
Tests were effected all along the Access Tunnel, along the auxiliary galleries, the recess tunnels and in the crown of the Cavern Pilot Tunnel (Agua y Energía, 1977-78-79).

Rock Mechanics laboratory tests. Panedile

225

Arg.(1979–80a) carried out triaxial tests on intact and jointed rock and tensile tests on core samples of the Access Tunnel.

Agua y Energía (1980) carried out uniaxial compression tests in their laboratories, on samples of drillings from the Access Tunnel. A group of these tests was effected with charge and discharge cycles, measuring the deformations of the middle third of the test-tube with mechanical comparators with the object of calculating the modulus of elasticity.

The values obtained are summarized in figures 4 and 6.

Failure criterion determination. In order to calculate the stability of the Cavern, the empirical criterion developed by Hoek and Brown was adopted. It is expressed as the relationship between the principal efforts maximun (σ_1) and minimun (σ_3):

$$\sigma_1 = \sigma_3 + \sqrt{m\,\sigma_c\,\sigma_3 + s\,\sigma_c^2}$$

where m and s are parameters peculiar to the material. The parameter m appears to be sensitive to the type of rock, to the angle of friction between mineral particles or rock particles when this is fractured; while s depends on the tensile strength of the rock mass; it takes values between 1 for the intact rock and 0 for the intensely jointed rock.

This model of failure allows for an analysis of the behaviour of the intact rock, the rock with some joints (anisotropic behaviour) and that of the full scale rock mass (considered isotropic); the parameters m and s varying for each case; m as much as σ_c were obtained from the results of the tri-axial tests on intact samples through the analysis of a lineal regression (fig. 5).

Consistent with the need to obtain values of these parameters for the rock mass and given the difficulties and high cost of the triaxial tests on large jointed samples, the authors of this model related the parameters peculiar to the material with the ratings of the rock mass classifications of NGI and CSIR discriminating the large lithological types of rock, permitting a discerning election of the values of m and s corresponding to the ratings assigned on the point of Geostructural Surveys (fig. 5).

These values were employed as input data for the analysis of the displacements and stresses induced by the excavation of the Cavern through the mathematical model of Boundary Elements (B.E.M.) in order to evaluate the ratio strength/stress, possible faults, their type and location.

Rock mechanics in situ tests. Plate bearing tests: undertaken by Bolognesi-Moretto (Fanedile Arg. 1978-79–80).

The object of these tests was to determine the modulus of deformation of the rock mass. Three tests were effected within the compass of Cerro Pelado, in recess tunnels excavated for the purpose (fig. 1).

1. Access Tunnel - Chainage 694 - recess 1
2. Access Tunnel - Chainage 1356- Gallery 1 - recess 4.
3. Cavern - Auxiliary Gallery 2 - recess 6

All the recesses were rectangular section excavated by perfectly controlled drilling and blasting.

Number 1 and 2 tests were carried out in

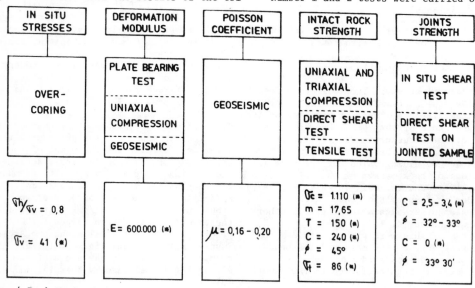

Fig. 4 Rock Mechanics Tests
(*) kg/cm2

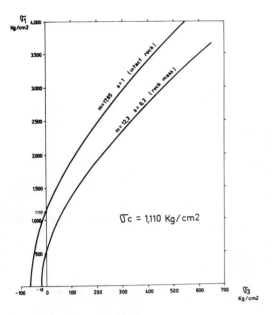

Fig. 5 Failure Criterion

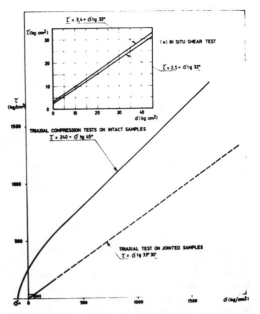

Fig. 6 Mohr-Coulomb's Failure Criterion

a vertical direction, N°3 in a horizontal one.

The appliance assembled for the first consisted of four hydraulic jacks which worked against the floor and the roof through mortar-levelled surfaces.

For N°3 two jacks were used, placed so that their actual bases leant against both sidewalls on surfaces smaller than the first, also levelled with cement mortar.

In every case the averages of the deformations measured by pairs of opposed deflectometers so as to eliminate errors introduced by displacement of the reference system, were used.

The calculation of the modulus of elasticity was effected using Newmark's influence graphs and Boussinesq's expression to determine the contact settlements under a uniformy charged area.

For each charge, the pairs strain-stress were taken and the average ratio was calculated by means of lineal regression, after eliminating the erratic values.

The resulting modulus was the average of the values thus calculated.

Given the elastic behaviour of the mass, the secant modulus proved to be the same as the tangent modulus (fig. 4).

Shear test: carried out by Bolognesi-Moretto (Panedile Arg. 1978). Site: Recess Tunnel N°1.

With the purpose of measuring the parameters of shear strength of a standard joint, one test was effected in situ (fig. 6) on a block of 0.7 x 0.56 x 0.35 m, cut with very

close diamond drillings with the object of producing the least possible disturbance.

The jack that was producing the shear force was placed in a horizontal form in order to go through the centre of the surface so as to avoid generating overturning moments.

In situ stress measurements. Carried out by Bolognesi-Moretto and Golder Associates (Panedile Arg. 1979-80b).

Determinations were made with two devices. In both cases the overcoring method was used.

Bolognesi-Moretto used a borehole deformation meters device from U.S. Bureau of Mines. They performed determinations in the N°2 recess in the Access Tunnel (chainage 694); and recess 5 of gallery 1 and in recess 8 in the Cavern vault, at the bottom of the Pilot Tunnel (fig. 1).

At each point three not parallel perforations were effected in which repeated measurements were made by turning the meters rosette. The values thus obtained refered to a special coordinates system for each perforation, attained a unique system coinciding with the coordinated system of the site.

It was possible to define three components of stress at a point in each perforation treating all the values of tensions calculated as from the deformations measured knowing the elastic modulus of the sample, through the method of minimun squares.

In all cases a perforation of 38 mm diameter (EX) was performed where the measuring device was lodged and then an overcoring was made with a thin 150 mm diameter bit taking care of the concentricity of both, an indispensable requisite for the later laboratory test of the core sample in biaxial camera to determine the elastic modulus of the rock: E=540,000 kg/cm2 was adopted.

The main problems which made the measurements difficult were: the presence of joints, excentricity of the perforation and breakage of the conductor cable.

Golder Associates used the Hollow Inclusion Cell (HI cell) of the Scientific and Industrial Research Organization of the British Community, made in Australia.

With this method ten measurements were totalled in recesses 5 and 9 (fig. 1) out of which four were considered successful and the remaining six were discarded for some of the following reasons: breakage of conductor cable, badly performed perforation making water drainage difficult, the noting of air bubbles in the rockcell contact cement, and presence of joints in metre zone.

The cells consist of a set of strain gauges in a tube of epoxi resin. In this way the six components of vector of tension may be determined in one perforation. The cell is located in an EX diameter drilling which it adheres to by resin injected from the bottom of the borehole pushed by a piston which hits against the rock. Then coring takes place with a thin bit of larger diameter (150 mm) while readings are taken and graphed with respect to the advance of the coring.

All the values obtained by both methods were evaluated, discarding those that were inconsistent. The rest was averaged and for practical reasons of design it was decided to adopt a scheme of principal tensions in which σ_1 is parallel to the axis of the Cavern, σ_2 is vertical and σ_3 is horizontal (fig. 1).

The horizontal stress/vertical stress ratio resulted in:

k = 32/41 = 0.8

Due to the significant height of the Cavern the value of   had to be considered variable with the depth in the mathematical model.

3 DEFORMATIONS STUDIES AND MEASUREMENTS

For the theoretical study of the displacements and stresses induced around the excavation, two mathematical methods were employed, based on the discretization of the rock medium assumed to be elastic, homogenous and isotropic, solved by iterative means:

1. Finite Element Method (FEM).
2. Boundary Element Method (BEM).
FEM was used in the preliminary approxi-

mations, when the natural stress ratio was still unknown. The numerical calculations were realized by the Geocomp Bracknell Society (UK), by order of the projector Studio Ing. G.Pietrangeli.

BEM was employed when the natural stresses had already been defined as regards magnitude and orientation, and due to the coincidence of the principal directions of the axes of the Cavern and the homogeneity of the rock mass, the consultant of rock mechanics Golder Associates decided to adopt this model for its simplicity of adaptation and its low cost.

Following is a sketch of the principal studies made with both methods in synthetic form, and the conclusions arrived at with their implications in preparing the definitive project of the Cavern.

3.1 Finite Element Method

The tests were realized adopting different natural stress ratio k = 0.5; k = 1.0; k = 2.0, which, according to what was esteemed, represented a spectrum in which Río Grande rock mass could be included, guided by the data obtained from Back-Analysis of the monitoring with extensometers realized in the Access Tunnel.

Sixteen distinct cases were considered:
1. Four for the first stage of excavation (vault) - K variant.
2. Ten for the complete excavation (including Drainage Gallery) k variant and support pressure (bolting).
3. Two for the total excavation with the Drainage Gallery separated - K variant.

This group of alternatives provided a first solid orientating idea of the stability of the cavity and concerning the support to be employed.

In fig. 7 is shown the result of the bidimensional analysis of the complete section, the input data of which are as follows:
1. Geometry of the section (note that the section studied was that of the original project).
2. Coordinates of the nodes.
3. Overburden, 200 m.
4. Specific rock weight, 2.7 tn/m3.
5. Modulus of elasticity, E= 300,000 kg/ cm2 (value corresponding to the decompressed rock around the cavities).
6. Poisson's coefficient, 0.18.
7. Natural stress ratio, K = 1.0

This study permitted the detection of two critical zones of tensile stresses: the notched haunches cut into the Cavern walls for the crane bridge and the Drainage Gallery.

The first problem was solved by eliminating the notchs. The concavity of the arch

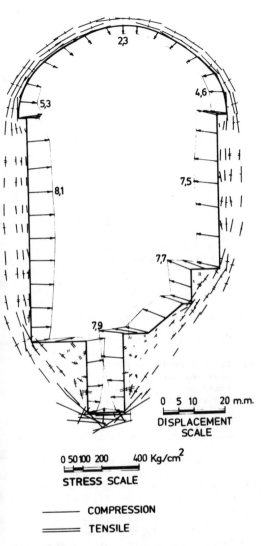

0 5 10   20 m.m.

DISPLACEMENT
SCALE

0 50 100 200   400 Kg./cm^2

STRESS SCALE

——— COMPRESSION

=== TENSILE

Fig. 7 Finite Element Method Results

in the vault was also increased.

These changes clearly favoured the stability of the excavation, as shown by the studies realized with BEM on the modified section which are revised in the next headline.

With relation to the Drainage Gallery, the project was not modified in spite of the state of stress existing, as it was considered advisable to support the rock, faced with the alternative choice of having to execute it as a gallery separated from the rest of the excavation.

3.2 Boundary Element Method

These studies were effected by Agua y Ener-

gía Eléctrica with a programme provided by the consultant Golder Associates.

Six different cases were analysed: one for each stage of the excavation from I to IV, and two for V: one for the section of the draft tube and another for the section between turbine pits.

In figure 8 the result of the last case is shown, the least favourable one, diagramming the displacements and shadowed zones which represent different categories of the factor of safety. To obtain this last datum the programme incorporates the failure criterion dealt with in 2.4'

The input data were:

1. Geometry of the section and coordinates of the ends of the segments.

2. Uniaxial compression strength of the intact rock, 1,110 kg/cm2.

3. Tensile strength of the rock mass, 18 kg/cm2.

4. Coefficients reduction, m = 12.3–s=0,2.

5. Elasticity modulus, E = 600,000 kg/cm2.

6. Poisson's coefficient μ= 0.2

7. Equivalent depth of floor, 170.8 m.

8. Specific rock weight = 2,7 tn/m3.

9. Natural stress ratio, K = 0,8.

It is interesting to note that the tensile zones in the intersections vault-sidewall have disappeared after the modifications described above, and that the problem of the Drainage Trench subsists although limited to the periphery of the excavation (not more than 3 m into the rock mass).

The Draft Tube section, which is marked by a broken line in fig. 8 produces a more favourable distribution of stresses.While the situation in the vault does not vary much, the tensile zones raised by the slender walls of the Drainage Gallery disappear, and the sidewall downstream is less in demand owing to the stress being transmitted at greater depth.

The difference in the values of displacement between figures 7 and 8, principally owing to the different modulus of elasticity adopted for each model, must also be observed.

The excavation was considered self-supporting, and the support to be employed was designed on account of the geological structures that affected the cavity in order to avoid the dismenberment of the blocks that were exposed by the excavation.

3.3 Deformation Measurements – Monitoring

Objective: to control the behaviour of the rock mass during the excavation and during the life-time of the Plant.

In January '79, when the construction of the Pilot Tunnel was beginning, the following ideas about the monitoring project of

229

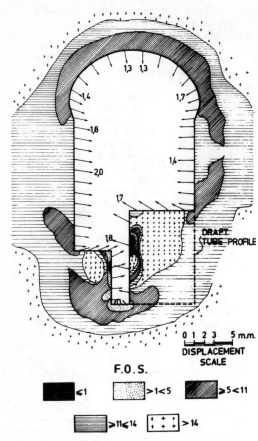

Fig. 8 Boundary Element Method Results

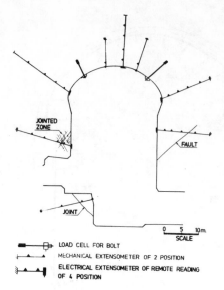

Fig. 9 Monitoring Section

the Powerhouse were counted on:

1. Number of monitoring sections: four.

2. A not systematic disposal of the instruments but in accordance with the geostructural problems.

3. Adoption of electric instruments of remote reading for a long-term control, together with the mechanical ones, preferably the first.

The four sections defined a priori with the object of controlling the behaviour of the principal types of the Powerhouse sections, are marked in fig. 3.

These sections were instrumented in the vault where, due to the presence of important geological discontinuities towards the South wall, a fifth section was instrumented. In view of the exceptional behaviour of the vault, after stages 1 and 2 had been excavated, it was decided that in the sidewalls (stages 3, 4 and 5) instruments would be placed only to control outstanding structural features, that is, without conditioning their situation to the foreseen sections (fig. 9).

The following types of instruments were installed:

1. Mechanical extensometers of 2 positions

2. Electrical extensometers of remote reading of 4 positions.

3. Load cells for bolts.

4. Fixed points for measurements of convergence with an extensometer tape.

During the construction of the Cavern the most useful information was extracted from the mechanical and electrical extensometers in that order.

The mechanical extensometers were installed during the excavation of the vault, while the electrical ones were placed in the vault when excavation of the third stage had been finished.

Access to the instruments was maintained by a system of scaffolds suspended from the rock bolts of the vault. Owing to the breakage of the scaffolds due to the blasting, the readings were interrupted on several occasions.

The mechanical extensometers of 2 positions were of much use during the excavation due to the simplicity and robustness of the system and to the design of the surface anchorage which makes it particulary resistant to the effects of the blastings and throw of debris.

The electrical extensometers were read during the construction in manual form by means of deflectometers of 0.01 mm.

As an experience of their behaviour it may be concluded that the data obtained in the first group of readings, that is, from their installation until after stage 4, they were not clear and required careful selection in order to be used.

Several points of reference threaded in the rods worked loose after the initial reading had been obtained, due to the effect of blasting, annulling the readings taken up to that moment.

The graphs of fig. 10, provide information about the displacement values registered by the extensometers in the different stages of excavation of the Cavern. The mean values were compared with the displacements prognosticated by the mathematical model of BEM (fig. 8) and a satisfactory relation was found between them.

With regard to the extensometric tape for measurements of convergence, its use was not successful due to the large dimensions of the cavity which made access to the points fixed to the rock very difficult.

The load cells were checked infrequently, through the use of a manual reading device; and during the construction they were duly protected by means of metal caps.

At the date of the writing of this report, work was being done on the connections of the transducers and cable laying to a switchboard of measurements, and therefore, representative data of this stage of remote measurements could not be counted on when the task of blasting had already been finished.

3 EXCAVATION AND SUPPORT - METHODOLOGY OF WORK

3.1 General Considerations

In the following points a general description will be made of the different steps taken to achieve the culmination of the work with regard to the methodology of excavation, support and sequence of interrelated tasks.

In order to accede to the different levels, auxiliary galleries were projected, with the same dimensions and maximun slope (8%) as the Access Tunnel (fig. 1).

The works of access were started at the end of '76, finishing the Pilot Tunnel of the Cavern vault at the end of '78, completing the excavation at the beginning of 1981, for which approximately 100,000 m3 had to be removed using the following equipment: 2 three-arm jumbos, 1 four-arm jumbo, 1 bull-dozer, 6 thirty-five ton trucks, 3 elevator machines, 1 elevator platform, 4 track drills, 2 wheel loaders.

The excavation was carried out in 5 stages (fig. 11), each one with a particular methodology, oriented and defined by the limitations of the accesses, parallel excavations, heights of bench and the support necessary for its definitive stabilization.

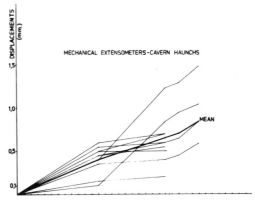

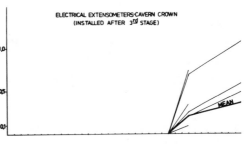

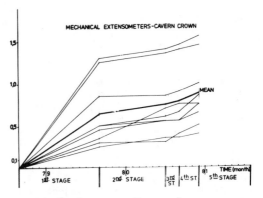

Fig. 10 Displacements Measured

3.2 Stage I

This stage, the most important one, because it exactly defined the characteristics and state of the rock mass in the implantation zone of the Cavern, was approached with caution in spite of the fact that, at that state of the works, there was sufficient information to permit applying it to said zone, and arriving as nearly as possible at a prognostication of the behaviour of the structure to be built. Therefore it was attacked in 2 phases: Pilot Tunnel in the crown (A) and lateral extensions (B) (fig. 12.a).

The access at this stage was effected from

231

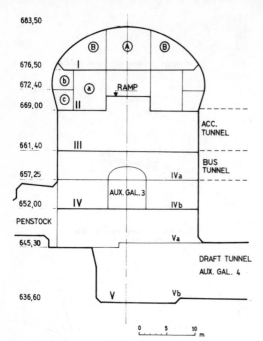

Fig.11 Transversal Section of the Cavern
      Excavation Stages

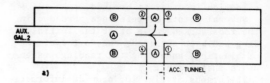

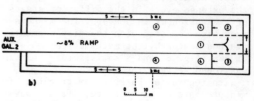

Fig. 12 Plan Views of the Cavern.a) Stage I
        and b) Stage II

the Access Tunnel in chainage 1522, by means
of the Auxiliary Gallery N°2.

Phase A consisted of a longitudinal Pilot
Tunnel 8,oo m wide and 7,oo m high, whose
roof was coincident with the Cavern vault,
and a transversal one in the middle, fulfi-
lling the following objectives:

1. To execute a detailed geological survey.

2. To install monitoring instruments to
check the excavation behaviour in all its
evolution.

3. To perform in situ tests and geophysical measurements.

4. To develop the support project defining
the criterion it would be faced with, bearing in mind the records and data obtained
on the former points.

5. The installation of primary bolting
projected, achieving in this manner the partial stabilization, before exposing the surface of the rest of the vault.

After that, lateral extensions were undertaken (B), establishing an alternative heading methodology, the sequence of which is
shown in fig. 12 a, permitting:

1. To give greater agility to the drilling, charging, blasting and muckpile transport.

2. To verify the geological structure predicted during Pilot Tunnel excavation and
in this manner adjust the support project
to the real structural conditions.

3. To effect the marking and installation
of the required bolting in each of the headings before completing the section of that
stage, in order to be able to take the most
advantage of the physical properties of the
discontinuities, because the support of the
blocks realized at the wrong time causes a
diminishing of the safety factor produced
by the opening of the joints due to the relaxation of the rock mass.

As regard the blasting patterns used, phase A was executed with one similar to that
practiced in the whole length of the Access
Tunnel: smooth blasting, with parallel hole-
cut, double spiral type, with headings of
3,50 m. Electrical delay detonators in mili-
second and half a second were used for ignition.

In the phase B, a very important condition
to be taken into account was the protection
of the support and the monitoring instruments installed in A, attaining this with
the minimun throw, so that charge zones of
explosives were fixed, the density (qi) of
which increased towards the side-wall, as
the same proportion as the confinement (fig.
13). Also, it made necessary to blast separately the remainder area, in broken line,
to avoid overbreak.

Note that the corner was included a priori in stage II, phase b.

The first design of the support of the Cavern was effected on the basis of the geological extrapolations practiced on the excavations of the Access Tunnel and the Diversion Tunnel, as well as on the exposed
surface of Cerro Pelado. Because of this,
and bearing in mind empirical formulae and
previous experiences, a bolt pattern was
projected with Ø 25 mm bolts, 5 - 10 m long,
and 1 - 2 m spacing.

As the excavation of the pilot Tunnel in
stage 1 advanced (Phase A), installing systematic bolts 5 m long and Ø 25 mm according

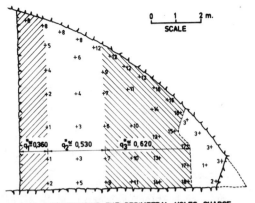

■ (Kg/m3) EXCLUDING THE PERIMETRAL HOLES CHARGE
+7 DELAY SEQUENCE

Fig. 13 Blasting Pattern. Detail of the La-
     teral Extension of Stage I

to the former scheme, it was observed that:

1. The spacing of structural geological
features was great, generally of 1 to 2 m.

2. The intact rock was fresh, homogeneous
and competent.

Consequently it was steemed that the Cavern vault would remain stable without the
systematic bolt installation (Agua y Energía,
1979).

The project criterion adopted to define
the support was that of preventing the fall
or sliding of blocks limited by specific
geological features (Hoek, 1979).

The decision to use structural bolting was
also endorsed by the result of the mathematical model effected for the Cavern, which
indicated that the strength of the rock mass
was very superior to the stresses induced
around the excavation.

The blocks treated were those limited by
three discontinuities and a free surface,
as also those originated by one or two geological fault planes, and the remaining surfaces being formed by the failing of the rock
mass, due to the effect of the blastings or
to the development of tensile stresses of
buckling, as the rock, by its own weight,
tends to move towards the excavation (Panedile Arg. 1980).

Two types of blocks were defined: gravita
tional wedges and sliding wedges. The support design for the first ones was made in
order to keep their own weight. For the second ones the stabilizing effect by friction
was considered. In both cases the safety
factor was two (2).

The stabilizing effect created by the development of tangential stresses around the
excavation was not considered, as the values
predicted for the zone near the surface
could not be trusted.

In the vault six potentially unstable blocks
were detected (fig. 3), which were treated
by means of a primary bolting consisting of
bolts ∅ 25 mm and 3 to 10 m long.

The structural bolting was practiced also
to avoid the development of instabilities o-
riginated by a joint and the failure of the
rock mass. The treatment of the lips thus
defined was practiced with bolts ∅ 25 mm and
from 3 to 10 m long, distributed over two
rows parallel to the line of intersection
of the joint and the vault, and with a spacing of two meters trying to cut perpendicularly the fault plane.

The design of the primary bolting was based on the inspection of the vault and the
detailed geological survey.

As a secondary bolting, bolts of ∅ 19 mm
were installed for the support of smaller
blocks. The design was practiced after a
visual evaluation of same.

As an additional support, a layer of reinforced gunite with a thickness of 6 cm was
placed in 7 zones where the rock was highly fractured (fig. 3). In addition, a ∅
3.4 mm galvanized wire mesh with an 8 cm
rhomboid opening was installed. This mesh
was attached to the bolts by means of an a-
dditional plate and nut; where the separation of these was greater than 1.25 m, untensioned grouted dowel of ∅ 19 mm and 60
cm long were installed.

3.3 Stage II

This stage (fig. 11), was initiated once
the final excavation and support of stage 1
were concluded.

The access was effected through the Auxiliary Gallery N°2, with a longitudinal ramp
trench 8 m wide and 7.50 m maximum height,
and a transversal bench at floor level (669)
(fig. 12 b).

The area defined by the ramp and the final profile of the vault was approached in
3 phases a, b and c (fig. 11); the dimensions, height and width were fixed in order
to achieve an easy circulation and accessi-
bility to the zone of confined vault of stage I and perform the necessary support. where, due to the fact that the perforation e-
quipments disposable were unable to operate,
it was not practiced with the rest.

Phase (a) was executed in bench, with vertical drillings and presplitting on the ramp
boundary to avoid breakage . This phase provided an outlet to phases (b) and (c) which
were performed with horizontal drillings and
smooth blasting owing to the curvature of
the profile.

Three zones were detected where the geological structures were unfavourably oriented,

233

which were treated with primary bolting consisting of bolts ∅ 25 mm and 19 mm and 3.5 m long.

The secondary bolting was realized after the visual analysis of the excavated zones and following the same criterion of stage I.

The placing of the galvanized mesh was continued. The mesh placed in stage I also had to be replaced due to the deterioration caused by the blasting in stage II.

In the zones where access was not recuperable, the repairing will be accomplished when the crane is disposable, so that this point deserves to be analysed as it will present a major cost difficult to evaluate, which can only be fixed when the work has been completed.

In stage II the mesh was placed only, as far as the elevation 672,40, where it was required (fig. 11).

3.4. Stage III

The access to this stage was effected through the Access Tunnel (fig. 11) being initiated simultaneously with the installation of the support of stage II, which conditioned the heading sequence implemented in 5 phases (fig. 14).

Phase 1 was fixed to the effect of creating two fronts of bench towards the two extremes of the Cavern (phase 2 and phase 4), and to dump in this zone the muckpile of the access ramp of stage II to be extracted, achieving a quick advance, without interfering with the works of support of stage II, following the sequence indicated in fig. 14.

Simultaneously, the support of the sidewalls of this stage was executed.

The general diagram of blasting of the whole stage was a bench inclined at 72°with respect to the horizontal, spacing E = 2.50 m, burden V = 2.00 m, drilling diameter ∅ = 64 mm and specific charge q = 400 g/m3.

At the most 4 rows of drill holes were blasted, corresponding to a volume of 1,200 m3.

The presplitting was performed with drillings of ∅ = 64 mm and spacings of 0.60 m.

Given the velocity of the bench with respect to the evolution of the presplit holes it was necessary to adopt the methodology of simultaneous blasting, this not being the way to obtain the best results.

To palliate this deficiency it was decided to blast the one corresponding to each bench, and approximately 50% of the following one. In the ignition, delay detonators were used, so that, in order to diminish the instantaneous charge, 4 drillings at the most were charged with the same delay. The result obtained was not to the quality expected, lessened also by the celerity of

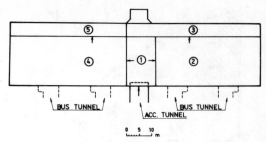

Fig. 14 Plan view of the Cavern. Stage III

production.

The primary bolting was performed in order to deal with a fault with a dip of 20°and a 200°dip direction, which had been anticipated by two diamond drillings and by the extrapolations performed from the excavations of the cable shaft and of the penstocks. The corresponding support was installed 0.50 m below the intersections of the fault with the sidewall and with an angle of 30°above the horizontal. The bolts used were ∅ 19 mm and 3 to 5 m long.

The secondary bolting was used to support slabs and bloks generated by two families of conjugated joints, running sub-parallel to the axis of the Cavern. The bolts used were ∅ 19 mm and longitudes up to 4 m which were placed with an incline of 10°above the horizontal to guarantee a proper grouting.

3.5 Stage IV

This stage was executed by approaching the Auxiliary Gallery N°3, which intersects the North sidewall of the Powerhouse (fig. 1).

Parallel to the excavation of the present stage, the Bus Tunnels, one for each generator, that intersect the downstream sidewalls of the Cavern in El 657.25, had to be executed, (fig. 11).

This condition determined the necessity of –dividing the stage into two benches:substage IVa from El 661.40 to 657.25 substage IVb from El 657.25 to 652.oo.

Substage IVa as being low (h = 4.15 m) was excavated with the total width of the Cavern (25 m), on the other hand substage IVb was limited by the ramps of access to the Bus Tunnels.

Presplitting was realized in all the perimeter of the stage with a total height of 9.40 m.

The geological features discovered on executing the excavation were the same as those found in stage 3; therefore the treatment of the blocks thus formed was analogous to the one realized in the previous stage.

Furthermore, two faults were discovered,

234

one of 25°/030° that dips towards the side-wall downstream, and another one of 22°/144° Both were treated with bolts of ∅ 19 mm and 2 to 4 m long.

In the intersections of the Bus Tunnels with the Cavern, and in order to pass the fault found in stage 3, bolts of up to 5 m were used.

3.6 Stage V

This stage of the excavation, (fig. 11), was executed in 2 substages limited by the height of the benches and its accesses.

Substage Va was carried out with access by Gallery N°3 from El. 652.00 to 645.30 co-rresponding to the spherical valves level, by means of a ramp and following the sequence indicated in fig. 15.

In substage Vb, of great geometric comple-xity owing to the variation of levels and dimensions of the different components of the Drainage Gallery and Draft Tubes, a ge-neral elevation (636.60) was fixed, practi-sing the excavations of detail later.

The principal conditions for programming the phases, and their corresponding heading sequence, was to protect the rock blocks that delimited the turbine pit, therefore a bench was begun from the Draft Tubes (pha-ses 1, 2, 3 and 4) leaving and adjacent thickness of rock on the turbine pit, to ca-refully blast in later.

As for the blasting diagrams, a variant was introduced in the presplitting with res-pect to the one used in the previous stages; maintaining the density of charge per area (0.550 kg/m2), the spacing was diminished to 0.40 m corresponding to the turbine pit and to 0.50 m for the rest of the perimeter of the stage, substantially improving the results obtained formerly.

In table 1 the characteristics of the di-fferent schemes used in the excavations are detailed.

Comparing those executed on the surface, especially in the Intake with those under-taken in the Cavern, both emplaced in rocky environments geotechnically similar, a di-fference in the diagrams is observed which, given equal results, leads to the following conclusions:

The state of natural confinement of the rock and the stresses induced by the opening have their influence; this may be measured in the greater energy per area necessary to produce the crack between adjacent boreho-les. With respect to the support, only some bolts were placed, to sustain the highly unstable blocks. The civil work, the initia-tion of which took place inmediately after the excavation was finished, was calculated

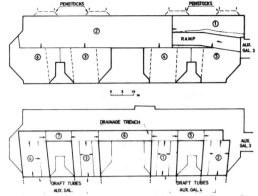

Fig. 15 Plan Views of the Cavern. Above Sta-ge Va, Below Stage Vb.

to provide an integral support to the Drai-nage Gallery, providing grouting where the rock mass was found to be strongly altered by the blastings.

3.7 Methodology of bolt installation

The anchorage used was of the mechanical ty-pe, fig. 16.

The boltshanks used were high resistance steel bars (σ_{sk} = 4,400 kg/cm2).

Each bolt was tensioned by means of hydrau-lic jack, carrying it up to the half load of failure that in the case of 25 mm diameter bolts was of 14 tn and for those of 19 mm was of 9 tn (fig. 16). On beginning the su-pport works, the tensioning of the bolts was realized by means of a torsion wrench and controlled by a torsiometer. This methology was replaced because the grouting hoses coi-led around the rod.

At times the bolts were grouted inmedia-tely after the first tensioning in order to ensure that the bolt did not lose charge through the sliding of the anchorage.

Table 1. Presplitting characteristics

∅ (mm)	E(m)	kg/m	Explosi ve Type	kg/m2	Site
64	0.70	0.180 0.280	GELAMON (VF 80%)	0.260 0.400	Intake
64	0.60	0.330	"	0.550	Cavern st.III & IV
64	0.50	0.275	"	0.550	Cavern st. V
64	0.40	0.220	"	0.550	

In most of the bolts the grouting was effected several days after the original tensioning. In these cases the bolts were retensioned and the grouting had to be done within the following 24 hs.

To effect the grouting, two plastic hoses were disposable; a short one and another long that reached the anchorage, one being the inlet tube and the other the return tube, according to the inclination of the bolt with respect to the horizontal.

Before executing the grouting the washing of the drilling and bolt were realized, thus detecting the cracks of the rock mass opened by the blastings, which were sealed, as also the face plate of the bolt, to avoid later escapes of grout during the injection.

The mixture injected was a grout with a ratio w/c= 0.5 in weight. The equipment used consisted of a mixer and a piston hand pump.

The bolts of Ø 25 mm and longitudes greater than 5 m were executed by means of two bars joined by nipples. In these cases and in order to guarantee the functioning of the coupling, the bolts were taken to 24 tn at the moment of tensioning, holding that load during 5 minutes and then lowering them to the service load (14 tn).

Destructive tests were realized on bolts with the anchorage without grouting; without anchorage and grouted to determine the development of bond strength, and lastly, tests with anchorage and grouted.

In all cases the results were satisfactory being the failure in the majority of cases through the rod.

But the most important and direct test was the one that was realized by the installation methodology in that this constituted a test of one to one.

3.9 Evaluation of the works results

At the date of the realization of this paper the tasks of excavation and support of the Cavern have been concluded.

The result of the excavations were not satisfactory due fundamentally to the errors in drilling, which caused an increase in the secondary bolting and in the volumes of concrete.

The functioning of the support has been

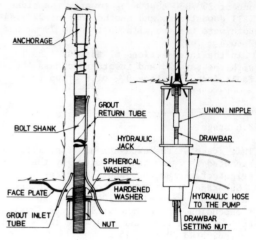

Fig. 16 Rock Bolt Scheme. Tensioning Equipment.

correct. The change from systematic bolting (Table 2) to structural (Table 3) signified a saving of 60% as regards the support of the vault.

As an interesting alternative of additional support, the authors consider the possibility of having covered all the Cavern vault with gunite: this would have made it possible to dispense with the mesh, that due to its sensitivity to the blastings, has given rise to greater cost.

The safety factor adopted for the structural bolting, of the blocks of the vault (=2) has been conservative, as in the calculation hypotheses the stabilizing effect created by the tangential stresses that developed around the excavation were not considered. It being possible, according to the authors, to have considered it ≃ 1.3. Nevertheless, this reduction in the safety factor, owing to the excellent quality of the rock mass, would not have contributed a significant saving, as the blocks considered were only six.

4 CONCLUSIONS

The authors wish to emphasize the following points:
  1. In the building of great underground

Table 2. Systematic Bolting (Vault only) (Panedile Arg. 1979)

Ø	Quantity of Bolts per Longitude (m)					Total		Average Bolt Length (m)
(mm)	5.0	6.0	7.0	8.0	10	Bolts	Length (m)	
25	926	121	54	361	86	1,548	9,482	6.125

Table 3. Structural bolting (realized)

	STAGE	Ø (mm)	Quantity of Bolts per Longitude (m)									Total		Total per Stage (m)	Average Bolt Length
			2.0	2.5	3.0	3.5	4.0	5.0	5.5	7.5	10	Bolts	Length(m)		
VAULT	I	19	-	834	-	5	-	-	-	-	-	839	2,102.5	3,580.0	3.00
		25	-	8	32	37	-	204*	4	16	7	308	1,477.5		
	II	19	-	400	-	82	4	7	-	-	-	493	1,338.0	1,365.0	
		25	-	1	-	7	-	-	-	-	-	8	27.0		
WALLS	III	19	-	26	61	130	76	19	-	-	-	312	1,102.0	1,152.0	3.22
		25	-	-	-	-	-	10	-	-	-	10	50.0		
	IV	19	75	15	196	21	52	-	-	-	-	359	1,057.0	1,057.0	
	V	19	-	29	12	5	11	-	-	-	-	57	170.0	170.0	
TOTALS												2,386	7,324.0	-	3.07

* 138 bolts were placed in the Pilot Tunnel, according to the project of systematic bolting.

works, an exhaustive study of the rock mass is essential before any definition of a project.

2. A project of this magnitude requires close collaboration between the technicians specialized in the different subjects involved in the design stage as much as during its construction.

3. The realization of a permanent control of tasks, undertaken by a team whose number and capacity is in accordance with the importance of the work, is fundamental.

4. The development of work programmes must be based on a deep understanding of the tasks and the real resources available.

5. ACKNOWLEDGEMENT

The authors wish to thank AGUA Y ENERGIA ELECTRICA for the authorization and support given them in the accomplishment of this paper.

6. REFERENCES

Agua y Energía Eléctrica 1972, Río Grande N°1 - Documentación para Licitación, Tomo I. Córdoba, Agua y Energía Eléctrica.

Agua y Energía Eléctrica 1977-78-79, Estudios de Microsísmica en las Excavaciones Subterráneas de Río Grande N°1. Mendoza, Internal Reports.

Agua y Energía Eléctrica 1979, Estudio Geotécnico de la Excavación de la Bóveda de la Central en Caverna del Aprovechamiento Hidroeléctrico Río Grande N°1. Río Grande, Internal Report.

Agua y Energía Eléctrica 1980, Ensayos en Laboratorio de la Roca de la Caverna de Río Grande. Córdoba, Internal Report.

Fig. 17 Powerhouse Cavern Río Grande I

Barton, N., Lien, R., Lunde, J. 1974,Engineering Classification of Rock Masses for the Design of Tunnel Support, Journal 106. Oslo, Norwegian Geotechnical Institute.

Bieniawski, Z.T. 1976, Rock Mass Classification in Rock Engineering, Vol. 1. Johanesburg, Proc. Symposium on Exploration for Rock Engineering.

Gordillo, C.E., Lencinas, N.L. 1979, Geología Regional Argentina, Vol. 1. Córdoba, Academia Nacional de Ciencias.

Harrington, H.J. 1968, Desarrollo Paleogeográfico de Sudamérica, Misc. N°26. Tucumán, Instituto Miguel Lillo.

Hoek, E. 1979, Report on Excavation Support Design for Underground Excavations in the Río Grande N°1 Pumped Storage Project. Córdoba, Agua y Energía Eléctrica, Internal Report.

Hoek, E., Brown, E., Underground Excavation in Rock, Restricted Circulation Draft.

Panedile Argentina 1978, Ensayo de Corte in Situ. Río Grande, Internal Report.

Panedile Argentina 1978-79-80, Ensayos de Carga In Situ I, II y III.Río Grande, Internal Reports.

Panedile Argentina 1979, Central en Caverna, Mecánica de Rocas, Memoria Estática.Río Grande, Internal Report.

Panedile Argentina 1979-80a, Ensayos de Mecánica de Rocas. Río Grande, Internal Reports.

Panedile Argentina 1979-80b, Mediciones de Tensiones In Situ. Río Grande, Internal Reports.

Panedile Argentina 1980, Informe sobre el diseño del Soporte de las Excavaciones Subterráneas de Río Grande N°1. Río Grande, Internal Report.

GEO-ENGINEERING EVALUATION OF PROBLEMS OF A LARGE UNDERGROUND CAVITY FOR TEHRI PROJECT (INDIA)

Ingenieurgeologische Auswertung von Problemen bei einer grossen unterirdischen Kaverne für das Tehri Projekt (Indien)

Interprétation au moyen de la géologie de l'ingénieur des problèmes relatifs à une grande caverne souterraine du projet de Tehri (Inde)

A.K.DUBE, J.L.JETHWA & B.SINGH
Central Mining Research Station, Dhanbad, India
BHAWANI SINGH & R.S.MITHAL
University of Roorkee, India

SUMMARY:

An irrigation cum power scheme called Tehri Dam project is under construction across river Bhagirathi near the township of Tehri located about 80 km from Rishikesh. The greatest challenge to the designers is the construction of a huge cavern (250 m long, 50 m high and 22.5 m wide to house the power plant for generating 2000 MW) especially, when adequate geological and geotechnical investigations could not be possible. An attempt has been made in the present paper to analyse the available data so that some guidelines could be prepared for the designers. Barton's rock mass quality Q and Bieniawski's rock mass rating RMR have been estimated for different catagories of rock masses likely to be encountered during the excavation of the cavern. Further, the values of deformation modulus estimated from RMR and diametrical tunnel-closure observations have been compared with those measured by flat jacks. A fair agreement between the measured and predicted parameters suggests that lack of adequate pre-construction geotechnical investigations could be compensated to some extent by judicious application of the available classification systems to generate some reasonably reliable design parameters.

ZUSAMMENFASSUNG:

Am Bhagirathi Fluss in der Nähe von Tehri, ca. 80 km von Rishikesh entfernt wird das Projekt "Tehri-Damm" zur Bewässerung und Stromversorgung, entwickelt. Die grösste Herausforderung an die Planer ist die Konstruktion einer grossen Kaverne (250 m lang, 50 m hoch und 22,5 m breit), die ein 2000 MW Kraftwerk beherbergen soll, insbesondere weil ausreichende geologische und geotechnische Untersuchungen nicht möglich waren. In der vorliegenden Arbeit wurde der Versuch unternommen, die vorhandenen Daten zu analysieren, so dass ein Leitfaden für die Planer vorbereitet werden konnte. Die Gebirgsqualität Q nach Barton und die Gebirgsgüte RMR nach Bienniawski wurden für verschiedene Gebirgskategorien, die wahrscheinlich beim Bau der Kaverne angetroffen werden, abgeschätzt. Weiterhin wurden die aus den RMR-Werten und aus Konvergenzmessungen abgeschätzten Werte für den Verformungsmodul mit denen aus Druckkissenversuchen verglichen. Eine gute Übereinstimmung zwischen den gemessenen und vorhergesagten Parametern legt nahe, dass das Fehlen von geotechnischen Untersuchungen vor Baubeginn bis zu einem gewissen Grade durch eine sachgemässe Anwendung der vorhandenen Klassifikationssysteme zur Herleitung von vernünftigen und sicheren Entwurfsparametern kompensiert werden kann.

RESUME:

Le projet d'irrigation et d'alimentation en courant, "Barrage Tehri", a été éxécuté sur le fleuve Bhagirathi, non loin duquel est situé Tehri, à environ 80 km de Rishikesh. Le plus grand défi aux projeteurs constitue la construction d'une grande caverne (250 m de long, 50 m de haut et 22.5 m de large) devant loger une centrale électrique de 2000 MW, car il n'était pas possible d'entreprendre des investigations géologiques et géotechniques suffisantes. Dans cette étude l'analyse des données existantes a été tenté, de telle sorte qu' un guide puisse être préparé pour les projeteurs. La qualité du terrain Q, estimée selon Barton, sa qualité RMR, évaluée d'après Bieniawski, ont été déterminées pour les diverses catégories de terrain qui probablement seraient rencontrées durant la construction de la caverne. De plus, les valeurs qui ont été estimées à partir de la valeur-RMR et des mesures de convergence pour le module de déformation ont été confrontées avec celles des essais de vérin plat. Une bonne correspondance entre les paramètres mesurés et prédits montre que l'absence d'investigations géologiques avant le début de la construction peut êtr jusqu'à un certain degré, compensée par une utilisation appropriée des systèmes de classification existants en vue d'en déduire pour la conception des paramètres raisonnables et sûrs.

1 INTRODUCTION

Tehri Dam Project is an irrigation cum-power project near the township of Tehri about 80 km from Rishikesh. The project consists of a 260.5 m high earth and rock-fill dam across river Bhagirathi about 1.5 km downstream of its confluence with river Bhillangana, an underground powerhouse of 2000 MW installed capacity, a chute spillway to drain the excess discharge and four diversion tunnels (T1, T2, T3 and T4) each of 11.0 m finished diameter (Fig. 1). A portion of the two diversion tunnels (T1 and T2) will be used as tail race tunnels.

The powerhouse cavity is proposed to be 250 m long, 50 m high and 22.5 m wide. Construction of such a huge cavern for engineering utility is a challenging task, particularly in inaccessible and hostile terrain of the Himalayas.

The scheme of the Tehri Dam Project was envisaged several decades ago. Its construction, however, could not be taken up earlier due to various reasons. One of the main reasons was inhospitable and inaccessible terrain which precluded systematic preconstruction geo-technical investigations and would have created several impediments during the construction stage. The project has now been accorded top priority in view of the present oil crisis and improved communication during the last decade.

The designers and the construction engineers were sceptical initially about the construction of such a huge underground structure on account of the following questions:

1. What is the most rational and practical method for predicting the rock loads and excavation conditions ?
2. What should be the criteria for the design of supports for the roof arch and the walls of the cavern ?
3. How to conduct geotechnical investigation ?
4. What additional precautions are necessary in the tectonically active and fragile rock masses of the Himalayas ?

An effort has been made in the present paper to analyse the available data and generate some reasonably reliable design parameters in order to provide answers to the above questions.

2 GEOLOGICAL INVESTIGATIONS

Geological investigations for this project were conducted by the Geological Survey of India and reported by Shome and Kumar (1979). They studied the regional tectonic setting and critically examined the proposed locations of the various engineering structures of the Tehri Dam Project. The area is still under investigations, however, the tentative location and orientation of the cavern has been fixed (see Figs. 1 through 3).

The main rock formations are phyllites of Ordovician-Silurian age, locally known as Chandpur series. These phyllites are banded in appearance, the bands being constituted of argillaceous and arenaceous materials. The degree of these contents an and the magnitude of tectonic deformations give the phyllites varying shades of physical form. The phyllites are being grouped in three grades as grade I, grade II and grade III depending upon the magnitude of the rock defects.

Grade I phyllites are mainly arenaceous, massive in character and distinctly jointed. However, the foliations are the least developed. Grade II phyllites are banded structures formed due to rapid alternations of arenaceous and argillaceous materials. The thickness of these bands varies from 5 to 100 mm. The rock masses are impregnated with quartz veins along and across the foliations. Grade III phyllites are mainly composed of the argillaceous material, criss-crossed with quartz veins. Many closely spaced foliation planes, cleavages and joints are present. Minor **fold**ing and puckering are also observed.

The general strike of these formations is due N 55° W–S 55° E to N 70° W–S 80° E with a dip of 35°-55° in South-Westerly direction. The formations are sheared and jointed and these joints and shears have been traced on the surface. In the absence of drill holes, these traces were projected to prepare longitudinal and transverse cross-sections of the powerhouse cavity as shown in Figures 2 and 3 respectively. These cross-sections show that the shears may be critical for determining the stability of the roof and walls of the cavern. Differences between the actual geology encountered during

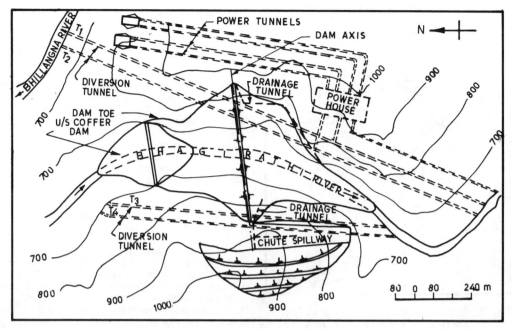

Fig. 1 _ Layout of works of Tehri Dam Project (After Gupta et al, 1979)

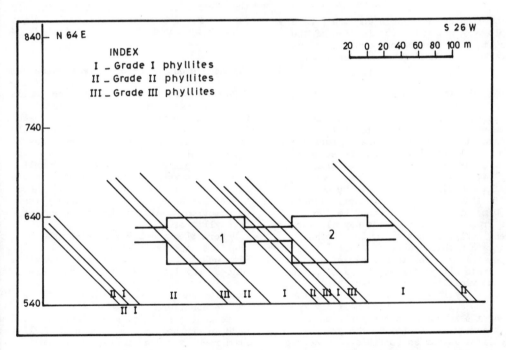

Fig. 2_ Tentative geological longitudinal section of powerhouse cavity
of Tehri Dam Project (After Shome and Kumar, 1979)

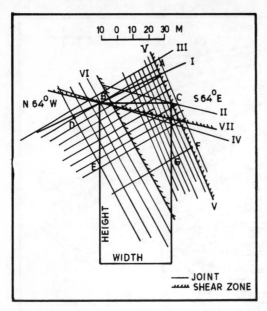

Fig. 3 _ Tentative geological transverse
section of powerhouse cavity (2)
of Tehri Dam Project (After Shome
and Kumar, 1979)

excavation of the cavern and the predicted
geology is not ruled out in view of the
fact that the geological cross-sections
have been prepared from surface data.

3 ORIENTATION OF CAVERN

It is clear from the above that the
planners had to depend more on their
judgement than on the reliable subsurface
geological details. It may be seen in
Fig. 2 that the widest band of Grade I
phyllites is about 120 m wide, less than
half the designed length of the cavern.
It is thus clear that the entire length
(250 m) of the cavern cannot be located in
the grade I phyllites. It may also be
seen in Fig. 2 that a couple of other
moderately thick bands of grade I phyllites,
seperated by a few thin bands of grade II
and grade III phyllites, are also present
in the vicinity of the widest band of the
grade I phyllites. It was decided, therefore, to split the machine hall cavity
along its length into two parts so that
each cavity is located in the grade I
phyllites as far as possible. These two
cavities are proposed to be connected by
appropriate galleries passing through the
grade II and grade III phyllites.

The orientation of the cavity has been

kept across the strike to ensure the most
favourable excavation conditions. Fig. 3
depicts the position of major joints and
shears vis-a-vis the crown of the cavern.
This position has been considered after a
very careful evaluation of the influence
of various joints and shears on the stability of the crown. The influence of the
intersection of the discontinuities III
and V has been considered to be critical
and the present alignment minimizes its
influence on the stability of the cavern.
Thus, the wedges CFG and BDE were found to
be very disconcerting for the stability of
the side walls of the cavern.

4 GEOTECHNICAL ASSESSMENT OF ROCK
CONDITIONS

In view of inadequate geological investigations it may not be possible to predict
accurately the rock mass behaviour in the
cavern. The best alternative under these
circumstances is to assess the various
geotechnical parameters from available
rock exposures in the region. As such,
data collected from a few drill holes and
drifts excavated in similar rock masses
during early investigation stages have
been used. This has been supplemented by
the observations in the diversion tunnels
presently under construction on the right
bank of the river Bhagirathi (Fig. 1).

4.1 Assessment of Deformation Modulus

Deformation modulus of rock masses could
be determined by flat jacks or plate
bearing tests insitu. It is also possible
to determine it emperically with the help
of rock mass classification approaches.
A third method is to estimate it from the
back analysis of observations of tunnel
closure (convergency measurements) in the
right bank diversion tunnels. All these
approaches have been used to assess the
deformation modulus of the three grades
of phyllites.

Deformation modulus was determined by
the flat jack tests at a few locations.
Although these tests were performed at
places away from the cavern, they were
done is the rock masses similar to those
expected in the cavern. As such, these
may be considered reliable.

Bieniawski's (1975) geomechanical ratings
were determined for all grades of phyllites
from rock exposures in the diversion
tunnels. The deformation modulii of rock
materials were determined in the laboratory
The relation between the ratio of the
modulii of rock mass and rock material and

the geomechanical ratings was then used to estimate the modulus reduction factor. This modulus reduction factor was ultimately used to obtain the modulus of deformation of the rock mass from the deformation modulus of the rock material.

In the third method, tunnel closures in one of the 12 m diameter right bank diversion tunnels were measured in grade II phyllites (Fig. 4). The closure-time plot is linear for the first 25 days and became non-linear thereafter. The linear part of this curve has been used for calculating the modulus of deformation from the following well known formula:

$$E = \frac{2a\ P\ (1 + \vartheta)}{\text{diametrical tunnel closure}}$$

where

E = deformation modulus,
a = radius of the opening,
P = cover pressure and
ϑ = Poisson's ratio of rock mass

The back calculated deformation modulus for the grade II phyllites works out to be 0.36×10^5 kg/cm^2. The values of deformation modulii obtained from the above three approaches have been given in Table 1. It may be observed that the

Table 1. Comparison of measured and estimated modulus of deformation in phyllites

Grade of phyll-ites	Modulus of Deformation, 10^5 kg/cm^2		
	Measured by Flat Jacks	Estimated From	
		Geom. Approach	Tunnel closure
I	0.68	1.3	not available
II	0.18–0.58 (0.38)*	0.43	0.36
III	0.19–0.39 (0.29)*	0.18	not available

* average value

values worked out from the three different approaches agree well.

4.2 Assessment of Rock Pressure

The observed tunnel closures were less than 1 percent of the tunnel size. As such, the rock conditions are assumed as non-squeezing. The empirical approaches are applicable for assessing rock pressure under such conditions. Amongst the various classification systems in use throughout the world, the one developed by Barton et al (1974) has been considered here.

The input information needed for Barton's classification system were not readily available in the desired format. Hence, those had to be generated. General geological information for this purpose were obtained from the reports of investigation of the Geological Survey of India. The rock exposures were also studied inside one of the right bank diversion tunnels which was under construction and some missing data were assumed judiciously.

The geotechnical data collected in this way were used for estimating Barton's rock mass quality (Q) for all the three grades. These Q-values have been used to predict rock pressures. The estimated Q-values and the predicted rock pressures for the three grades of phyllites are given in Table 2.

Rock loads on steel ribs were measured at two locations in one of the diversion tunnels on the right bank. One of these locations was in the predominantly grade I phyllites whereas the other was in the predominantly grade II phyllites. Vertical rock pressures estimated from these observations are also given in Table 2.

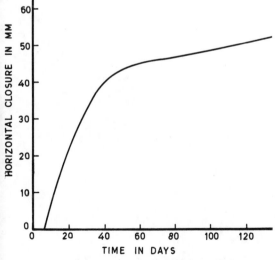

Fig. 4 _ Time - closure relation in 12.0 m diameter right bank diversion tunnel through grade II phyllites

243

Table 2. Comparison of measured and predicted vertical pressure

Grade of Phyllites	RQD*	RMR+	Q++	Rock pressure kg/cm²	
				measured	Predicted**
I	75	67	5	0.4	0.8
II	50	35	0.8	1.1-1.4	2.1
III	25	29	0.15	-	3.8

* assumed; + Bieniawskis' rock mass rating; ++ Barton's rock mass quality ** from Barton's approach

5 DISCUSSION OF RESULTS

It may be noted that three different approaches adopted for determining the modulus of deformation of grade II phyllites yielded comparable results (Table 1). This gives confidence to estimate E-values from geomechanical approach and tunnel closure observations. However, tunnel closures should be measured at several locations in all the three grades of phyllites for getting reliable representative E-values.

The rock loads were measured only at two places in two different grades of phyllites. It may be seen in Table 2 that the rock load for grade I phyllites were lower than these observed in grade II phyllites. This is natural because better rock masses are likely to exert lower rock loads.

The observed and the estimated vertical rock pressures have also been compared in Table 2. It may be seen that the observed pressures were lower than those estimated with the help of geomechanical data. The differences reflect the conservatism associated with the method of prediction. The rock loads have been measured in a 12 m diameter tunnel whereas the cavern is 22.5 m wide. But according to Barton et al (1974) the rock pressure is independent of the size of the opening. As such, the rock pressures estimated from the measured rock loads may be applicable for the design of the supports for this cavern. This is not to suggest that the rock loads will also be the same. The total rock loads will be greater in the caven than those observed in the tunnel and hence the support dimensions will also be greater.

It is desirable that rock loads are measured while supporting the cavern in order to generate confidence in the design approach.

6 CONCLUSIONS

The near agreement between the predicted and measured values of rock pressure and modulus of deformation has been observed only at a couple of locations. However, this has given confidence that lack of sufficient geotechnical data at the design stage could be compensated to an extent by judicious estimates of geomechanical parameters from surface and underground exposures and instrumentation at the construction stage of the cavern.

7 REFERENCES

Barton, N., J. Lien and J.Lunde,1974, Engineering classification of rock masses for the design of tunnel supports. Rock Mech. Vol. 6, No. 4, pp. 189-236.

Bieniawski, Z.T. 1975, Case studies - prediction of rock mass behaviour by the geomechanical classification. 2nd Australia-NewZealand Conf. on Geomechanics, Brisbane, pp. 36-41.

Gupta, S.K. and Lawania, B.V.K., General layout of works, Proc. of Workshop on Tehri Dam Project, Dec. 4-6, 1979, Roorkee University, Roorkee.

Shome, S.K. and Kumar, V., 1979, Geological and Foundation treatment of the Tehri Dam Project, U.P., India, Proc. of Workshop on Tehri Dam Project, Dec. 4-6, 1979, Roorkee University, Roorkee.

LES FACTEURS QUI LIMITENT LA TAILLE DES CAVITÉS
Factors limiting the size of caverns
Einschränkende Faktoren für die Grösse von Kavernen

PIERRE DUFFAUT
Ecole Nationale des Ponts et Chaussées, Paris, France

SUMMARY:

Civil engineering caverns do not span over 35 m and most are below 25 m. Mine openings and natural caves provide stable caverns spanning up to 100-200 m. Arch masonry bridges reach 60-70 m. A scale effect works by reference to the fracture intercept, but more through the action of gravity on the loosened zone. It works also in a more psychological way through the increased results of any cave-in. The influence of the natural ground structure and the working method is by far more important than the one of depth of cover. Prestress by tendons associated to natural arching might allow to easily reach spans about 100 m.

ZUSAMMENFASSUNG:

Die Spanweiten bautechnisch errichter Kavernen liegen maximal bei 35 m und meistens unter 25. Dagegen sind bei bergmännisch hergestellten Hohlräumen und in natürlichen Höhlen standfeste Kavernen bis zu 100 - 200 m Spannweite möglich, während gemauerte Gewölbe Spannweiten von 60 - 70 m erreichen können. Der **Massstab spielt mit Rücksicht auf den Abstand der** Trennflächen, aber besonders hinsichtlich der Schwerkraft der aufgelockerten Zone eine Rolle. Hinsichtlich der weitreichenden Folgen bei einem Einsturz haben die Abmessungen **wei**terhin noch einen psychologischen Effekt. Viel wichtiger als die Überdeckung ist der Einfluss der natürlichen Gebirgsstruktur und der angewendeten Ausbruchsmethode. Eine Vorspannung mit Felsankern in Verbindung mit dem natürlichen Gewölbeeffekt lässt es möglich erscheinen Spannweiten von ca. 100 m zu erreichen.

RESUME:

Les cavernes de génie civil ne dépassent pas 35 m de portée et la plupart sont inférieures à 25 m, alors que les mines et les grottes montrent des cavités stables de 100 et 200 m de portée, et que les voûtes des ponts en maçonnerie atteignent 60-70 m. L'effet d'échelle joue par rapport à la maille de la fracturation, mais surtout par l'action de la pesanteur sur la zone décomprimée. Il joue enfin de façon psychologique par l'augmentation des conséquences d'un éboulement. L'influence de la structure du terrain et celle de la méthode d'exécution sont beaucoup plus importantes que celle de la profondeur. La précontrainte par tirants associée à l'effet de voûte devrait permettre d'atteindre aisément une portée de l'ordre de 100 m.

INTRODUCTION

Dans beaucoup de cas, l'échelle des ouvrages humains tend à croître avec le développement des civilisations. Par exemple les portées des ponts sont en augmentation constante depuis l'antiquité. Mais contrairement à ceux des ouvrages d'art aériens, les projeteurs d'ouvrages souterrains ne semblent pas désireux de dépasser les dimensions déjà illustrées par un nombre relativement grand de cavernes en service. Cette timidité limite le recours au sous-sol pour implanter des activités qui pourraient y bénéficier de nombreux avantages. En particulier et pour citer un seul exemple, le développement de centrales nucléaires souterraines est au point mort faute de confiance dans des cavernes un peu plus grandes que les dimensions déjà classiques (WATSON et al.)

Jusqu'à une époque très récente (moins de vingt ans), la stabilité des cavernes n'était pas soumise au calcul. L'empirisme étant la seule garantie de l'ingénieur, on pouvait comprendre sa prudence. L'usage du calcul s'est affirmé depuis, notamment pour la belle caverne de Veytaux (aménagement hydroélectrique Hongrin-Leman, Suisse) (RESCHER). En même temps est apparue la technique des tirants précontraints qui a permis de résoudre élégamment des problèmes difficiles en toute sécurité.

Il paraît donc paradoxal que les garanties nouvelles apportées par des méthodes de calcul puissantes et des méthodes de soutènement non moins puissantes n'aient pas été mises à profit pour faire un pas vers des cavités de plus grande taille. Il paraît paradoxal aussi que ce problème de taille n'ait jamais été traité dans les nombreuses réunions consacrées depuis vingt ans aux cavernes artificielles, en particulier Oslo 1969 (Large permanent underground openings), Phoenix 1971 (Underground rock chambers), Lucerne 1972 (Symp. int. sur la construction de cavités souterraines), Stockholm 1977 et 1980 (Rockstore), Madrid 1981 (Uso industrial del subsuelo). C'est seulement à Hanovre 1981 (Underground siting of nuclear power plants) que divers projets de grandes cavités ont été dessinés schématiquement et que des recherches sur leur stabilité ont été envisagées (PAHL)

Le Comité français de mécanique des roches a donc chargé un groupe de travail de préparer quelques réflexions sur ce sujet, en profitant de l'expérience accumulée notamment par les centrales hydroélectriques souterraines et par les stockages souterrains. Les grottes et les cavités minières sont mises à profit aussi.

I RETOUR SUR LE PASSE

1.1 Evolution des portées des tunnels et cavernes

Les premiers tunnels dont on a retrouvé les restes, destinés au captage ou à l'amenée de l'eau sont de portée très modeste, de l'ordre du mètre. Le gabarit du tunnel était une section minimale pour les ouvriers qui le creusaient. Toutefois quelques rares chambres de temples hypogées ou de tombeaux avaient une largeur de quelques mètres, de même que le tunnel routier du Posilipo à Naples creusé sous le règne d'Auguste.

En France, c'est probablement Riquet qui le premier a eu besoin d'un gabarit plus grand pour faire passer le canal du Midi. Le tunnel du Malpas près de Béziers n'a que 180 m de long et une couverture très modeste, mais il a été ouvert en 1680 et il est toujours en service. Sa portée de 7,5 m

est très proche de celle des tunnels ferroviaires à double voie qui allaient se développer dans toute l'Europe au 19ème siècle (portées de 7,6 m à 8 m). Pendant longtemps les tunnels routiers se sont contentés eux aussi de sections du même ordre.

Au vingtième siècle le record de portée a été repris par un tunnel de navigation, le tunnel du Rove qui fait communiquer l'Etang de Berre avec le port de Marseille, 22 m entre piédroits. Le premier tunnel français pour autoroute a été creusé en 1935 sous la colline de St Cloud avec 17 m entre piédroits. La grande majorité des tunnels et cavernes de génie civil creusés aujourd'hui dans le monde reste à l'intérieur de la limite de portée 22 m. Ceci s'applique aux cavernes de défense nationale (PC souterrains), aux abris de défense passive, aux arsenaux souterrains de la marine suédoise, aux salles de sport norvégiennes, aux magasins et surtout aux cavernes de stockage pour hydrocarbures en vrac. Ceci s'applique aussi à la plupart des stations de métro. A l'intérieur de Paris, les trois stations de la ligne nouvelle du Réseau Express Régional atteignent 23 m à Etoile, 24 m à Auber, 25 m à Nation. Ces portées ne sont dépassées que dans des stations construites sous forme de tubes parallèles tangents ou sécants suivant une pratique développée d'abord à Moscou. Il subsiste alors toujours des files de robustes piliers.

Ceci s'applique aussi au plus grand nombre des centrales hydroélectriques souterraines. Quelques rares centrales atteignent 25 m (la Bathie et Montézic, France ; Mica, Canada) ; 26 m (Churchill Falls et la Grand II, Canada) ; 27 m (Coo-Trois Ponts, Belgique) ; 30,5 m (Veytaux, Suisse) ; 33,5 m (Waldeck II, Allemagne fédérale, Imaichi, Japon, cette dernière actuellement en construction). Sauf omission, la portée record est détenue depuis 1930 par la salle en partie souterraine de la centrale du Sautet, près Grenoble, avec 35 m de diamètre intérieur, 36,5 avant bétonnage. Il paraît significatif que ce record soit antérieur au grand développement des centrales souterraines pendant les dernières décennies.

Hors des centrales hydroélectriques, des cavernes de 42 m sont en construction en Finlande et une salle de sports de 50 m est projetée en Norvège. Il y a donc un petit espoir que des conditions particulières de terrain et de technologie permettent de franchir la limite des 35 m.

1.2 Hauteur, élancement, forme des voûtes

Si la plupart des tunnels ont une section ramassée dont la hauteur h est du même ordre que la portée 1, beaucoup de cavernes s'écartent de cette forme, qu'elles soient aplaties, l>h, c'est le cas de salles de sport et d'une manière générale de beaucoup de magasins, c'est le cas aussi de stations ferroviaires souterraines à plusieurs voies, ou au contraire élancées, l<h, c'est le cas des cavernes de stockage d'hydrocarbures, et de beaucoup de centrales hydroélectriques. Dans le premier cas l'élancement permet d'optimiser le coût du creusement en augmentant la part du stross en gradins tirés par mines verticales par rapport à la part de la calotte, tirée par mines horizontales plus coûteuses. En outre la limitation de la portée évite de recourir à un soutènement.

Dans le second cas l'élancement tient au gabarit des matériels, turbine et alternateur superposés le long d'un axe vertical, ainsi qu'à l'espace nécessaire au-dessus pour la manutention de ces matériels. Certaines turbines-pompes ont une grande hauteur (pompes à 5 étages de la Coche, France) et certaines centrales de transfert d'énergie par pompage superposent sur un même axe la pompe, la turbine et l'alternateur. Dans ces deux cas l'élancement est grand, 2,5 à la Coche pour h = 30 m, 2,5 à Lago Delio, Italie, pour h = 60 m. Il s'agit alors de cavités "en trou de serrure" dont la hauteur peut devenir plus critique que la portée. En effet les hautes parois verticales sont peu stables par nature. Même avec un élancement modéré, elles sont très sensibles à la présence de fractures naturelles à pendage vers la cavité.

Beaucoup de projets ont été dessinés comme si la hauteur ne comptait pas ; Une fois que la voûte est ouverte, la cavité peut descendre aussi bas que l'on veut. Au moins dans un cas, le creusement du stross a conduit à une déformation de la voûte trop grande pour le béton déjà mis en place (Tumut, Australie, PINKERTON et GIBSON).

Le dessin de la voûte compte beaucoup pour la stabilité d'ensemble. Dans le passé, la voûte en demi-cercle était d'emploi pratiquement général. Le tunnel de Riquet est en plein cintre, les tunnels ferroviaires sont en plein cintre, les égoûts de Paris construits par Belgrand au 19ème siècle sont tous en plein cintre. Les stations du métro de Paris sont en ellipse aplatie qui se rapproche davantage du gabarit nécessaire. Les voûtes des cavernes de stockage et des centrales hydroélectriques sont souvent un peu surbaissées. En outre les voûtes en béton sont encastrées au sommet des parois verticales. Le creusement nécessaire est d'ailleurs dangereux pour la stabilité des parois. Dans de

nombreux cas, la voûte déborde largement les parois verticales et la cavité prend une forme "en champignon". Souvent alors les rails du pont roulant sont posés sur le rebord de la section. Il est toutefois nécessaire de rétablir une poutre en béton armé car le mineur ne sait pas tailler un angle saillant (du moins à l'explosif).

Cette forme est pratiquement abandonnée aujourd'hui et de nombreux exemples au contraire tendent à supprimer aussi les hautes parois verticales. La section prend alors une forme ovoïde (à Waldeck II, Porabka Zar, Pologne, et Imaichi), une forme en fer à cheval avec des parois planes qui se rapprochent vers leur base (la Saussaz II, France, Venaus, Italie), ou une forme où le cercle dépasse le diamètre horizontal (Montézic). Comme exceptions notables il faut citer d'une part Veytaux et le Sautet dont le plein cintre domine un plancher horizontal (dans les deux cas les machines sont à axe horizontal) et d'autre part Batang Padang (Malaisie) dont la section approche le cercle complet (BECKER)

Dans tous les cas cités, centrales ou autres cavités, il s'agit de cavernes allongées perpendiculairement à leur section. Un projet avait été dessiné en France (pour une chute dite Montpezat 2 qui n'a pas été réalisée) avec un développement de la salle des machines en anneau circulaire, (une disposition analogue des machines a été utilisée, mais pas en souterrain, à Djatiluhur, Indonésie).

1.3 Les cavités multiples, parallèles ou croisées

Dans une centrale hydroélectrique, le circuit hydraulique comporte des vannes en amont des turbines, des batardeaux à l'aval, et quelquefois une chambre de mise en charge du canal de fuite. Cette chambre est obligatoirement une cavité distincte de la salle des machines, parfois très importante comme à Churchill Falls. Par contre vannes et commandes des batardeaux peuvent ou non se trouver dans des cavernes parallèles. Les transformateurs peuvent aussi être séparés des alternateurs ou rapprochés. Il y a donc choix entre deux types de solutions : cavernes multiples dont aucune n'a une grande portée, comme à la Coche, fig.1, ou caverne unique de portée sensiblement augmentée, comme à Montézic, fig. 2. Les cavernes multiples sont en outre reliées par de nombreux tunnels : aussi les "piliers" rocheux qui les séparent se trouvent souvent dégradés et affaiblis.

Les distances entre cavités parallèles devraient être au moins de l'ordre de la

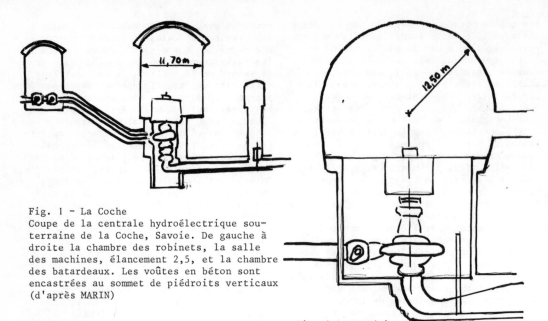

Fig. 1 - La Coche
Coupe de la centrale hydroélectrique souterraine de la Coche, Savoie. De gauche à
droite la chambre des robinets, la salle
des machines, élancement 2,5, et la chambre
des batardeaux. Les voûtes en béton sont
encastrées au sommet de piédroits verticaux
(d'après MARIN)

Fig. 2 - Montézic
Coupe de la centrale hydroélectrique souterraine de Montézic, Aveyron. Les robinets
et les batardeaux sont dans la même salle
que les groupes (d'après MARIN)

hauteur de la cavité la plus haute.

Lorsque les cavités parallèles sont identiques ou presque, le schéma se rapproche
des chambres parallèles d'exploitations
minières. C'est le cas par exemple de la
station de traitement des eaux usées de
Käppala, Suède, et aussi à plus grande
échelle de certains stockages à cavités multiples, comme Lavéra, Donges et Vexin en
France. Les cavités peuvent se développer
aussi à angle droit, comme dans les stations
de surveillance NORAD aux Etats-Unis et au
Canada (BLASCHKE). D'une façon très générale
les structures géologiques sont anisotropes
et il est rare que les deux directions des
cavités croisées soient également favorisées
par le terrain.

Les intersections entre cavités, et plus
généralement les bifurcations de tunnels et
les branchements de tunnels sur les cavernes
sont toujours difficiles à découper, et l'é-
quilibre du terrain y est en général menacé
deux fois de suite. Des procédés d'exécution
minutieux doivent être mis au point, et appliqués avec beaucoup de soin.

1.4 Les cavités minières de grande dimension

L'exploitation des mines conduit à ouvrir
des cavités de grande taille, soit pour ex-
traire des minerais, soit aussi pour instal-
ler des matériels spécifiques : concassage,
machines d'extraction, etc... Ce deuxième
cas ne diffère en rien des cavités de génie
civil examinées précédemment. Par exemple
une cavité formée de deux salles perpendi-
culaires a été étudiée pour une mine du

Pérou (BOUVARD). Parmi les intersections
de cavités, on trouve plus souvent qu'en
génie civil des puits verticaux de grand
diamètre.

Quant aux cavités qui résultent directement de l'exploitation de minerai, leur
stabilité à long terme n'a évidemment pas
la même importance qu'en génie civil. Toutefois certaines restent longtemps stables
et il est bon de considérer les dimensions
qui sont ainsi obtenues. Deux cas remarquables sont cités en Scandinavie : dans
la mine Skorovas, Norvège, l'exploitation
se fait par chambres parallèles soutirées
de largeur 80 m et hauteur 45 m (HAUGEN
et MYRVANG) ; dans la mine Tyrtyri, Finlande, une cavité non supportée reste
stable avec des dimensions d'environ
100 x 100 x 100 (mais la section comporte
des pans coupés qui limitent le volume bien
au-dessous de 1 hm3). Cet exemple sert à
LUNDE d'argument pour affirmer que la construction de très grandes cavités est possible en toute sécurité. Malheureusement
ces deux articles sont en norvégien, et
leur diffusion a été limitée.

Dans beaucoup de mines sédimentaires
l'exploitation se développe dans des couches relativement minces, et les cavités
de grande portée sont caractérisées par
un toit plan et un élancement très petit.
Par exemple la mine de fer de May sur Orne

(France) comporte des portées dépassant parfois 120 m sans pilier (MAURY). Il s'agit toutefois de salles inclinées suivant les flancs d'un synclinal, l'un à 25°- 30°, l'autre proche de 50°, où l'action de la pesanteur est moins critique que dans des salles horizontales. Au Québec la mine d'Oka où le pendage est plus faible montre des portées libres jusqu'à 150 m.

Un autre témoignage favorable vient des Etats-Unis (JACOBY) et concerne une mine de sel de Louisiane (Avery Island). L'exploitation s'est faite d'abord par chambres de section carrée 20 x 20 m. Cette dimension a été portée à 30 x 30 vers 1950, puis 30 x 40, et 46 x 47 en 1970. En 1976 l'auteur prévoit que la section 61 x 61 sera prochainement introduite. Dans une telle exploitation, les piliers ont aussi une section carrée et un élancement unité. Plus ils sont grands, mieux ils se comportent. L'auteur recommande seulement de laisser un chanfrein sur les bords du toit plat, afin d'atténuer la concentration des contraintes.

Bien entendu le sel est connu aussi pour les cavités qui y sont creusées par dissolution. Parmi celles-ci seules sont intéressantes les cavités de forme relativement régulière creusées pour le stockage. C'est dans ce cas qu'on obtient les plus grandes portées et les plus grands volumes : diamètre jusqu'à 100 m, hauteur de plusieurs centaines de mètres, volume jusqu'à 500 000 m3. Leur forme de révolution améliore la stabilité, mais cette stabilité est aussi subordonnée au maintien d'une pression de fluide à l'intérieur. La plus grande cavité de stockage d'un seul tenant creusée dans le sel par dissolution est celle de West Hackberry (Etats Unis) qui atteint 2 hm3. Elle se développe sur 300 m de haut et sa partie inférieure comporte une chambre horizontale de 180 à 260 m de portée. En France la plus grande cavité du stockage de Manosque atteint 500 000 m3 (Fig. 3).

1.5 Cavités naturelles : grottes de grande dimension

Les grottes aussi sont creusées par dissolution et beaucoup d'entre elles dépassent la portée de 30 ou 35 m évoquée ci-dessus. Sous réserve de découvertes futures, la plus grande salle connue est la Torca del Carlista, Espagne (COURBON) dont les dimensions sont : portée 230 m, hauteur 125, longueur 500, (le volume dépasse largement le million de mètres cubes)(Fig. 4). Deux autres salles suivent de près d'après le même auteur, la Verna, France, Pyrénées,

(180 x 150 x 230) et Grotta Gigante, Italie (180 x 138 x 240). Quant à la grotte de Carlsbad, New Mexico, souvent citée par les auteurs américains comme record de portée (189 à 200 m), elle aurait une hauteur faible, un plan très irrégulier, et de nombreux piliers

La dissolution est le phénomène principal pour les boyaux et galeries karstiques. Pour toutes les grandes salles des éboulements ont joué aussi un rôle majeur et se sont arrêtés lorsqu'une position stable a été atteinte. Il convient de noter l'influence possible des séismes, pourtant les grottes souffrent peu de séismes : parmi les plus importants séismes récents en France depuis 20 ans, celui du Vercors n'a eu aucune influence sur les fines stalactites de la grotte de Choranche longues de plusieurs mètres, et celui d'Arette n'a pas troublé les spéléologues qui visitaient alors la salle de la Verna toute proche

Fig. 3 - Coupe schématique d'une cavité de stockage obtenue par lessivage à partir d'un forage (Manosque, hauteur totale 330 m dont 60 remplis d'insolubles, diamètre maximum environ 87 m, volume 500 000 m3)

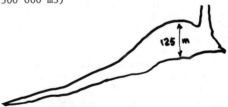

Fig. 4 - Coupe schématique de la grotte Torca del Carlista, Espagne, dont la portée (perpendiculairement à la coupe) atteint 230 m (d'après COURBON)

En matière de cavités karstiques, les puits ouverts en surface sont également très remarquables : El Sotano del Barro, Mexique, a 410 m de profondeur. La section du puits est 420 x 210 m en haut, 200 x 100 en bas, son volume est donc de l'ordre de 10 hm3.

Si les cavités minières peuvent paraître trop jeunes pour que l'expérience confirme suffisamment leur stabilité, les grottes ont au contraire un âge hors de proportion avec la durée des constructions humaines. Des éboulements y sont souvent visibles mais les concrétions qui les fossilisent permettent de calculer de très longues durées de stabilité.

1.6 Retour sur les ponts en voûtes

L'histoire des ponts construits en voûtes peut être invoquée aussi d'après un cours déjà centenaire (CROIZETTE DESNOYERS). Dès avant l'ère chrétienne plusieurs ponts en maçonnerie franchissaient le Tibre à Rome avec des portées comprises entre 18,5 et 24,5 m. Trois de ces ponts sont encore en service aujourd'hui. La portée de 30 m a été atteinte en Espagne en 98 par l'arche unique du pont d'Alcantara sur le Tage. Autour de 1200 3 ponts ont été construits sur le Rhône avec des arches jusqu'à 33 m (Avignon, Pont St Esprit, Lyon). Au 14ème siècle le pont de Céret sur le Tech atteint 45 m, et au 15ème le pont de Vieille Brionde sur l'Allier 54 m, cependant que se construisent en Italie un pont sur l'Adige à Vérone de 48,7 (1354) et un pont sur l'Adda à Trezzo de 72,25 m (1377). Malheureusement ce dernier pont a été détruit peu après à l'occasion d'une guerre locale. Le record appartient donc à un pont de 61 m construit à Chester, Royaume Uni, sur la Dee, en 1834, puis il passe aux Etats Unis pour un aqueduc sur le Potomac, à Cabin John dont l'arche couvre 67,1 m.

Au 18ème siècle toutefois le métal vient concurrencer la maçonnerie. Des voûtes en fonte, puis en tôle, et enfin en treillis permettent d'atteindre 165 m (viaduc de Garabit construit par Eifel sur la Truyère) puis 518 (Firth of Forth, Ecosse) mais ce n'est plus une voûte pure. D'ailleurs l'emploi du métal en traction diminue l'intérêt pour les voûtes et les poutres droites deviennent compétitives lorsque l'esthétique les tolère. Dès lors il ne reste plus qu'à attendre le béton précontraint, encore que les plus grandes portées soient évidemment haubannées ou suspendues.

Une histoire parallèle aurait pu être fournie par les voûtes des grands édifices.

2 LA RECHERCHE DES FACTEURS PRINCIPAUX

Les grottes et les cavités minières prouvent surabondamment que la limite de 30-35 m est franchissable. Dans le cas des mines une structure favorable est parfois mise à profit, les bancs qui encadrent la couche exploitée pouvant se comporter comme des dalles épaisses. Dans le cas des grottes c'est la méthode même du creusement, la dissolution, qui tend à donner une forme favorable puisqu'elle attaque sélectivement les zones en traction et respecte les zones comprimées. Ces deux leçons doivent être soigneusement enregistrées.

2.1 L'effet d'échelle

Dans un site donné, nature du terrain et profondeur restant constantes, ainsi que la méthode d'exécution, il est bien connu qu'il y a une limite supérieure à la portée d'une cavité stable sans soutènement. Si la profondeur est faible par rapport à la résistance du terrain, cette limite est ressentie comme en rapport avec la maille de la fracturation. Toutefois cette argumentation est de faible poids dès qu'un soutènement minime empêche le mouvement relatif des blocs le long des surfaces de discontinuité.

Lorsque la résistance est faible devant la profondeur (cas des sols en général et des tunnels très profonds dans les roches) l'effet d'échelle est bien représenté par l'emploi du graphique classique de LAUFFER qui fixe la durée de stabilité suivant la portée libre du tunnel. Toutefois ce graphique empirique n'est pas l'expression d'une loi mécanique applicable de façon générale aux matériaux rocheux. Au contraire la solution élasto-plastique met d'abord en évidence un comportement qui ne dépend pas de l'échelle : anneau plastifié séparant le tunnel du massif élastique. Mais cette analyse est bien incapable de faire intervenir l'échelle puisqu'elle est obtenue en milieu infini non pesant, chargé à l'infini. Lorsqu'on étudie l'effet de la pesanteur sur l'anneau plastifié, on retrouve évidemment l'effet d'échelle (PANET). Lorsque la cohésion résiduelle est faible, il n'y a que de très petites cavités qui peuvent rester stables sans soutènement, celles pour lesquelles la pesanteur est justement négligeable. Or le volume soumis à la pesanteur augmente comme le carré du diamètre du tunnel. Toute autre force à action locale, pression d'écoulement, secousse sismique, s'ajoute à la pesanteur et abaisse donc la limite de

250

stabilité sans soutènement.

Mais si un soutènement convenable limite les déformations plastiques et surtout les dégradations qu'elles entrainent dans ce qu'il est convenu d'appeler la zone décomprimée, ce soutènement restera très modeste par rapport au poids de la couverture : la maîtrise de la convergence par un confinement apporté dès que possible est une méthode générale non limitée par l'effet d'échelle. En l'absence d'essais convenables il paraît probable que l'effort de confinement nécessaire augmente moins vite que le carré du diamètre.

Ce qui est certain en revanche, c'est que l'homme qui creuse la cavité est très sensible à l'échelle. Il se rend compte parfaitement de ce que les difficultés qu'il aborde augmentent très rapidement avec le diamètre et la hauteur. En outre les moyens d'action immédiate qu'il sait employer dans un petit tunnel en cas d'éboulement lui paraissent dérisoires dans une grande caverne. C'est donc le risque d'accident incontrôlable qui constitue la limite psychologique. Lorsque la portée augmente, les précautions à prendre pour maîtriser les déformations doivent devenir de plus en plus strictes parce que les conséquences d'une rupture locale deviennent rapidement catastrophiques.

2.2 L'effet de la profondeur

Un raisonnement très sommaire peut être fait pour une cavité cylindrique à axe vertical et toit plan, de rayon R et couverture H : supposant que la stabilité tient uniquement à la résistance au cisaillement τ sur la paroi du cylindre vertical au-dessus de la cavité, l'équilibre s'écrit : poids = résistance, c'est-à-dire :

$$\pi R^2 H \rho g = 2\pi RH\tau$$

cette équation donne évidemment un rayon limite $R = 2\tau/\rho g$, et il est remarquable que la couverture H s'élimine. Pourvu que la résistance au cisaillement reste constante, la même cavité est en équilibre quelle que soit la profondeur. Bien entendu le schéma de calcul utilisé devient très pessimiste lorsque la cavité n'est pas très superficielle ; dès que H est nettement plus grand que 2 R, la descente verticale du toit est improbable et l'effet de voûte peut assurer une stabilité bien meilleure. Si le terrain est stratifié en bancs horizontaux, l'équilibre du toit est étudié banc après banc. Les contraintes de flexion augmentent cette fois comme R^2/e où e est l'épaisseur du banc. A moins de trouver au toit des bancs d'épaisseur plus grande,

c'est bien le carré de la portée qui commande l'action de la pesanteur. Ici encore la couverture ne joue aucun rôle : grâce à la flexion des bancs superposés du toit, et sous quelques réserves concernant leurs rigidités, le poids de la couverture est entièrement reporté autour de la cavité. C'est l'équivalent de ce qu'on appelle dôme de Fayol au-dessus des exploitations minières. On retrouve toutefois l'effet de la couverture sur les piédroits de la cavité, avec un coefficient multiplicateur qui dépend de l'élancement et de la forme de la cavité. En particulier les angles "attirent" une forte concentration de contraintes.

2.3 L'effet de la structure du terrain

Les solutions analytiques ne sont valables que pour un terrain continu homogène, ou pour un empilement de bancs étudié banc par banc. Le second cas correspond assez bien aux carrières de pierre de taille et aux mines sédimentaires, le premier plutôt aux roches très massives, ou bien parcourues de plusieurs réseaux de diaclases. Mais aucune étude n'a été faite pour des structures géologiques aussi répandues que les plis des terrains sédimentaires. Le modèle des exploitations par chambres et piliers dans une série de bancs horizontaux est assez comparable au bâtiment traditionnel, tout en bénéficiant d'épaisseurs qui écartent les instabilités de flambement. Par contre la voûte en maçonnerie, celle des ponts, et des grandes nefs, n'a pas d'équivalent en ouvrage souterrain.

Pour trouver un équivalent et bénéficier en conséquence d'une stabilité considérablement meilleure que celle des chambres à toit plat, il y aurait lieu de rechercher des coeurs d'anticlinaux. C'est d'ailleurs ce qui s'est fait pour les stockages de gaz dits en aquifère, puisqu'une structure étanche en cloche sert de couvercle. Il reste à vérifier comment vont réagir les unes sur les autres les voûtes superposées d'un anticlinal naturel.

2.4 Effet de la forme de la cavité

Le problème a été déjà évoqué en 1.2 et 2.2 et il suffit de rappeler ici quelques conclusions classiques :
- importance d'un accord global entre l'élancement de la section et l'élancement du tenseur contrainte initiale, à corriger suivant les anisotropies de module et de résistance du terrain,

- importance d'un accord de détail entre les surfaces des cavités et les surfaces de discontinuité majeures.

Lorsque les contraintes initiales ont un niveau critique, c'est l'accord global qui est le plus important, toutefois il convient aussi d'éviter tout angle rentrant. Lorsque les contraintes initiales sont faibles par rapport aux résistances, les discontinuités s'ouvrent facilement et c'est l'action de la pesanteur qui doit guider le dessin. Dans tous les cas la mobilisation d'un effet de voûte est souhaitable.

2.5 Effet des méthodes d'exécution

Dès que le gabarit du tunnel a dépassé la pièce de boisage qu'un homme peut mettre en place, la pratique de la section divisée s'est introduite et elle a été ensuite étendue en tant que de besoin jusqu'aux plus grandes sections. Pour les cavernes on peut distinguer trois types de sections divisées qui trouveraient leurs racines dans les méthodes de creusement des tunnels de chemin de fer européens au siècle dernier :

a) creusement de la voûte d'abord, permettant son soutènement, avant de descendre ensuite par tranches parallèles. Le cas échéant les piédroits sont soutenus aussi au fur et à mesure, c'est la méthode la plus couramment employée.

b) creusement des piédroits d'abord et construction des murs latéraux susceptibles de porter la voûte au fur et à mesure. Le stross n'est abattu qu'après revêtement complet (exemple Porabka Jar)

c) creusement de plusieurs galeries le long du contour, à partir desquelles un pré-soutènement est mis en place, permettant ensuite l'ouverture à pleine section (exemple Veytaux).

C'est évidemment l'introduction des tirants qui a permis l'emploi de cette dernière solution, et c'est le seul moyen de soutènement dont l'encombrement à l'intérieur de la section n'augmente pas quand l'échelle augmente. En outre, c'est un moyen de confinement remarquablement adaptable et même règlable. La tension du tirant peut être mesurée et surveillée, elle peut être modifiée en fonction des phases de construction et des convergences mesurées simultanément.

Il est toujours facile de reporter les zones d'ancrages des tirants au-delà des grands blocs susceptibles de mouvements le long des surfaces de discontinuité majeures, et comme leur longueur n'est pas limitée, ils constituent un moyen de sou-

tènement applicable à de très grandes cavernes, au moins jusqu'à une portée de l'ordre de 100 mètres.

Il ne devrait donc pas être nécessaire de recourir au type de solution proposé par STILLBORG sous le nom de *Rib in Roc*

CONCLUSIONS

Les facteurs qui limitent la taille des cavités ont été identifiés au long des chapitres précédents, les fortes contraintes et les faibles résistances ne sont pas les principaux, les surfaces de discontinuité comptent assurément, la crainte d'éboulements difficiles à maîtriser est au premier rang. Enfin il n'y a pas lieu évidemment de concevoir des cavités tellement grandes qu'on n'en aurait pas l'usage.

Réciproquement si des méthodes sûres et relativement peu coûteuse permettent d'exécuter des cavernes sûres, les usages suivront certainement. Deux démarches s'opposent, celle du projeteur de tunnel, chargé de relier un point à un autre, et dont le tracé est imposé à peu de choses près ; et celle du projeteur de caverne exceptionnelle qui bien souvent peut choisir le site qui lui apporte les meilleures conditions de matériau et de structure. Les stockages pétroliers ont ainsi recherché l'économie par une stabilité sans aucun soutènement ou presque. D'autres usages sont susceptibles de supporter le coût de soutènements conséquents.

La solution au soutènement des grandes cavernes est fournie par les tirants précontraints. Mais cette précontrainte n'intervient qu'en complément d'une précontrainte naturelle, fournie gratuitement pourvu qu'on sache l'utiliser. Dans l'effet de voûte, c'est le poids propre du matériau qui équilibre les réactions horizontales. En souterrain, le poids propre ne coûte rien et cette précontrainte est la moins coûteuse. Les voûtes en maçonnerie sont exposées au flambement et sensibles à tout déplacement de leurs appuis, ce qui a limité leur portée à 60-70 m. Les voûtes en rocher qui échappent à ces deux problèmes devraient pouvoir dépasser allègrement ces valeurs.

Il y a donc lieu de réfléchir à la fois sur les méthodes de calcul de ces cavernes, qu'exigeront par exemple les autorités chargées de la sûreté nucléaire, et sur les méthodes de reconnaissance susceptibles de découvrir le bon emplacement et d'en garantir la qualité. Il reste donc beaucoup de travail à faire sur le sujet.

REFERENCES

BECKER H. Bergdruck und Seine Beherrshung in der Praxis, CR Symp. Int. de la Construction des cavités souterraines, Lucerne, Sté Suisse de Mécanique des sols et des roches, 1972

BLASCHKE T.O. Underground Command Centre, Civil Engineering 34,36 mai 1964

BOUVARD A. Etude d'une cavité minière (titre exact non connu) CR journées d'études int. Ass. Franc. Travaux en souterrain, Nice 1981, à paraître début 1982, éditions Sepaly, Lyon

COURBON P. Atlas des grands gouffres du monde, édition 1972

CROISETTE DESNOYERS P. Cours de construction de ponts, Ecole nationale des ponts et chaussées, Dunod, Paris, 1885

DUFFAUT P. Site reservation policies for large underground openings, Proc. Int. Symp. Rockstore, Stockholm 1977, reprinted in Underground space vol 3 n° 4, 187-193, 1979

HAUGEN A. et MYRVANG G. Large openings at Skorovas mine (en norvégien) Fjellsprengningsteknikk og Bergmechanikk, Oslo 1974

JACOBY C.N. Creation and stability of large sized openings, Proc. 3rd RETC, Las Vegas 1976, published by AIME 591-608

LAUFFER G. Gebirgs Klassifierung für Stollenbau, Geologie und Bauwesen n° 24 Vol 1, 1958

LUNDE J. Large underground openings (en norvégien) Fjellsprengningsteknikk og Bergmekanikk, Oslo 1974

MARIN G. La construction des grandes cavernes artificielles, Exemple des centrales hydroélectriques souterraines, Industrie Minérale, Mine nov. 1978

MAURY V. Environmental protection, monitoring and operation at the May sur Orne underground oil storage facility, Proc. Int. Symp. Rockstore, Stockholm 1977

PAHL A. Geological studies for large caverns (exact title not known) Proc. Int. Coll. Underground siting of nuclear power plants, to be published Bundesanstalt für geologie und Rohstoffe Hannover 1981

PANET M. La mécanique des roches appliquée aux ouvrages du génie civil - Ass. Am. Ing. des Ponts et chaussées Paris 1976

PINKERTON I.L. et GIBSON E.J. Tumut 2 Underground power plant Proc. ASCE n° 3835, mars 1964

RESCHER O.J. Soutènement de la centrale de Veytaux par tirants en rocher et béton projeté, Bull. Techn. Suisse Romande, 7 sept. 1968

STILLBORG B. The Rib in Roc prereinforcement system for large underground openings, Proc. 4th RETC, Atlanta 1979 published by AIME

WATSON M.B., KAMMER W.A., LANGLEY N.P., SELZER L.A. et BECK R.L. Underground nuclear power plant siting, Nuclear Eng. Design 33, 269-307, 1975

REMERCIEMENTS

L'auteur a plaisir à remercier les collègues et amis qui l'ont aidé par leurs conseils et contributions, tout particulièrement Messieurs Pierre BEREST, Gilbert MARIN, Vincent MAURY, Marc PANET et Robert THEROND.

VORSCHLÄGE FÜR BAUVERFAHREN FÜR DAS AUFFAHREN SEHR GROSSER UNTERTÄGIGER RÄUME
Proposals for methods of construction for the excavation of very large caverns
Propositions concernant des procédés d'excavation des cavernes souterraines de très grandes dimensions

ARNOLD EBER
Technische Universität München, Bundesrepublik Deutschland

SUMMARY:
The excavation of such cavities requires special rock characters and an adapted method of excavation. In order to have early geological information and enable measurements to be taken, it is proposed to excavate a spiral-formed pilot tunnel on the periphery of the planned cavern. During the excavation of this pilot-tunnel the final supports are placed in position, and the increase of the secondary tension is slowly introduced before the removal of the core. It also serves as a supply tunnel for the core excavation, while the muck is removed through a central shaft.
To break away the walls of a large cavern smoothly, the use of a rotary slit- cutter is suggested. The slit- cutter is guided along the periphery of the cavern between the pilot-tunnels, thus detaching the core through a tangental cut.

ZUSAMMENFASSUNG:
Die Anlage solch großer Hohlräume erfordert bestimmte geomechanische Eigenschaften des Gebirges, ebenso aber auch ein angepaßtes Bauverfahren. Um einen frühzeitigen geologischen Aufschluß zu erhalten, rechtzeitig Messungen ansetzen und die notwendige Sicherung einbauen zu können, wird die Anordnung eines spiralförmigen Erschließungsstollens entlang der Peripherie des zukünftigen Bauwerks vorgeschlagen. Durch den Ausbruch dieses Stollens wird das Anwachsen der Sekundärspannungen eingeleitet, bevor der Kern ausgebrochen ist. Die Verformungen können gemessen und die notwendigen Sicherungen gesetzt werden. Der Spiralstollen dient gleichzeitig als Zugangs- und Versorgungsstollen beim Ausbruch des Kerns, während über einen zentralen Schacht geschuttert wird.
Um eine Kaverne möglichst schonend auszubrechen wird vorgeschlagen entlang der Peripherie zwischen zwei Erkundungsstollen eine Schlitzfräse zu führen und den Kern durch einen tangentialen Schnitt vom umgebenden Gebirge zu lösen.

RESUME:
L'intéret croissant à situer de grandes centrales d'énergie et des dépots importants en souterrains entraine non seulement des problèmes relatifs au choix des emplacements en ce qui concerne la qualité des sols, mais aussi des exigences particulières relatives aux procédés de construction.
Certaines de ces exigences se rapportent à l'information géologique, à l'observation et la mesure des déformations et des variations de contraintes, à l'assainissement de zones perturbées, à la réalisation prématurée de soutènements et au lent déplacement des efforts pour aboutir à un nouvel état d'équilibre. On peut suffir à ces exigences au moyen de galeries de reconnaissance. Sur l'exemple d'une caverne circulaire de 65 m de diamètre et de 70 m de hauteur on a concu une telle galerie de reconnaissance au tracé hélicoidal en périphérie de l'ouvrage futur. Le présent article énumère ses fonctions correspondant aux exigences susmentionnées, décrit ses principes constructifs

et explique les avantages d'exploitation qui en résultent pour l'excavation du noyau de la caverne.

D'autres exigences concernent le ménagement du sol environnant par des procédés de construction appropriés. Le système Kunz à entaille fraisée par exemple est décrit dans l'article avec ses particularités constructives et l'explication de ses avantages d'exploitation.

Il consiste essentiellement dans la réalisation d'une entaille fraisée séparant du sol environnant le bloc rocheux restant après le forage d'une galerie de reconnaissance.

1. Geologie und Bauverfahren:

Aus vielfältigen Gründen besteht in der Öffentlichkeit immer mehr Interesse, große Energieanlagen oder Lagerräume unterirdisch anzuordnen.

Die Anlage solcher übergroßer Hohlräume setzt aber ein Gebirge voraus, dessen felsmechanische Eigenschaften einem Katalog von Mindestforderungen entsprechen müssen. Solche Voraussetzungen sind für die Standortwahl mit bestimmend.

Die Herstellung von Großraumkavernen verlangt aber auch ein Bauverfahren, an das besondere Anforderungen gestellt werden. Diese können auf folgende 5 Grundforderungen reduziert werden:

2. Forderungen an das Bauverfahren:

1 Gründlicher geologischer Aufschluß im Stadium der Planung durch Erkundungsbohrungen, am gründlichsten aber durch Erkundungsstollen.

2 Beobachtung und Messung der Verformungen und Spannungsänderungen durch den Einbau von Meßgeräten, am besten bei größerer Überlagerung von Erkundungsstollen aus.

3 Frühzeitige Sanierung von Störzonen und Einbau der erforderlichen Sicherung, am besten von Erkundungsstollen aus und im Zuge des Vollausbruches.

4 Langsame Kraftumlagerung in einen neuen Gleichgewichtszustand durch entsprechende Anordnung der Teilausbrüche, wobei Erkundungsstollen als solche angesehen werden können.

5 Schonender Ausbruch durch besondere Ausbruchsverfahren. Es ergibt sich, daß für die Erfüllung dieser Forderungen Erkundungsstollen ein geeignetes Mittel darstellen.

3. Anordnung der Erkundungsstollen:

Die Anordnung und Größe der Erkundungsstollen soll aber so gewählt werden, daß sie auch den betrieblichen Erfordernissen entgegenkommen.

Die Erkundungsstollen können innerhalb, an der Peripherie oder außerhalb des zukünftigen Hohlraumes angelegt werden.

1. Die Lage des Erkundungsstollens innerhalb des späteren Bauwerks liefert nur nähere geologische Aufschlüsse und bietet einige betriebliche Erleichterungen, erfüllt aber nicht die Erfordernisse nach Ziffer 2, 3 und 4.

2. Die Anordnung der Erkundungsstollen an der Peripherie dagegen erfüllt alle Forderungen unseres Kataloges und eröffnet bei einer guten Vorplanung eine Fülle von betrieblichen Erleichterungen.

3. Die Situierung der Erkundungsstollen außerhalb des zukünftigen Bauwerks bringt ebenfalls Vorteile; so besonders die Möglichkeit der frühzeitigen Sicherung des zukünftigen Hohlraums vor Beginn der Ausbrucharbeiten.

4. Vorschlag für die Anordnung von Erkundungsstollen an der Peripherie des zukünftigen Bauwerks in Form einer Spirale:

Beispielhaft ist diese Methode für eine kreisförmige Kaverne mit 65 m Durchmesser und 70 m Höhe in den Bildern 1 und 2 dargestellt. Zwei Bauzustände sind aufgezeigt.

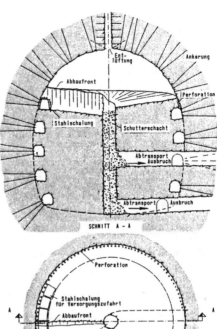

Bild 2 Betriebsweise beim Kernausbruch

Diese Bauweise erfüllt folgende Aufgaben:

- Die Peripherie des Hohlraums wird systematisch für geologische Untersuchungen und felsmechanische Messungen erschlossen. Diese Messungen können während des Auffahrens des Spiralstollens und während des Ausbruchs des Kerns fortgeführt und die Veränderungen der Meßwerte beobachtet werden.

- Die nach Auswertung der Aufschlüsse und Messungen erforderlichen Sicherungsarbeiten können vor Ausbruch des Kerns durchgeführt werden.

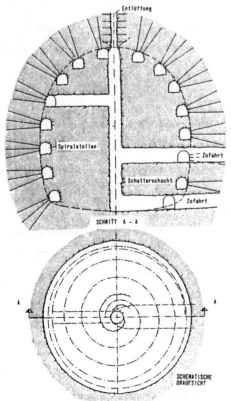

Bild 1 Auffahrung des Spiralstollens zur Erschließung und Sicherung

- Störungen im Gebirge können von diesem Spiralstollen aus frühzeitig erkannt, sorgfältig saniert und beobachtet werden, ohne den Ausbruchsbetrieb zu stören oder ihn einstellen zu müssen.

- Das spiralförmige Sicherungsband bleibt bis zum Kernausbruch auf die jeweilige Ausbruchssohle zugänglich. Nachträglich notwendige Verstärkungen, wie etwa zusätzliche Anker, können mühelos und ohne Störung des übrigen Betriebes eingebaut werden.

- Die Sekundärspannungen werden sukzessiv in dem gesamten Baukörper geweckt. Sie werden mit dem fortschreitenden Ausbruch des Spiralstollens kontinuierlich, jedoch wegen der zwischen den einzelnen Gängen verbleibenden Felsbank nicht in voller Höhe, erzeugt. Die Sicherung kann aber im vollen erwarteten Umfang dem Vortrieb des Spiralstollens folgend, eingebaut werden. Eine Teilvorspannung der Felsanker in dieser Bauphase ist möglich.

- Bei einem von oben dem Spiralstollen folgenden Abbau des Kerns kann die noch vorhandene Verbindung des Kerns mit dem umgebenden Gebirge durch Bohrungen oder auf andere Weise reduziert werden. Er ist damit fast vollständig abgelöst und kann ohne störende Einwirkung auf Gebirge und Sicherung abgetragen werden.

Konstruktive Gesichtspunkte

Die Abmessungen und die Steigung des Spiralstollens richten sich nach den geologischen u. betrieblichen Erfordernissen.

Die Querschnittsform wird nicht konstant sein, sondern sich jeweils an die tangierende Wand oder Kalotte der Kaverne anpassen, um eine genügend große Fläche für die Unterbringung des Sicherungsbandes mit den Vorspannankern zu erschliessen.

Der Spiraltunnel wird beim nachträglichen Ausbruch des Kerns als Zugangsstollen benutzt. Er muß auch für diesen gleislosen Verkehr dimensioniert werden und den Transport der dann verwendeten Geräte und Einrichtungen ermöglichen.

Die Breite muß das Bohren und Setzen von Vorspannankern erlauben, die entweder als Einzelstabanker zusammengekoppelt oder als Stabbündel eingefädelt werden.

Die Steigung soll so gewählt werden, daß zwischen den einzelnen Spiralgängen ein Felskörper erhalten bleibt, der nach dem Stand der Erkenntnisse in der Lage ist, denjenigen Teil der erwarteten Kräfte auf den Kern zu übertragen, der nicht schon durch die vom Spiraltunnel aus gesetzten Felsanker übernommen werden kann. Diese Restkräfte müssen dann durch Anker im Bereich dieses Felskörpers aufgenommen werden, sobald im Zuge des Kernausbruchs diese Fläche zugänglich wird.

Die Steigung kann auch variiert und den unterschiedlichen geologischen Verhältnissen innerhalb eines Bauwerks angepaßt werden.

Allzugroße Steigungen sind wegen der betrieblichen Erfordernisse zu vermeiden.

Auch im Bereich der Kuppel läßt sich etwa die gleiche Steigung beibehalten, wenn man die Ganghöhe dem verkürzten Durchmesser anpaßt.

Betriebliche Vorteile

Mit dem Vortrieb des Spiralstollens wird auch ein zentraler Schutterschacht von unten nach oben aufgebrochen. Er sollte so frühzeitig fertig sein, daß er über Querschläge schon beim Auffahren der Spirale zur Abkürzung der Schutterwege benutzt werden kann.

Der Kern wird spiralförmig von oben nach unten abgebaut. Die Abbauwand dreht sich dabei um den zentralen Schutterschacht. Ihre Höhe entspricht der Ganghöhe der Spirale. Sie kann bei Bedarf in zwei Abbaustufen unterteilt werden.

Um eine große Ladeleistung zu ermöglichen, wird im Beispiel sowohl auf der oberen wie unteren Zufahrtssohle geladen.

Der Spiralstollen dient der Versorgung der jeweiligen Arbeitssohle. Um den Zugang bei den einzelnen Abschlägen freizuhalten, wird eine schwere Stahlschalung in Einzelelementen eingesetzt und mit Fortschreiten des Kernausbruchs im Spiralstollen zurückgebaut.

Er dient auch der Belüftung der Arbeitssohle. Ein Entlüftungsschacht im Scheitel der Kuppel führt schlechte Wetter ab. Der Lade- und Fahrbetrieb im Zugangsstollen ist getrennt zu bewettern.

Im Zuge des Kernausbruchs werden alle noch notwendigen Sicherungsarbeiten, wie das Setzen und Nachspannen von Ankern, und alle Spritzbetonarbeiten mitgeführt.

Durch das vorgeschlagene Bauverfahren wird die Verformung langsam eingeleitet und steigt gegen den Ausbauwiderstand auf ihre volle Größe. Durch die schrittweise nachgebaute Sicherung vergrößert sich auch die Stützkraft fortlaufend und wächst durch Vorspannung stufenweise an. In der Zeit bis zur Beendigung der Ausbrucharbeiten hat sich annähernd ein neuer Gleichgewichtszustand eingestellt, und die Verformungen sind im wesentlichen abgeklungen. Durch begleitende Messungen wird dieser Vorgang kontrolliert.

Eine allenfalls notwendige wasserdichte Schale wird erst nach dem Abklingen der Bewegungen im Zuge der Ausbauarbeiten unter günstigen Arbeitsbedingungen von unten nach oben betoniert.

5. Vorschlag für das schonende Lösen des Kerns von dem umgebenden Gebirge nach der Schlitzfräsmethode System Kunz:

Nach diesem Vorschlag wird das zwischen den Erkundungsstollen - seien es Spiralstollen oder parallele Längsstollen - stehen bleibende Felsband durch eine geführte Schlitzfräse vom umgebenden Gebirge getrennt. Die Führungsschienen werden nach der gewünschten Profilform gebogen und im oberen und unteren Richtstollen verspannt. Das Bohrklein wird im unteren Stollen abgefördert.

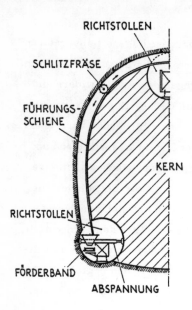

RICHTSTOLLEN
SCHLITZFRÄSE
FÜHRUNGS-SCHIENE
KERN
RICHTSTOLLEN
FÖRDERBAND
ABSPANNUNG

Bild 3 Schlitz-Fräs-Verfahren
System Kunz

Konstruktive Gesichtspunkte

Die Schlitzfräse besteht aus einem Fräsrad mit Antrieb. Die Ortsbrust wird von der Seite her angeschnitten, so daß bereits 2 Ebenen entspannt sind und nur tangentiale Kräfte an der Peripherie entstehen. Die Konstruktion der Maschine kann daher leicht gehalten werden. Die Schlitzfräse selbst ist für verschiedene Profilformen verwendbar, nur die Führungsschiene muß jeweils angepaßt werden.

Die Höhe des Schlitzes kann von einem Minimaldurchmesser des Fräsrades bis zu 2 m variieren, der Schnitt wird je nach Gebirge 0, 3 - 0, 5 m tief sein.

Ähnliche Fräsmaschinen sind aus dem Bergbau bekannt. Mit der Firma Wirth & Co. ist ein Versuchsgerät entwickelt

und im Dolomit erfolgreich erprobt worden.

Betriebliche Gesichtspunkte

Läßt man den Kernausbruch abschnittsweise folgen, so ist Raum zum Einbau noch erforderlicher Sicherungen, soweit sie nicht schon von den Erkundungsstollen aus gesetzt waren.

In dem entstehenden Schlitz kann aber auch vor dem Kernausbruch ein Betongewölbe entweder direkt oder mittels einer Schalung eingebaut werden.

Schlußbemerkung

Diese Überlegungen sind als weiterer Diskussionsbeitrag zu dem interessanten Thema der Herstellung von ungewöhnlich großen untertägigen Hohlräumen gedacht, wobei u.a. noch keine statischen Untersuchungen angestellt wurden und die Frage nach Bauzeit und Kosten noch unbeantwortet blieb. Auch die betrieblichen Einrichtungen und die Organisation des Bauablaufs für den je nach Verwendungsart unterschiedlichen Innenausbau sind nicht angesprochen und bedürfen weiterer Untersuchungen.

STABILITY OF LARGE UNDERGROUND OPENINGS UNDER VARIOUS GEOLOGICAL CONDITIONS

Die Stabilität grosser Felskavernen unter verschiedenen geologischen Bedingungen

La stabilité des cavernes rocheuses de grandes dimensions dans de différentes conditions géologiques

A.B.FADEEV & V.V.KUZEVANOV
Leningrad Civil Engineering Institute USSR

I.I.PROTOPOPOV, Yu.D.ORLOV & Yu.S.AFANASYEV
All-Union Institute of Mine Geomechanics & Shaft Surveying, USSR

SUMMARY

The information of actual size of the chambers and of the pillars applied in some ore deposits of the USSR is concerned, and the results of experimental studying the pillar deformation as well as those of evaluating the stable spans of the chambers under different geological conditions are analysed.

ZUSAMMENFASSUNG

Auf der Grundlage der umfanreichen Untersuchungen in einigen Erzlagerstatten der UdSSR werden tatsachlige Abmessungen von Pfeilern und Kammern angegeben. Die Ergebnisse der experimentallen Untersuchungen zum Verformungsverhalten von Pfeilern und zur Einschatzung von standfesten Kammerspannweiten in verschiedenen geologischen Bedingungen sind angefuhrt.

RESUME

Les données réeles des dimensions des chambres et des piliers, utilisés aux certains gisements minérals de l'URSS et les résultats des etudes experimentales de l'aptitude à la deformation des piliers et d'estimation des travées stables des chambres dans les conditions géologiques differents sont exposées.

INTRODUCTION

The mining practice has accumulated a rich experience of studying the stability of large underground openings. Especially great diversity of geological conditions is observed in the course of exploiting the ore deposits. Ore bodies usually have a bed-like form distorted by folds or disjunctives, which results in considerable variability of their inclination and thickness. During the working of deposits the room-and-pillar systems are often applied that cause the formation of rooms (chambers) whose section is large and length is considerable. The bearing members are ore pillars formed like separate columns or strips arranged uniformly if seen on a contour plan (see Fig.1).

Some data on the geological conditions, chambers and pillars at different ore mines in the USSR are given in Table 1 (in accordance to [1]).

STABILITY OF PILLARS

The ore pillars left are either lost or extracted in the course of the further mining of the deposit. In the first case it is desirable to leave the least size pillars at an optimum ratio between the pillar cross-section and the span (the width) of the chambers. The problem consists in the evaluation of the strength of the rocks in the pillars and the load on them which depends upon the areas of the extracted ore.

To study the behaviour of pillars under the increasing load, experiments were carried out at some mines. These experiments consisted in subsequent extracting a certain number of the pillars and in observing the neighbouring pillars. The stress and the strain (longitudinal and lateral) were measured in the pillars, and their characteristics were also evaluated (ultrasonic tests and electrometry).

Table 1

Chamber and Pillar Stability Performance at Some Mines in the USSR

Deposit Location	Mining Depth	Ore and Rocks	Thickness and Inclination of Ore Body	Ore and Rock Strength (MPa)	Pillar Size (Cross-Section and Height)	Chamber Span	Conditions when Stability Breaks
Jezkaz-ghan	80 to 240	Mineralized sandstones	$m=5-14$ m $\alpha=0-10°$	40 to 200 (50-150 mainly)	5 x 7 m $h=5-14$ m	12 to 16 m	Roof and pillar caving is localized to the synclinal folds with thin bedding (10 cm to 15 cm)
Mirga-limsigh	90 to 350	Dolomitic limestones	$m=3-12$ m $\alpha=0-7°$	120 to 280	4 x 6 m $h=3-12$ m	8 to 12 m	Pillar caving is localized to regions with heterogeneous structure of ores, considerable jointing
Kaula	100 to 400	Mineralized phyllites, breccias, serpentinites	$m=8-40$ m $\alpha=35°$	70 to 180 for phyllites; 10 to 40 for breccias and serpentinites	Strips 8 m wide $h=8-40$ m	9 to 32 m	Stable rocks
Kotsel-vaara	80 to 350	The same as at Kaula mine	$m=5-12$ m $\alpha=25-33°$	The same as at Kaula mine	Strips 8-12 m wide $h=5-12$ m	9 to 40 m	Pillar caving occurred in the synclines at considerable jointing; 12 joints per 1 m
Belousov-skoye	300 to 450	Quartz-sericitic, chlorite schists	$m=9$ m $\alpha=20-40°$	120 to 160 for ore	Strips 9 m wide $h=9$ m	10	Stable rocks
Norilsk	300 to 1200	Sulphide ores, gabbro-dole-rites	$m=5-40$ m $\alpha=0-30°$	40 to 120 for ores; 120 to 180 for rocks	Strips 3 m wide $h=6$ m	4 to 12	Caving occurs in considerably jointed rocks; up to 20 joints per 1 m
Communarov-sky mine	250	Porphyraceous diorites	$m=15$ $\alpha=35-65°$	240	15 to 25		Stable rocks
Nikitovski gypsum mine	80 to 100	Limestones, dolomites, gypsum, clay	$m=3-9$ $\alpha=0-20$	2 to 6; 100 for dolomite	Strips 8 m wide	12	Stable rocks

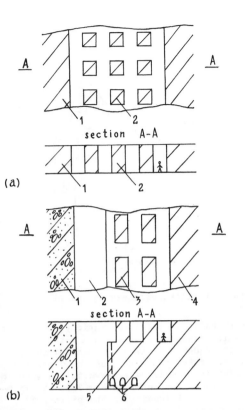

(a)

(b)

Fig.1. Room-and-pillar systems
  a - with opened worked space
  1 - barrier pillars, 2 - pillars-columns
  b - worked space filled with a hardening
  cementous filling
  1 - filling, 2 - chamber, 3 - pillars of
  upper undercutting, 4 - orebody,
  5 - blastholes, 6 - haulage level

Experience accumulated during many years
of observation shows that there are at least four stages in the process of pillar
deformation for which peculiar dependences
between the stress and the strain are typical. Fig.2 illustrates typical diagram
" $\sigma - \varepsilon$ " as well as the corresponding rheological model.
  Stage I of pillar loading is pure elastic
behaviour with Young modulus E_o. Only occasional fractures appear at this stage. When
the stress exceeds some level σ^e -limit of
elasticity - stage II of visco-elastic creep begins. The edge zones of the pillar begin getting demolished, and separate cracks
appear in the central part of it. Stage II
is imitated on the rheological model by
block consisting of elements E_1, η_1, σ^e.
Stages I and II are stable. If the stress
exceeds the long-term strength of the rock
σ^l - stage III of viscous creep begins.

Now considerable destruction of the edge
zones is in progress, the number and the
size of fissures in the central part of the
pillar increase.
  If the load onto the pillar is not diminished stage III gradually passes to post-

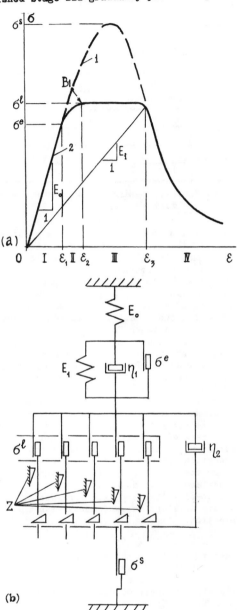

(a)

(b)

Fig.2. Stress-strain diagram and rheological model
  I, II, III, IV - deformation stages
  E_o, E_1 - elasticity elements
  η_1, η_2 - viscosity elements
  σ^l, σ^s - friction elements

263

Table 2. Pillar Deformation Stages according to Results of Sonic Tests and Electrical Logging Measurement

Pillar Deformation Stage	Longitudinal Speed, m/s	Electrical Specific Resistance, Ohm·m
I	4500–7500 / Exceeds 3500	Below 5 x 10³ / –
II	3500–4500 / 2200–2800	5 x 10³ – 5 x 10⁵ / –
III	2000–3500 / 1300–2200	5 x 10⁵ – 7 x 10⁵ / –
IV	Below 2000 / Below 1300	Exceeds 7 x 10⁵ / –

Note. Numerator – Mirgalimsigh mine, denominator – Norilsk mine

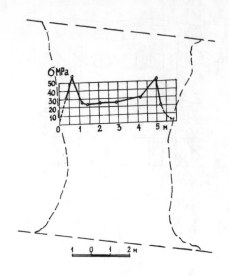

Fig.3. Vertical stresses in the pillar

failure unstable stage IV. Now a greater part of the pillar loses its bearing capacity, and the pillar becomes destroyed with formation of inrushes.

At the rheological model stages III and IV are simulated by a number of friction (strength) elements with common strength which are subsequently excluded from action by the fixed teeth "Z".

Table 2 contains some data on geophysical properties of pillars under various stages of deformation. The electrical resistance of Norilsk sulphide ore was too small for its variations could be registered.

The stresses in the pillars were measured by means of a relief method at stages I and II (see Fig.3). At stages III and IV, when the state of the pillar is inelastic, the stress measurement is not effective, and the pillar stress state should be determined on the basis of strains and their rates. Experiments have shown that at stage II (visco-elastic creep) the progress of the strain develops in conformity with the Equation:

$$\varepsilon^{(1)} = \varepsilon_o^{(1)}\left(1 - e^{-at}\right)$$

where: $\varepsilon_o^{(1)}$ – the final strain of visco-elastic creep,
t – the time.

The viscous creep of stage III is characterized by the Equation:

$$\varepsilon^{(2)} - \varepsilon_o^{(2)}\left(e^{at} - 1\right)$$

where: $\varepsilon_o^{(2)}$ – the initial strain of viscous creep,
t – the time,
a – the creep parameter.

When the loads increases rapidly, the relationship between the stresses and the deformations is characterized by branch 1 in Fig. 2a. After the rapid loading up to point B1, the stresses will relax down to the slow loading level (branch 2 in Fig.2a). The absolute limit of loading on the pillar, σ^s, may be called the short-term strength. For hard rocks the σ^s is close to the σ^l.

IN-SITU ROCK PROPERTIES

The most significant characteristics of the pillar stability – the Young modulus, E_o, and strength σ^l – can be found on the basis of laboratory-scale tests.

Table 3. Values of λ Depending upon Fracture Orientation in Respect of Load Action and Joint Spacing

Number of Joints per 1 m	4	5–8	10–15	15
Angle between Joints and Load Direction				
0 to 20°	0.90	0.70	0.60	0.35
21 to 30°	0.70	0.60	0.40	0.30
31 to 45°	0.42	0.40	0.30	0.20
46 to 90°	0.80	0.60	0.50	0.30

The generalization of the experience of the in-situ tests and observations and the laboratory tests makes it possible to propose the Equation for finding the long-term strength, σ^l :

$$\sigma^l = \lambda \sigma_o (1 - 0.25 \, lg \sigma_o)$$

where: λ – the scale effect coefficient due to jointing (see Table 3),
σ_o – the strength of the laboratory specimen, MPa.

The Young modulus, E_o, can be directly estimated by laboratory testing. The ultimate pillar deformation can be estimated approximately by the secant modulus, E_i, (see Fig. 2a) that may be defined as $E_i = \lambda E_o$.

The load on the pillars and the conditions of their deformation are defined by the degree of the underworking, the depth of mining and upon the dislocation of the rocks.

The degree of the underworking is characterized by the geometrical parameters: the depth of the mining, H, and the least size of the underworking contour, L (see Fig. 4).

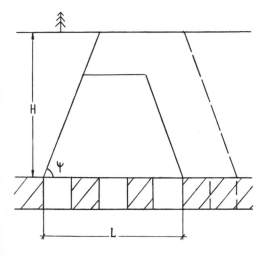

Fig.4. Pillar loading diagram
ψ – underworking angle

When L/H < 1.0, the load on the pillars is lowered to approximately 0.7 of the column full weight due to the arching effect. The pillars are under the conditions of stiff loading.
If L/H is greater than 1 – 1.5, the whole weight of the rock mass lies heavy on the pillars, and they become deformed under the conditions of soft loading. This critical L/H ratio was obtained by the full-scale observation data and the FEM calculations.

It should be noted that for the FEM calculations the strength properties of the overlying rocks are to be evaluated realistically since their properties define the arching effect and the stress state of the pillars.

The limited loading of pillars at L/H less than 0.5 to 1.0 permits to extract the ore in local areas of the deposit with the reduced size of pillars. The upper limit of critical ratio L/H depends upon the structure of the rocks that defines their stability. The least values are typical for the stratified massifs affected by disjunctives while the highest values are typical for the non-stratified rocks of magmagene origin with a low degree of dislocation.

STABILITY OF UNSUPPORTED ROOF

The stability of the immediate roof of the chambers depends upon the geometrical dimensions of the room and the degree of the tectonic dislocation of rocks. The methods of calculating the ultimate spans of stratified roofs analogous to the beam calculation method were proposed [3] and appeared to be effective. For non-stratified rocks there are no reasonable schemes, and therefore the selection of the ultimate roof spans is based on the results of the full-scale mining experiments only. The experiments consisted in widening the chambers up to the first caving, and these experiments were accompanied by measurements and observations of the roof foliation (stratified rocks) and of the roof deformation in the non-stratified rocks.

The results of a number of such experiments carried out in stratified and non-stratified rocks indicate that a roof is stable if:

$$\frac{x \cdot y}{2(x+y)} \leqslant k$$

where: x, y – linear dimensions of the roof exposure,
k – an empirical coefficient;
lies within the range of 10 to 12 for the stratified rocks and for the jointed non-stratified rocks while equals from 16 to 20 for the poorly jointed rocks.

The 15 m chamber spans (the length is unlimited) were found experimentally for gypsum; as to the stratified rocks of the Mirgalimsigh mine, the value varied from 8 to 10 while the experimental spans reached 12 or 18 m respectively. At the Kotselvaara mine the stable span achieved 100 m at the fixed

265

inclined length of the chamber of 40 m. The increasing of the bearing ability of the roof can get obtained by different technical means, in particular, by fixing the roof with the help of wedge-shaped and ferroconcrete rods. The stable roof spans increase in the inclined ore beds in inverse proportion to the cosines of the inclination angle.

If the horizontal tectonic stresses are high and distinctly overcome the vertical ones, the peculiarities of the roof behaviour are well seen: the openings whose orientation is perpendicular to the action of the highest horizontal stresses get demolished with the formation of a high arch (the ratio of the height of the arch to its width exceeds 1 or 2) while the openings with a long axis parallel to the direction of the principal stress maintain their initial shape quite well.

REFERENCES

1. Methodological Instructions for Ascertaining the Size of Chambers and Pillars at Room-and-Pillar Systems of Working the Non-Ferrous Metal Ores. Leningrad, edited by VNIMI, 1972 (in Russian).
2. Mining Journal. Moscow, NEDRA, No.2, 1981, p.50-52 (in Russian).
3. Kuznetzov G.N. and oth. The Study of Rock Pressure Phenomenon on Models. Moscow, OUGLETEKHIZDAT, 1959 (in Russian).

ASEISMIC DESIGN OF LARGE CAVERNS
Berücksichtigung der Seismik beim Entwurf grosser Kavernen
Considération du séisme dans le dimensionnement des grandes cavernes

K.FUJITA, Y.HAGA, K.UEDA, K.NAKAZONO & H.YOICHI
Hazama-Gumi Ltd., Tokyo, Japan

SUMMARY:
A study is made on the stability against an earthquake in the case that the rock caverns are placed parallel to one another.
If the caverns are placed with more than a certain interval in the rocks having the larger dynamic strength than the static strength, it is generally assumed that the cavern which completed the excavation properly is also stable against the strong earthquake to be considered.

ZUSAMMENFASSUNG:
Die Forschung handelt über die Stabilität gegen ein Erdbeben für den Fall, wo sich die Felsenhöhlen miteinander parallel definden.
Wenn Höhlen in mehr als einem gewissen Abstand im Felsen liegen, dessen Stärke mehr dynamisch als statisch ist, ist es im allgemeinen angenommen, die Höhle, die die Aushöhlung angemessen vollendet hat, auch gegen das starke Erdbeben stabil sein soll.

RESUME:
Une étude est faite sur la stabilité contre un tremblement de terre dans le cas ou les cavernes rocheuses sont placées en parallèle à l'une de l'autre.
Si les cavernes sont placées avec un intervalle plus grand gu'un certain intervalle guand les roches ont la résistance dynamique plus grande que la résistance statique, généralement c'est assumé que la caverne dont l'excavation est accomplie comme il faut, est aussi bien solide contre un fort tremblement de terre consideré.

1 INTRODUCTION

With regard to the underground pumped-storage power plant constructed in Japan, the examination of the stability against earthquake acting on the cavern has almost never been done so far because the structure built inside the cavern after the excavation increases the safety to the cavern. However, it will be necessary to make an aseismic design upon the large cavern such as underground nuclear power plants.
Researches concerning the method to analyze the stability of the rock around caverns during the earthquake as well as observations on the behaviours of the cavern during the actual earthquake are carrying eagerly. And yet, the aseismic design standard has still not been established.
This paper deals with the way to make a rough estimate of the stability of caverns against an earthquake upon carrying out the aseismic design of caverns to be built parallel to one another.

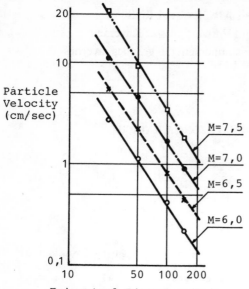

Particle
Velocity
(cm/sec)

M=7,5

M=7,0

M=6,5

M=6,0

Epicentral Distance (Km)

Fig.1. Particle Velocity (Kanai-1966)

2 ASSUMPTIONS USED IN THE STUDY

2.1 Seismic Waves Acting on the Cavern

All the above-ground nuclear power plants are built on the rock foundation in Japan. As to the aseimic design, the active fault located some distance away from the power plant is assumed as the hypocenter, and the seismic analysis is done in consideration that the ground motion having a particle velocity and a peak acceleration, which are obtained by Figure 1 as Kanai proposed.

In many cases, the input of seismic wave is made where the rigid base is placed approximately 200 meters deep below ground level. Figure 2 shows the result of computation on the distribution of seismic acceleration from the rigid base to the ground surface at a certain nuclear power plant construction site. The quality of rock at the said site was not so preferable. However, the magnitude of acceleration is a same grade at the depth of about 50 meters or deeper, which is about 40 percent of that at the ground surface.

Similar results were obtained at the other sites as well. Therefore, to make a seismic analysis for the

cavern deeper than 100 meters, it can be said that the magnitude of acceleration shall be the same as that of the rigid base, which means that the earthquake forces to be considered are much smaller than that of the surface structures.

2.2 Depth of Seismic Wave Input

According to the result of the earth quake observation done at Shiroyama underground pumped-storage power plant by Kamada and Hayashi (1979), it is not necessary to locate the place of the seismic wave input deeper than the bottom of the cavern for the aseismic design.

2.3 Estimation of Rock Strain

Yokoyama et al. (1980) made the following suggestion after their observation of earthquakes at the tunnel in the Kamaishi vicinity:

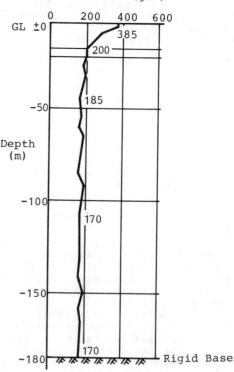

Fig.2. Computed seismic acceleration distribution

a) The strain of rock around a cavern is assumed to be same as the strain in the surrounding rock without cavern.

b) The strain of rock caused by the vertical propagation of seismic motion shall be computed considering the seismic wave reflects on the surface.

c) The horizontal propagation of seismic motion can be considered as progressive waves. The strain of rock caused by this seismic motion is estimated by getting the ratio of the particle velocity and the propagating velocity.

2.4 Analysis of Cavern Stability

As a method of analyzing the cavern stability at the time of excavation, the visco-elastic and visco-plastic finite element method, proposed by Hayashi et al., has been applied for around twenty underground pumped-storage power plants in Japan. The release of the initial stress by excavation causes to form the new stress condition of rocks around the cavern.

Figure 3 shows the Mohr's stress circle and the failure envelope of the rock. In case the former is the stress field of the rock around the cavern and the latter is the triaxial strength of the rock, the shortest distance of these two curves, expressed by d_{min} indicates the margin of the strength of the rock around the cavern.

The stability number is given by the following equation:

$$S_I = d/(d - d_{min})$$

The area where $S_I \leq 1$, Poisson's ratio $v \geq 0,45$ is called relaxed zone as shown in Figure 4. The design of the cavern is carried out so that such a zone will not appear, otherwise it is necessary to strengthen that the particular area by means of rock-bolting with or without concrete lining.

2.5 Estimation of Stress during Earthquake

Applying the wave equation to the strain caused by logitudinal wave (P-wave) that propagates horizontally and vertically, Owen et al.

(1979) proposed a method to estimate the dynamic stress in the rock caused by earthquake.

They estimated also the stress in the rock around the cavern during earthquake by combining the said dynamic stress and the static stress caused by overburden as well as they assessed the stability of the cavern using this result.

2.6 Dynamic Properties of Rock

Hayashi et al. (1973) gave the relation between the elastic modulus in dynamic E_d and the elastic modulus in static E_s as following:

$$E_d = (1,3 \sim 1,7) \ E_s$$

The value of E_d is obtained by the in-situ dynamic loading test, and the Poisson's ratio v_d is $0,2 \sim 0,3$.

Price et al. (1969) explained that the tensile strength will increase about up to 1,5 times that of the static value at the time of quick loading.

3 STRESS INCREMENT OF ROCK DUE TO EARTHQUAKE

3.1 Strain and Stress Caused by Seismic Waves

Seismic waves consists of the body waves such as the longitudinal wave (P-wave), the shear wave (S-wave) and the surface waves such as Love

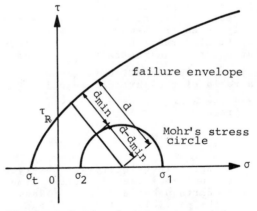

Fig.3. Relation between triaxial stress and failure envelope (Hayashi-1970)

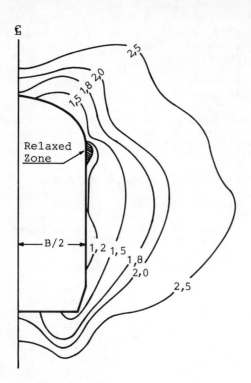

Fig.4. Stability number around cavern

wave and Rayleigh wave. Because of the ground motion by S-wave makes the most influence on the aseismicity of structures, the estimation of strain to be examined in this study is made only on the ground motion caused by S-waves.

As the S-wave reaches closer to the surface from the deep underground, it gradually propagates in a nearly vertical direction. Generally, when the S-wave propagates in vertical direction from a deep elevation, the shear strain γ_{xy} caused by the seismic motion is given as a ratio of the particle velocity V_0 and the propagating velocity V_s as follows:

$$\gamma_{xy} = - V_0/V_s \qquad (1)$$

The particle velocity was observed in the numerous records at the time of an earthquake, and Kanai (1966) gave the particle velocity in the equation (2) as well as Figure 1, when M: magnitude of earthquake and X: epicentral distance in km.

$$V_0 = 10^A$$

$$A = 0,61M - (1,66+3,6/x)\log_{10}x - (0,631+1,83/x) \qquad (2)$$

Hence, where the maximum particle velocity is $_{max}V$, the maximum shear strain $_{max}\gamma_{xy}$ is estimated by the following equation (3) in case of Vs is obtained by means of site investigations.

$$_{max}\gamma_{xy} = - _{max}V/Vs \qquad (3)$$

If the elastic modulus in dynamic E_d and the Poisson's ratio in dynamic ν_d are given, the maximum shearing stress $_{max}\tau_{xy}$ in the rock caused by the seismic wave is obtained by the following equation.

$$_{max}\tau_{xy} = \frac{E_d}{2(1+\nu_d)} _{max}\gamma_{xy} \qquad (4)$$

3.2 An Example of Dynamic Stress Caused by Earthquake

Where the maximum velocity $_{max}V$ is assumed to be 20 cm/sec as refered in Figure 1 and the propagating velocity of S-wave Vs is observed by in-situ investigation, the strain of rock $_{max}\gamma_{xy}$ is given as follows:

$$_{max}\gamma_{xy} = \pm 100 \times 10^{-6}$$

Assuming the elastic modulus in dynamic E_d is $15,3 \times 10^3$ MN/m^2 and Poisson's ratio ν_d is 0,3, the dynamic stress caused by an earthquake to be applied is estimated as follows:

$$_{max}\tau_{xy} = 0,58 \text{ MN/m}^2$$

4 AN EXAMPLE OF CAVERN STABILITY DURING EXCAVATION

4.1 Stability of Single Cavern

Figure 4 shows the distribution of the stability number obtained by the result of the analysis for the rock around the cavern at the end of excavation. Table 1 shows the rock mechanical properties used in this analysis. The relaxed zone where $S_I \leq 1$ and $V \geq 0,45$ were recognized in a certain area.

Table 1. Rock mechanical properties

Rock Overburden	H	80 m
Unit Weight	γ_t	26 KN/m³
Deformation Mudulus	D_0	12×10^3 MN/m²
Shearing Strength	τ_{R0}	2,5 MN/m²
Tensile Strength	σ_{t0}	0,4 MN/m²
Poisson's Ratio	ν_0	0,25

4.2 Stress Increment of Rock Caused by Excavation in Case of Several Caverns Placed in Parallel

Due to the excavation of caverns, the weight of overburden rock on the cavern is distributed to the surrounding rocks. This means that the stress conditions of the rock between the caverns differ the initial one. The increment of stress due to the excavation is expressed by a curve that decreases corresponding to the distance from the cavern.

Figure 5 shows the increment of the minimum principal stress σ_1,

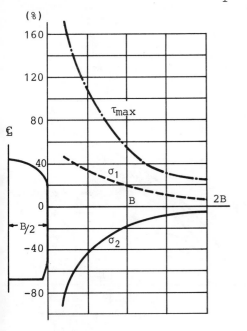

Fig.5. Stress increment due to excavation

the maximum stress σ_2 and the maximum shearing stress τ_{max} which correspond to Figure 4. In addition, at the corner of the cavern, the large increment is appeared due to the stress concentration.

When several caverns are placed in parallel to one another, the stress of rock between the caverns is added as each excavation of cavern is executed. Figure 6 shows the increment of the stress when the distance between the caverns is as shown by B, 1,5B and 2B.

5 STABILITY OF CAVERN AGAINST EARTHQUAKE

5.1 Total Stress of Rock Around Caverns

Where the rock is formed in uniform conditions, the stress of the rock around the cavern could be expressed approximately by the combination of the following items which are specified previously:
1) Initial stresses (σ_i, τ_i)
2) Increment of stress due to excavation of the cavern (σ_c, τ_c)
3) Increment of stress due to excavation of adjacent caverns (σ_p, τ_p)
4) Increment of stress caused by the earthquake (σ_e, τ_e)

Therefore the following equations could be described the total stress of the rock at the particular point around the cavern:

$$\sigma_1 = \sigma_{i1} + \sigma_{c1} + \sigma_{p1} + \sigma_{e1} \quad (5)$$

$$\sigma_2 = \sigma_{i2} + \sigma_{c2} + \sigma_{p2} + \sigma_{e2} \quad (6)$$

$$\tau = \tau_i + \tau_c + \tau_p + \tau_e \quad (7)$$

5.2 Assessment of Stability Against Earthquake

Figure 7 shows a Mohr's stress circle describing the concept of the total stress around the cavern at the time of an earthquake obtained by the combination of the static and dynamic stresses. Table 2 indicates the stress of each function during the both excavation and earthquake, refering the equations (5), (6) and (7).

With regard to the maximum shearing stress τ_{max}, the dynamic stress

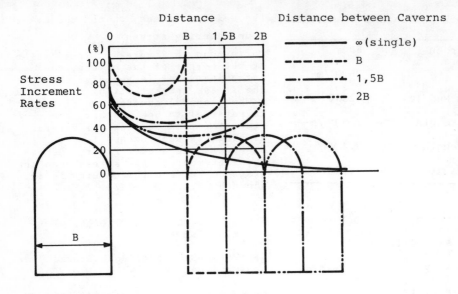

Fig.6. Relation between stress increment and
distance between caverns

indicates less than about 35 percent of that during the excavation. As the overburden depth of the cavern becomes deeper, the static stress during the excavation also becomes larger while the dynamic stress is constant. This means that the cavern in a deep depth is much stable than that in a shallow depth.

The failure envelope shown in Figure 3 is described using the tensile strength σ_t and the shearing strength τ_R of the rock around the cavern. At the time of assessing the stability of cavern against an earthquake, σ_t and τ_R in a dynamic state which probably being 1,5 times of those in a static state could be considerable. Figure 6 illustrates the relation between the stress condition and failure envelop during an earthquake.

As a result, the cavern which is stable in a static condition may remain stable also against an earthquake.

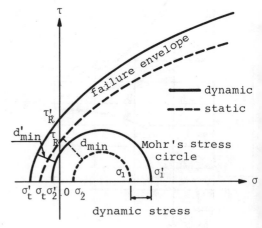

Fig.7. Combination of static and
dynamic stresses

Fig.8. Assessment of stability
during earthquake

Table 2. Combination of stresses

(1) Rough Estimate

(MN/m²)

	Stress		Position on Side Wall		
			Top	Middle	Bottom
σ_1	①	σ_{i1}	-2,20	-2,40	-2,60
	②	σ_{c1}	-1,10	-1,20	-1,30
	③	σ_{p1}	-0,22	-0,24	-0,26
	④ ①+②+③		-3,52	-3,84	-4,16
	⑤	σ_{e1}	-0,58	-0,58	-0,58
	⑥ ④+⑤		-4,10	-4,42	-4,74
	⑦ ⑤/④		(16%)	(15%)	(14%)
σ_2	⑧	σ_{i2}	-1,10	-1,20	-1,30
	⑨	σ_{c2}	+0,88	+0,96	+1,04
	⑩	σ_{p2}	+0,11	+0,12	+0,13
	⑪ ⑧+⑨+⑩		-0,11	-0,12	-0,13
	⑫	σ_{e2}	+0,58	+0,58	+0,58
	⑬ ⑪+⑫		+0,47	+0,46	+0,45
τ_{max}	⑭	τ_i	+0,55	+0,60	+0,65
	⑮	τ_c	+0,96	+1,05	+1,14
	⑯	τ_p	+0,14	+0,15	+0,16
	⑰ ⑭+⑮+⑯		+1,65	+1,80	+1,95
	⑱	τ_e	+0,58	+0,58	+0,58
	⑲ ⑰+⑱		+2,23	+2,38	+2,53
	⑳ ⑱/⑰		(35%)	(32%)	(30%)

(2) Estimate considering Direction of Principal Stresses

			Top	Middle	Bottom
σ_1	⑤'	σ_{e1}	-0,32	-0,14	-0,45
	⑦' ⑤'/④		(9%)	(4%)	(11%)
σ_2	⑫'	σ_{e2}	+0,32	+0,14	+0,45
τ_{max}	⑱'	τ_e	+0,32	+0,14	+0,45
	⑳' ⑱'/⑰		(19%)	(8%)	(23%)

Note: The distance between caverns is 1,5 times of the width of the cavern.

6 CONCLUSION

At the time of planning caverns preliminarily, the followings can be assumed for the first assessment of the stability.

a) With regard to the group of caverns for the underground power plant or similar placed in parallel to one another having an overburden depth of about 100 to 200 m, if the distance between the caverns equals the cavern's width, the stress of the rock increases by 30 percent compared to that of the single cavern. When the distance between caverns is 1,5 times of its width, the stress increment will be 10 to 15 percent. The percentage of the stress increment does not change so much even though the distance between caverns made larger.

b) In case that an earthquake of the same grade that should be applied on the aboveground nuclear power plant in Japan acts on the group of caverns mentioned previously, the shearing stress increment of the rock around the cavern will be less than around 35 percent of the total stress in the static conditions.

Generally the dynamic strength of the rock is larger than 50 percent compared to that of the static state. Therefore, the stability of cavern will be sufficiently enough during an earthquake.

Therefore, the selection of the representative triaxial strength – especially the shearing strength – both in static and dynamic states interpretating the investigated test results shall be conducted carefully for the assessment of the cavern stability considering the location of joints, the direction of joints etc.

7 REFERENCES

Dowding, C.H. & Rozen, A., Damage to Rock Tunnels from Earthquake Shaking, Journal of the Geotechnical Engineering Division, ASCE, Vol. 104, pp. 175-191, 1978.

Hayashi, M. & Hibino, S., Visco-plastic Analysis on Progressive Relation of Underground Works, Proc. of the 2nd Congress of the International Society for Rock Mechanics, Beograd, 1970, No. 4-25 (Vol. II), pp. 565-575.

Kanai, K., Improved Emperical Formula for Characteristics of Strong Earthquake Motions, Proc. Japan Earthquake Symposium, 1966 (in Japanese).

Komada, H. & Hayashi, M., Earthquake Observation around the Site of Underground Power Station, Research

Report of Central Research Institute of Electric Power Industry, No. 379013, 1979.9 (in Japanese).

Owen, G.N.,Scholl, R.E.&Brekke, T.L., Earthquake Engineering of Tunnels, RETC Proceedings, pp. 709-721, 1979.

Price, D.G.&Knill, J.L., A Study of the Tensile Strength of Isotropic Rocks, Proc. of the 1st Congress of the ISRM, Vol. 1, pp. 439-442, 1969.

Ichikawa, Y. & Ariga, Y., Some Observations of Movement of the Underground Caverns during Earthquakes, 15th Symposium on Earthquake Engineering, JSCE, pp. 169-172, 1976.

EXCAVATED ANTISEISMIC DWELLINGS AT SANTORINI ISLANDS IN YOUNG VOLCANIC TUFFS

Ausgegrabene erdbebensichere Behausungen auf Santorini in jungem vulkanischem Tuff

Logements munis d'installation de protection contre les séismes, mis à jour à Santorini, dans le jeune tuf volcanique

CONSTANTIN N.GARAGUNIS
National Technical University, Athens, Greece

SUMMARY:

Santorini is an island of the Southern Cyclades of Greece. Its history begins from the prehistoric times. Around 1500 B.C. however its Civilisation was destroyed by an explosion of its volcano. Later on the Dorians arrived in the island and built the city of Thira. This city is preserved until today. Santorini has a long and rich history to show from ancient times till today. Geologically Santorini belongs th the volcanic arch of the Southern Aegean Sea. The pedestral of the stratigraphic column of the island consists of mesozoic limestone. The rock that constitutes its geological structures is pleistocene until recently volcanic.

The volcanic activity of the island from the pleistocene period until today is due to (7) seven volcanic centers, most of which consist of many volcanoe Santorini is often hit by dense, strong earthquakes and for this reason, Santorinis houses should have a good resistance to earthquakes. As such dwellings, the houses carved into the pumice stone (volcanic rock) were constructed. These, besides the humidity which they present, have an excellent behavior to earthquakes, do not undergo collapses and are very economical because they are constructed very easily.

There are two kinds of such excavated dwellings in Santorini:
a) The Dichoro (Two-space) and b) The Didymo (Twin). These excavated constructions usually repeat themselves from the point of view of height one over the other up to 5 or 6 constructions. Especially in the western side of the city of Fira over the volcanic center Kameni of Santorini island.

ZUSAMMENFASSUNG:

Santorini ist eine Insel der Kykladen in Griechenland. Ihre Geschichte fängt schon in der prähistorischen Zeit an. Um 1500 v.Ch. wurde ihre Zivilisation durch eine Vulkanexplosion vernichtet. Später kamen auf die Insel die Dorier, die die Stadt Thera erbauten. Santorini hat eine reiche und jahrhunderte alte Geschichte, die von der Antike bis zur heutigen Zeit reicht.

Geologisch gesehen gehört Santorini zum vulkanischen Bogen des Attikokykladischen Bogens im Ägäischen Meer. Das Liegende der Vulkanite besteht aus mesozoischen Kalksteinen. Die Gesteine, aus denen das geologische Profil besteht, sind pleistozän bis jungvulkanisch. Die vulkanische Tätigkeit seit dem Pleistozän ist auf sieben vulkanische Gebiete beschränkt, von denen die meisten aus mehreren Vulkankratern bestehen.

Santorini erlebt oft häufige und starke Erdbeben, deshalb mußten Santorinis Häuser in alter Zeit ein gutes Verhalten den Erdbeben gegenüber haben. Schon die alten Griechen haben ihre Häuser, wie auch in der Neuzeit in Bimsstein (vulkanisches Gestein) ausgeschachtet, um sich vor den Erdbeben und dem Jungvulkanismus zu schützen. Der Bimsstein hat eine geringe Feuchtigkeit, die das Gestein im Kornverband zusammenhält. Im trockenen Zustand zerfällt das Gestein.

Es gibt zwei Arten dieser ausgeschachteten Häuser:
1. zweiräumige Art; 2. Zwillingsräume

Diese ausgeschachteten Bauten werden in der Regel in der Höhe wiederholt, bis zu 6 Stockwerken. Sie sind besonders an der westlichen Seite der Stadt Thera oberhalb des vulkanischen Zentrums Kamini der Insel Santorini verbreitet.

RESUME:

La greque Île Santorini appartient aux Kyklades dans la partie méridionale de la mer
Egée. La histoire va de l'antique jusqu' aujourd'lui. Elle commence déjà dans le temps
prehistorique. A 1500 a C. la civilisation a été anéanti par une explosion volcanique.
Plus tard les Dorins ont bâti la ville Thera.
Sur le plan géologique Santorini fait partie de l'arc insulaire attikokykladique dans
la mer Egée. Les roches volcaniques au mur consistent en calcaire mésozoique. Les roches, qui forment le profil géologique sont pleistocène jusque à néo-volcanique.
L'activité volcanique depuis le pleistocène est bornée aux sept régions, qui se compo-
sent de plusieurs cratères volcaniques.
Comme Santorini est souvent secouée par les seismes violents, les habitants, au temps
jadis comme aujourd'hui, construisent leures maisons dans le pierre ponce (roche volcanique). Par l'état hygrométrique, le pierre ponce recoit sa stabilité. En l'état sec,
la roche se désagrègent.
Il y a deux sortes des maisons excavées:
1. Le "Dichoro" (deux pièces); 2. Le "Didymo" (jumeau - piece)
Normalement, cettes structures excavées se répètent jusque'aux six étages. On trouve
cette architecture particulièrement dans la partie occidentale de Thera, au - dessus
de Kamini, la centre volcanique.

INTRODUCTION

In this work the excavated buildings
of Santorini island are studied. Santorini is an island of the Southern Cyclades of Greece and geologically belongs
to the volcanic arch of Aegean Sea.

The excavated constructions are
dwellings carved in the pumice stone
(volcanic rock). Initially they were made
to be the dwellings of poor inhabitants
of the island because it was easy to
built them and also because they resisted
to the weight of possible ash deposits
in their roof. Later on however, they
proved to be strong antiseismic constructions, which withstood all the seismic
vibrations that took place in the island.
For this reason, this work was oriented
to the study of the construction of these dwellings, the examination of the
geological background which they are constructed, the way of construction, their
technical characteristics, and the reasons that they are withstanding antiseismic dwellings.

As until now the reaction of these
constructions to the frequent earthquakes
of Santorini island has not been studied
from the technical geological point of
view, this study is attempting to clarify
for the forst time the conditions of the
western part of the city of Thira over
the volcanic center Kamini of Santorini
island.

1. Geographical Position

Santorini of Thira is one of the Cyclades islands. Together with Anafi island
it forms the Southern part of the Cyclades islands complex.
Santorini island occupies a range of 76
square kilometers and its populations is
6169 inhabitants in accordance with the
1971 census elements.

Santorini island consists of a complex of small volcanic islands. These islands are Thira, Thirasia, Aspronisi,
Old and New Kameni. The small islands of
Thira, Thirasia, Aspronisi, form a ring
which contains a sea-basin, at the center of which the islands of Old and New
Kameni are seen (s. figure 1).

2. History of Santorini

During prehistoric times the island
was prospering as member of the peaceful
and sea-ruling commonwealth of the Aegean
Sea, which was dominated by Crete. Around
1500 B.C., after a strong earthquake, the
volcano was awakened. A strong explosion
followed, accompanied by the puring out of
large masses of pumice stone, which covered all the surface of the island destroying this civilisation.

The history of the classical period
of Santorini island has its roots in the
beginning of the first millenium B.C.
when Dorians arrived at the island under
the leadership of Thiras Authesion, who
was a relative of the royal house of
Sparta. He built the Thira and became
its first king.

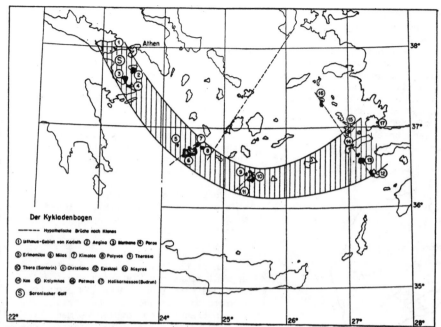

Fig. 1: Attiko-Kykladenbogen/Greece

During the Medic wars, Thira did not take part in the fighting, contrary to their participation in the Peloponnesian war.

In the beginning of the Peloponnesian war, Thira was an ally of Sparta. However later on, it became a member of the first Athenian alliance. After the Athenian defeat in Aeghos rivers in 404 B.C., Thira acquires its independence.

During the Hellenistic times, Thira falls under the rule of the Ptolemeans and thereafter it falls under the Roman Empire. It then acquires a sort of autonomy for local matters and is included in the province of Asia. During the Roman rule the Therians are converted to Christianity, through a Jewish community existing there. After the conquest of Constantinople by the Franks, in 1204 B.C., the ruler of Naxos, Markos Sanoudos, gave Thira to the Venetian Jiakomo Barocci, whose descendants kept the island until 1336. From 1336 to 1579, when it was captured by the Turks, it constituted a Dukat of Naxos.

In the revolution of 1821 it took an active part offering ships, crew and wine for the fleet.

The island was named Santorini for the first time in the 14th century and it seems that this name was established by the Italian Portogals of this era.

3. Geology of Santorini

The island of Santorini geologically belongs to the volcanic arch of the Southern Aegean Sea, which begins from Korinthos and passing through the volcanic centers of Aegina, Methana and Dodekanissions, ends in Asia Minor, near Alikarnassos (s. fig.2).

Fig. 2: Location of Santorini Island

The island of Santorini mainly consists of Pleistocene up to recent volcanic rock. Only the southeast part of the main

277

island of Thira, consists of pre-Pleisto-
cence and mainly non-volcanic rock, which
constitute the pedestal. From the Pleistocene until today there was volcanic activity, which was interrupted by countless
periods of small or large duration periods
of non-volcanic activity. Due to these
volcanic phenomena, a thick layer of lava
and pyroplastic material, which extended
the boundaries of the initially small
non-volcanic island to the size of
Strongyli island. (s. fig. 3 - 4).

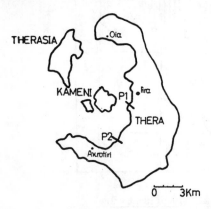

Fig. 3: The Santorini Group in the Aegean
Sea P1 and P2 are the Locations
of the schematic profiles of
fig. 4

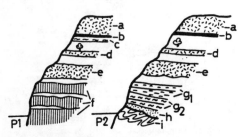

Fig 4: Schematic profiles at Localities
P1 and P2 on fig. 3.
a = upper pumice, b = palaeosol,
g_2c = ignimbites, d = middle
pumice, e = Lower pumice, f = Lavas,
g_1 = red scorial, h = white vitric
tuffs, i = Lower Tertiary phyllites
(acc. to H. PICHLER, H.L. FRIEDRICH)

Volcanic activity from the Pleisto-
cence till today is due to a minimum of
(7) volcanic centers (PICHEER) most of
which consist of several volcanoes.
These 7 volcanic centers are:

1. The volcanoes of the site Acrotiri
2. The volcanoes of the site Thira
3. The volcano of Skaros
4. The volcano of Small Prophet Helias
5. The volcanoes of the site Great
   Mountain
6. The volcanoes of the site Therasia
7. The volcanoes of the site Cammenae

Initially, before the volcanic activity took place in the island, there was
a small island in the southern part of
Thira, which consisted of sheet and
crystallic from of mesozoic limestone.

These rocks sprang from the remains
of the Aegeis which was partitioned and
sunken and were situated near the site
"Prophet Helias".

The pedestal of the stratigraphic
column of the island consists mainly of
crystal limestone, in which Megalodon
rock has been found (PAPASTAMATIOU 1958).
Therefore their age is upper triadic.
Within transformed complex we meet granite porphyries slightly transformed. The
transformation took place during the
Eocene era.

Around 100.000 years B.C. (PICHLER),
some volcanic eruptions took place in
Thira during which white pumice stone
was produced with thickness that varies
in various sites of Thira. It goes un-
interrupted from "Acrotiri Tourlas".

Around 50.000 years B.C. (PICHLER)
another volcanic explosion took place in
Thira during which about 10 meters thick
dacitic pumice stone of grey colour was
produced, which covered the entire
ancient surface of Strongyli island. Today this layer of pumice stone constitutes a characteristic horizon.

After a period of vocanic tranquilli-
ty a new phase followed during which
eruptions of rhyodacitic lava took place,
which had a high viscocity, in several
sites between Theressia and the city of
Fira.

Later on, at least two effusions of
ignimbrite took place at one or more
cracks or annular fissures. These higher
ignimbrites, which spread over the entire
surface of Strongyli island and which
consist of two layers, have a very small
thickness between 0.5 and 12 meters. The
eruptions of ignimbrite were the last
event in Strongyli island before the great
explosion which took place during the

period of Copper around 1500 B.C. These two
events, are separated between them by a
period of 15.000 years of volcanic tran-
quillity.

Finally in 1500 B.C. the explosion
of the volcano of Thira took place cal-
lend of the Copper Age, during which the
higher layers of pumice stone were formed, pumice stone and perlite (glass). These rocks belong to a subgroup of volcanic
rocks, characterised by a glass fibre and
formed by sudden cooling of the lava.

Pumice Stone is a porous rock
(sponge-like) with circular, ellipsoid
and elongated pores. In these emty spaces
gases and steam in bubble form have been
enclosed during the sudden freezing.

Due to the increased porousness,
pumice stone has an apparent weight of
0.35 to 0.40 and floats on the surface of
the water, whereas its specific weight is
about 2.5. As sizable crystals cannot be
traced in the glassy tissue, chemical analysis is necessary fcr the determination
of the composition of these rocks. The
colour of pumice stones is usually ash-
grey or white-ash.

Pumice stone presents a decreased
resistance to fracture and it is a brittle
(breakable) rock. The property, which mar-
kes this rock useful is its great insu-
lating ability against heat and sound.
For this reason it is used widely in building under the form of bricks or plates
or even as an intermediate layer. It is
also used as aggregate for cement mortar.

These layers have a medium weight of
about 30 m and are composed of three
layers. Later the upper layer has undergone aprocess, in which it was redeposi-
ted as a residue from the rinsing of the
rain water. During this explosion the
entire pre-existing Aegean Civilisation
which had flourished in the town of
Acrotiri was destroyed.

The geological evolution of Santorini island is depicted in fig. 5.

4. History of the earthquakes (acc. to
Georgalas)

The earthquakes, which interest us
are those that manifested after the settlement of inhabitants on the island during the historic times.

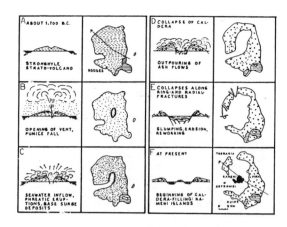

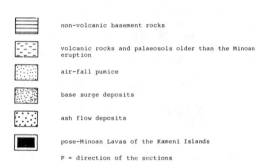

	non-volcanic basement rocks
	volcanic rocks and palaeosols older than the Minoan eruption
	air-fall pumice
	base surge deposits
	ash flow deposits
	pose-Minoan Lavas of the Kameni Islands

P = direction of the sections

Fig. 5: Schematic representation in sec-
        tion and plan of the phases and
        the mechanism of the Minoan erup-
        tion of Thera showing the deve-
        lopment of the Santorini group
        from 1700 B.C. till today
        (acc. to G.A.WAGNER, H. PICHLER)

So in 197 B.C. an eruption took
place mentioned by Stabon during which
the island of Thira was formed by the
lava. The remaining eruptions took place:

1. In 19 A.D. when from its explosion
   the island of Thira was formed, to-
   days Old Cammenae.
2. In 46 A.D. a new small island was formed in the same way.
3. In 726 A.D. a new small island was formed, which united with Thira island
   and then dissapeared.
4. In 1570 A.D. Small Cammenae was
   created.
5. In 1650 the explosion took place in
   the underwater region at a point
   situated about 6.5 km northeast of
   the cape Colombos of Thira.
   At this point a small island was formed which later on was destroyed from
   sea errosion.

6. In 1707-1711 the island of New Cammenae was formed.
7. In 1866-1911 the dome of Dafni was formed, which united the small islands of Small and New Cammenae.
8. In 1928 the dome of "Nautilus" was formed in the islands of New and Small Cammenae.
9. In 1939-1941 the new domes were formed of: Thirds A, Thirds B, Ktenas, Fouke, Smith A, Smith B and George A.
10. In 1950 this explosion took place through the cracks of lava of the domes George A and Dafni. During this, the dome of Liatsikas was formed. This also has been the last explosion till today.

   Today this volcano is at rest. In many points of the island however, vapours, warm waters and sulfurus exhalations are coming out of the opening of the hole, around which they form sulfuric crystals. The temperature of the volcanic steam varies. The highest observed reached 86°C.

5. Excavated constructions of Santorini island

   In the island of Santorini caves were used already from the Paleolithic age as a basic form of dwelling. This happend for three reasons mainly. In the first place the inhabitants of the island should be protected from the frequent and strong winds (etesian winds) that blow in the island. In the second instance, the dwellings inside the earth presented a better behavior to the dense earthquakes that stroke and still strike the island (and still strike the island) and finally the inhabitant of Santorini should respect the economy and the environment of his island.

   So, many centuries ago, the Santorinian craftsman thought and realised simple, intelligent, and financially faultless solutions, always combining the right aesthetic aspect. The constructions in Santorini island have the shape of a dome because this shape has a better behaviour to earthquakes. The most resistant houses to earthquakes, are those which are carved inside the rock, as attested by the control commitee of the buildings after the earthquakes of 1950. The above commitee ascertained that the excavated buildings had only been damaged in the wall plaster, whilst the built houses of Santorini had cracked presented cracks, as stated by architect Mrs. Roussea, member of the commitee.

This happens, because pumice stone in its geological backround (in situ) presents better resistance than when it is taken as a specimen. As we know, pumice stone presents a reduced resistance to fracture and is a brittle rock. However when it is situated in its geological background it acquires a great cohesion, especially when there is humidity. From observations on the spot we ascertained that pumice stone without humidity (because it was situated in adequately ventilated spaces) was a lot more breakable than that which was humid.

The excavated houses do not give the impression of a cavern. They are high-ceiling houses and spacious. In the summer they are cool and in the winter they are hot. This happens because they are carved inside the pumice stone, which as we know has excellent thermo-insulatory qualities. And due to the excellent sound-insulation of pumice stone. However, they also have a terrible defect, they are humid. The inhabitants of Santorini suffer a lot from humidity, in an island where there is a great shortage of water.

Humidity is created as follows: During the day and especially during the summer months, when temperatures are very high, sea water evapourates. When it gets to the highest, cold layers of the air are formed enter the cool excavated parts, it liquifies and creates droplets, which deposit on the cheeks of the excavated dwellings. As in these subterranean constructions there is complete cirquit of ventilation, humidity is created.

This problem is partly faced by the creation of high domes, which increase the volume of the house and help, in this way, ventilation and lighting, especially of the spaces situated in depth, which if they had a low ceiling with natural draught then a low ceiling would be uninhabitable.

Adequate ventilation could be achieved in two ways:

a) By creating a circuit of ventilation. This could be achieved if we opened a well from the depth of the excavated part till the surface, in which case due to natural draught a circuit of ventilation would be created. However this is impossible because it demands expenses for the opening of the well, it is not aesthetic and is dangerous for an inhabitable space to have an opening in the ceiling. Functionally it is also bad because the well should pass trough all the excavated dwellings above it. For these reasons this solution is rejected.

b) By creating a circuit of artificial ventilation with either recessive or blowing ventilatiors, which will force the air to renew itself. This solution is also anti-economical and anti-functional because it demands a permanent instalation of ventilators inside the house. In addition, these ventilators when they function they create considerable and annoying noise.

For these reasons and also for the reason that the Pumice stone when humid presents a better behaviour to earthquakes, we avoid making exhaustive ventilation of the excavated dwellings today.

The only technically feasible solution seems to be the ventilation of the excavated dwellings by air conditioning. But this solution also is not easy to realize due to financial reasons because, the excavated dwellings belong to mainly poor families of the island, who do not have the financial means to install air conditioning in their homes and for this reason the problem of humidity of the excavated dwellings, remains unsolved.

The excavated·dwellings of Santorini constitute special and unique dwellings in their kind. For this reason they follow certain special rules of building. These rules where codified in the 18th century and defined special principles: "This houses which are excavated in the hill-side should not be built in such a height so as to be an obstacle to the view of the houses situated on top of them", "a carved house should not spead in with in a way that enter the foundations of the neighbouring houses", "the planting of a vineyard or other trees is prohibited above houses excavated in the ground", "the owner of a house needing repair should execute the required works of supporting since his house is dangerous for the dwelling underneath. If he does not execute them, then the other owner of the community has the right to demolish it."

6. Types of cavern houses on Santorini

In Santorini we distinguish two types of excavated dwellings. Type A or "dichoro" and type B "didymo".

A. The dichoro is the simplest form of a house in Santorini. This is entirely or partly excavated in pumice stone, the so called aspa (s. fig. 6 - 7). Favourable circumstances for the construction of this home is the existence of pumice stone that is cohesive enough.

These houses are narrow-fronted for the following reasons:

a) Due to the narrowness and the unevenness of the ground.
b) This is done because it is so required from the resistance of the pumice stone.
c) In this arrangement the houses are supporting one another with their long sides, this aquiring cohesion as a whole and resistance against seismic vibrations, which are so frequent in the island.

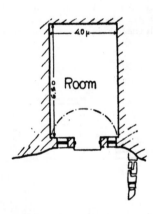

Fig. 6: Dichoron house. It is entirely excavated in pumice stone

The front is the only wall which can be seen of the excavated space, is usually built (normally). Rarely a thick wall of the same material of the aspa is left. They have a small door placed axially both on the right and on the left of a window, whilst there is sometimes a third window high over the door. The great and many windows are used in the lighting of the interior of the house which extends to a great depth.

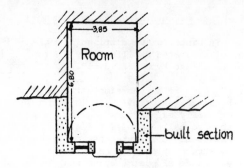

Fig. 7: Dichoron house. It is in one part
excavated. The other part is
builded.

The main house usually consists of
two spaces. One is in the front and is
called Salle. In this Salle, reception,
dining, work and even sleep take place,
when the family is large. The second space is situated in the depth and is called
Kamari. In this the family sleeps. The
two spaces are separated by a built wall,
which is idnetical to the wall of the
front side (s. fig. 8). The kitchen and
lavatory are always in the yard and the
covering of all the walls is done through
semi-cylindrical domes and pumice-cement/
concrete.

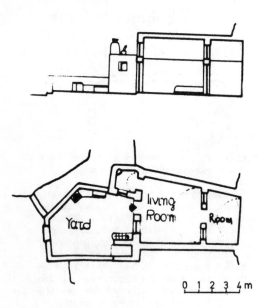

Fig. 8: Horizontal view and Section of
dichoron house

B. The didymo results from a repetition of
the dichoro in the plan view, as shown
in the (fig. 9). The two dichoro apart-
ments are sometimes of equal width and
sometimes of unequal width. Usually
the narrowest branch is the stable and
the widest is the dwelling.

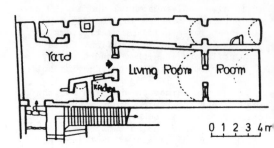

Fig. 9: Horizontal view of didymon house

Sometimes, however the stable is missing and the house extends only in
the two spaces.

Access to all these spaces takes place
from a small elementary yard. In front
of this yard a stone-paved road is
constructed.

These houses repeat themselves in the
sense of height one on top of the
other up to 5 or 6 houses, as shown
in (fig. 10).

Today the excavated dwellings constitute the touristic attraction of Santorini island. They are rented at high
prices to the tourists in the summer,
either because they prefer them all because they are unique in their kind, or
because they are excavated in the pumice
stone which gives them a good thermal
and a high sound insulation. Also, they
have a panoramic view to the volcano of
Santorini.

Finally it is worthwile noting the
existence of an excavated dwelling, which
crosses the island, and from which the
Santorinians could reach the other side
of the island when, during the Middle
Age, they suffered invasions by Pirates.

The excavated dwellings of Santorini
are not unique in their kind. There have
also been several houses carved inside
volcanic tuffs in Kappadocia of Asia
Minor, today's Turkey.

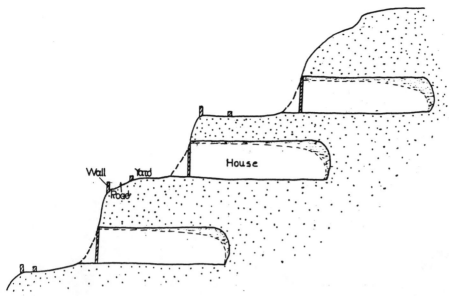

Fig. 10: Section of the houses as they repeat themselves in the sense of height one
on top of the other

The first excavated dwellings of Kappadocia where built before 800 B.C. The byzantine people also used to built there excavated churches.

Today in Kappadocia they continue to built excavated dwellings some of which are (suitably) modified for the tourists.

A sort of excavated dwellings carved inside volcanic tuffs are the catacombs of Milos island, which date back to the first christian centuries.

BIBLIOGRAPHY

Davis, El. 1975, Die jungvulkanischen Gesteine von Aegina, Methana und Poros und deren Stellung im Rahmen der Kykladen Provinz. Kommissions Verlag von Guggen, Bühl u. Huber, Schweizer Spiegel Verlag, Zürich.

Doumanis Or.B.-Oliver, P. 1974, Shelter in Greece Architecture in Greece, 1974. Printed in Greece Library of Congress Card Number 73-92747.

Georgalas, G. 1976, Santorini volcano manoskript. Bein der Exkursion in Santorini von der Intern. Cong. Ther. Waters Geoth. Energ. and vulcan of Mediter Area, Athen.

Koumanoudis, I.N. 1970, Popoular houses and churches of Santorini. Santorini.

Michelis, I.N. 1960, The Greece popular house, Athen.

Papastamatiu, J. 1937, Die neogenen Vulkane der Landschaft Krommyonia (Isthmus von Korinth). Hab. Schrift Univ. Athen.

Pichler, H. & Friedrich, W.L. 1978, Thera and Aegean World II. Proceedings of the Second International Scintific Congress Santorini, Greece.

Seward, D., G.A. Wagner & H. Pichler 1978, Thera and Aegean World I. Proccedings of the Second International Scintific Congress Santorini, Greece.

KORROSIONSGESCHÜTZTE FREISPIELANKER FÜR DEN KAVERNENBAU
Corrosion protected anchors for construction of underground chambers
Tirants protégés contre la corrosion pour la construction des cavernes

F.GRABER
Losinger AG, Bern, Schweiz

SUMMARY:

Rock anchors are the right means to secure large underground chambers during the excavation without the use of support structures. After excavation a supporting concrete lining is not required as the rock in connection with the prestressed anchors will create a support system in itself around the opening. The anchors, therefore, must be designed accordingly to fulfil their task during the entire service live of the structure. The steel tendon must be fully protected against corrosion. The free length of the anchor must be capable to compensate changes of loading due to fluctuations in the state of stress during excavation and later on during the period of stabilization. A full corrosion protection can be achieved by fully encapsulating the steel tendon by means of resistent PE-ducts which must be corrugated along the bond length to transfer the anchor load to the ground. By this means the steel tendon is fully insulated from the surrounding. Greased and PE-coated steel strands along the free length permit free movement of the tendon at any time. The anchors are grouted in the borehole with cement mortar and are prestressed to the required force. Anchors which are equipped with load measuring devices permit a control of the stresses in the cavern at any time during excavation and during service.

ZUSAMMENFASSUNG:

Felsanker sind beim Bau von grossen unterirdischen Hohlräumen das richtige Hilfsmittel um bei abstützungsfreier Ausbruchmethode den Hohlraum jederzeit zu sichern. Nach der Ausbruchsphase erübrigt sich eine steife Beton-Auskleidung des Hohlraumes, da das Felsmassiv mit den vorgespannten Ankern rund um den Hohlraum in sich ein tragfähiges Stützsystem ergibt. Die Anker müssen daher entsprechend der langen Funktions-,bzw. Lebensdauer aufgebaut und vor allem die Zugglieder von Korrosion wirksam geschützt sein. Im weiteren muss sich das Zugglied in der freien Ankerlänge jederzeit frei bewegen können, um Spannungsumlagerungen im Fels während der Ausbruchs- und später während der Stabilisierungsphase aufnehmen zu können. Ein wirksamer Korrosionsschutz wird erreicht durch ein vollständiges Umschliessen des Zuggliedes mit einem PE-Hüll-rohr, das entlang der Verankerungslänge zum Zweck der Kraftübertragung gewellt ist. Dieses Hüllrohr isoliert die korrosionsgefährdeten Stähle des Zuggliedes von der Umgebung. Gefettete und mit PE-umhüllte Litzen entlang der freien Ankerlänge gewähr-leisten die freie Bewegung des Zuggliedes (Freispieleffekt). Die Anker werden im Bohrloch mit Zementmörtel verpresst und auf die erforderliche Kraft vorgespannt. Anker, die mit Messdosen ausgerüstet sind, ermöglichen eine Kontrolle der Ankerkraft und somit des Spannungszustandes im Fels während der Ausbruchsphase und bei Bedarf während der ganzen Lebensdauer.

RESUME:

Lors de la construction de grandes cavernes souterraines, les tirants en rocher représentent la façon la plus traditionnelle d'assurer la voûte sans l'aide d'étayage lors des travaux d'excavation. Le massif rocheux garni de tirants précontraints forme après excavation un système porteur stable qui rend inutile la construction d'une voûte rigide en béton dans la caverne. Les tirants précontraints doivent être conçus en fonction de leur durée de fonctionnement ou de vie, notamment en ce qui concerne la protection contre la corrosion qui doit être exemplaire. Aussi, le tirant devra en tous temps pouvoir se mouvoir au niveau de sa longeur libre afin de supporter les modifications de tension engendrées par le rocher lors des travaux d'excavation et de l'établissement du régime secondaire des contraintes lors de la phase de stabilisation de l'enveloppe rocheuse. Une protection très efficace contre la corrosion est fournie par le confinement intégral des torons dans une gaine de polyéthylène, ondulée dans la zone de scellement. Cette gaine isole les aciers à haute résistance du tirant de l'environnement rocheux. Les torons graissés et individuellement enrobés dans du polyéthylène sur la longueur libre du tirant peuvent se mouvoir sans entrave sur ce tronçon. Les tirants sont injectés au mortier de ciment sur toute leur longueur et mis en tension à la force requise. Les tirants équippés de vérins de mesure permettant en tous temps un contrôle effectif de la force et par la même de l'état de tension du rocher que ce soit durant la phase d'excavation ou à long terme en service permanent.

1 EINLEITUNG

Der Ausbruch unterirdischer Hohlräume im Fels für Stollen, Tunnel und Kavernen führt zwangsläufig zu einer Aenderung des Spannungszustandes, die sich in Verformungen und Verschiebungen auswirkt und im schlimmsten Falle einen Einsturz zur Folge haben kann. Um einem solchen Ereignis zuvorzukommen, muss der Hohlraum gesichert werden. Dies kann durch den Einbau von Abstützungen und anschliessendem Betonieren einer steifen Auskleidung geschehen. Der wesentliche Nachteil dieser Lösung besteht im grossen Raumbedarf für die Ausführung der Arbeiten.

Die heutigen Kenntnisse der Felsmechanik und die moderne Felsankertechnik machen es möglich, grosse Hohlräume durch Vorspannanker und Spritzbeton zu sichern. Bei diesem Verfahren, das in den sechziger Jahren eingeführt wurde, haben die Anker die Aufgabe, im Felsmassiv rund um den Hohlraum einen tragfähigen Ring zu schaffen, der eine Entspannung und merkliche Verschiebungen des Felses während des Ausbruchs verhindern soll.

Die Methode hat sich sowohl als Stützsystem an sich wie auch bezüglich der Ausführung der Ausbrucharbeiten als sehr erfolgreich erwiesen. Bessere Leistungen dank kontinuierlichem Bauablauf und genauerer Abbau bei erhöhter Sicherheit sind die Folge. Daraus ergeben sich Verkürzungen der Bauzeiten und Verringerungen der Baukosten.

Das Abstützsystem mit Ankern kann während des Ausbruchs jederzeit angepasst und korrigiert werden. Schwankungen des Spannungszustandes werden durch Messanker überwacht, die wie normale Anker unmittelbar nach dem Ausbruch eingebaut werden, im Gegensatz zu diesen jedoch mit Messeinrichtungen versehen sind. Sie erlauben eine dauernde Kontrolle bis zum Abschluss der Stabilisierungsphase, d.h. bei Bedarf während vieler Jahre.

VSL Felsanker wurden zum ersten Mal im Jahr 1957 angewendet und bereits im Jahre 1961 wurden sie in einer Kaverne (Vianden, Luxemburg) erfolgreich eingebaut. Insgesamt 10 Kavernen sind bis heute mit Hilfe von VSL Felsankern gesichert.

Mit all diesen Arbeiten wurde eine grosse praktische Erfahrung auf dem Gebiet der Ankertechnik erworben und der Aufbau des Ankers verfeinert, um den speziellen Anforderungen gerecht zu werden.

Eine spezielle Aufmerksamkeit wurde seit jeher einem wirksamen Korrosionsschutz geschenkt, da die Sicherheit der Kavernen direkt von der Lebensdauer der Anker abhängt.

Die nachfolgenden Ausführungen behandeln den konstruktiven Aufbau von voll korrosionsgeschützten Freispielankern wie sie heute von VSL angeboten werden.

2 AUFBAU VON VOLL KORROSIONSGESCHUETZTEN VSL FREISPIELANKERN

Die Anker bestehen grundsätzlich aus den folgenden drei Teilen:
- Verankerungslänge)
- Freie Ankerlänge) Zugglied
- Ankerkopf als Abstützung des Ankers auf dem verankerten Bauteil.

2.1 Zugglied

Die Zugglieder bestehen aus 7-drähtigen Spannstahllitzen mit Nenndurchmesser 13 mm (0,5") und 15 mm (0,6"), deren Kennwerte den im Spannbetonbau verwendeten Litzen entsprechen. Die Einzeldrähte der Litzen sind patentiert und kaltgezogen.

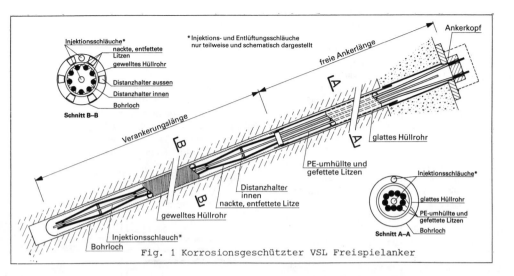

Fig. 1 Korrosionsgeschützter VSL Freispielanker

Nach dem Verseilen werden die Litzen angelassen oder stabilisiert. Die Bruchfestigkeit liegt zwischen 1600 und 1800 N/mm2. Relaxationswerte bei einer Belastung von 70% Bruchfestigkeit und bei einer Temperatur von 20° C liegen nach 1000 Stunden bei 7% bei Normalrelaxationsqualität bzw. bei 2,5% für Qualität mit tiefer Relaxation.

Die Verwendung von Litzen hat folgende Vorteile:

- Grosse "Elastizität" der Anker dank hoher Bruchfestigkeit des Spannstahles, so dass kleine Kriechverluste oder Kraftzunahmen bei Gebirgsdeformationen entstehen.
- Grosse Biegsamkeit der Litzen erleichtert Transport, Lagerung und Einbau auch unter erschwerten Bedingungen mit beschränkt verfügbarem Raum, wie zum Beispiel in unterirdischen Hohlräumen.
- Keine Kupplungen erforderlich, unabhängig von der Länge der Anker.
- Anker grosser Tragkraft können dank der hohen Bruchfestigkeit der Litzen mit einem relativ kleinen Durchmesser ausgebildet werden. Dies führt zu entsprechenden Kosteneinsparungen bei den Bohrarbeiten.

Die einzelnen Litzen der Zugglieder von korrosionsgeschützten VSL Freispielankern sind entlang der freien Ankerlänge gefettet und mit einem PE-Rohr umhüllt und gewährleisten daher jederzeit eine ungehinderte Bewegung der einzelnen Litzen. Diese Umhüllung wird entweder vom Hersteller im Werk oder aber direkt bei der Herstellung der Anker aufgebracht. Im ersten Fall muss die Umhüllung und das

Fett entlang der Verankerungslänge vor dem Zusammenbau der Anker entfernt werden. Dabei wird der Entfernung des Fettes eine spezielle Aufmerksamkeit geschenkt, um eine Verminderung des Haftvermögens zwischen Spannstahl und dem umgebenden Mörtel zu verhindern. Die einzelnen Drähte der Litzen werden geöffnet und mit Dampf gewaschen.

Da diese Arbeit ziemlich aufwendig ist hat VSL ein Verfahren entwickelt, wobei nur die freie Ankerlänge kurz vor dem Zusammenbau gefettet und in ein PE-Rohr von mindestens 1 mm Wandstärke gestossen wird. Eine einfache Vorrichtung gewährleistet, dass auch der Zentrumsdraht der Litzen gefettet wird. Das Verfahren ist einfach und kann auch auf einer provisorischen Ankerherstellungsanlage auf einem Bauplatz eingesetzt werden.

2.2 Verankerungslänge

In der Verankerungslänge werden die Kräfte des Zuggliedes auf den Baugrund übertragen. Die Uebertragung der Zugkraft auf

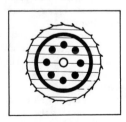

Fig. 2 Querschnitt durch die Verankerungslänge

den Zementmörtel und den umgebenden Fels erfolgt in Form von Haftspannungen.

Die mehrmals gespreizten Litzen (Fig. 1) sind von einem gewellten PE-Hüllrohr umgeben, das das Zugglied völlig von der Umgebung isoliert (Fig. 2).

Die Einleitung der Zugkraft des Ankers in den Fels geschieht über den Mörtel, der das Zugglied umgibt, über die Wellung des Hüllrohres und über das Verpressgut zwischen Hüllrohr und Fels.

Innere Distanzhalter (Fig. 1) gewährleisten eine einwandfreie Ueberdeckung der einzelnen Litzen des Zuggliedes mit Verpressmörtel.

Aeussere Distanzhalter (Fig. 1) zentrieren den Anker im Bohrloch.

Beim Uebergang zwischen Verankerungslänge und freier Ankerlänge ist das gewellte Hüllrohr mit dem glatten Hüllrohr mittels einem Blechrohr verbunden. Um eine absolute Dichtigkeit zu gewährleisten, wird ein Schrumpfschlauch über diese Trennfuge angebracht. An dieser Stelle beginnt die Kraftübertragung und sie ist daher stark korrosionsgefährdet wegen der Risse, die im Verpressgut auftreten.

Am äussersten Ende der Verankerungslänge wird eine Ankerspitze aus Plastik oder galvanisiertem Stahl, die mit dem Zugglied verbunden ist, montiert und die Verbindungsstelle mit dem gewellten Hüllrohr mit einem Schrumpfschlauch abgedichtet.

Die Verankerungslänge wird aufgrund der geotechnischen Eingenschaften des Felses und anhand der Resultate von Versuchsankern bestimmt. Sie schwankt zwischen 3 und 10 m je nach Art des Baugrundes und der Gebrauchskraft des Ankers.

2.3 Freie Ankerlänge

Als freie Ankerlänge wird die Distanz zwischen dem Beginn der Verankerungslänge und dem Ankerkopf bezeichnet. Sie entspricht also derjenigen Länge, in der sich das Zugglied beim Spannvorgang unbehindert verlängern kann.

Die Ausbildung der freien Ankerlänge ist eine Funktion der an den Anker gestellten Anforderungen, welche für korrosionsgeschützte Freispielanker zum Beispiel sein können:
- erforderlicher Schutzgrad bezüglich Korrosion und mechanischen Beschädiggungen

- die Möglichkeit, eventuelle Querverschiebungen des Bodens zu ertragen.

In Tabelle I sind verschiedene Möglichkeiten gezeigt.

In jedem Fall ist jedoch das Zugglied mit einem glatten PE-Hüllrohr umgeben und der Hohlraum zwischen Hüllrohr und Bohrloch mit Verpressgut verfüllt. Einzelne Längen des Hüllrohres werden mit Schrumpfmuffen gekuppelt. Aeussere Distanzhalter zentrieren den Anker im Bohrloch.

2.4 Ankerkopf

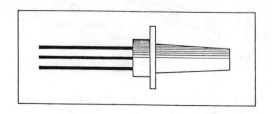

Fig. 3 VSL-Verankerung Typ E

Der Ankerkopf besteht aus einer VSL-Spannverankerung Typ E, die sich im wesentlichen aus einer Ankerbüchse, Klemmen und einer Ankerplatte zusammensetzt (Fig. 3). Ein Schutzdeckel, der mit Zementmörtel oder einer dauerplastischen Korrosionsschutzmasse verfüllt ist, gewährleistet einen dauernden Korrosions- wie auch Sprengschutz des Ankerkopfes. Ein Stahlrohr dient als Uebergang zwischen PE-Hüllrohr der freien Ankerlänge und der Ankerplatte. Das Stahlrohr wird über das PE-Hüllrohr geschoben und der Ringraum mit einer Dichtungsmasse verfüllt.

Alle Litzen des Zuggliedes eines Ankers werden gleichzeitig gespannt aber einzeln mittels Klemmen in einer konischen Bohrung in der Ankerbüchse verkeilt. Die zur Verfügung stehende Reihe von VSL-Verankerungen ermöglicht das Spannen von Ankern von 1 bis 55 Litzen, wobei das Verankerungsprinzip stets dasselbe ist.

Die Verankerungen werden, je nach besonderen Anforderungen, denen ein Anker unterworfen werden kann, entsprechend konzipiert. Dies ist hauptsächlich nötig, wenn der Anker
- ein Kontrollanker ist
- später nachgespannt werden muss
- abgelassen und wieder gespannt werden muss.

In Tabelle II sind schematisch verschiedene Möglichkeiten der Ausbildung der Spannverankerung aufgezeigt, falls der

Tabelle I Freie Ankerlänge, Ausführungsmöglichkeiten

Variante	Injektion	Korrosionsschutz	Anwendungsgebiet	Geeignet für Kontrollanker	Ablassen u. Nachspannen
1	Gleichzeitige Injektion aller Hohlräume in einem Arbeitsgang	Litzen einzeln gefettet und PE-umhüllt, Litzenbündel in PE-Hüllrohr, Zementmörtel inner- und ausserhalb des Hüllrohres	Freispiel-Daueranker	ja	ja
2	Nur Primärinjektion (Verankerungslänge und Ring um das glatte Hüllrohr im Bereich der freien Ankerlänge)	Litzen einzeln gefettet und PE-umhüllt, Litzenbündel in PE-Hüllrohr, Hüllrohr von Zementmörtel umschlossen	Freispiel-Daueranker bei zu erwartenden Querverschiebungen	ja	ja

Tabelle II Ausbildungsarten des Ankerkopfes für Kontrollanker

Lösung	A	B	C
Schematische Darstellung			
Ankerkopf	Typ E normal	Typ E mit Gewinde	Typ E mit Gewinde
Kraftmessung	mit Spannpresse	mit Spannpresse über Kupplungsstück	mit dauernd oder bei Bedarf aufgesetzter Kraftmessdose
Litzenüberstand	erforderlich	keinen	keinen

Anker für Kurz- oder Langzeitkontrollen bestimmt ist. Die Wahl des geeigneten Typs hängt von der Zugangsmöglichkeit zum Anker, die Dauer der Kontrollen sowie wirtschaftlichen Ueberlegungen ab.

Wenn Kraftverluste infolge von Bauwerksverformungen zu erwarten sind, wird der Ankerkopf so ausgebildet, dass er nachgespannt werden kann.

Die Lösungen A und B der Tabelle II eignen sich für diesen Zweck. Beim Nachspannvorgang wird die Ankerbüchse von der Ankerplatte abgehoben und der Zwischenraum, der entsteht, mit Unterlagen der entsprechenden Form und Dicke gefüllt. Als dritte Möglichkeit bietet sich die Verwendung einer Verankerung Typ E_R an, die mit einer Reguliermutter versehen ist, mit welcher die Spannkraft angepasst werden kann (Fig. 4).

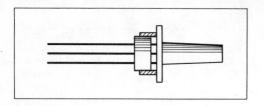

Fig. 4 VSL-Verankerung Typ E_R

Für ein späteres Ablassen des Ankers müssen Spezialklemmen eingesetzt werden, die mittels einem Spannpressenzubehör nach Belieben entkeilt und wieder verkeilt werden können, um den Anker auf diese Weise in einer oder mehreren Stufen völlig zu entspannen und unter Umständen wieder nachzuspannen.

Falls die Litzen jedoch nicht über die Verankerung hinausstehen dürfen, kann eine Verankerung Typ E_A eingesetzt werden, die auf dem Prinzip der Reguliermutter arbeitet (Fig. 5). Das Ablassen wird mit Hilfe einer Kupplung ausgeführt.

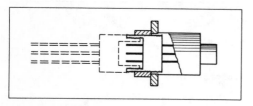

Fig. 5 VSL-Verankerung Typ E_A

Um nach dem Ausbruch eine rasch wirkende Gewölbesicherung zu erhalten, wird der Ankerkopf in vorfabrizierte Elemente einbetoniert. Diese Elemente werden an Montageankern befestigt und der Zwischenraum zwischen Gewölbewand und Element mit Beton hinterfüllt.

3 EINBAU DER ANKER

3.1 Versetzen der Anker

Je nach Länge und Grösse werden die Anker von Hand oder mit Seilwinden in das Bohrloch versetzt. Bei diesem Arbeitsgang muss vor allem darauf geachtet werden, dass die Umhüllung, d.h. das gewellte Hüllrohr und damit der Korrosionsschutz des Ankers, nicht beschädigt wird.

3.2 Injektion der Anker

Um eine einwandfreie Injektion zu gewährleisten wird das Bohrloch nach dem Bohren mit Zementmörtel unter Druck verpresst um Klüftungen und Risse im Baugrund zu verfüllen, aufgelockerte Zonen zu verfestigen und ein Zusammenfallen des Bohrloches zu verhindern. Nach Erhärtung des Verpressgutes wird das Bohrloch wieder aufgebohrt. Die Dichtigkeit des Bohrloches wird danach mit einem Wassertest kontrolliert.

Die Verankerungslänge von Ankern kleiner Gebrauchslast mit Verankerungslängen bis zu 6 m und namentlich steigende Anker werden mit Zementmörtel vorinjiziert.

Neuere Spezifikationen verlangen eine Verfüllung des inneren Hohlraumes mit Epoxy oder Polyester Kunststoffmörtel, d.h. ein duktiles Verpressgut bei dem unter dem Aufbringen der Vorspannkraft keine Risse auftreten sollten. Es ist jedoch zu beachten, dass das Arbeiten mit Kunststoffmörtel eine grosse Erfahrung des Baustellenpersonals erfordert um eine einwandfreie Qualität mit genügender Festigkeit und gutem Kriechverhalten zu erhalten.

Eine Vorinjektion gestattet eine eingehende Kontrolle der Verankerungslänge bevor der Anker versetzt wird. Der Nachteil dieses Verfahrens ist jedoch eine gewisse Behinderung bei der Lagerung, beim Transport und Versetzen des Ankers mit steifer Verankerungslänge, namentlich unter beschränkten Platzverhältnissen in Kavernen. Beim Transport des Ankers können im Injektionsgut zudem Risse auftreten. Bei Ankern mit Gebrauchslasten über 2000 kN und Verankerungslängen über 6 m wird die Vorinjektion aus praktischen Gründen nicht ausgeführt.

Die Anker werden im wasserdichten Bohrloch mit einem nicht-schwindenden Zementmörtel mit einem Wasser/Zement Faktor von max. 0,45 verpresst.

Falls die Verankerungslänge nicht vorinjiziert ist, werden der Hohlraum innerhalb des Hüllrohres sowie der Ringraum zwischen Hüllrohr und Bohrlochwand simultan verpresst. Normalerweise erstreckt sich diese Verpressung auf die ganze Länge des Ankers in einem Arbeitsgang. Infolge der Pfahlwirkung der äusseren Verpressgutsäule wird die Verankerungskraft "weich" in den Untergrund eingeleitet. Falls dies nicht erwünscht ist und die Einleitung der Verankerungskraft an einer ganz bestimmten Stelle erfolgen muss, wird vorerst nur die Verankerungslänge primär verpresst und die freie Ankerlänge

nach dem Vorspannen mit einer Sekundär-
Verpressung. Für steigende Anker wird im
letzteren Fall ein Packer beim Uebergang
zwischen Verankerungslänge und freier Ankerlänge montiert.

Ebenso wird ein Packer an dieser Stelle
verwendet falls die Verankerungslänge unter Druck verpresst werden muss. In diesem Fall jedoch muss der innere Hohlraum
der Verankerungslänge vorinjiziert sein.

Das Verfüllen des Hohlraumes unmittelbar hinter der Spannverankerung geschieht
nach dem Vorspannen mit Zementmörtel oder
einer dauerplastischen Korrosionsschutzmasse zusammen mit dem Verfüllen des
Schutzdeckels über dem Ankerkopf.

4 SCHLUSSBETRACHTUNG

Felsanker sind ein nicht mehr wegzudenk-
endes Hilfsmittel für den Bau von unterirdischen Hohlräumen. Sie gestatten dem
Projektverfasser eine weitgehende Frei-
heit in der Formgestaltung des Hohlraumes, sie sichern diese Hohlräume während jeder Bauetappe und lassen sich den
örtlichen Verhältnissen anpassen. Kontrollanker in einer genügenden Anzahl
über den ganzen Hohlraum verteilt lassen
sich einfach überwachen und geben jederzeit eine genaue Analyse des Verformungs-
zustandes.

Nachfolgend ist eine Uebersicht von mit
VSL Felsankern gesicherten unterirdischen
Hohlräumen:

1. Kaverne Pumpspeicherwerk
   Vianden, Luxemburg   1961-63
2. Maschinenkaverne Säckingen,
   BR Deutschland   1964-66
3. Kraftwerkszentrale Veytaux,
   Schweiz   1965-67
4. Kraftwerkszentrale El Toro,
   Chile   1967-70
5. Zentrale Reconvalgrande,
   Italien   1967-70
6. Kaverne Pumpspeicherwerke
   Tulough Hill, Irland   1970-71
7. Kaverne Waldeck II,
   BR Deutschland   1970-72
8. Maschinenkaverne Wehr,
   BR Deutschland   1971-73
9. Lüftungszentrale Huttegg
   des Seelisbergtunnels, Schweiz 1972-75
10. Kaverne des Pumpspeicherwerkes
    Taloro, Italien   1975-76

BAU VON KAVERNEN UND DRUCKSCHÄCHTEN
FÜR DIE WASSERKRAFTANLAGE OYMAPINAR IN DER TÜRKEI
Construction of caverns and pressure shafts for hydroelectric power plant Oymapinar/Turkey
Construction des cavernes et des puits sous pression de la centrale hydroélectrique
d'Oymapinar en Turquie

KLAUS HORN
Bilfinger & Berger Bauaktiengesellschaft, Wiesbaden, Bundesrepublik Deutschland

SUMMARY

The construction of caverns and pressure shafts for a dam project in Turkey
is reported. The related hydrological and geological conditions are presented, as they are important for planning and execution of the subsurface rock
work. Dimension and stability criteria for the two caverns are explained.
Furthermore the procedure for driving and securing the calottes and benches
is described. The measured deformations are presented typically for two
measuring points. For the execution of the penstocks and pressure shafts
operational considerations were prevailing. It is demonstrated how the execution of a system of galleries situated at the bottom of the cavern could
smoothen the construction schedule.

ZUSAMMENFASSUNG

Es wird über den Bau von Kavernen und Druckschächten im Rahmen eines Tal-
sperrenprojektes in der Türkei berichtet. Die hydrologischen und geologischen Randbedingungen werden aufgezeigt. Sie bestimmen wesentlich Planung
und Durchführung auch der Felshohlraumbauten. Abmessungen und Standsicher-
heitsüberlegungen der beiden Kavernen werden erläutert. Im weiteren Verlauf wird die Vorgehensweise beim Auffahren und Sichern der Kalotten und
Strossen beschrieben. Die gemessenen Verformungen werden exemplarisch für
zwei Meßpunkte dargestellt. Bei der Behandlung der Triebwasserschächte und
-stollen stehen die baubetrieblichen Belange im Vordergrund. Es wird dargelegt, wie durch die Schaffung einer tiefliegenden Angriffsebene der Bauablauf entstört wird.

RESUME

Il est rendu compte de la construction de cavernes et de puits sous pression dans le cadre d'un aménagement hydro-électrique en Turquie. Les données
hydrologiques et géologiques sont enoncées. Elles ont grandement influencé
la conception du projet et sa réalisation, entre autres, pour ce qui est
des ouvrages souterrains. Les dimensions et réflexions relatives à la stabilité des deux cavités sont explicitées. Puis la méthode d'exécution pour
l'abattage et la préservation de la stabilité des calottes et des stross
est décrite. Les déformations mesurées en deux points caractéristiques
sont relevées. Pour ce qui est de l'exécution des puits sous pression et
des galeries forcées, il faut tenir compte de ce que les impératifs de conduite du chantier sont prépondérants. Il est montré comment, grâce à la
mise en oeuvre d'un front d'attaque profond, le déroulement du reste du
chantier n'a pas été perturbé.

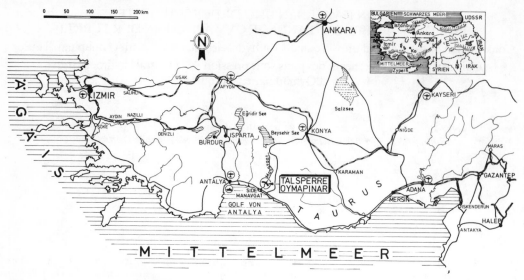

Abb. 1   Lage der Baustelle in der Türkei

1 EINFÜHRUNG

Wie viele Länder der Erde, muß auch
die Türkei die Industrialisierung
vorantreiben. Eigene Ölvorkommen
sind unbedeutend. Die z.Zt. ausge-
beuteten Kohlevorkommen reichen
nicht aus, um den steigenden Energiebedarf zu decken. Einzig die Was-
serkraft wäre zukünftig in der Lage,
die teuren Ölimporte zu drosseln.
Noch ergießen sich viele Flüsse un-
genutzt in die angrenzenden Meere.
Ausbaufähige potentielle Wasserkräf-
te von 25.000 MW sind planerisch erfaßt.

Die Türkei ist seit Jahren bemüht,
die Planungen in die Tat umzusetzen.
Z.Zt. werden mehrere Großprojekte
ausgeführt.

Eines davon ist die Talsperre Oymapinar mit einer Leistung von 540 MW.
Sie liegt in der Provinz Antalya un-
weit der südlichen Mittelmeerküste.
Vorhandene Quellfassungen und Was-
serleitungen in Form von Aquädukten,
Kanälen und Tunnelstrecken zeugen
von historischer Vergangenheit. Über
eine Distanz von 20 km wurde Trink-
wasser aus dem geplanten Talsperren-
bereich in die zu Zeiten der Römer
bedeutende Hafenstadt Side geleitet
(s. Abb. 2).

Abb. 2   Römische Wasserleitung
(Aquädukt)

Schon 1939 befaßten sich erste Studien mit dem Bau eines Wasserkraftwerkes am Manavgat-Fluß. Seit 1963
wurden intensive hydrologische und
geologische Untersuchungen angestellt. Sie bildeten die Grundlage
für das vorliegende Talsperrenpro-
jekt, das die Türkei 1976 international zur Ausschreibung brachte.
Bauherr der Anlage ist der türki-
sche Staat, vertreten durch das Amt
für Wasserkraftanlagen (DSI) in Ankara. Die Planung und Beratung erfolgt durch Consulting Engineers
Coyne et Bellier, Paris und Aknil
Engineers, Ankara.

Die Ausführung einschließlich der
Stahlwasserbauten liegt in Händen
der Bilfinger + Berger Bau AG, Aus-
landsbereich Wiesbaden. Im Mai 1977
wurde mit den Arbeiten begonnen.

2 HYDROLOGIE UND GEOLOGIE

Die mittleren Abflußmengen des
Manavgat-Flusses schwanken jahreszeitlich zwischen 50 und 700 m³/sec.
Das 100-jährige Hochwasser wird mit
1200 m³/sec. angegeben. In einer
kritischen Bauphase wurde die Baustelle zweimal in kurzem Abstand
mit 1100 m³/sec. heimgesucht. Die
Grundlast des Wasserzuflusses, besonders in der trockenen Jahreszeit,
wird von Karstquellen getragen. Die
bedeutendste ist die Dumanli-Quelle.
Sie liegt zwei km oberhalb der Sperrenstelle und gehört mit max.
100 m³/sec. zu den größten Karstquellen der Welt.

Vom Meer aus betrachtet liegt die
Sperrenstelle in dem ersten höheren
Gebirgsrücken, der sich aus der
Schwemmlandebene erhebt. Der Fluß-
durchbruch bildet ein enges und
steiles V-förmiges Tal (s. Abb. 4).

Die Gebirgsrippe hat in Höhe der
Wasserlinie eine Mächtigkeit von
ca. 300 m. Sie besteht aus dolomi-
tischem Kalkstein (Fatmalar). Ober-
und unterwasserseitig ist das Kalk-
steinmassiv begrenzt von metamor-
phem Schiefergestein (Calk-Schist).
Die Grenzflächen zwischen den For-
mationen sind steilstehende Störungen mit Verkarstungen (F_2 und F_4).
Innerhalb der Verwerfungen F_2 und

Abb. 4 Blick von der Unterwasserseite in die Schlucht

F_4 ist der Gebirgskörper durchzogen
von Kluftsystemen unterschiedlicher
Richtung. Die Trennflächen sind z.T.
auskristallisiert und geschlossen
bzw. erweitern sich spaltenartig
zu meterweiten Spalten, die z.T. be-
gehbar bzw. besteigbar sind.

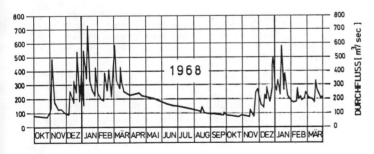

Abb. 3 Beispiel einer Jahresabfluß-
kurve des Manavgat-Flusses

295

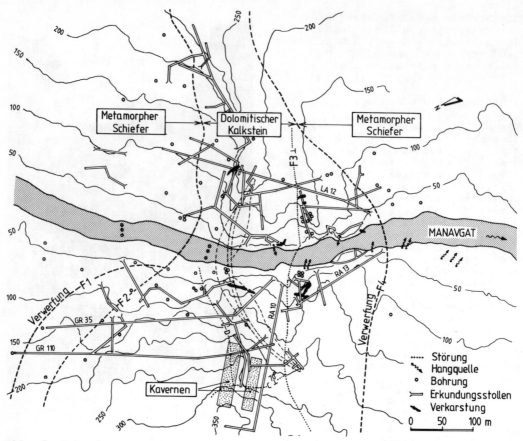

Abb. 5 Erkundungen und Geologie

Viele dieser Klüfte und Störungen kommunizieren untereinander. Besonders am linken Hang steigt während der Regenzeit der unterirdische Wasserspiegel auf 10 m über das Niveau des Manavgat an. Zwischenzeitlich erstellte Zugangs- und Injektionsstollen verwandeln sich dann in reissende Bäche mit einem Durchfluß von 5 - 6 m³/sec.

Die Beherrschung dieser unterirdischen Wasserströme in Form von Dichtungsschleiern und Verfüllungen ist Bestandteil der Injektionsarbeiten. Sie nehmen mit 25% des Gesamtauftrages einen unverhältnismäßig breiten Raum ein. Es handelt sich um schwierige Arbeiten, deren erfolgreiche Bewältigung eine Voraussetzung für das Gelingen des Gesamtprojektes bilden. Leider ist es im Rahmen dieses Beitrages nicht mög-

lich, näher auf diese sehr interessanten Arbeiten einzugehen.

3 GESAMTANLAGE

Topographie und Geologie zwingen zu einer sehr gedrängten Anordnung der über- und untertägigen Bauwerke. Abb. 6 zeigt die Gesamtanlage der Talsperre mit den Einzelbauwerken.

Die linksseitige Gebirgsrippe ist verhältnismäßig schwach ausgebildet. Aus diesem Grund konzentrieren sich die zentralen Hohlraumbauten einschließlich der Hochwasserentlastungstunnel im ausgedehnteren Teil des rechtsseitigen Fatmalarmassives. Die räumliche Zuordnung verdeutlicht Abb. 7.

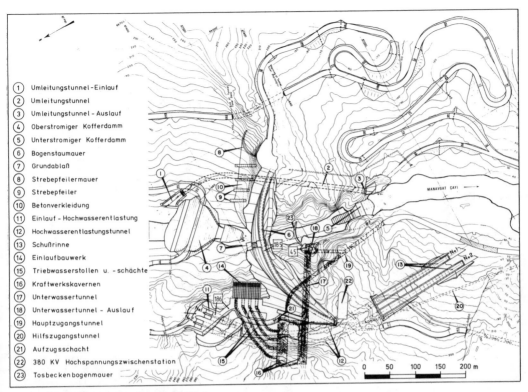

① Umleitungstunnel-Einlauf
② Umleitungstunnel
③ Umleitungstunnel - Auslauf
④ Oberstromiger Kofferdamm
⑤ Unterstromiger Kofferdamm
⑥ Bogenstaumauer
⑦ Grundablaß
⑧ Strebepfeilermauer
⑨ Strebepfeiler
⑩ Betonverkleidung
⑪ Einlauf - Hochwasserentlastung
⑫ Hochwasserentlastungstunnel
⑬ Schußrinne
⑭ Einlaufbauwerk
⑮ Triebwasserstollen u. -schächte
⑯ Kraftwerkskavernen
⑰ Unterwassertunnel
⑱ Unterwassertunnel - Auslauf
⑲ Hauptzugangstunnel
⑳ Hilfszugangstunnel
㉑ Aufzugsschacht
㉒ 380 KV Hochspannungszwischenstation
㉓ Tosbeckenbogenmauer

Abb. 6   Talsperre Oymapinar

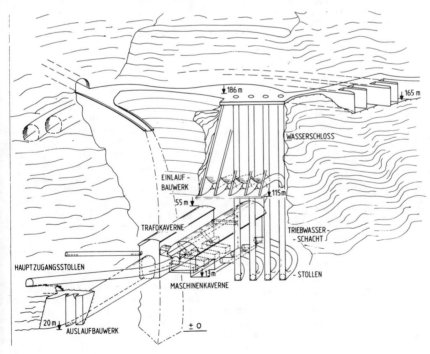

Abb. 7   Kraftwerkszentrale

297

4 HERSTELLUNG DER MASCHINEN- UND TRANSFORMATORENKAVERNE

4.1 Anordnung und Dimensionen

Die beiden größten Hohlräume sind außerhalb der Primärklüfte F_3 und C angeordnet (s. Abb. 8).

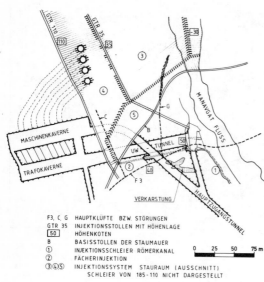

F3, C, G   HAUPTKLÜFTE BZW. STÖRUNGEN
GTR 35   INJEKTIONSSTOLLEN MIT HÖHENLAGE
[50]   HÖHENKOTEN
B   BASISSTOLLEN DER STAUMAUER
①   INJEKTIONSSCHLEIER RÖMERKANAL
②   FÄCHERINJEKTION
③④⑤   INJEKTIONSSYSTEM STAURAUM (AUSSCHNITT)
           SCHLEIER VON 185-110 NICHT DARGESTELLT

0   25   50   75 m

Abb. 8   Hauptkluft- und Injektions-
         systeme im Kavernenbereich

Die Kluft C liegt bergseitig des In-
jektionsschleiers am rechten Ufer
und führt in Höhe der Kavernensohlen
kein Wasser. Die Kluft F_3 ist stark
verkarstet und flußseitig wasserführend. Wegen des erheblichen Wasser-
überdruckes von ca. 23 m (MW = 35
u. NN, tiefste Sohlaushubkote in der
Maschinenkaverne = 12 ü. NN) ist
der tiefer liegende Kavernenaushub
durch einen Injektionsschleier zu
schützen. Dieser besteht aus dem
Vertikalschleier im Römerkanal und
der Fächerinjektion aus einer Nische
im Zugangstunnel. Die Injektionen
der Kluft F_3 wurden gleichzeitig mit
Beginn der Vortriebsarbeiten in An-
griff genommen und erwiesen sich als
voll wirksam.

Abbildung 9 zeigt beide Kavernen mit
den maximalen Spann- und Ausbruch-
weiten und komplettem Betonausbau.

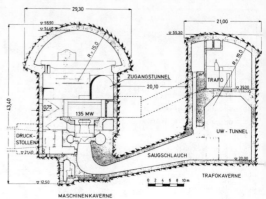

Abb. 9   Kavernenquerschnitt, End-
         zustand

Die Hohlraumlängen betragen 105 m
bzw. 86 m.

4.2 Standsicherheitsbetrachtungen

Bauherr und Consulting beurteilten
das Tragverhalten und die Standsicherheit des Gebirges als wenig problema-
tisch. Grundlage für diese Einschätzung bildeten umfangreiche geologische Untersuchungen (8000 m Erkundungsstollen und 40.000 m Kernboh-
rungen im gesamten Projektgebiet).
Außerdem hatte man Erfahrungen gesammelt beim Auffahren des Zufahrts-
tunnels und des Umleitungsstollens
mit einem Größtdurchmesser von 11 m.
Die Standsicherheitsuntersuchungen
erfolgten u. a. mit Hilfe von zwei-
dimensionalen FE-Berechnungen der
Maschinenkaverne unter Annahme homo-
gener, isotroper und elastischer Un-
tergrundeigenschaften und einer maximalen Überlagerung von 300 m. Kluftflächen und die sich aus dem Bauablauf ergebenden Ausbruch- und Beto-
nierphasen werden nicht berücksichtigt. Verlauf und Größe der Haupt-
spannungen gestatten die Abschätzung
des Gebirgskörpers, der nach Abklingen der Verformungen das Betongewölbe belastet.

Spannungskonzentrationen im Kämpfer-
und Sohlbereich deuten auf eine nicht
optimale Formgebung hin. Die ein-
springende Ecke beim Übergang vom
Gewölbe zur Auflagerbank birgt die
Gefahr einer keilförmigen Ablösung
zum Hohlraum hin.

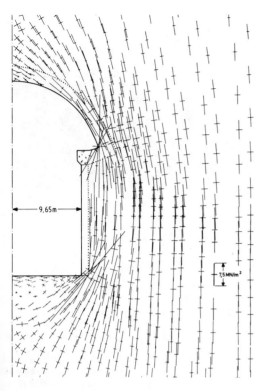

Abb. 10   Hauptspannungsfeld

Die wesentlichen, das generelle Vorgehen bestimmenden Aussagen, lassen
sich wie folgt zusammenfassen:

- Die Kalotten beider Kavernen
sind für die Dauer des Ausbruches
bis zum Einbringen der Gewölbe stabil.
- Sicherungsmaßnahmen können lo-
kal beschränkt bleiben.
- Die Systemanker in den Wänden
dienen der Verankerung der Kavernenwände gegen einen möglichen Wasser-
druck, der sich, bedingt durch Klüfte und Undichtigkeiten, aufbauen
könnte.

4.3 Ausbruch und Sicherung

Beide Kavernen wurden gleichzeitig
wie folgt aufgefahren:

1. Auffahren der Kalotten
2. Betonieren der Auflager und
   Gewölbe

3. Strossenabbau
4. Durchörterung des Pfeilers
   zwischen den Kavernen
5. Betonausbau

4.3.1 Kalottenvortrieb

Der Ausbruch der Kalotte von 56 NN
auf 42 NN vollzog sich in den in
Abb. 11 dargestellten Phasen. Diese wurden durch die Reichweiten der
Bohrgeräte und durch die Forderung
nach gebirgsschonendem Abbau bestimmt. Die Arbeitsebene für Phase 2
wurde durch einen befahrbaren Stollen vom Zugangstunnel aus erschlossen.

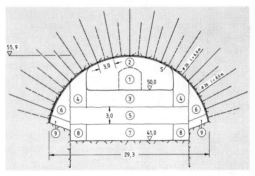

① ERSCHLIESSUNGSSTOLLEN   ③-⑨ REIHENFOLGE DER TEILAUSBRÜCHE
② KALOTTENAUSBRUCH   S = SPRITZBETONSICHERUNG

Abb. 11 Ausbruchphasen und Siche-
        rung

Nach dem Niederbruch eines Felskeils
von ca. 20 m³ in der Schnittlinie
zweier zunächst nicht erkannter
Kluftflächen wurde das ursprüngliche Sicherungskonzept revidiert. Vorgespannte Perfoanker in Kombination
mit Spritzbeton bildeten im weiteren
Verlauf die notwendige temporäre Sicherung. Noch während der Vortriebs-
und Profilierungsarbeiten im vorderen Kavernenbereich begann die takt-
mäßige Erstellung der schweren Auflagerbalken und des unbewehrten Ge-
wölbes (s. Abb. 12).

Abb. 12 Aufgefahrene Kalotte der
Masch.-Kaverne, Gewölbe-
betonierung

Abb. 13 a Strossenaushub
Maschinenkaverne

4.3.2 Strossenabbau

Die Vorgehensweise im Strossenbe-
reich kann sprengtechnisch begründet werden (vgl. 4.3.4). Wegen der
starken Staubentwicklung mußte naß
gebohrt werden. Bohr- und nachsik-
kerndes Bergwasser wirkten sich auf
das Sprengergebnis z.T. sehr nach-
teilig aus, weil das in der Türkei
hergestellte Dynamit bei längerer
Verweildauer im Wasser unbrauchbar
wurde. Daher wurde die Abschlagstie-
fe auf 3 m begrenzt (s. Abb. 13 u.
13 a).

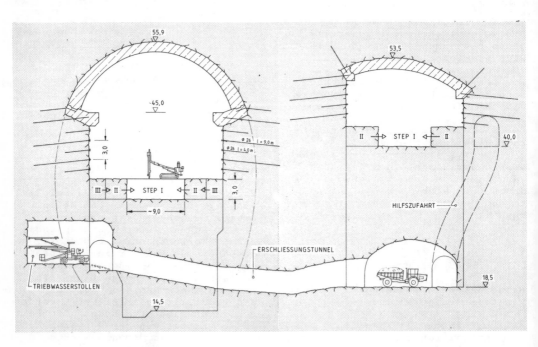

Abb. 13 Strossenabbau

Die Art der Sicherung der Felswände
in beiden Kavernen ist als Kompro-
miß zwischen Bauherrschaft und Un-
ternehmung anzusehen. Die weiter-
gehende Forderung des firmenseiti-
gen Gutachters sah ein System vor-
gespannter Anker im 1,5 m-Raster
vor. Die ursprünglich erst beim Betonieren der Wände einzubringenden
9 m-Anker wurden sofort eingebaut.
Die dazwischen angeordneten Felsnä-
gel dienten der oberflächennahen
Sicherung der freien Felswände. Beide Typen sind schlaffe Mörtelanker.

genden Kabelkammern und -tunnel verhindern einen statisch günstigen
Kraftfluß. Der Ausbruch der Saugschläuche mußte daher möglichst ge-
birgsschonend in zwei Phasen ausgeführt werden:

1. Vorstollen 3 x 3 m
2. Restauffahrung des endgültigen
   Profils

Firste und Wände wurden in geklüfteten Bereichen durch vorgespannte Anker und Spritzbeton gesichert.

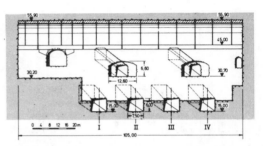

Abb. 15   Maschinenkaverne, Längs-
          schnitt mit Pfeileransicht

Abb. 14 Trafokaverne, Aushub been-
        det

4.3.3 Pfeilerdurchörterung

Eine Besonderheit bei den anfallenden Felsarbeiten stellte die acht-
fache Durchfahrung des Felspfeilers
zwischen den beiden Kavernen dar.
Die Saugschläuche haben einen recht-
eckigen Querschnitt. Die darüberlie-

4.3.4 Sprengtechnik

Die technischen Spezifikationen ver-
langten die Anwendung eines gebirgs-
schonenden Sprengverfahrens (smooth
blasting). Folgende Forderungen
standen dabei im Vordergrund:

1. Sauberes Abscheren in den frei-
   gelegten Felswänden
2. Weitgehende Vermeidung von Auf-
   lockerungen des umgebenden Gebirges

Ein Beispiel eines unter obigen Gesichtspunkten ausgearbeiteten
Sprengschemas ist der 3-Phasen-Aus-
hub in den Strossen der Kavernen.

Charakteristika:
Bohrlochabstand im Feld = 1,3 x1,3 m
Perimeterreihe   a =0,75 m
Spez. Sprengstoffverbrauch= 330g/m³
Sprengstoffmenge je Zündstufe= 12 kg
Bohrloch Ø 45 mm

4.4 Verformungsmessungen

Ursprünglich war ein komplettes Meßprogramm des üblichen Umfanges vorgesehen. Durch vertragliche Schwierigkeiten und Verzögerungen bei der
Lieferung der Meßausrüstung kam es
zu einer Reduzierung der Meßstellen
(s. Abb. 16). In der oberen Hälfte
des Strossenabbaus wurden z.T. lediglich Konvergenzmessungen durchgeführt.

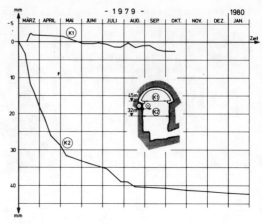

Abb. 17   Konvergenzen K_1 und K_2 (II)

baut. Trotz Lückenhaftigkeit der gewonnenen Ergebnisse, ergaben die ver
bliebenen Messungen einen wertvollen
Anhalt über das Langzeitverhalten
der Kavernenwände (s. Abb. 18).

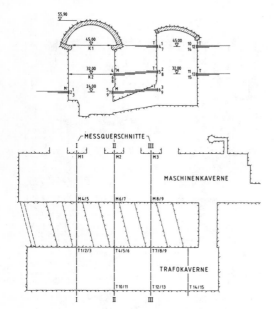

Abb. 16   Lage der Meßstellen

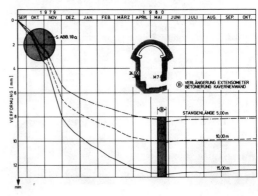

Abb. 18   Extensometer M_7

Bedingt durch die aussteifende Wirkung der Auflagerbalken und des Ge-
wölbes waren die Verformungen in der
Kranbahnebene klein (s. Abb. 17).
Die in Höhe 32 m gemessene Gesamt-
konvergenz von rd. 45 mm müßte an-
teilig auf beide Ausbruchflächen
verteilt werden. Da eine Verformungs-
berechnung nicht vorlag, konnte ein
Bezug hierzu nicht hergestellt werden.

In den übrigen Bereichen wurden Drei-
fachstangenextensometer (5,10 und
15 m) mit manueller Ablesung einge-

Vergleicht man die Meßergebnisse bei
der Hohlräume, so fällt auf, daß die
Absolutwerte der Trafokaverne weit
unter denen der Maschinenkaverne lie
gen. Meßstelle M_7 weist für Niveau 2
die größten Verformungen auf. Diese
sind u. a. dadurch zu erklären, daß
hier größere Felspartien aufgrund

302

tektonischer Einwirkungen mit klein-
klüftigem Gefüge anstehen.

Alle Verformungen zeigen jedoch die
Tendenz, sich noch während der Aus-
hubarbeiten asymptotisch einem Endwert zu nähern. Sobald der Wandbeton
die jeweilige Meßstelle erreichte
(Kletterschalung), trat kein weiterer Verformungszuwachs auf. Abb. 18a
macht das Verformungsverhalten bei
Standzeiten und Sprengungen deutlich.

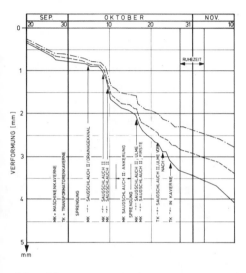

Abb. 18 a   Ausschnitt aus Abb. 18

Abb. 19 Maschinenkaverne, Primär-
ausbau beendet

5 TRIEBWASSERSCHÄCHTE

5.1 Übersicht

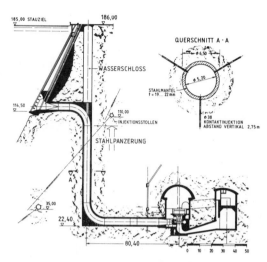

Abb. 20   Vertikalschnitt Schacht I

Die Triebwasserleitung besteht aus
den horizontalen Ästen, die sich auf
der Einlauf- und Turbinenebene befinden, und Schächten, die von der
Funktion her in den gepanzerten
Triebwasserbereich und das darüber-
liegende Wasserschloß zu unterteilen
sind. Der Ausbruchquerschnitt beträgt einheitlich 33 m² (Ø 6,50 m).

5.2 Bauablauf

Das Konzept der Schachtauffahrung
bestand darin, daß im ersten Arbeitsgang ein Schutterschacht (2x2 m)
mit der Aufbruchbühne (System Alimak)
hergestellt wurde. Danach erfolgte
die Aufweitung auf den Endquerschnitt
(Ø 6,50 m) von der Plattform 186 ü.
NN abwärts.

Die Stollen und Schächte mußten von
der Maschinenkaverne angegangen werden. Die Hintereinanderfolge von Kavernenaushub und anschließendem Auffahren der Triebwasserstollen schied
aus Gründen des Bauablaufes aus. Die
Problemlösung bestand in der Erschließung durch ein Stollensystem
auf der Sohlebene der Kavernen.

Durch den Einsatz von gleichzeitig
zwei Bohrjumbos konnten die vier
Triebwasserstollen im Vollausbruch
in kürzester Zeit aufgefahren werden.
Damit war der Weg frei für das Öffnen der Schächte (s. Abb. 22).

5.3 Ausbruch, Sicherung, Ausbau

Das Auffahren vergleichbarer Querschnitte hatte gezeigt, daß Stand-
sicherheitsfragen i.a. keine wesentliche Rolle spielten. Beim Aufweiten
wurde nach jeder 2.Sprengung die Felsoberfläche mit ca. 5 cm Spritzbeton
versiegelt. Der Spritzbeton wirkte
einer Gebirgsauflockerung entgegen

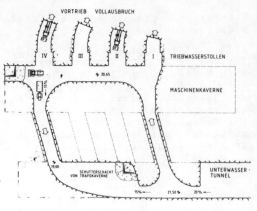

Abb. 22 Erschließung der Trieb-
         wasserstollen und -schächte

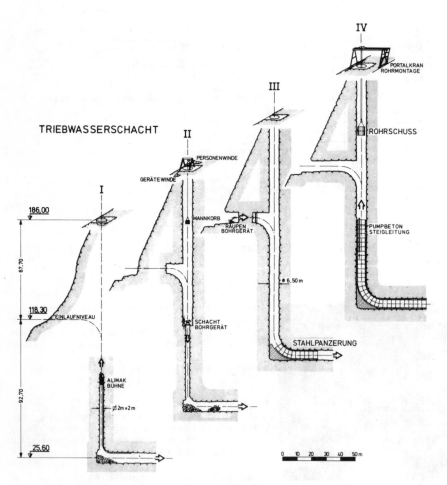

Abb. 21 Triebwasserschächte, Darstellung gleichzeitig ablaufender Arbeits-
         vorgänge

304

und diente primär als Schutz der Schachtmannschaft gegen herabfallendes Gestein. Alle Betriebsphasen vom Aufbruch des Schutterschachtes bis zum Einbau der Stahlpanzerung sind in Abb. 22 dargestellt. Abb. 23 zeigt die Einrichtung auf der Plattform 186 mit Portalkran, Rohrschüssen und Schachtgerüst (s. auch Abb. 24).

Bei den Sprengungen für die hangnahen Schächte erwuchsen Schwierigkeiten aus einer ausgeprägten vertikalen Klüftung des Gebirges.
Der Gasdruck entwich z.T. durch Klüfte an die Oberfläche. Erneutes Bohren und Nachsprengen waren die Folge.

Die Erfahrung mußte in solchen Fällen die rechnerisch vorgegebenen Sprengstoffmengen korrigieren.
Das Schuttern des Ausbruchmaterials durch die Maschinenkaverne überschnitt sich mit den dort beginnenden Betonierungsarbeiten. Durch Herstellen von Querschlägen zwischen den Triebwasserstollen und eine Abwicklung gelang eine hinreichende Entstörung. Das Konzept einer zweiten Angriffsebene wurde durch die Praxis voll bestätigt.

Abb. 23 Einrichtung der Plattform 186

Abb. 24 Einlaufebene der Triebwasserschächte, linke Bildhälfte: Sperrenaushub und Kabelkrangegenfahrbahn

305

6 SCHLUSSBETRACHTUNG

Für die beschriebenen Hohlraumbauten umfaßte der Felsaushub 300.000m³.
Der größte Teil der Ausbruch- und
Ausbauarbeiten wurde in den Jahren
1978-1980 abgewickelt.

Fügt man die Untertageaktivitäten
in die Gesamtbaumaßnahme ein, so liegen z. B. am rechten Hang drei bis
vier Plattformen, Bauwerke und Hohlraumbauten in der Vertikalen über-
einander.

Während des Felsaushubs mußten in
jeder Schicht Sprengungen, Schub-,
Schutter- und Transportvorgänge
durchgeführt werden. Es wird deutlich, daß umfangreiche Maßnahmen in
betrieblicher und sicherheitstechni-
scher Hinsicht erforderlich waren, um
einen reibungslosen und unfallfreien
Bauablauf zu gewährleisten.

7 LITERATURHINWEISE

1. EIE-Manavgat: Oymapinar Project
   Arch Dam Site, report on the
   grouting tests, Nov. 1976

2. Rune Gustafsson: Swedish Blasting
   Technics

3. Dr. M.Baudendistel: Auszüge aus
   den felsmechanischen Gutachten
   zum Oymapinar-Projekt (unveröf-
   fentlicht)

SOME DYNAMIC BEHAVIORS OF CAVERN WALLS DURING EARTHQUAKES
Einige dynamische Verhaltensmerkmale von Kavernenwänden während eines Erdbebens
Quelques comportements dynamiques de murs de cavernes pendant les tremblements de terre

Y.ICHIKAWA, H.SHIMIZU & M.KAWANOBE
Electric Power Development Co.Ltd., Japan

SUMMARY:
In establishing the seismic design method for underground structures, it is important to
make clear the characteristics of underground seismic motions and to know behaviors of
structures during an earthquake.
Electric Power Development Company (EPDC) has started the seismological observations
since 1976 at three existent underground hydro-power plants. In these six years, nearly
a hundred earthquakes have been observed including the Miyagiken-Oki earthquake with a
magnitude of 7.4. The peak accerelation amplitude ratio shows half to one-third for
far-field earthquakes. This result is the same as those observed and given in other
references. While, for near- and very-near-field earthquakes this ratio evidently shows
smaller. The peak displacement of cavern wall is proportional to the Spectrum Intensity
(S.I.) and accerelation amplitude has no correlation to wall displacement.

ZUSAMMENFASSUNG:
Hinsichtlich der seismischen Konstruktionsmethode für unterirdische Bauten ist wichtig,
dass die unterirdischen seismischen Bewegungscharakteristiken, und das Verhalten der
Bauten während eines Erdbebens, erkannt werden.
Die Electric Power Development Company (EPDC) hat im Jahre 1976 mit der seismologischen
Beobachtung von drei bereits vorhandenen unterirdischen Wasserkraftwerken begonnen.
Während dieser sechs Jahre wurden etwa einhundert Erdbeben, einschliesslich das Miyagi-
ken-Oki Erdbeben mit einer Stärke von 7.4. Das maximale Beschleunigung Amplitude-
verhältnis zeigt die Hälfte bis zu einem Drittel, Bei entfernten Erdbeben. Dieses
Resultat ist das gleiche wie vorherige Resulte, während für nahe oder unmittelbare
Erdbeben das Verhältnis nachweislich geringer ist. Die maximale Verschiebung von Wänden
unterirdischer Hohlräume ist proportional zu Spektrums stärke (S.I.) und das Beschleuni-
gungsverhältnis hat keine Beziehung zur Wandverschiebung.

RESUME:
Au sujet de la méthode d'étude sismique pour les constructions souterraines, il est important de préciser les caractéristiques des mouvements sismiques souterrains, de même
que de connaître les comportements des constructions pendant les tremblements de terre.
Electric Power Development Company (EPDC) a commencé un programme d'observations sis-
mologiques en 1976 à trois centrales hydro-électriques existantes. Au cours de ces six
dernières années, pas loin d'une centaine de tremblements de terre avec une amplitude
ont été observés, y compris le tremblement de terre Miyagiken-Oki avec une magnitude de
7,4. Le rapport d'amplitude d'accélération maximum diminue de moité jusqu'à un tiers
pour les tremblements de terre lointains. Ce résultat est identique aux résultats
obtenus précédemment. Alors que pour les tremblements de terre proches et très proches,
ce rapport est évidemment plus faible. Le déplacement maximum du mur d'abri est pro-
portionnel à l'Intensitéde Spectre (I.S.), et l'amplitude d'accélération n'est pas en
corrélation avec le déplacement du mur.

1 INTRODUCTION

The procedure of seismic design for underground caverns is shown schematically in Fig.-1. Among the items shown in the procedure, the following must be specifically examined, 1) whether or not stress-strain characteristics of rock can be known by means of conventional test methods when rock mass is subjected to the large seismic load, 2) whether or not the dynamic stress and strain of non-uniform rock mass including non-linear behavior can be analysed reasonably and accurately by practical means, 3) whether or not the characteristics of input seismic motion underground are different from those at the ground surface ordinally known and 4) how an actual cavern behaves during an earthquake.

In order to clarify these issues, we believe that it is the best way to obtain the underground observation data from an actual earthquake and simulate the observations by analysis using an analytical method based on the unified theory.

This seismological observations have been started since 1976 as a part of the study on underground nuclear power plant.

2 EARTHQUAKE OBSERVATION SYSTEM

EPDC has 11 underground hydro-power plants. Considering the regional characteristics of seismicity in Japan, the geological conditions, the dimensions of underground caverns and the maintenance conditions of the plant, the earthquake observatory system was installed at three plants for observation of earthquake motions. The observed records at the ground surface and underground were then compared. The locations of three plants are shown in Fig.-2 along with the magnitudes and locations of earthquakes observed. Table-1 lists an outline of the observation of each of the three plants. The earthquake motions are detected by velocity sensors, and then are recorded by recorder controllers (differential amplifier, integral amplifier). In order to prevent the mal-operation of equipment caused by the start-up of a generator or by the air-vibration of line-switches, the recorder is so designed as to start operation, except for the Miboro-plant, when the starters simultaneously detect the earthquake motion of over 0.05 kine in velocity both at the ground surface and underground.

The relatively strong earthquake motion has not yet been observed at the Miboro

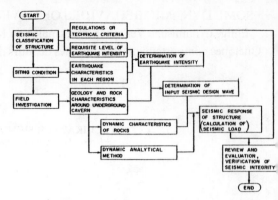

Fig. 1 Flow Chart of Seismic Design of Underground Cavern

plant. The cavern at the Ikehara plant is located at shallow rock. In this paper we describe mainly about the result obtained from the Numappara plant. When required, the data obtained at Ikehara are referred. The installation points of seismographs at Ikehara are shown in Fig.-3 and at Numappara in Fig.-4-1, 4-2 and 4-3.

Numappara lies 160 km north of Tokyo. The rock mass is composed of granite and the ground surface is covered with tuff of Miocene age. This area is composed of non-volcanic topography of Tertiary period and well-dissected steep mountain. Most of mountain slopes face west. The underground cavern at Numappara was constructed at a depth of 250 m from the ground surface in granite with the primary wave velocity (V_p) of 4 km/sec. This cavern is 22 m wide in the east-west direction, 45 m high and 130 m long in the north-south direction. Seismographs for recording underground motions are installed at the gallery tunnel and at the side wall of machine hall.

3 OBSERVED RESULTS

3.1 General

The distribution of earthquake epicenters at Numappara are shown in Fig.-2. The number of recorded earthquakes is eight in the south, four in the east, nine in the north-east. Distance-wise it is three with an epicentral distance of over 500 km (far-field earthquake) and seven with an epicentral distance of below 30 km (near-field earthquake). Table-2 shows some records obtained to date. In these records, the Miyagiken-Oki earthquake of magnitude 7.4 is the largest. In this earthquake, the maximum displacement of 423 micron was

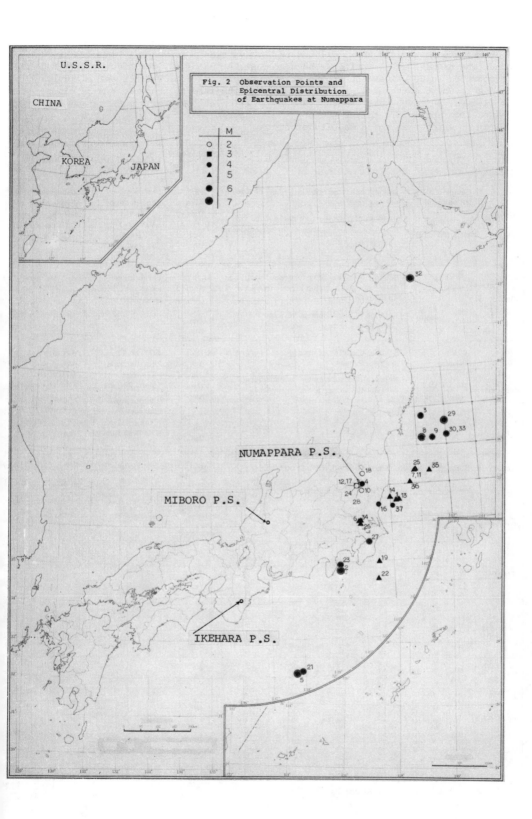

Fig. 2 Observation Points and
Epicentral Distribution
of Earthquakes at Numappara

U.S.S.R.

CHINA

KOREA JAPAN

M
○ 2
■ 3
● 4
▲ 5
● 6
● 7

NUMAPPARA P.S.

MIBORO P.S.

IKEHARA P.S.

caused and the maximum acceleration of 8 gal at the ground surface and 3 gal underground. The highest acceleration we have ever observed in 30 gal at the ground surface due to No. 6 earthquake.

At Ikehara, 40 earthquake records were obtained from April 1977 to the end of 1980, 18 of which being of a magnitude of 3.5 to 4.5. The acceleration of over 1 gal have been observed only in seven earthquake out of 40. The highest magnitude observed was 4.8, which resulted in 108 micron in displacement, 4.4 gal in acceleration at'the ground surface and 3.6 gal underground.

Site	Location	Purpose of Observation	Component of Sensor	Observed Data	Remarks
Ikehara	Center of the Kii peninsula lat. 34°03'N long.135°58'E	· Seismic behavior of underground cavern in shallow rock mass · Relation of displacement between Ground Surface and Underground in homogeneous rock mass	G.S. Acc.-2 Dis.-3 U.G. Acc.-2 Dis.-6	1977.4.13 – Acc. Records 17 waves Max. 4.3gal Dis. Records 33 waves Max. 100μ	observation of cavern wall dis. since 1981.3
Miboro	Center of Honshu lat. 36°08'N long.136°55'E	· Seismic behavior of underground cavern in deep rock mass during large earthquake of inland type · Relation of displacement between Ground Surface and Underground	G.S. Acc.-3 Dis.-3 U.G. Acc.-1 Dis.-3	Large inland earthquake has not been observed	
Numappara	160km north of Tokyo lat. 37°06'N long.139°56'E	· Seismic behavior of underground cavern in deep rock mass · Relation of displacement and acceleration between Ground Surface and Underground	G.S. Acc.-3 Dis.-3 U.G. Acc.-3 Dis.-3 Cavern Wall Dis.-6	1977.12.17 – Acc. Records 29 waves Max. 30gal Dis. Records 32 waves Max. 517μ Wall Dis. Records 25 waves	rock mass Vp= 4.0km/sec

Table. 1 Summary of Seismological Observation

Note : G.S. = Ground Surface
U.G. = Underground

DIRECTION OF HYPOCENTER	NUMBER	DATE	MAGNITUDE	EPICENTRAL DISTANCE (km)	HYPOCENTRAL DISTANCE (km)	PEAK ACCELERATION AMPLITUDE OF GROUND (gal)	RATIO OF PEAK ACCELERATION AMPLITUDE GROUND/UNDERGROUND	PEAK DISPLACEMENT AMPLITUDE OF UNDERGROUND (μ)	RATIO OF PEAK DISPLACEMENT AMPLITUDE GROUND/UNDERGROUND	PEAK DISPLACEMENT AMPLITUDE OF CAVERN WALL (μ)
NEAR FIELD	4	78. 3. 6	4.0	22	55	5	7.2	15	3	—
	24	80. 7. 7	3.0	10	10	25	17	10	17	26
	28	81. 1. 1	2.6	10	10	6	8	10	3	11
	17	80. 3. 8	2.6	10	14	9	7	3	10	4
	18	80. 3. 10	2.5	22	37	7	3	8	3	11
	12	79. 6. 17	2.4	10	14	3	8	2	9	3
	10	78. 6. 17	—	27	27	12	16	10	13	22
SOUTH	2	78. 1. 14	7.0	266	266	0.8	2.6	56	1.5	—
	23	80. 6. 29	6.7	250	251	1	3	41	1.4	64
	27	80. 9. 25	6.1	178	195	4	3	100	1.6	105
	22	80. 5. 8	5.7	290	296	0.5	1.5	24	1.6	31
	19	80. 3. 12	5.6	244	257	1	2	13	1.5	16
	6	78. 3. 20	5.5	113	124	30	2.8	344	1.3	—
	26	80. 9. 24	5.4	126	150	14	6	56	3	71
	34	81. 1. 28	5.0	104	120	14	7	64	3	84
EAST	13	79. 7. 11	5.9	135	141	9	5	116	1.4	129
	14 15	79. 11. 25	5.4	106	139	20	9	44	2	37
	1	77. 12. 17	5.3	126	132	10.9	4.9	98	2.5	—
	16	79. 12. 17	4.3	91	109	7	6	8	3	9
NORTHEAST	8	78. 6. 12	7.4	229	232	8	3	423	1.1	397
	29	81. 1. 19	7.0	315	315	1.2	1.7	135	1.1	164
	30 31 3	78. 2. 20	6.8	271	274	3.7	4.2	164	1.8	—
	9	78. 6. 14	6.3	256	259	0.6	3	95	0.6	70
	33	81. 1. 23	6.2	301	301	—	—	34	0.8	39
	11	79. 3. 11	5.5	160	165	6	4	48	1.4	70
	7	78. 5. 11	5.4	167	172	3	5	46	1.3	78
	25	80. 7. 16	5.2	169	174	1.5	3	27	0.9	30
FAR FIELD	5	78. 3. 7	7.8	587	659	4.4	2.5	517	1.5	—
	32	81. 1. 23	7.1	622	635	—	—	22	1.3	29
	21	80. 4. 22	6.6	579	704	10	3	55	2	77

Table. 2 List of Observed Records

3.2 Characteristics of underground earthquake motion

(1) Peak amplitude ratio

The ratio of peak horizontal acceleration amplitude at the ground to that underground obtained at Numappara are shown in Table-2. In the case of very-near-field earthquakes, the mean ratio amounts to 10, while it amounts to 2.7 in the case of far-field earthquakes of an epicentral distance of over 200 km. But according to the results obtained at Ikehara, the mean ratio amounted to only 1.1 for near-field earthquakes of an epicentral distance of below 60 km. Furthermore, it was 1.0 in the far-field earthquakes of an epicentral distance of over 120 km. The difference in the ratio of peak horizontal acceleration amplitude between the near-field earthquake and the far-field earthquake was not recognizable. The ratio of peak vertical acceleration amplitude was approximately the same as the above mentioned ratio for horizontal acceleration amplitude of the

very-near-field earthquake, but it seems to become a little smaller for the far-field earthquake.

The ratio of peak displacement amplitude at the ground surface to that underground are also presented in Table-2. This ratio was 9.0 for the very-near-field earthquake, while the mean ratio was 1.0 for the far-field earthquake with an epicentral distance of over 200 km. So the difference in displacement between at the ground surface and underground is not recognizable. According to the results obtained at Ike-

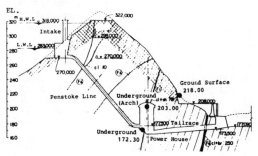

Fig. 3 Arrangement of Seismometer at Ikehara

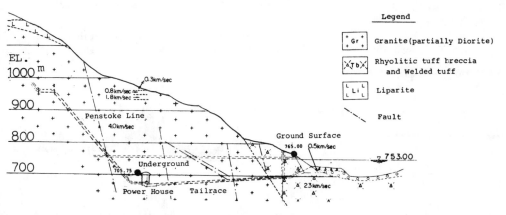

Fig. 4 Arrangement of Seismometer at Numappara

Legend

Gr	Granite(partially Diorite)
Tb	Rhyolitic tuff breccia and Welded tuff
Li	Liparite
	Fault

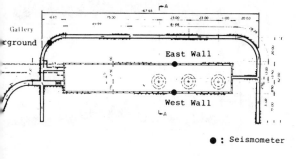

● : Seismometer

Fig. 4-2 Floor Plane

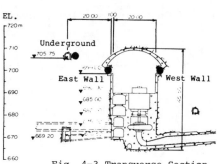

Fig. 4-3 Transverse Section (A-A Section)

311

hara, this ratio ranged from 0.9 to 2.4 and the mean ratio amounted to 1.33 for the near-field earthquake, while for the far-field earthquake, the ratio and the mean ratio were 0.9 to 2.1 and 1.0, respectively.

The results are plotted in Fig.-5 where the epicentral distance is represented by abscissa and the peak acceleration ratio in each component by ordinate at Numappara.

(2) Transfer function

In order to grasp the frequency characteristics of observed earthquake records, power spectrum analysis was conducted and the results are shown in Fig.-6. Transfer function is defined as the ratio of the square root of the power spectrum of a ground surface motion to that of an underground motion at each frequency. Nine earthquake motions were selected for the analysis, which differ in magnitude, epicentral distance, duration, peak amplitude and frequency characteristics. Transfer functions of the same component of nine

earthquake motions thus derived are given on the same plot as indicated in Fig.-7. From Fig.-7, it was found that 1) in the case of horizontal motion the peak value of transfer function is in the range of 6 to 11 Hz and in the case of vertical motion it is in the range of 10 to 15 Hz, 2) the amplitude ratio of vertical motion is, in general, smaller than that of horizontal motion, 3) in the range of 0 to 5 Hz, the amplitude ratios of both vertical and horizontal motions are small and distinct difference in the frequency characteristics between the horizontal and vertical motions is not seen, 4) though it

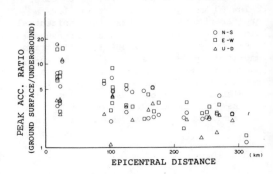

Fig. 5 Peak Accerelation Ratio versus Epicentral Distance at Numappara

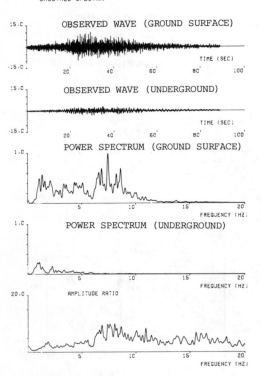

Fig. 6 Power Spectra at the ground surface and underground

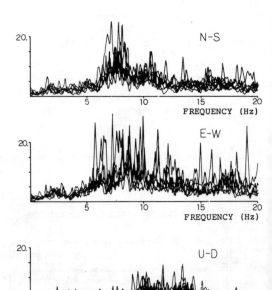

Fig. 7 Transfer Functions (N-S, E-W, U-D)

can be considered that the characteristics of seismic wave are affected by various factors, the similar frequency characteristics are observed for the different earthquake records.

This means that the transfer function depends largely on the rock mass property at the observation point and not so much on the source mechanism of an earthquake.

(3) Response spectrum

Normalized acceleration response spectra for a damping factor of 0.05 are produced and indicated in Fig.-8, in which the spectra are grouped according to the following classification; near-field earthquake [Δ < 200 km, M < 6], far-field earthquake [Δ ≥ 200 km, M > 6], horizontal motion, vertical motion, ground surface motion and underground motion. It is noticed that the characteristics of spectra for the near-field earthquakes are different from those for the far-field earthquakes. In general, it is seen that the predominant period lies in the region of a short period for the near-field earthquakes and in the region of a long period for the far-field earthquakes. This tendency is observed both in the horizontal and vertical motions, and is especially remarkable in the horizontal motion. In many cases, the difference in the response spectrum between the horizontal and vertical motions is fairly distinct in the case of the far-field earthquakes. It was found that response spectrum of underground motion decreases towards the shorter period, and that its peak appears in the longer period region than that of ground motion. Generally, the response amplification

ratio of ground surface motion in larger than that of underground motion. However, in certain periods, the latter becomes larger in some cases than the former, while the above mentioned seldom occures in the case of the absolute acceleration response spectrum.

(4) Summary

A summary of the characteristics of underground earthquake motion identified from the study is presented below.

a) In the case of Ikehara with shallow rock cover (20 m in depth), the ratio of peak acceleration amplitude at the ground surface to that underground has no distinct difference. It could be explained by the fact that the cavern is, from the topographical viewpoint, contained in a relatively small steep mountain in addition to being embedded into shallow rock, as indicated in Fig.-3. In terms of the peak acceleration amplitude, underground motion, whose intensity depends on various conditions, is not necessarily less severe than ground surface motion.

b) In the case of Numappara with deep rock cover (250 m in depth), the frequency characteristics was found that no peak appears in the short period region and that the peak moves toward the long period region. The peak acceleration amplitude ratio (underground to ground surface) shows 1/3 to 1/2 for the horizontal motion of the far-field earthquakes with large magnitudes. The displacement ratio (underground to ground surface) does not exceed that of acceleration amplitude. But both acceleration and displacement ratios sometimes are smaller than 1/10 for the near-field earthquakes.

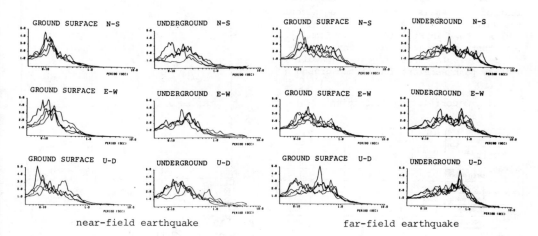

near-field earthquake   far-field earthquake

Fig. 8 Normalized Acceleration Response Spectra

While, in the vertical motion, there exists no remarkable difference in both acceleration and displacement ratio. Thus, the characteristics of underground earthquake motions observed in caverns deep in rock are identified. It can also be said that the large damping effect might be expected especially for the near-field earthquakes.

c) It is thought that those characteristics are governed by the difference between body wave and surface wave, the effect of reflection wave at the ground surface, the amplification through earthquake propagation path and dynamic properties of the observation point.

More theoretical investigations about these subjects are required in the future.

3.3 Behavior of underground cavern wall during earthquakes

(1) List of observed records

25 records of the behavior of cavern wall during earthquakes have been obtained at Numappara as shown in Table-2.

(2) Displacement of cavern wall during earthquakes

The correlation between the peak displacement of west-side wall and various observed values are given in Table-3. The following findings are obtained from Table-3.

a) The correlation between the peak displacement of west-side wall and that of east-side one is considerably significant regardless of the epicentral direction (Fig.-9). From Fig.-9, the peak displacement of both walls was found to be almost the same.

b) As shown in Fig.-10, it was found that there seems no correlation between the peak displacement of west-side wall and the peak acceleration at the ground

surface.

c) There exists good correlation in the peak displacement between the west-side wall and the ground surface and underground. Especially, as shown in Fig.-11, there is a nearly linear relation with the peak displacement underground.

d) There seems no close correlation between the peak displacement of west-side wall and the magnitude and epicentral distance of an earthquake.

It can be said from the above findings

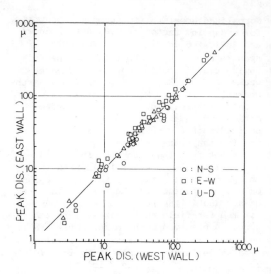

Fig. 9 Correlation of Peak Displacement between West-Wall and East-Wall

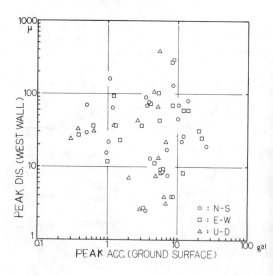

Fig. 10 Correlation between Peak Displacement of West-Wall and Peak Acceleration of Ground Surface

Table. 3 Correlation Coefficient Table

CORRELATION WITH WEST-WALL		NEAR FIELD	NORTH-EAST	EAST	SOUTH	TOTAL
DISPLACEMENT OF EASTWALL		0.94	0.99	0.98	0.94	0.99
ACCELERATION	GROUND	0.77	0.76	0.07	0.68	0.08
	UNDERGROUND	0.20	0.86	0.48	0.53	0.40
DISPLACEMENT	GROUND	0.76	0.95	0.82	0.92	0.92
	UNDERGROUND	0.72	0.95	0.97	0.95	0.96
SPECTRAL INTENSITY	GROUND	0.67	0.90	0.50	0.80	0.67
	UNDERGROUND	0.61	0.91	0.70	0.67	0.83
MAGNITUDE		0.91	0.81	0.85	0.08	0.58
EPICENTRAL DISTANCE		0.03	0.20	0.99	(-0.68)	0.24

that the cavern wall is governed by the
displacement caused by the earthquake motion and vibrates with the neighboring
rock mass. It seems that the motion of the
cavern itself is not recognizable. If so,
considering that the ratio of peak displacement amplitude between the ground
surface and underground is nearly 1.0, the
seismic design of underground caverns
would result in the problem of estimating
the displacement of underground. For this
reason, we investigated the displacement
records taken from underground at the
west-side and east-side walls during
earthquakes.

(3) Comparison between cavern wall
    behaviors and underground earthquake
    motions

Four earthquake records are shown in Fig.-
12 as an example; namely No. 8 (Miyagiken-
Oki earthquake) of magnitude 7.4, No. 29
of magnitude 7.0, No. 13 of magnitude 5.9
and No. 27 of magnitude 6.1. Except for
No. 8, close agreement is seen between the
records of underground and the side wall.
The behavior of No. 8 is different from
others because the cavern wall responded
to higher frequency components of the
earthquake motion.

(4) Investigation of the records obtained
    at the both side walls

In order to investigate the behaviors of
side walls, time-dependent displacement
records obtained at both side walls were
compared with emphasis on the wave-forms
of the two records. As a result, it was

found that both side walls move in phase
or out of phase depending on earthquakes.
Time-dependent displacement records at the
west-side wall and time-dependent relative
displacement, which is estimated as the
difference in displacement between the
west-side wall and east-side wall, were
investigated in the frequency domain. This
investigation has led to the finding that
the spectrum is sensitive to the epicentral
distance. Thus for the purpose of study,
the records were classified into near-
field and far-field types.

In the case of far-field earthquakes,
as shown in Fig.-13, the spectra for both
west- and east-side walls are simple in

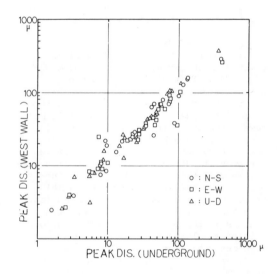

Fig. 11 Correlation of Peak Displacement
between West-Wall and Underground

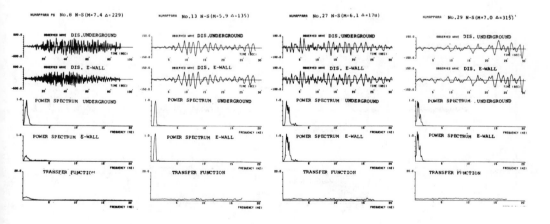

Fig. 12 Comparison of Displacement between West-Wall and Underground

315

shape and look similar. It can also be
seen that their predominant periods range
from 1 to 5 Hz. Some peaks were, however,
found to appear in the high frequency
region in the relative displacement records.

In the case of near-field earthquakes,
Fig.-13, their spectra are complex in shape
and their predominant period are about 5
Hz. It will be seen that there are peaks
in the higher frequency region in comparison with the far-field earthquakes.

(5) Non-parallel behavior

On the basis of the time-dependent displacement records taken during earthquakes
to date at the east- and west-side walls,
the cavern wall behavior was investigated.
Fig.-14 shows the time-dependent displacements and their directions, in which the
displacement at the east-side wall is
plotted at abscissa, which that of the
west-side wall at ordinate. It can be
noticed from Fig.-14 that they exhibit two
different types of behaviors. One is the
motion in phase where both side walls move
toward the same direction almost simultaneously. The other is the motion out of
phase where both side walls move toward
the opposite direction almost simultaneously. We call the former the parallel behavior and the latter the non-parallel
behavior. In the case of vertical motion,
only the parallel behavior was observed,
whereas in the case of horizontal motion,
both parallel and non-parallel behaviors
were observed. Non-parallel behavior is
considered to be a very important factor
in terms of the integrity of caverns.

(6) Summary

A summary of the findings concerning the
cavern wall behavior is given below:
a) Displacement of cavern wall is governed by that of the neighboring rock mass.
Cavern wall and the neighboring rock mass
behave as one body.
b) Displacement of underground cavern
wall can be stimated from that of rock
mass to some extent.
c) Characteristics of cavern wall behavior depend highly on epicentral distance, especially in the case of near-
field earthquakes.
d) Side walls exhibit non-parallel behavior in the horizontal motion during
some earthquakes.
In order to grasp the characteristics of
underground earthquake motion in more detail, it seems necessary to continue observing earthquakes by this observation
system.

3.4 Estimation of displacement of cavern
      wall

The ratio of the peak displacement of
cavern wall to that of underground is obtained at nearly 1.0. So, it is considered
that the former can be estimated from the
latter. An attempt was made in the study
to estimate the peak displacement of
cavern wall as a function of the seismic
intensity, which was expressed by the
Housner's spectrum intensity (S.I.). The
results thus derived are plotted in Fig.-
15, in which S.I. of underground is represented by abscissa and the peak displacement of west-side wall by ordinate
both on logarithmic scale. It is evident

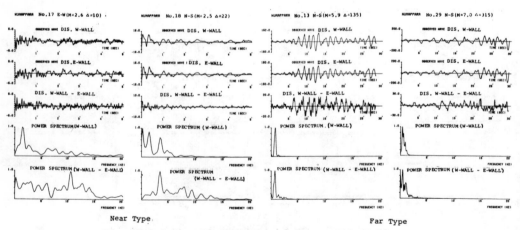

Near Type   Far Type

Fig. 13 Relative Displacement of Cavern Side Wall

316

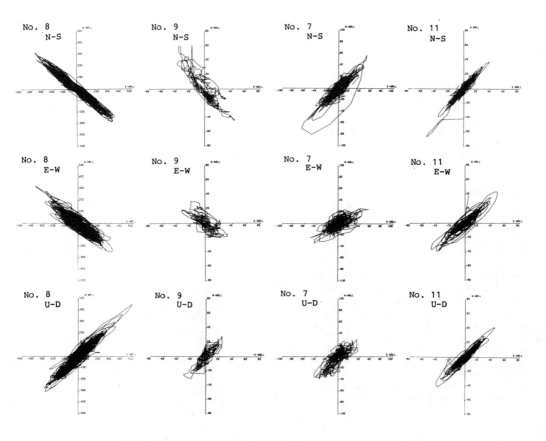

Fig. 14 Characteristics of Cavern Side Wall behavior

from Fig.-15 that there exists an approximately linear relationship between these two values. The same relationship is indicated in Fig.-16 for the larger earthquakes with a magnitude of over 7.0. Again a linear relationship is seen in Fig.-16, and the peak displacement of underground at Numappara was found to be equivalent to 2 to 3% of S.I. for large earthquakes.

4 ANALYTICAL APPROACH TO SEISMIC DESIGN OF CAVERN

Static analysis methods for estimating the structural intensity of underground cavern during excavation have already been developed. Taken into consideration in the static analysis are such rock mass parameters as non-linearity, heterogenety, anisotoropy, viscosity and dimensions of cavern. The validity of these analytical methods has been well demonstrated by actual construction experiences. In comparison with the static analysis, however,

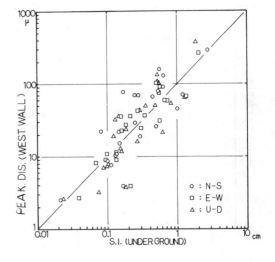

Fig. 15 Peak Displacement of West-Wall versus Spectrum Intensity

analytical methods for estimating the structural integrity of cavern subjected to dynamic loading have been in the early stage of development. Especially, the adequacy of analytical results by some dynamic analysis methods have not been well verified due to lack of understanding of dynamic properties of rock mass. In view of this, dynamic analysis methods for cavern are being developed for this study, and some results obtained by the above methods are described below as a reference.

(1) Transfer function

The finite element model used for the analysis is shown in Fig.-17. The seismic motion with an acceleration equivalent to 400 gal at the ground surface was input at the base rock 500 m deep. Transfer function were obtained at three points, ground surface, underground and cavern wall. The results are given in Fig.-18 for comparison. As can be seen, the difference in short period region seems to be attributed to the existence of cavern in rock. It is also seen that the response of cavern is sensitive to the short period components of a given seismic motion. This analysis result is generally in good agreement with the observations mentioned above.

(2) Stress analysis results

A time-dependent analytical method was used to estimate the stress during an earthquake. The stresses induced by both static and seismic loads are shown in Table-4. It appears that the stress induced by an earthquake can be estimated reasonably well. The stress at the side wall is negligibly small if the cavern integrity is taken into account.

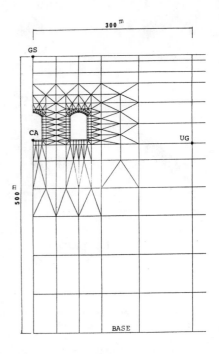

Fig. 17 Analytical Model

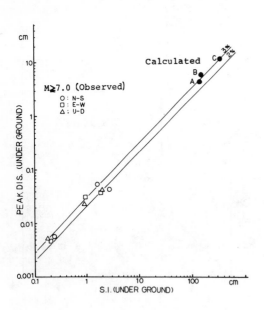

Fig. 16 Peak Underground Displacement versus Spectrum Intensity

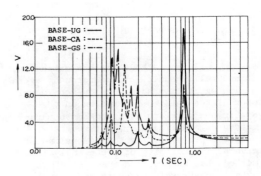

Fig. 18 Comparison of Transfer Function

318

(3) Evaluation of cavern integrity

Shaded portions in Fig.-19 show the elements where Mohr's stress circles exceeds the rupture envelope. The analysis was conducted on the same model by using a quasi-static loading method, and its result is indicated in Fig.-20. As a result, close agreement was obtained between Fig.-19 and Fig.-20.

(4) Relation between displacement of side wall and S.I.

Analysis was performed for three different motions to know the relation between displacement side wall and S.I. by extrapolating the observed data. The analytical result is depicted in Fig.-16, where the same relation for the observed records are given. It is evident that close agreement was again achieved. Table-5 gives the

Table. 4 Calculation of Principal Stress

REPRESENTATIVE POINT			σ_1 (t/m^2)			σ_2 (t/m^2)			τ_{max} (t/m^2)		
			STATIC	SEISMIC	TOTAL	STATIC	SEISMIC	TOTAL	STATIC	SEISMIC	TOTAL
ROCK	A1	ARCH CROWN	12	6	18	69	19	88	28	6	34
	B1	ARCH ABUT	-628	-167	-795	-56	19	-37	286	21	307
	C1	SIDE WALL	-587	-7	-594	31	1	32	310	4	314
	D1	CORNER (L)	-1008	-29	-1037	-156	402	246	426	216	642
	E1	" (R)	-975	-438	-1413	-152	26	-126	411	232	643
CONCRETE LINING	A2	ARCH CROWN	-58	6	-52	-0	94	94	29	44	73
	B2	ARCH ABUT	-21	-59	-80	3	-18	-15	12	21	33
	C2	SIDE WALL	-4	-7	-11	7	6	13	5	6	11
	D2	CORNER (L)	-106	42	-64	-12	293	281	47	125	172
	E2	" (R)	-107	-314	-421	-14	-45	-59	47	135	182

Note 1) Seismic stress is the value at the time when stress state of arch is severest.
2) Seismic load is applied toward right.
3) Symbol (-) means compression.

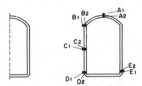

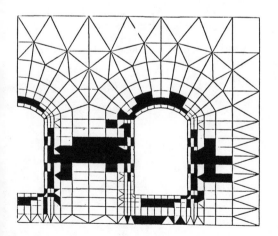

Fig. 19 Result of Analysis
(Time Series Analytical Method)

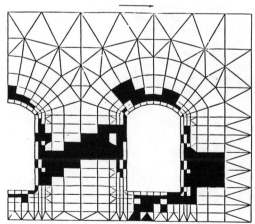

Fig. 20 Result of Analysis
(Quasi-Static Loading Method)

numerical results (peak displacement of side wall) derived from both the quasi-static loading and time-dependent analytical methods.

Table. 5 Calculation of Peak Displacement of Cavern Sidewall

INPUT MOTION	S.I. 0.02 (cm)	MAX. DIS. OF SIDEWALL (CALCULATION) (cm)					
		QUASI-STATIC LOADING METHOD			TIME SERIES ANALYTICAL METHOD		
		SINGLE TYPE	TWIN TYPE	TRIPLE TYPE	SINGLE TYPE	TWIN TYPE	TRIPLE TYPE
A WAVE	124.9	–	5.19	3.75	–	5.45	4.05
B WAVE	141.2	6.45	6.85	8.8	7.30	6.94	5.84
C WAVE	334.8	–	10.9	11.0	–	11.60	11.50

(5) Summary

In the light of a review of the above-mentioned analytical results and a lack of sufficient understanding of various dynamic properties and rupture mechanism of rock mass, it can be said that the quasi-static loading method is practical.

5 CONCLUSION

Some outstanding characteristics unique in the underground earthquake motions have been clarified by means of the field observations and analyses. It is noteworthly that high damping effect can be expected in the motions induced by very-near-field earthquakes. It was found that underground earthquake motions have quite a peculiar feature that they are dependent upon the magnitude, epicentral distance and epicentral direction of an earthquake and so on. It seems that underground earthquake motions can fall into the body wave and surface wave. The displacement of under-ground cavern wall is, except for some special cases, governed by the displacement of neighboring rock mass. Cavern wall and neighboring rock mass behave as one body during an earthquake. Therefore, it is possible to estimate the displacement of cavern wall from that of rock mass with the use of the same method as is usually used to estimate the displacement of underground seismic motion.

The analytical method we employed for the study to date is imcomplete. Needless to say, however, an analytical approach should eventually be developed as a tool to prove the structual intensity of underground cavern under the given design conditions. Therefore, it is our wish that the continuation of field observations together with the continuous effort for developing an appropriate analytical tool would lead to the successful completion of our study aimed at clarifying the dynamic behaviors of cavern wall during earthquakes.

ACKNOWLEDGEMENT

The authors wish to express their sincere gratitude for the guidance and encouragement received from Prof. K. Kubo. The authors also wish to express their thanks to a number of people who engaged in the maintenance of measuring system and in the analysis of observed data.

REFERENCES

Kanai, K., T. Tanaka & Yoshizawa 1959, Comparative studies of earthquake motions on the ground and underground (multiple reflection problem), Bulletin of the Earthquake Research Institute, Vol. 37.
Okamoto, S. 1973, Introduction to earthquake engineering. New York - Toronto, University of Tokyo Press.

SOME ASPECTS ON HOW TO USE NUMERICAL ANALYSIS IN ROCK DESIGN – AN APPLICATION TO THE DESIGN OF A CAVERN WITH 30 M SPAN

Einige Gesichtspunkte für den Gebrauch numerischer Berechnungen beim felsmechanischen Entwurf – Eine Anwendung beim Entwurf einer Kaverne mit 30 m Spannweite

Quelques aspects des procédés d'utilisation de l'analyse numérique dans le dimensionnement du rocher – Une application au dimensionnement d'une caverne de 30 m de portée

ULF KEIJER & TORBJÖRN HAHN
Teknisk Databehandling, Stockholm, Sweden

SUMMARY

In this paper some methods utilized for studying the stability of large rock caverns are described. These methods were applied to a practical case, a fairly large cavern in Sweden with a width of the span just above 30 m. The cavern is under excavation at present.

It is emphasized that numerical analysis in rock mechanics must be treated with caution implying that a stepwise refinement of the numerical analysis should be advisable. Relatively simple methods based on manuals are often sufficient. The finite element method (FEM) offers, however, the possibility of describing the geometry of a cavern more accurately. Mostly, an elastic model of the rock material will yield enough guidance. If further refinements are desirable, joints can be introduced into the FEM model and adequate material properties for these joints can be defined.

A vast amount of work is associated with FEM modelling and the generation of the input data for the FEM program to be used in the calculations. For this work, however, a versatile and flexible interactive graphics input data generator, called GEORGE, has been utilized. Besides considerable time saving the preprocessor, as it is designed, can imply further insight and understanding of the finite element method and its actual limitations in rock design.

ZUSAMMENFASSUNG

Dieser Beitrag beschreibt einige Verfahren zur Stabilitätsprüfung grosser Felskavernen. Sie kamen in Schweden bei einem praktischen Fall, einer ziemlich grossen, z.Z. im Bau befindlichen Kaverne mit gut 30 m Spannweite, zur Verwendung.

Es wird betont, dass numerische Analyse in der Felsmechanik nur mit Vorsicht zu verwenden ist und tunlichst stufenweise verfeinert werden sollte. Oft genügen auf Lehrbücher fussende, verhältnismässig einfache Verfahren. Die Finite-Element-Methode (FEM) ermöglicht jedoch, die Geometrie einer Kaverne genauer zu beschreiben. Meistens reicht es dabei, von einem elastischen Modell auszugehen. Sind weitere Feinheiten erwünscht, lassen sich Klüfte mit ins FEM-Modell einbauen und für die Klüfte geeignete Materialeigenschaften festlegen.

Derartige FEM-Modelle zu entwickeln und die für Berechnungen mit dem FEM-Programm benötigten Ausgangsdaten einzugeben, erfordert viel Arbeit; die Aufgabe wurde jedoch mit einem flexiblen, interaktiven Graphik-Programm namens GEORGE bequem gelöst. Neben wesentlicher Zeitersparnis gewährt dieses Programm in seiner heutigen Form auch tieferen Einblick in die Finite-Element-Methode und Verständnis für deren faktische Begrenzung bei felsmechanischen Entwürfen.

RESUME

Ce document fait la description de quelques méthodes utilisées dans l'étude de stabilité des grandes chambres souterraines creusées en pleine roche. Ces méthodes ont été appliquées sur un chantier en Suède, consistant au creusement d'une grande chambre d'une portée légèrement supérieure à 30 m. L'excavation est actuellement en cours.

En mécanique des roches, il est à remarquer que l'analyse numérique doit être traitée avec beaucoup d'attention pour pouvoir faire une approche successive devant mener à un résultat convenable. Des méthodes relativement simples, basées sur des manuels, sont souvent suffisants, mais la méthode des éléments finis (MEF) permet de décrire plus exactement la géométrie d'une chambre. Dans la plupart des cas, un modèle élastique de la roche fournira des renseignements assez consistants pour tracer une ligne de conduite. Pour celui qui désire améliorer les performances, des joints pourront être introduits dans le modèle MEF après avoir défini les propriétés du matériau adéquat pour ces joints.

De très nombreux ouvrages sont compatibles au modelage MEF et les données d'entrée sont générables dans les calculs du programme MEF. A cet effet, un générateur graphique, appelé GEORGE, a été utilisé pour introduire les données. Ce processeur, versatile et très souple, a permis des gains de temps considérables et a, de par sa conception, abouti à une meilleure compréhension de la méthode des éléments finis et de ses limites actuelles en mécanique des roches.

1 INTRODUCTION

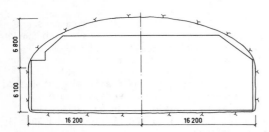

Figure 1. A section of the cavern with con-tour lines of the internal structure.

A cavern with a free span of 30 m is under excavation at present. The size and the shape of the cavern were determined from general functional and service requirements based on demands from defense authorities in Sweden. One of the main questions in this respect was whether the relatively large span and the shallow shape of the cavern would seriously affect its stability, also taking the actual site constraints into consideration.

Originally, the cavern was designed as two separate smaller rooms. It was quite clear, however, that the total construction costs would be higher for a two-room-alter-native than for a larger single-room-alter-native, provided that the costs for addi-tional reinforcement could be limited for the second case. Consequently, the interest was focussed on the rock mechanical aspect during the design stage including investi-gations of the real conditions in the rock mass at the actual site.

Considering the parameters affecting the stability of the cavern, already a simple elastic analysis shows that the tangential stresses in the roof are not very dependent on the overall size of the cavern for ordinary ratios between the horizontal and vertical virgin stresses of the mass. For small horizontal stresses, however, the roof will be affected by tensile stresses which, in combination with unfavourable joint conditions, may cause stability prob-lems and corresponding risks for substantial increase of necessary reinforcement. There-fore, the geological conditions in regard to structures, joint patterns and virgin stresses were considered to be of vital importance for problems to be expected during the excavation of the cavern.

2 GEOLOGY

Geological mapping showed fairly good rock conditions at the actual site. Some weak zones visible at the surface were investi-gated by core-drilling. A part of the rock massif was selected where no severe dis-turbances could be found and where access tunnels with acceptable length could be arranged. See Figure 2.

In the vertically drilled bore-hole three-dimensional stress measurements were made utilizing methods developed by the Swedish State Power Board. The results from the measurements principally showed low primary stresses.

The vertical stresses correspond roughly to the weight of the overburden of the rock mass. The horizontal stresses were about the same along the longitudinal axis of the cavern and near zero in the perpendicular direction. See Figure 3.

Some smaller zones with soft material were discovered in this bore-hole. The directions of these zones were unfavourable in regard to the overall orientation of the cavern. These weak zones are considered in the numerical analysis while other joints, with rough surfaces and irregular orienta-tions have been disregarded. Some shear tests were made where this assumption was

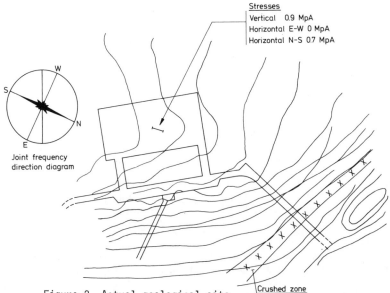

Figure 2. Actuel geological site.

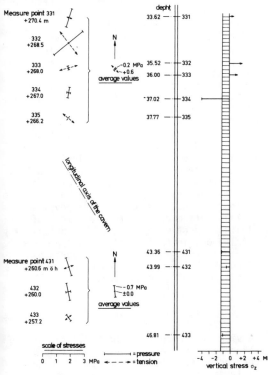

Figure 3. Results from stress measurements.

justified. The behaviour of this latter type of joint was similar to that of homogenous rock material.

3 THE FINITE ELEMENT METHOD IN ROCK DESIGN

3.1 General aspects

The finite element method (FEM) has been applied to rock mechanical problems for many years in Europe as well as overseas. Calculations have been carried out for studying design problems both in mining and tunnelling.

In Sweden the finite element method has been introduced later, mainly due to the fact that the stability of jointed hard rock has not been considered to be critical for ordinary caverns and tunnels. In connection with some large projects in Sweden it has been found desirable to introduce FEM as a tool for the analysis of the behaviour of the rock mass. Here the Näsliden project (mining) and two major projects concerning nuclear waste disposal can be mentioned.

Also in the project presented here, numerical analysis has been applied to a relatively large extent including the finite element method. However, it could be maintained that, for the time being, there is a general uncertainty about the practical benefits from applying numerical analysis, in particular the FEM technique, for the design of rock caverns and tunnels. Some reasons for this will be mentioned.

At first, it can be pointed out that the FEM calculations carried out in Sweden for the above mentioned projects have been very comprehensive, have taken a very long time and have cost a lot of money.

Further, analytical calculations produce results in terms of numerical values. In structural engineering, for example, these values can be compared with values given in codes of practice. Thus, criteria exist for judging whether a suggested structural solution can be accepted or not. In rock mechanics, in general, such criteria are not available. Therefore, the results from the calculations will always be judged with a a considerable degree of subjectiveness.

Thirdly, a finite element model cannot perfectly simulate the rock mass to be modelled. Especially, there is an uncertainty of the distribution of the mechanical properties of the joints. In addition, FEM calculations of rock problems are calculated mainly with two-dimensional models. This is certainly a simplification, still more emphasizing that it is very advisable to interpret results from FEM calculations with caution.

The finite element method implies that considerable work has to be accomplished by establishing required input data for a given problem. This work takes several days, even for fairly simple models. For more complicated models the time can be considerable. Among other things, this implies that the results from the calculation cannot be obtained for some time. Maybe, at that time the results, either they are right or wrong, will not be asked for any longer.

The above mentioned reasons lead to the conclusion that the finite element method can only be considered as a complement to other possibilities for improving the total available information for the design of the tunnel. Figure 4 tries to describe the idea.

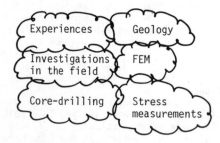

Figure 4. A model describing the idea of the integration of the application of the finite element method with other activities and experiences utilized in rock design.

The curly contours aim at illustrating the fact that the available information, regardless of its kind, is relatively "soft". For example, stress measurements in situ give only approximate results. Besides, for economical reasons only a limited number of places can be provided with measuring devices. Stress measurements as well as core drilling are often neglected due to the costs. Neither, in general, is the geological information complete and the responsible geologist or engineer can obtain only partial guidance from his own earlier experiences.

The conclusion is that the finite element method, which generally requires "hard" input data and produces "hard" results, must be, in one way or the other, adapted to the pattern in the picture. Its contours must be "softened". A rock designer must be able to utilize FEM as he utilizes all other available information, including his own experience. Typically, the procedure for obtaining results from analytical calculations are too "hard" (in the sense used here) to be fully utilized in ordinary rock design.

If, however, a "softer" application of the finite element method is possible, some additional demands on the computer programs to be used must be fulfilled. The following seems to be most essential.

The input data should be established quickly and easily for a given problem and the presentation of the results from the calculation should be problem-oriented, which in this case means that it must be conceivable in terms adapted for the actual decision-making situation of the designer. Just as well as the input data for a model must be easy to create, these data must be easy to modify, reflecting changes of the model. The results from the calculations raise, in general, new questions. Sensitivity analysis for different physical parameters may be desirable, e.g. residual stresses in the rock mass or material properties as well as refinements of the very mesh of the finite element model. Thus, the analysis is carried out in an iterative way. In consequence of this a simpler FEM program can often be chosen, usually based on linear elastic material properties.

3.2 Analysis step by step

In view of the current uncertainties of the structure and the material properties of the rock mass, there is no reason in an early design stage for carrying out more comprehensive analyses, for example with FEM. It is more essential to obtain at least a rough estimate of the actual situation by investigations in the field. If possible, core-drilling and stress measurements should be included. An analysis is then performed in a stepwise manner; first simple calculations, thereafter, if practical, more elaborate analyses are carried out.

For the actual project the analysis has included the following steps, which will be described later in detail:
1. A simple analytical model (not FEM).
2. An elastic FEM model (joints not considered).
3. Joints included (opening of joints possible).

As a fourth point a final run can be added using a non-linear FEM program describing more accurately the influence from the behaviour of the joints. Such a run may be justified as a confirmation of the results obtained from earlier runs, maybe, with simpler material models.

By proceeding step by step in this way the responsible designer can take part also in the numerical analysis. Accordingly, he can decide whether the results obtained are satisfactory or if further analysis is required.

4 THE INTERACTIVE PROGRAM

In order to support the ideas discussed above, a computer program called GEORGE (for GEOmetry and REstraints GEneration) has been developed. It consists of a number of separate programs principally for the generation of the complete input data of finite element programs. The so called preprocessor is not confined to be used togethe with a special FEM program. On the contrary, it has been considered valuable to be able to compare results from different analyses. It is well known that they might differ.

The program permits the user to draw the desired geometry of the finite element structure direct on the graphics terminal, perform modifications and prescribe loadings and other boundary conditions in a direct dialogue with the computer model. Thereby the non-computer expert, for example the rock designer, can fully control the model and decide what changes he wishes to make.

The finite element meshes shown in this report have all been created using GEORGE. A substantial saving of time has been achieved. As a rule, 75-95% of the time normally required for establishing a FEM model has been eliminated.

5 ANALYSIS

5.1 Stresses in the roof determined by simple theory of elasticity.

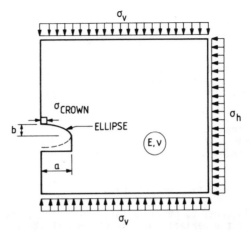

Figure 5. Model of a cavern in elastic homogenous rock subjected to a horizontal pressure σ_h and a vertical pressure σ_v. The roof of the cavern conforms with an ellipse with the principle axes 2a and 2b.

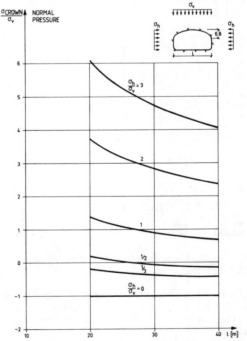

Figure 6. A diagram showing the horizontal pressure at the crown as a function of the span and the relationship between horizontal and vertical virgin stresses in the rock mass. The diagram is valid for an elliptic shape of the roof of the cavern.

As a first step, as mentioned above, the theory of elasticity was applied. Assuming the shape of the roof of the cavern being elliptic, formulas from handbooks can be utilized.

The results obtained as per Figure 5 are compiled in a diagrammatic form in Figure 6. The tangential stress at the crown of the roof is plotted versus the total span of the cavern for different relationships between the horizontal and vertical virgin stresses in the rock mass.

It is interesting to note that the actual stress is only slightly influenced by the width of the span for low horizontal stresses.

5.2 Elastic analysis with FEM

In order to obtain a more complete picture of the variation of the tangential stress along the roof, the finite element method was applied. In particular the real non-elliptic shape could be modelled more accurately. Different FEM meshes were generated. Figure 7 shows one of the chosen models. Still, linear elastic material properties were assumed.

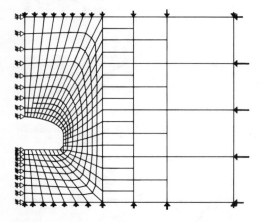

Figure 7. Element mesh, boundary conditions and loadings.

The calculations were carried out for two different load cases corresponding to two different orientations of the cavern at the site:

1. Originally suggested orientation according to Figure 1. Measurements at the site gave σ_h = 0 MPa and σ_v = 0.9 MPa.

2. A perpendicular orientation. In this case σ_h = 0.7 MPa. σ_v is of course still 0.9 MPa.

Figure 8 shows the resulting variation of the tangential stress along the roof

for the two cases. For comparison, the variation for the previously assumed elliptic shape is shown as well.

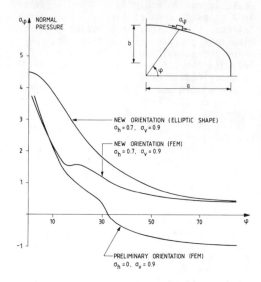

Figure 8. Variation of the tangential stress along the roof of the cavern for two different orientations of the cavern.

5.3 A method for an approximate treatment of joints in the rock mass

The discussion above has assumed that the rock mass is homogenous and elastic. Core-drilling, however, revealed that joints in the mass could have some influence on the stability of the roof of the cavern. A third step of the analysis was carried out in order to obtain a more complete picture of the possible effects of these joints. In particular, one specific joint seemed to be more severe than the others in this respect. A relatively coarse element mesh was created with the actual joints included. See Figure 9. The leftmost joint in the figure was allowed to open successively.

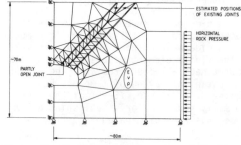

Figure 9. Finite element mesh and loadings utilized for the analysis of the opening of a joint.

Figure 10 shows in detail how the elements are connected to a given node at a joint. Note particularly how the ordinary degrees-of-freedom in the horizontal and vertical directions are transformed into degrees-of-freedom with displacements along the joint and perpendicular to the joint.

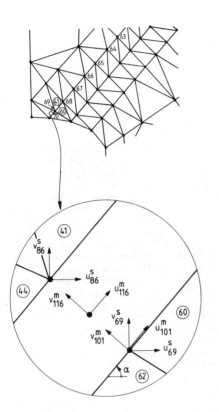

Figure 10. Introduction of additional nodes (degrees-of-freedom). Particularly it is shown how node 69 is substituted by four new nodes, viz. 69, 86, 101 and 116. α is the angle between the horizontal x axis and the direction of the joint under consideration.

The procedure of the calculation will be the following. At first calculations are performed assuming the rock mass being completely elastic. The friction is big enough to prevent any slipping from occuring in the joint.

The Mohr-Coulombs criterion $\tau_c = c + \sigma \tan \emptyset$, where c is the cohesion and $\emptyset$ is the friction angle, can be applied. τ_c is the critical shear stress which implies slipping if it is exceeded.

If the calculated value of τ exceeds τ_c

in a given node of the joint, beginning with the lowest one, and at the same time tension stresses are prevailing, the joint is decoupled at this node. The calculation is repeated and the next node along the joint is checked. The procedure goes on until complete failure or until no more nodes tend to slip.

The results are, of course, very much depending on the assumed material parameters. After the investigation of material specimens from the joint (core cylinders) c = 0.05 MPa and $\emptyset$ = 22° were applied. With these values only the lowest node at the very contour of the roof opened. The subsequent calculations indicated stable conditions.

On the other hand, if c = 0 MPa and $\emptyset$ = 18° were applied, the opening of the joint did not stop before the fourth node from the bottom.

5.4 Conclusions

It is worth stressing once more that the results are not more accurate than the assumed input data and the correspondence between the assumed properties of the mathematical model and the real rock mass. With this in mind, however, the different analyses gave valuable information for the project. Above all, it supported to a large extent the single-room-solution and contributed substantially to the judgement that the necessary additional reinforcement for this solution should be very limited. It can also be said that these FEM calculations performed might probably have been neglected if not such a versatile tool as the utilized input data generator had been available.

6 ROCK MECHANICAL ASPECTS ON THE EXCAVATION

Mathematical analysis, discussed above, is only one of several aspects on the question of safety and economy for large underground caverns. Neither can calculations nor pre-investigations cover all details of the rock behaviour under the excavation stage. As the probability for unfavourable combinations of joints increases with the size of the cavern, higher demands on carefulness, control and checking during the excavation of a large cavern will be required.

For this project the excavation sequences will be as illustrated in Figure 11. At first the top heading (I) is to be excavated to a span of about 15 m. After that the remaining parts of the heading (II and III) are excavated by smooth stoping to full span. The bench (IV) will then be excavated by

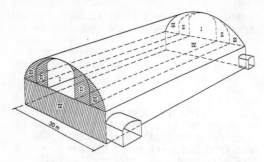

Figure 11. Sequences of excavation of the actual cavern.

bench blasting. The deformations will be measured with extensometers for each sequence of the excavation and will be continued after the completion of the cavern until satisfactory convergence is recorded. The measuring devices are planned to be placed according to Figure 12.

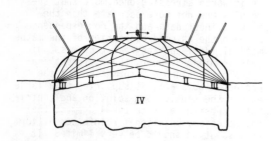

Figure 12. Planned arrangement of extensometers and distometer measurements.

The measurements are intended to fulfil the following three functions:
1. to provide information for the design of final rock reinforcement
2. to check the calculations
3. to develop new ideas for measuring during the construction phase of underground caverns.

In May 1982 the measuring program will still be going on and, hopefully, some results from this program will be presented at the conference.

7 CONCLUSIONS

Preinvestigations, calculations and measurements are all important factors in the design of underground caverns. For larger caverns these factors are of increasing importance. It is, however, not possible to decide the contribution of each factor in advance. By an iterative and interactive design philosophy, within the different stages of the design and the constructions as well as between these stages, it is possible to obtain a final product which corresponds more closely to essential requirements regarding economy and safety.

8 REFERENCES

Bjurström, S. 1973, Rock bolts in jointed rock (in Swedish). Royal Swedish Fortifications Adm., 121:3, Stockholm.

Goodman, R. et al. 1968, A model for the mechanics of jointed rock, ASCE Proc., J. of the Soil Mech. and Found. Div., 94:185-203.

Hahn, T. et al. 1981, Aspects on the use of the finite element method in rock design (in Swedish). Royal Swedish Fortifications Adm., 134:4, Eskilstuna.

Hiltscher, R. and Ingevald, K. 1971, Rock mechanical investigations concerning the influence of a rock burst zone on the brench excavation in the headrace tunnel at Suorva-Vietas hydropower plant (in Swedish). Academy of Engineering Science, 38, p. 153-164, Stockholm.

Keijer, U. 1979, Interactive computer graphics. An application to modelling finite element structures, Proc. Digital Equipment Computer Users´Society, vol 6, Maynard, Mass.

Keijer, U. 1980, Contributions to interactiv computer-aided design in structural engineering. Royal Swedish Fortifications Adm., 134:3, Stockholm.

Kovari, K. (ed.) 1977, Field measurements in rock mechanics. Rotterdam, Balkema.

Swan, G. 1980, Stiffness and associated joint properties of rock. Proc., Conf. on rock mechanics to cut-and-fill mining, 2:91-118, Luleå.

DESIGN AND CONSTRUCTION OF UNDERGROUND POWER CAVERNS IN TAIWAN

Entwurf und Bau von unterirdischen Kraftwerkskavernen in Taiwan

Dimensionnement et construction de centrales souterraines à Taiwan

S.C.LIU
Taiwan Power Company, Taipei, China

ROGER Y.CHENG & C.S.HSIEH
Sinotech Engineering Consultants Inc., Taipei, China

SUMMARY:

This paper is intended to present a description of the historical development and progress of the design approaches for the construction of a total of nine (9) underground power caverns in Taiwan over the past three decades. The design approaches of the caverns in Taiwan are roughly classified into the classical and the more recent methods for discussion in this paper. The first five caverns constructed during the period of 1955 through 1973 were mostly designed in accordance with the classical approach. The other four power caverns, however, were designed in accordance with the more recent approach based on recently developed principles and theories of rock mechanics. As an illustration of this more recent design approach, the design procedure of the Minghu power cavern, which is 20 m in clear span and about 120 m in length, are discussed in detail in this paper. Techcal problems related to geological investigation and orientation of the power caverns built in Taiwan are also reported in this paper. Furthermore, for reference purposes, the paper also embodies a description of the progress of rock mechanics tests, construction method and sequence which have been undertaken in Taiwan for construction of power caverns as well as the instrumentations installed in the caverns in Taiwan over the past 30 years.

ZUSAMMENFASSUNG:

In diesem Beitrag soll für die letzten 3 Jahrzehnte die geschichtliche Entwicklung und der Fortschritt beim Entwurf von Kavernen anhand von neun unterirdischen Kraftwerkskavernen in Taiwan dargestellt werden. Die Entwürfe für die Kavernen in Taiwan werden in diesem Beitrag grob in klassische und modernere Methoden unterteilt. Die Entwürfe der ersten fünf Kavernen, die im Zeitraum von 1955 bis 1975 gebaut wurden, lehnen sich an die klassische Methode an. Die anderen 4 Kraftwerkskavernen wurden in Übereinstimmung mit den modernen Verfahren, die nach den Theorien und Prinzipien der Felsmechanik entwickelt wurden, gebaut. Zur Anschauung dieser moderneren Entwurfsmethoden wird hier der Planungsablauf bei der Minghu Kraftwerkskaverne, mit einer Spannweite von 20 m und einer Länge von 120 m, im Detail durchgesprochen. Von den technischen Problemen bei der geologischen Erkundung und bei der räumlichen Orientierung der in Taiwan gebauten Kraftwerkskavernen wird in diesem Beitrag ebenfalls berichtet. Weiterhin beinhaltet der Bericht für ähnliche Fälle eine Beschreibung der Entwicklung von felsmechanischen Untersuchungen, Baumethoden und -abläufen, als auch eine Beschreibung der in den letzten 30 Jahren in den Kavernen von Taiwan eingebauten Messeinrichtungen.

RESUME:

Cet exposé a pour but de présenter une description du développement et de la progression historique des approches de dimensionnement dans la construction d'un total de neuf (9) centrales souterraines à Taiwan durant les trois dernières décades. Les approches de dimensionnement de ces usines souterraines sont classées approximativement parmi les méthodes classiques et les plus récentes à discuter dans cet exposé. Les cinq premières centrales, construites durant la période 1955 à 1973, ont été dimensionnées selon l'approche classique. Cependant les quatre autres ont été calculées d'après une approche plus récente, basée sur les théories et les principes de la mécanique des roches. Comme illustration de cette plus récente approche de dimensionnement, les procédés de calcul de l'usine souter-raine Minghu, d'une portée de 20 m et d'une longueur approximative de 120 m, sont discutés en détail dans cet exposé. Les problèmes techniques relatifs à l'investigation géologique et à l'orientation des centrales souterraines construites à Taiwan sont présentés dans cet exposé. De plus, à des fins de références, cette étude embrasse également une des-cription de la progression des essais de mécanique des roches, de la séquence et de la méthode de construction qui ont été appliquées à Taiwan lors de l'exécution des usines souterraines ainsi qui les instruments installés dans les centrales de ce pays durant les 30 dernières années.

1 INTRODUCTION

In Taiwan, a total of six underground power caverns have so far been successfully com-pleted and are presently in service. In addition, two more caverns are being de-signed and constructed and one more cavern is in the geological exploration and pre-liminary design stage. Highlights of the underground power caverns in Taiwan are summarized in Table 1.

Of the aforementioned nine power caverns, seven are for conventional hydro power schemes with the clear span ranging from 7.5 m to 21.0 m. Two other caverns, the Minghu and the Mingtan caverns, which are respectively in the detailed and prelimi-nary design stages, are for pumped storage schemes. These two caverns involve the construction of caverns of relatively large spans (20.0 m and 22.8 m clear span) in sandstone stratum with fairly develop-ed joint systems occasionally intercalated with clay seams.

Construction of the first underground power cavern in Taiwan may be traced back to the 1950s. At that time, the science of rock mechanics was still in its embry-onic stage. Consequently, no rigorous theories, standardized testing methods, and sophisticated testing instruments were available to evaluate the rock properties for design use. The design and the stabi-lity analyses of the first five power ca-verns in Taiwan, namely the Tungmen, the

Table 1: Highlights of Underground Power Caverns in Taiwan

Status	Name of Power-Plant	Cross-Section of Cavern	Unit No. and Installed Capacity	Dimension			Completion Date (or Scheduled)
				Clear Span (m)	Length (m)	Height (m)	
Completed	Tungmen	Mushroom	3 @ 7 MW = 21 MW	7.5	50.5	21.7	Feb. 1955
	Lungchien	Mushroom	1 @ 46.8 MW = 46.8 MW	10.0	45.0	19.0	May 1959
	Kukuan	Mushroom	4 @ 45 MW = 180 MW	13.8	85.0	32.0	Dec. 1961 (2 units)
	Chingshan (Lower Tachien)	Mushroom	4 @ 90 MW = 360 MW	17.5	89.5	36.0	Dec. 1970 (2 units)
	Tsengwen	Cylindrical with dome	1 @ 50 MW = 50 MW	⌀21.0	–	36.5	Oct. 1973
	Techi (Tachien)	Mushroom	3 @ 78 MW = 234 MW	17.5	75.0	38.5	Sept. 1974
Under design or construc-tion	Minghu	Mushroom	4 @ 250 MW = 1,000 MW	20.0	119.2	44.5	1985
	Chipan	Mushroom	2 @ 80 MW = 160 MW	15.1	63.1	30.0	1988
Under planning	Mingtan	Under study	8 @ 200 MW = 1,600 MW	22.8	173.5	39.2	1989

Lungchien, the Kukuan, the Chingshan and the Tsengwen caverns, were mostly performed through the adoption of the traditional and classical approach (To facilitate further discussion, this design method shall hereinafter be known as the classical design approach).

Along with the development of the rock mechanics science and the worldwide development of more advanced underground construction methods, the design approach for the other four subsequent underground power caverns at Techi, Minghu, Chipan and Mingtan in Taiwan has considerably improved.

In 1970, the computer oriented finite element method was first introduced into Taiwan for analysis of the stability of the Techi power cavern. This was a milestone in the history of the advancement of power cavern design in Taiwan. Thereafter, the new design method (to be hereinafter known as the "recent design approach") has been successively to assess of the stability of power caverns now under construction, design or planning.

The recent design approach adopted for design of the Minghu power cavern will be illustrated in the following section of this paper.

The power caverns in Taiwan are characterized by the following points:

i) All caverns are of the so-called mushroom shape, except the Tsengwen power cavern, which is of the cylindrical shape with a dome, and the Mingtan power cavern of which the shape is presently under study.

ii) Because of the above, the entire cavern is structurally divided into two elements, the roof arch and the sidewall, for execution of its design.

iii) Since Taiwan is an island of which the geological age is rather young, its abundant rainfall has brought about a high under-groundwater table. Thus, the rock formation of nearly all the power cavern sites in Taiwan has been found to be characterized with rather pronounced joint systems.

iv) Concrete lining has been adopted to help increase the stability of the cavern. Up to now, there is no cavern in Taiwan which void of lining.

2 GEOLOGICAL INVESTIGATION AND ORIENTATION OF POWER CAVERNS

2.1 Exploration Adit and Boreholes

It is customary in Taiwan that prior to determining the orientation of a power cavern, an adit of 2 m high by 1.8 m wide would be driven in the area of the proposed location of the power cavern to carry out a thorough investigation into the geological settings at the site and the rock type(s) and quality, strike of bedding or schistosity, dipping, joint systems, groundwater table, shear, fracture or fault zones and other structural defects or discontinuities which should be ascertained at each and every cavern site. It is intended that the exploration adit would hit directly, or reach the cavern site as close as possible. However, past experiences indicate that the exploration adits were always driven about 40 to 50 m above the proposed elevation of the cavern because the adit was designed for excavation in an upward grade to facilitate drainage and mucking operation. Thus, progress of the cavern site at an earlier date so that the aforementioned geological information may be obtained.

After the adit has reached the site at about 40 to 50 m above the proposed cavern elevation, boreholes were then sunk from the adit (this portion of the adit would be enlarged to 5 m high by 4 m wide to facilitate drilling operation) for the purpose of collecting the geological information required.

The exploration adit could be re-shaped at a later date and for use as a mucking tunnel during the construction stage, or as a part of the permanent structures, such as the ventilation tunnel, the emergency exit, or a headtank for storage of the cooling water of the plant.

Geological conditions, exploration and orientation of power caverns in Taiwan are provided in Table 2 below for reference.

2.2 Orientation of Power Cavern Axis

Based on the geological information collected from the exploration, the power caverns in Taiwan were generally oriented by taking into consideration such factors as the bedding, the schistosity, the existing initial stress pattern, the joint systems, the weak strata and the hydraulic require-

Table 2: Geology and Orientation of Power Caverns in Taiwan

Power Caverns	Rock Cover (m)		Brief Description of Rock Condition	Bedding or Schistosity and Dipping	Prominent Joint System	Orientation of Major Axis of Cavern	Exploratory Work
	In Vertical Dir.	In Horizontal Dir.					
Tungmen	100	40	Sericite-quartz-schist with graphite	N70°E/30°SE	Not prominent	N17°W	Adit: 115m
Lung-chien	320	700	Massive crystalline limestone with layer thickness more than 80 m	Schistosity not prominent	Not prominent	N48°W	–
Kukuan	110	200	Alternation of quartzite, slate and slaty quartzite	N40°E/90°	Not prominent	N40°W	Adit: 673m Borehole: 70m
Ching-shan (Lower Tachien)	200 (60 m below river-bed)	100	Quartzite occasionally intercalated with thin slate band	N10°E/30°NW	1) N15°W/80°E∿80°W 2) N50°W/75°E∿75°W 3) N80°W/85°E∿85°W	N70°W	Adit: 1,000m Borehole: 140 m
Tseng-wen	200	75	Rather thickbed sandstone intercalated with thin beds of shale	N30°E/30°SE	1) N35°W/80°NE 2) N70°W∿N80°E/55°NE	–	Adit: 645m Borehole: 1,000 m
Techi (Ta-chien)	180	250	Alternation of quartzite and slate intercalated with graphite slate	N30°E/65°SE	1) N55°W/75°NE∿75°SW 2) N40°E/30°NW	N60°W	Adit: 277m
Minghu	135	270	Sandstone layer intercalated with thin siltstone and coaly shale layers	N60°E/35°SE	1) N60°W/80°SE 2) N25°E/60°NW 3) N5°W/60°W	N13°W	Adit: 834m Borehole: 1,175m
Chipan	150	180	Hard and fresh gneiss with moderately developed joint system	Schistosity not prominent	1) N-S/40°E 2) N30°E/90°	N25°E	Adit: 600m Borehole: 200 m
Mingtan	300	230	Sandstone with intercalation of thin siltstone layers	N45°E/35°SE	Very irregular	N13°W	Adit: 816m Borehole: 725 m

ments of a waterway system. Such factors are described below:

2.2.1 Bedding or Schistosity

The sidewalls of the power caverns in Taiwan are structurally cantilever element of which the foundation is fixed, leaving the top-end free and without any support. An overhead crane is installed astride and over these free top-ends of two opposite sidewalls. The crane travels in the direction of the longitudinal axis of cavern to lift and haul power equipment. In case these free top-ends deflect too much in the direction normal to the longitudinal axis of the cavern, operation of the crane will be crippled. Therefore, the sidewall shall be designed with an adequate rigidity to reduce its deflection, and, at the same time, the cavern shall be oriented in such a manner so that the side rock pressure will be minimized.

All the power caverns in Taiwan were oriented in the manner described above. It may be noted from Table 2 that the angles sustained between the bedding and the major axis of the power caverns are 87° for Tungmen, 80° for Kukuan, and 90° for Techi. Thus, the side rock pressure would be minimized and at the same time a rather uniform rock load could be expected to act on the roof arch to reduce unstable rock wedges during the course of excavation.

2.2.2 Joint Systems or Discontinuities

At several power cavern sites, joint systems or discontinuities were found and were very much developed and pronounced. Accordingly, consideration of such a weak plane would be made at the time for determination of the orientation of power caverns. For instance, in the Chingshan power cavern, the orientation was selected to intersect the bedding plan at an 80° angle and to intersect the most prominent joint plan at a 55° angle (please refer to Table 2). Thus, a sharp angle of intersection was eliminated to minimize the possibilities of the development of unstable rock wedges during the course of excavation.

Fortunately, the joint systems or the discontinuities at the old power cavern sites, such as Tungmen, Lungchien and Kukuan were not so much developed. However, for the Chingshan cavern, the joint system striking N15°W and dipping 80°E to 80°W was observed, and the cavern was accordingly oriented in order to meet with the geological conditions. It should be specifically pointed out that in some cases, the rock formation of a proposed cavern site contains both the bedding plane and the weak planes of joint systems or discontinuities, the choice of the most optimum orientation of the cavern axis would be very difficult and would require more extensive studies and analyses.

With regard to the classical design approach, joint systems or discontinuities in the rock formation of the proposed power cavern site were merely identified by inspection and observation made by highly qualified geologists through an exploration adit. If the site contained more than one weak plane, it would be difficult to tell which was the decisive and the crucial one. As for the recent design approach, the identification of weak planes or discontinuities and joint systems is carried out through the application of the stereographic (Wulff) projection which is very scientific and can provide more reliable bases for identification of the most prominent joint systems at the cavern site.

As an example, for the Minghu power cavern, which is now under construction, about 240 measurements were made to locate and identify the prevailing discontinuities through the exploration adit which is about 834 m in length. These data were plotted on the stereographic net and the counting net was used to examine the concentration of the discontinuities. Finally, a discontinuity contour diagram was worked out as shown in Fig. 1.

2.2.3 Hydraulic Requirements

From the hydraulics point of view, the orientation of a power cavern is also closely related to the penstock and tailrace alignments. Much efforts were generally made to work out short waterways and the smooth alignment with the waterway system for the purpose of reducing head loss so as to achieve the goal of building an economical and highly efficient power plant.

After a close examination of their geological conditions, the power caverns of Minghu and Chipan now under construction or being designed were oriented and are located on the best quality of rock formation available at the proposed sites, having their major axes of the caverns intersected the pronounced joint system with a fairly large angle and also having very

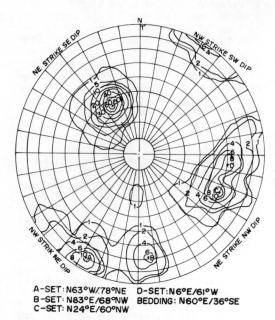

A-SET: N63°W/78°NE   D-SET: N6°E/61°W
B-SET: N83°E/68°NW   BEDDING: N60°E/36°SE
C-SET: N24°E/60°NW

Fig. 1: Discontinuity Contour Map of Minghu Cavern Site

smooth alignment with respect to the upstream penstock and downstream tailrace.

3 ROCK MECHANICS TESTS

Rock mechanics tests carried out for collection of design parameters for use in the design and construction of power caverns in Taiwan are briefly explained below:

3.1 For those Caverns Designed Using the Classical Approach

No specific rock test was performed for building the power caverns of Tungmen, Lungchien, Kukuan and Chingshan. Only samples of the soft materials intercalated in between the beddings or the clay seams encountered in the cavern area, were sampled for tests in laboratory for determination of their mechanical properties. No test for the aforesaid power caverns was attributed to the following reasons:

i) All rock formations of the selected cavern sites were generally very fresh, sound and competent, except the existence of a number of minor joints and small cracks

ii) The cavern openings were relative small.

iii) Before 1970, the development of the rock mechanics science was rather limited and its application was not as popular as it is nowaday.

3.2 For Caverns Designed Using the Recent Approach

The new development of the rock mechanics science, and the application of such a new technology to the construction of power caverns have caught the keen interest of the Chinese engineers in Taiwan. Starting from the construction of the Tsengwen power cavern, numerous rock tests have been performed both in the laboratory and at the job sites, including general rock property tests in the laboratory, and in-situ shearing strength tests and plate loading tests.

Furthermore, in order to apply the computer-aid finite element method to the stability analysis of power caverns, the scope of rock mechanics tests has been gradually expanded to cover in-situ tests of plate loading, shearing and initial stress measurements and the conduct of axial and triaxial tests in laboratories. For the Minghu cavern, the following rock tests have been performed:

i) 3 sets of plate loading tests,
ii) 14 borehole deformation tests performed in six (6) boreholes,
iii) 5 over-coring tests, and
iv) 4 triaxial tests.

As a result, the following findings have been obtained from the tests:

i) From the plate loading tests

Strata	E (kg/cm^2)	Creep Ratio (α)	Retardation Modulus (β/min.)
Fresh and hard sandstone	88,500	0.220	2.5×10^{-2}
Sandstone adjacent to shale layer	58,300	0.149	3.26×10^{-2}
Extremely soft, fractured siltstone	19,000	0.226	2.99×10^{-2}

ii) From the borehole deformation tests at a sandstone layer adjacent to the shale layer.

$$E = 40,000 \text{ kg/cm}^2$$

iii) From the over-coring tests for sandstone layer:

Maximum principal stress $\quad \sigma_3 = 53 \text{ kg/cm}^2$
Minimum principal stress $\quad \sigma_1 = 10 \text{ kg/cm}^2$
Vertical stress component $\quad \sigma_z = 27 \text{ kg/cm}^2$

It was noted that the direction of the initial stress was almost parallel to the plane of the bedding and was also well coincident with that of the maximum slope of the mountain.

4 DESIGN

4.1 Classical Design Approach

Using this design approach, the roof arch and the sidewalls were respectively designed as follows:

4.1.1 Roof Arch Design

The roof arch was treated as a plane structure with a parabolic cross-section and a rise-span ratio of the section was in the range of 0.24 to 0.3. Thus, the line of normal thrust at any section of the arch under various loadings was made to be close to the center line of gravity without causing the development of any excessive tensile stresses in the arch. The least work method was mostly used for solving this statically indeterminate structure.

The loadings taken into design consideration were as follows:

i) Rock Load

The pattern and the intensity of the rock load adopted for the design were selected on the basis of the rock conditions and width of span of the cavern through the application of Prof. K. Terzaghi's method. Generally, a uniform load with an intensity of 0.25 B·γ to 0.6 B·γ (where B is the span width and γ is unit weight of the rock) was selected. For competent rocks, the rock load selected for design was seldom exceeding 0.5 B·γ.

ii) Seismic Load

According to the available seismic data of each individual area, an adequate intensity was chosen and the Pseudo-static method of analysis was applied to each and every cavern.

iii) Temperature and Concrete Shrinkage Effects

It was considered that the surrounding rock mass of a cavern was always of a constant temperature, all the year around regardless of the seasonal variations. However, the ambient air temperature in the cavern would vary according to the outside air temperature due to functioning of the ventilation system installed to expel the excessive heat generated by the power equipment. The difference of temperature variations inside and outside of cavern varies from project to project, and was carefully selected for design use based on the long-term data of air-temperature and also on the design information available on the ventilation system.

Similar to temperature stresses, stresses induced by the shrinkage effect of concrete was also taken into consideration in designing the roof arch, which was physically curve-member and structurally fix-ended at both abutments. Thus, it has been a customary practice to reinforce the arch concrete with equal steel on the extrados and intrados faces.

iv) External Hydrostatic Pressure and Grouting Pressure

As a power cavern is located deeply below the surface of the ground or inside a hill, the outside groundwater pressure at certain locality was very considerably high and was properly taken into consideration during the course of design.

In a rather permeable rock strata, having a high groundwater table or are close to a reservoir, where a power cavern would be constructed, it was customary to provide a drainage system to reduce the external hydrostatic pressure. The intensity of hydrostatic pressure selected for design of cavern depends on topographical configuration, permeability of surrounding rock mass, and provision of drainage system.

After lining of arch concrere, grouting was performed to fill up the gap which exists between the concrete and the rock. The grouting pressure would be around 1 to 2 kg/cm^2, which was also taken into consideration for design.

Details of the roof arch of the old power caverns designed with the aforesaid loadings are tabulated in Table 3 below for reference.

Table 3: Arch Design Loadings of Old Power Caverns in Taiwan

Caverns	Description	Loadings			
		Rock	Seismic	Temperature Variation	External Hydrostatic or Grouting Pressure
Tungmen	Clear span - 11 m Clear rise - 3.3 m Concrete thickness: Crown - 0.4 m Abutment- 1.8 m	Uniform load, $q = 0.6\,B \cdot \gamma$ $(\gamma = 2.7\ T/m^3)$	0.1 g	$\pm 20^{\circ}C$	None
Lungchien	Shape - Parabolic curve Clear span - 12.2 m Clear rise - 2.9 m Concrete thickness: Crown - 0.4 m Abutment- 1.1 m	No data	No data	No data	No data
Kukuan	Shape - Parabolic curve Clear span - 16 m Clear rise - 4 m Concrete thickness: Crown - 0.5 m Abutment- 1.8 m	Inverted "U" shape uniform load, $q = 0.25\,B \cdot \gamma$ $(\gamma = 2.7\ T/m^3)$	0.15 g	$\pm 15^{\circ}F$	None
Chingshan (Lower Tachien)	Clear span - 22.5 m Clear rise - 5.6 m Concrete thickness: Crown - 1 m Abutment- 1.8 m	Inverted "U" shape uniform load, $q = 0.25\,B \cdot \gamma$ $(\gamma = 2.7\ T/m^3)$	0.15 g	$\pm 15^{\circ}F$	1 kg/cm^2

4.1.2 Sidewall Design

Except the oldest power cavern, Tungmen, in most power caverns, two layers of sidewalls were adopted. The outer wall, known as the structural wall, is designed to stabilize the surrounding rock mass and the inner wall, known as the false wall or the finishing wall, is constructed to meet the inner decoration requirements. Between these two walls a gap from 30 cm to 50 cm minimum clear space was maintained for installation of an inner drainage system within the cavern in order to keep the inside of the false walls dry. The columns supporting the overhead crane girders were built to line up with the false wall are to locate at a distance free from the structural wall so that any deformation developing in the structural walls due to side rock pressure would not be transmitted to the columns. Thus, the proper function of overhead crane could be ensured. However, in a very sound and competent rock formation, construction of the structural sidewalls was sometimes omitted.

This omission occurred in the cases of the construction of caverns for the Kukuan and Chingshan Projects.

The stability of structural walls was examined based on the assumption that rock wedges might slide towards the inside of a cavern along a pronounced joint system, seams or other geological discontinuities. In this examination, the seismic loads and external hydrostatic pressure were also taken into consideration in a manner similar to that for the roof arch design. In areas where the stability was found to be questionable, rock bolts or prestressed tendon were used for improvement of their stability. Details of the structural sidewalls of the old caverns are summarized in Table 4 for reference.

4.2 Recent Design Approach

The recent design approach has adopted the computer-oriented finite element method for assessment of the stability of power caverns. To facilitate discussion of this

336

Table 4: Details of Sidewalls of Old Power Caverns in Taiwan

Cavern	Rock Conditions	Structural Sidewalls	Stabilization Measures
Tungmen	Quartz-schist with graphite	Fully concrete lined; columns and walls subject to side rock load.	None
Lungchien	Fresh and massive crystalline lime-stone	Fully concrete lined.	1"∅ x 2.4 m rock bolts were installed where required
Kukuan	Alternation of quartzite and slate	Above generator floor unlined; below generator floor, concrete struc-tural sidewalls placed against rock.	25 T x 11 m and 20 T x 9m prestressed tendons spaced at 4 m to 5 m.
Chingshan (Lower Tachien)	Quartzite inter-calated with slate band	Same as above.	28 T x 10 m prestressed tendon spaced at 4 m to 5 m

method, the design performed for the Minghu power cavern will be described below as an illustration.

The input data involved were: i) inclina-tion or dipping of rock strata or bedding; ii) nodal point data; iii) physical pro-perties of rock strata; iv) element data inclusive of initial stresses; and v) con-struction sequence.

The design considerations, assumptions, parameters and methodology involved in the Minghu cavern are as follows:

i) The analysis was performed on the two-dimensional plane perpendicular to the longitudinal axis of the cavern with the surrounding rock mass represented as shown in Fig. 2.

ii) Meshes of finite elements were of the quadrangular shape and were selected in such a way that at some localities where high stress concentration or high stress gradient (such as corners) exists, smaller meshes were, where possible, used for analysis.

iii) The sequence of cavern excavation was assumed to proceed as shown in Fig. 3.

iv) As strike and dip of bedding and joint systems were not coincident with the longitudinal axis of the cavern, a trans-formation was performed according to the apparent dip calculation and the results obtained therefrom are as shown in Fig. 4 for the bedding and joint systems.

v) Since the cavern site was composed of jointed sandstone layers intercalated

within this siltstone band of low shear strength, the overall elastic moduli, E_1 and E_2, respectively parallel and normal to

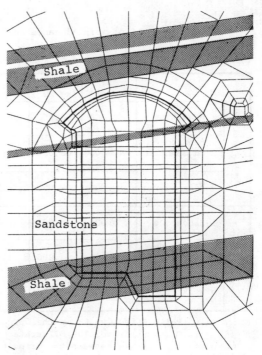

Fig. 2: Mesh and Geological Condition of Minghu Cavern

337

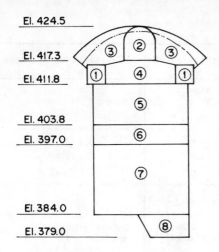

El. 424.5
El. 417.3
El. 411.8
El. 403.8
El. 397.0
El. 384.0
El. 379.0

Fig. 3: Stage Excavation of Minghu Power Cavern

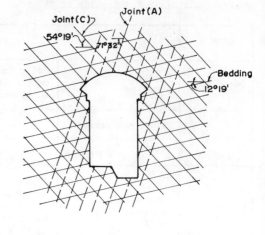

Fig. 4: Projected Joints and Bed of Minghu Cavern

the bedding, were figured out as follows:

$$E_1 = \alpha \cdot E_R + \beta \cdot E_L \text{ -------------- (1)}$$

$$E_2 = \frac{1}{\dfrac{\alpha}{E_R} + \dfrac{\beta}{E_L}} \text{ ---------------- (2)}$$

where

E_R, E_L: E-moduli of jointed sandstone

and siltstone

α, β : Percentage proportion the layer thickness of jointed sandstone and siltstone respectively, which are based on actual measurement in the exploration adit.

vi) The mechanical properties of the rock mass at the Minghu cavern site were taken as shown in Table 5 below for analysis:

Table 5: Mechanical Properties of Rock Mass of Minghu Power Cavern

	Type	E_1 (kg/cm^2)	E_2' (kg/cm^2)	G (kg/cm^2)	γ	ν_1	ν_2	τ_R (kg/cm^2)	ϕ_R (degree)
Normal condition	1 Sandstone	50,000	50,000	20,000	12°	0.25	0.25	15	55
	Sandstone 2 adjacent to shale layer	40,000	38,000	15,700	12°	0.25	0.24	0	50
	3 Weak zone	10,000	10,000	3,900	12°	0.28	0.28	0	40
After rock relaxed	1 Sandstone	5,000	5,000	2,000	12°	0.45	0.45	0	0
	Sandstone 2 adjacent to shale layer	4,000	3,800	1,570	12°	0.45	0.45	0	0
	3 Weak zone	1,000	1,000	390	12°	0.45	0.45	0	0

Notes: i) E_2' = Effective E_2 in the direction normal to the major axis of cavern
       ii) G = Shear modulus of strata
       iii) γ = Angle between the principal axes for the orthotropic material and the glob axes
       iv) ν_2 = Poisson's ratio normal to bedding planes

vii) The initial stresses prevailing at the cavern site are shown in Fig. 5, which were taken from the result of rock tests.

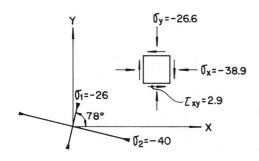

Unit of stress : kg/cm²

Fig. 5: Initial Stresses of Minghu Cavern Site

viii) Failure of rock mass will be assessed by the following equation (refer to Fig. 6):

$$\tau = \tau_R + \sigma \cdot \tan\phi_n \text{ -------------- (3)}$$

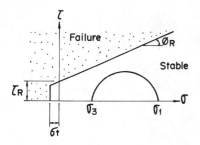

Fig. 6: Failure Criteria

where

σ_t : Maximum allowable tensile stress (2.0 kg/cm² is adopted in the analysis for the rock mass of sandstone)

ϕ_R : Internal friction angle of rock mass

τ_R : Shearing strength of rock mass

ix) Failure along weak stratum (such as the shear planes) will be examined as shown in Fig. 7.

where

σ_1, σ_3: Principal stresses in rock mass

θ: Angle measured from horizontal plane to principal stress

γ: Stratum inclination measured from horizontal plane

σ_C : Stress normal to weak stratum plane

$$= \frac{\sigma_1 + \sigma_3}{2} - \frac{\sigma_1 - \sigma_3}{2} \cos 2\ (\gamma-\theta)$$

τ_C : Shearing stress along weak stratum plane

$$= \left| \frac{\sigma_1 - \sigma_3}{2} \sin 2\ (\gamma - \theta) \right|$$

τ : Shearing strength of weak stratum plane

$$= C_j + \sigma_C \tan\phi_j$$

C_j : Cohesion of stratum

ϕ_j : Internal frictional angle of weak stratum

If $\dfrac{\tau_C}{\tau} > 1$ ----- The weak stratum is unstable

$0 < \dfrac{\tau_C}{\tau} < 1$ ----- The weak stratum is stable

$\dfrac{\tau_C}{\tau} < 0$ ----- The weak stratum is subject to tension failure

x) Based on the results of the analysis (as illustrated in Fig. 8), the extent of relaxed zone were defined, and prestressed tendons were designed as indicated in Fig. 9 for the purpose of stabilizing the sidewalls.

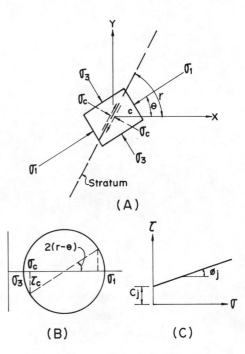

Fig. 7: Failure Along Weak Stratum

339

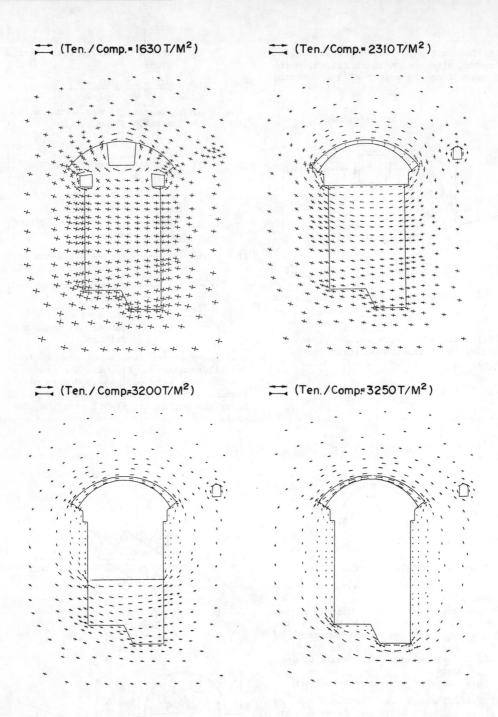

Fig. 8: Analyzed Principal Stresses of Minghu Power Cavern

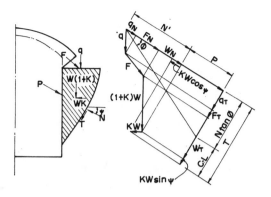

Fig. 9: Tendon Design

where

w : Weight of sliding wedge of the re-laxed rock mass under consideration

F : Reaction forces of concrete roof arch abutment

q : Surcharge load from the relaxed zone above arch abutment

p : Tendon force applied

ψ : Inclination of normal force

$\emptyset$: Internal friction angle of the rock mass

K : 0.1 (coefficient for blasting shock during construction which is assumed to act in all directions)

Normal force, N, to sliding surface

$N = P - KW \cdot \cos\psi + W_N + F_N + q_N$

where the subscript N means components of each force or load in the direction of normal force.

Tangent force, T, to sliding surface

$T = KW \cdot \sin\psi + W_T + F_T + q_T$

where the subscript T means components of each force or load in the direction of sliding surface.

Let $N' = - KW \cdot \cos\psi + W_N + F_N + q_N$

$\therefore N = N' + P$

For stabilizing sliding surface,

$N \tan\emptyset + C \cdot L > T$, namely

$(N' + P) \tan\emptyset + C \cdot L > T$ ------------(7)

The above equation (7) shall be always satisfied.

where

$\emptyset$: Friction angle for sliding surface = 50°

C : Residual shearing strength of slid-ing surface = 15 T/m^2

L : Arc length of sliding surface

$\therefore P > \dfrac{T - N'\tan\emptyset - C \cdot L}{\tan\emptyset}$ ----------(8)

Based on the equation (8), the required tendon force could be estimated, and the capacity and space of the tendons were de-termined accordingly.

As a result, the maximum principal stresses were found to be 1,630 T/m^2, and the maximum deflection of the sidewall was estimated at 34 mm, if tendon force was not applied.

The tendon force required at the upper part of the cavern was found to be 13 T/m^2. Therefore, a 60-ton tendon was applied at the spacing of 2.0 m by 2.0 m.

It is specifically pointed out that since the arch was regarded as the most import-ant structural element to resist the ver-tical rock load, its design was re-evalu-ated using a method similar to that used in the classical design approach to ensure its stability. However, since a computer is available as a tool, the finite element method is used to replace the manual com-putation for design. The loading condi-tions examined for the Minghu power cavern arch are as follows:

  i) Dead load

  ii) Combination of dead load plus rock load

  iii) Combination of dead load, rock load and thermal load with temperature inside cavern dropping by 10°C.

  iv) Combination of dead load, rock load and thermal load with temperature inside cavern rising by 15°C.

The grouting pressure and the external hydrostatic pressure were not considered in the design because only low-pressure contact grouting was deemed necessary to backfill gaps existing between the lined concrete and rock, and a drainage gallery will be provided to reduce the external hydrostatic pressure.

5 CONSTRUCTION

5.1 Old Power Caverns

For those old power caverns (such as the caverns of the Tungmen, Lungchien, Kukuan and Chingshan Projects), the construction performed was almost in the same fashion, except the mucking methods, which were different for each cavern due to the a-vailability of mucking adits.

  Generally speaking, more sophisticated

and efficient excavation equipment were employed project after project. However, the basic concept of setting up the construction sequence was the same. The following was the construction method adopted for the Chingshan Project which will be briefly illustrated as an example.

The roof arch was first excavated with two side drifts running along the abutments and then the transversal arch was excavated following the sequence indicated in Fig. 10 either alternatively (with a panel width of 4 to 5 m) or continuously along the main axis of the cavern, if the quality of the rock permits such an excavation.

Immediately following the completion of the arch ring-cut excavation, rock bolts or shotcrete were applied to stabilize the excavated face, depending on the necessity of the geological conditions. After that, concrete was placed against the rock surface which was carefully trimmed by manual or limited explosive charges to its finally designed line and grade. The central rock cores were maintained for use as a support to formworks, when the arch concrete was poured.

Upon completion of the entire arch concrete, the middle and the lower portions were excavated by the bench cut method with a height ranging from 2 to 3 m. During the excavation, special attention was

always paid to avoid overbreak and to disturb as little as possible the surrounding rock formation. In order to achieve this goal, the pre-splitting method was usually adopted for excavation for the sidewalls, when blasting came near to the designed excavation line.

Prestressed tendons and long rock bolts were installed, as designed, to the excavated sidewall face to secure stability in parallel with the progress of the bench cut excavation.

Pumpcrete fed by agitator or transit mixer was generally used in the placing of concrete for the arch and sidewalls.

5.2 Recent Power Caverns

For recent power caverns in Taiwan, or the caverns of the Techi and Minghu Projects, the construction method similar to the aforesaid has been adopted, except the following points:

i) In order to shorten the construction time, good performance and high efficiency of excavation and concrete equipment were employed.

ii) A sliding steel formwork was specially adopted for arch concreting in lieu of the conventional wooden form. Thus, one cycle time for excavation and concreting of a 4.5 m wide panel of roof arch could be kept within 10 days.

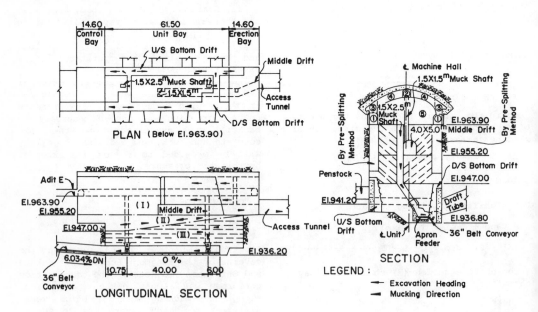

Fig. 10: Construction Sequence of Chingshan Power Cavern

342

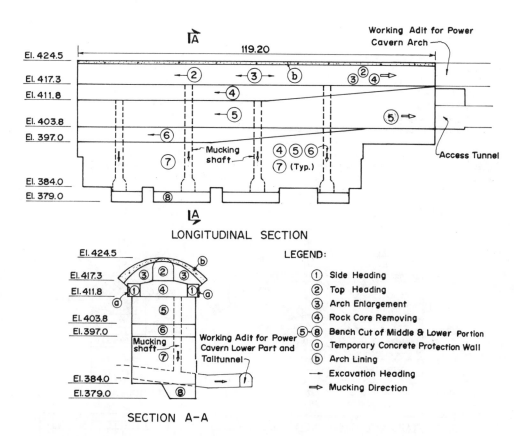

El. 424.5
El. 417.3
El. 411.8
El. 403.8
El. 397.0
El. 384.0
El. 379.0

Working Adit for Power
Cavern Arch

119.20

Mucking
shaft

Access Tunnel

② ③ ⓑ ③② ④

④
⑤ ⑤
⑥
④⑤⑥
⑦ ⑦ (Typ.)
⑧

LONGITUDINAL SECTION

El. 424.5
El. 417.3
El. 411.8
El. 403.8
El. 397.0
El. 384.0
El. 379.0

Mucking shaft

Working Adit for Power
Cavern Lower Part and
Tailtunnel

LEGEND:

① Side Heading
② Top Heading
③ Arch Enlargement
④ Rock Core Removing
⑤-⑧ Bench Cut of Middle & Lower Portion
ⓐ Temporary Concrete Protection Wall
ⓑ Arch Lining
→ Excavation Heading
⇒ Mucking Direction

SECTION A-A

Fig. 11: Construction Sequence of Minghu Power Cavern

iii) In coordination with the utilization of the excavation and concrete equipment, coping with the extremely large volume of excavation and concreting, construction and mucking adits was well planned and constructed in advance in order to facilitate the construction operations.

The construction sequence of the Minghu power cavern is shown in Fig. 11 for reference.

6 INSTRUMENTATION AND MEASUREMENT

6.1 Old Power Caverns

Among the old power caverns, instruments provided in the caverns for measurements were rather few. They were mostly stressmeters, strainmeters or thermometers provided to record the mechanical behavior of the concrete lining of the roof arch under loading conditions. For instance, in the Chingshan power cavern, 9 sets of stressmeter and 28 sets of strainmeter were embedded in the roof arch concrete.

The stresses measured with the stressmeters were found to be lower than the computed values. This has led to the conclusion that the rock loads actually acting on the roof arch were smaller than the designed values. Furthermore, based on the embedded thermometers, it was observed that the roof arch concrete was 22°C on the second day, rose up to 48°C on the seventh day, and then dropped gradually to the final stable temperature of 20°C on the 28th day after its placement.

At the upstream and downstream sidewalls, a total number of seven 4 m long and three 15 m long extensometers were installed to detect displacement of the sidewalls. The measured values were all within the reasonable range.

6.2 Recent Power Caverns

In order to understand the behavior of the concrete structures and rock formation in response to the excavation operation, more sophisticated measuring systems have been installed in the caverns which are recently under construction or design.

For the Techi power cavern, 18 sets of triple-point extensometer were installed in the sidewalls of the cavern. After the installation, reading for each extensometer was taken at regular intervals, ranging from 5 days during excavation to 10 days after sidewall concrete had been finished.

From the displacement recording as shown in Fig. 12 below, it was observed that no significant rock movement had occurred. In general, the amount of rock displacement is noted to have a close relation with the geologic conditions, the excavation procedures and the time for extensometer installation with respect to excavation. In the Techi cavern, the displacement has been found to be slightly less than the computed values (Refer to Fig. 13).

For the Minghu power cavern, which is now under construction, the following instrumentation are proposed for installation in places shown in Fig. 14 to provide a monitoring system.

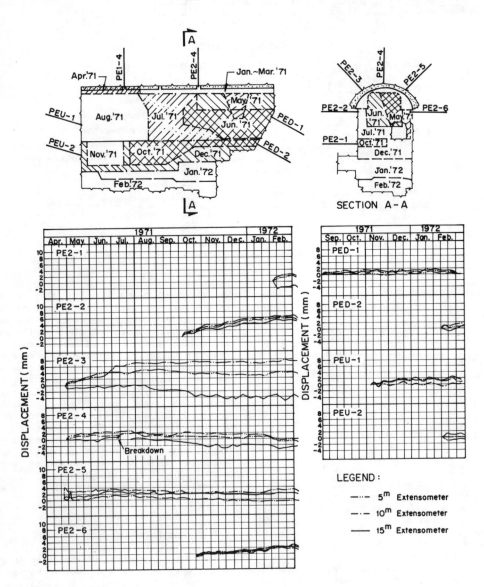

Fig. 12: Rock Displacement Recording of Techi Power Cavern

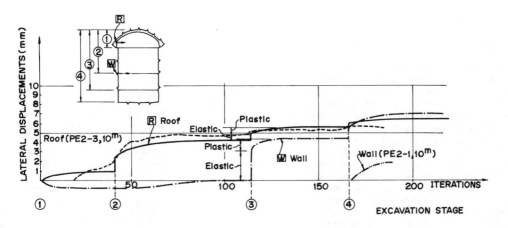

Fig. 13: Displacement Comparison for Techi Power Cavern

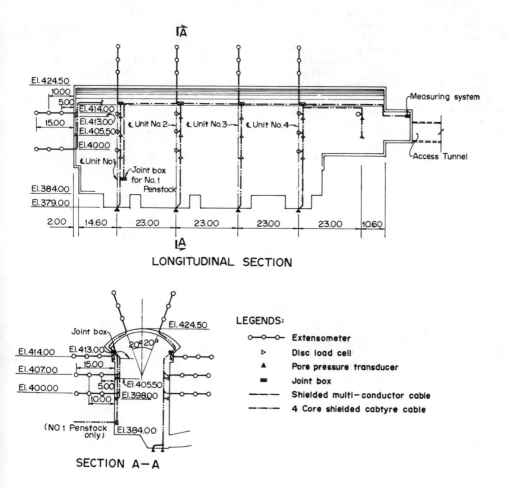

LONGITUDINAL SECTION

SECTION A—A

LEGENDS:

○—○—○— Extensometer
▷ Disc load cell
▲ Pore pressure transducer
▬ Joint box
——·—— Shielded multi-conductor cable
——··—— 4 Core shielded cabtyre cable

Fig. 14: Instrumentation of Minghu Power Cavern

7 CONCLUSIONS

The following conclusions are drawn up for reference:

i) The design and stability analyses of the old power caverns in Taiwan were mostly performed through an empirical approach rather than a theoretical approach. Because all of these caverns are located in competent and sound rock formations, a few problems have been encountered during the course of design and construction.

ii) Along with the development of the rock mechanics science and of the computer application, a more rigorous theoretical approach has been gradually adopted for design and construction of power caverns in Taiwan. The quality of design has greatly improved as a result of the adoption of the new approach and more rational designs were achieved.

iii) From the analyses carried out through the adoption of the recent approach method, it is noted that stresses of a roof arch will be seriously influenced by the excavation sequence of tunnels and openings in the vicinity of the cavern. In order to reduce the magnitude of stresses, the tunnels or openings in the vicinity of the cavern are better for excavation in advance of or simultaneously with the cavern excavation work.

iv) From the current design of the Minghu and Chipan power caverns, it is generally felt that rock mechanics tests carried out for each project can not cover satisfactorily the needs of design. Therefore, considerable design parameters are still assumed. This will sometimes affect the accuracy of the results of the analyses.

v) Since rock mass is a very complicated assembly of different materials and not isotropic, an accurate interpretation of the geology or the site geology represented with mathematic model is always found to be difficult.

vi) Up to now, all the power caverns in Taiwan are of the so-called mushroom shape. From the rock mechanical point of view, the egg-shape cavern section is also found to be very desirable. If the egg-shape cavern is adopted, it is noted that the interior arrangement inside a powerplant, especially cranes and other related equipment, and the construction method are very much different, when compared with those of mushroom-shape caverns. The possibility and economy of adopting the egg-shape cross section is subject to further studies and investigation.

THE DESIGN AND CONSTRUCTION OF THE IMAICHI UNDERGROUND POWER PLANT

Entwurf und Ausführung des unterirdischen Kraftwerkes Imaichi

Le calcul et la construction de la centrale souterraine d'Imaichi

T.MIZUKOSHI

The Tokyo Electric Power Co. Inc., Japan

Summary

The Tokyo Electric Power Co., Inc. is now in the process of excavating a large cavern--33.5 m wide, 51 m high, and 160 m long--to set a 1,050 MW pumped-storage power plant 400 m under the ground surface.
The cross section of the cavern is horseshoe-shaped, the first time that such a shape has been used in Japan. It is planned to redistribute the stress resulting from excavation along the walls. To this end, the supports and lining of the walls are designed to make effective use of the resistance of the surrounding rock.
The paper reports on the rock foundation tests, stability analyses using FEM, measurements plan, and the supporting and lining work carried out for the cavern stability.

Zusammenfassung

Tokyo Electric Power Company beschäftigt sich augenblickich mit dem Ausschachten einer riesigen Kaverne von 33.5 m Breite, 51 m Höhe und 160 m Länge, die in 400 m Tiefe ein 1,050 MW Pump-speicherkraftwerk aufnehmen soll.
Die Kaverne wird einen hufeisenförmigen Querschnitt haben und wird somit die erste dieser Form in Japan sein. Auf diese Weise beabsichtight man die durch die Ausschachtung au der Wandung Umlagerungs-Spannungen gleichmäßig zu verteilen. Die Ausbauwiederstand der neuen Wände werden so konstruiert, daß die Widerstandsfähigkeit des umgebenden Gesteins voll genutzt wird.
Die Abhandlung befaßt sich weiterhin mit den Untersuchungen des Gründungsgesteins, Festigkeitsnachweisen nach dem FFM-Verfahren, Meßprogramm, Ausbau und Auskleidung.

Résumé

Tokyo Electric Power Company est actuellement en train d'excaver une caverne importante (largeur 33.5 m x hauteur 51 m x longueur 160 m) qui abritera, à 400 m au-dessous de la surface du sol, une centrale hydroélectrique du type à pompage ayant une puissance de 1,050 MW.
Sa section transversale en forme de fer à cheval est employée premierement au Japon.
Les contraintes occasionnées par l'excavation est envisagé de redistribuer dans les parois de la carerne et, à cette fin, les supports et le revêtement de paroi sont étés conçu pour incorporer la résistance de la roche environnante.
Ce rapport présente les essais sur la roche, l'analyse de la stabilité par FEM, le plan de mesurement et les travaux des supports et du revetement de paroi.

1 INTRODUCTION

The Tokyo Electric Power Company has been constructing a large-scale pumped-storage power plant with capacity of 1,050 MW since Oct. 1979, which is located in a northern mountain area in Tochigi Prefecture. Civil Engineering works come to be

a peak stage in 1981.
The plant is of the underground type;
since its main transformer room and the
machine hall are set in the same cavern,
the dimensions of the power station
cavern -- 33.5 m in breadth, 51 m in
height, and 160 m in length -- rank it
among the largest in the world.(Figure 1)
The horseshoe-shaped cross section of the
cavern was adopted for cavern stability
and rationality of construction and had
never before been used in Japan.
At the present time (Dec. 1981), excavation of the station cavern is roughly 75
percent complete.

2 DESIGN OF THE POWER STATION CAVERN AND THE SUPPORTING AND LINING

2.1 Topography and geology of the station site

The underground power station is located
400 m below the surface of a ridge extending to the southeast at a slope of
40° from Gassan Mountain, a peak in the
eastern reaches of the Nikko Mountain
Range. Its horizontal distance from the
reservoir is approximately 600 m.
The geology of the station site is made
up of siliceous sandstone, breccia and
hornfels, to which sandstone and slate
belonging to the Chichibu paleozoic
strata were altered by the influence of
intrusion of magma accompanying acid
igneous activity during the end of the
Mesozoic period or the Paleozoic period.
The bedrock at the location of the plant
is composed primarily of siliceous sandstone, breccia and sandstone-slate in
alternating strata approximately 50 m
thick of which the strike and dip run
EW/50 N. (Figure 2)
Both components of the bedrock are hard

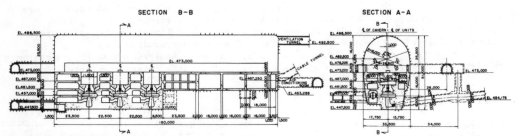

Figure 1. Cross section of power station

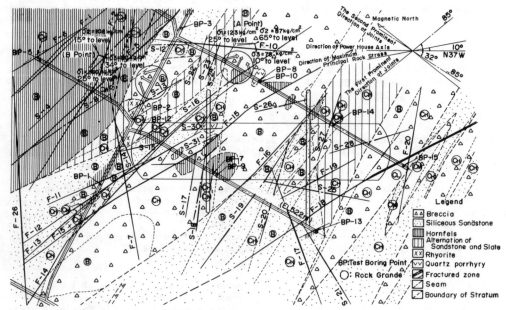

Figure 2. Geological map (EL 522 m)

and compact; their classification ranges for the most part between C_H and B class.

Hornfles is distributed from nearby the lower portion of the penstock on the mountain side of the plant to the upstream. This bedrock is hard and compact, too. But there is groundwater in some places, and its pressures is about 5 – 10 kg/cm^2.

There are several small fractured zones roughly 10 to 50 cm in width, surrounding the plant, but there hardly exists a continuous fractured zone that intersects the plant itself.

Joints are found at intervals from 10 to 40 cm; there are few in the breccia, while in the siliceous sandstone, sandstone-slate and hornfels they are relatively well developed. There is remarkable concentration, however: the strike and dip of the most predominant N 75 W/85 NE, and its percentage on the order of 6 %.

Since the joints and crucks in the bedrock at the plant site were filled with calcite etc. at the time of magma intrusion, the permeability of this bedrock is 70 % for less than 1 Lugeon and 99 % for less than 5 Lugeon, forming an impermeable zone with hardly any seepage water.

2.2 Properties of the bedrock

The tests performed on the bedrock before beginning construction work included deformation and shear tests, rock tests using boring cores, and initial in-situ stresses measurements. An outline of the properties of the bedrock are shown in Table 1.

a. Bedrock deformation tests
The results of bedrock deformation tests performed on both classes of rock (C_H – B), breccia and siliceous sandstone, at initial in-situ stress level using the fixed displacement jack method on a loading plate 30 cm in diameter are shown below. There was no noticeable difference in the modulus of elasticity by class of rock or by direction; on the whole, the bedrock is thought to be isotropic.

By classification:
Breccia
150 – 420 (average: 270) x 10^3 kg/cm^2
Siliceous sandstone
210 – 350 (average: 260) x 10^3 kg/cm^2
By direction:
Horizontal (NS)
210 – 390 (average: 260) x 10^3 kg/cm^2
Horizontal (EW)
210 – 420 (average: 290) x 10^3 kg/cm^2
Vertical
140 – 350 (average: 250) x 10^3 kg/cm^2

b. Rock shear tests
The results of shear tests performed on specimens of Class B bedrock, breccia and siliceous sandstone, are shown in Figure 3.

According to these results, there is hardly any observable difference between rock classes. When shearing strength is expressed in Coulomb's equation, the following result is obtained.

$\tau = 25 + \sigma \tan 58°$ (kg/cm^2)

Table 1. Properties of bedrock

	Items	Test Results (Mean Value)	
		Breccia	Siliceous Sandstone
Bedrock	Modulus of Deformation (kg/cm^2)	141000	168000
	Tangent Modulus of Elasticity (kg/cm^2)	267000	266000
	Creep Factor	α : 0.1 ~ 0.4 β : 1 ~ 30 (/DAY)	
	Shearing Strength	$\tau = 25 + \sigma$ TAN58°	
Rock	Density (g/cm^3)	2.6	2.6
	Uni-Axial Strength (kg/cm^2)	800	760
	Tensile Strength (kg/cm^2)	68	90
	Seismic Wave Velocity (km/s)	V_P : 4.7 V_S : 2.7	V_P : 5.2 V_S : 2.9
	Modulus of Elasticity (kg/cm^2)	356000	343000
Initial In-Situ Stresses	1st Principal Stress σ_1 (kg/cm^2)	123 (N47°W/25°)	160 (N97°W/25°)
	2nd Principal Stress σ_2 (kg/cm^2)	87 (N109°E/63°)	108 (N21°E/45°)
	3rd Principal Stress σ_3 (kg/cm^2)	78 (N142°W/10°)	80 (N155°E/34°)

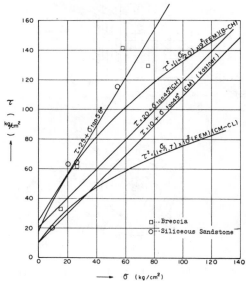

Figure 3. Shear strength of bedrock

349

c. Strain control triaxial compression tests

The results of strain control triaxial compression tests performed using a boring core (diameter: 40 mm) in order to discover the residual strength of the rock are shown in Table 2. Expressed in Coulomb's equation, residual strength is as follows (strain velocity = 0.1 %/minute):

Table 2. Results of tri-axial compression tests controlled by strain

		Breccia		Siliceous Sandstone	
		C (kg/cm^2)	Ø (°)	C (kg/cm^2)	Ø (°)
Peak Strength	Standard Test	103.3	58.2	60.7	62.1
	Multi-Stage Test	57.8	60.3	–	–
	Average	78.0	59.2	60.7	62.1
Residual Strength	Standard Test	2.4	50.3	13.7	51.4
	Multi-Stage Test	12.7	47.9	2.4	51.7
	Average	7.7	49.1	7.8	51.6
Specific Gravity		2.64		2.64	
Absorption (%)		0.83		0.45	
Effective Porosity (%)		2.16		1.18	
Velocity of P-Wave (km/s)		4.64		5.19	
Velocity of S-Wave (km/s)		2.73		3.45	
Dynamic Modulus of Elasticity (kg/cm^2)		4.98×10^5		6.05×10^5	
Dynamic Poisson's Ratio		0.234		0.247	
Splitting Tensile Strength (kg/cm^2)		52		77	

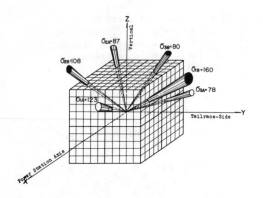

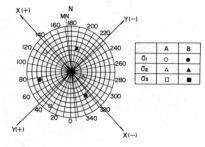

Figure 4. Distribution of initial in-situ stresses

$\tau = 8 + \sigma \tan 50^{\circ}$ (average)

$\tau = 3 + \sigma \tan 50^{\circ}$ (minimum)

d. Initial in-situ stresses

Five elements of a strain gage were buried in 56 mm diameter bore holes at two measuring points, A and B, within the exploratory tunnel shown in Figure 2. One element was directed parallel to the hole axis and four radially. The bore holes were overcored to a diameter of 218 mm and the initial in-situ stresses were measured (Figure 4).

According to the measurement results, at both measuring points, A and B, the direction of the primary principal stress was relatively close to the horizontal, and values ranged between 120 – 160 kg/cm^2. On the other hand, secondary principal stress showed values between 87 – 108 kg/cm^2, nearly equal to natural ground surface. If we regard this secondary principal stress as a vertical element corresponding to natural ground cover, a ratio of horizontal to vertical stress (K value) should be respectively 1.4 (measuring point A) and 1.5 (measuring point B), the horizontal element predominating.

At measuring point A, primary principal stress corresponded very closely to the direction of the ridge extending from Mount Gassan, which showed clearly that it was governed by the topographical condition.

At measuring point B, there is a fractured zone running East-West. Under the effect of local geologic circumstances, the primary principal stress that ran North-West may have been canceled out. In addition to the above reason, since the initial in-situ stresses working in the underground cavern of the power plant itself could be conceivable due to the pressure effect of magma intrusion, the results from measuring point A are thought to be typical of the initial in-situ stresses.

2.3 Power plant location

The location and positioning of the power plant were selected according to the procedure indicated below.

i) Since the dimensions of the cavern were to be extremely great, the first deciding factor for the site was to find a geologically stable, hard, and compact bedrock.

For this reason, attention was paid to the alternating layers of siliceous sandstone and breccia in choosing the site. It was decided that the hornfels regions

350

in the northern part, with their high water pressure, were to be avoided, as well as part of the western side, bounded by fractured zone F18, where there were relatively numerous open joints accompanied by seepage water.

ii) As related above, the primary principal stress of initial in-situ stresses ran N 47 W/25 S, and the horizontal direction predominated. It was thus desirable to align the main axis of the power plant with this direction. This also made smooth linkage with the waterway system possible, as well as selection of the narrowest feasible cavern section.

iii) Strike and dip for the most prominent of the systems of joints in existence at the site were N 75 W/85 NE, with a predominance of 6.1 %, followed by N 5 W/85 NE, with a predominance of 4.4 %. Positioning the main axis of the plant between these two would mean crossing obliquely at an angle of between 35° and 40°, but as the dip is nearly vertical, it was thought that the effect on the cavern would be relatively slight. In this case, the K value at measuring point A is found by measurement to be 0.84 and at point B, K = 1.24.

2.4 Stability analysis of the cavern

A behavior analysis of the surrounding bedrock at the time of excavation was performed in two dimensions for transverse sections of the power plant using a method of visco-plastic analysis on progressive relaxation of underground excavation works developed at the Central Research Institute of Electric Power Industry (Masao Hayashi and Toshio Hibino's method).

a. Comparison of horseshoe-shaped and mushroom-shaped sections analysis was performed on the following two cases.
Case A: K = 0.84
Bedrock classification C_H – B
Modulus of elasticity = 18 x 10^4 kg/cm^2
Strength characteristics
$2 = (1 + \sigma /2.0) \times 19^2$
Creep factor $\alpha = 0.4$
$\beta = 2/\text{day}$
Case B: K = 1.24
Other values same as Case A.
Figure 5 shows the horseshoe-shaped and mushroom-shaped sections and the excavation stage used in the calculations; Table 3 and Figure 6 show the calculation results.

b. Analysis of the stability of the horseshoe-shaped
Case C: K = 1.24
Bedrock classification C_M-C_L
Modulus of elasticity = 5 x 10^4 kg/cm^2
Strength characteristics
$\tau^2 = (1 + \sigma /1.7) \times 10^2$
This case hypothesizes that bedrock of classes C_M-C_L (found only locally in the surroundings of cavern) is found through- out the cavern.
Case D: Anisotropic bedrock
K = 1.24
In site tests, no noticeable anisotropy was observed in the properties of the bedrock, but since the boundary of rock class and joints have, relatively speaking, a predominant orientation N 75 W/85 NE, this was converted to the section of the plant; as shown below, this case hypothesizes anisotropic bedrock with different strength and deformation characteristics.

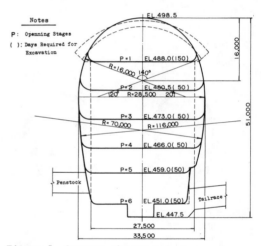

Figure 5. Opening shapes and stages at analyses

Table 3. Comparison of analysis between shapes of horseshoe and mushroom

Calculation Cases		A		B	
		Horseshoe Shape	Mushroom Shape	Horseshoe Shape	Mushroom Shape
Kvalue(σy/σz)		0.84		1.24	
Stress (kg/cm^2)	EL 488 Penstock Side	240	320	270	340
	Tailrace Side	250	320	230	390
	EL 452 Penstock Side	280	320	330	360
	Tailrace Side	280	320	460	450
Displacement (mm)	Vault	14	16	14	17
	Side Wall (Penstock-Side)	20	26	38	44
	Side Wall (Tailrace-Side)	20	26	36	44
Relaxed Zone (m)	Vault	1	1	3	3
	Side Wall (Penstock-Side)	1	9	1	6
	Side Wall (Tailrace-Side)	3	8	5	8

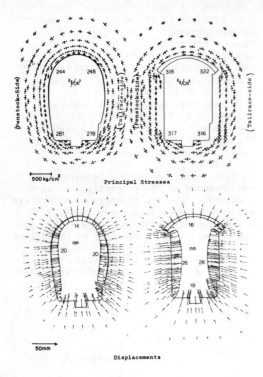

500 kg/cm² Principal Stresses

50mm Displacements

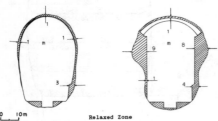

0 10m   Relaxed Zone

Figure 6. Result of FEM analyses (P=6)

The direction parallel to the joints:
$$\tau_1{}^2 = (1 + \sigma/1.7) \times 10^2$$
$$D_1 = 18 \times 10^4 \text{ kg/cm}^2$$
The direction cross to the points:
$$\tau_2{}^2 = (1 + \sigma/3.0) \times 26^2$$
$$D_2 = 5 \times 10^4 \text{ kg/cm}^2$$

c. Observations on the calculation results and decision regarding the section. The calculation results for each case are as shown in Table 4 and can be summarized in the following.

i) Comparison of the horseshoe-shaped and mushroom-shaped sections showed that the horseshoe shape was superior to the mush-

Table 4. Results of behavior analysis (Horseshoe shape)

	Cases	Isotropic Rock						Anisotropic Rock –	
		C_H-B Class				C_M Class			
		A (K=0.84)		B (K=1.24)		C (K=1.24)		D (K=1.24)	
Opening Stages		Vault	Side Wall	Vault	Side Wall	Vault	Side Wall	Vault	Side Wall
Displacement (mm)	1	15	4	16	4	61	38	18	28
	2	15	9	16	13	60	79	16	50
	3	15	11	16	22	60	105	16	75
	4	15	15	15	27	60	130	13	92
	5	14	18	15	32	60	130	11	100
	6	14	20	14	38	58	148	11	110
Relaxed Zone (m)	1	0	0	1	0	3	1	3	1
	2	1	1	1	1	6	3	3	3
	3	1	1	1	1	10	6	3	6
	4	1	1	3	1	10	8	3	6
	5	1	1	3	1	10	10	6	10
	6	1	3	3	5	10	10	6	10
Maximum Principal Stress (kg/cm²)	0	80		140		140		140	
	1	390		470		470		570	
	2	460		590		600		670	
	3	420		560		570		690	
	4	440		580		550		750	
	5	420		450		500		720	
	6	280		460		400		900	

room-shape as regards the degree of stress concentration, the extent of displacement, and the depth of the relaxed zone. From a comprehensive viewpoint, the behavior of the horseshoe-shaped was the most stable.

ii) In the case of a horseshoe-shaped section, with bedrock of classes C_H-B accounting for most of the rock present, and K = 0.84, there is an almost uniformly spread compressive stress along the walls of the cavern and no tensile stress is observed. The relaxed zone ranges from 1 to 3 m or so, extremely narrow, and deformation is little.

iii) In the case where K = 1.24 and the properties of the bedrock are hypothesized C_M-C_L, there is no noticeable stress concentration with the horseshoe-shape and there is a fully sufficient margin of safety relative to the strength of the bedrock. The depth of the relaxed zone, on the order of 10 m, can be sufficiently treated through the use of the type of supporting usually used in underground power plants.

iv) Bedrock behavior when anisotropy is considered shows intermediate behavior in cases B and C.

v) Judging from the results of the cases A and B, a mushroom-shaped cavern in cases C and D would require quite

352

extensive supporting and lining to ensure the cavern stability.

vi) In the light of the fact that, judging from past experience, it is predicted that there will be relatively little activity of the joints and displacement of the walls, and the fact that the surrounding bedrock forms a nearly impermeable layer, so that it is unlikely that seepage water will exert a deleterious effect, the adoption of a horseshoe-shaped cross section is judged to be fully appropriate from above-mentioned analyses.

From the standpoint of costs as well, although quantitatively the horseshoe-shaped cross section will require 200,000 m^3 of excavation – against 190,000 m^3 for the conventional mushroom-shaped cross section – the horseshoe-shape is economically advantageous when the total cost of civil engineering and electrical engineering, together with the reduction in vault lining and increase in available space, are considered.

As the result of a comprehensive judgment of the cavern stability, economic factors, etc., the final decision was made to adopt the horseshoe-shaped cavern, 33.5 m wide, 51 m high, and 160 m long, whose excavation section is shown in Figure 1.

2.5 Design of supporting and lining

In designing the supporting and lining of the underground cavern, it was decided to adopt the NATM concept as a basis, whereby the surrounding solid compact bedrock is used as effectively as possible. For supporting, rock anchor, rock bolting,

and shotcreting were used.

A basic pattern was established for supporting and lining design in which, in addition to visco-plastic analysis by FEM, and elasto-plastic analysis using the methods of Oka, Kastner, et al., calculations were made for collapsing of rock, due to loosening of the vault of the bedrock, and for the sliding of side walls.

Consideration was also given to the fact that above the floor level of the generator room (EL. 473 m), supporting would also serve as permanent lining without requiring any change.

There were also areas where, with these methods of calculation, the effects of joints and of heterogeneity of the bedrock could not be accurately reflected. This was compensated for through the use of the so-called observational method, related below, linking the detailed measurements to increasing or decreasing supporting appropriately.

a. Supporting and lining design studies using FEM visco-plastic analysis and elasto-plastic analysis

Table 5 show the results of calculations made to determine the relaxed zones and wall displacement affected by the input of supporting using Hayashi and Hibino's method of visco-plastic analysis and Oka and Kastner's method of elasto-plastic analysis. Although most of the bedrock surrounding the cavern is of class C_H – B, in our studies, classes B – C_L too were covered. Figure 3 shows the strength characteristics of the bedrock used in the calculations.

With regard to the supporting pattern, since there were no large fractured zones or predominant groups of joints of the

Table 5. Elasto-plastic boundary vs. induced force

Cases		FEM Analyses		Elasto-Plastic Analyses (Methods by Oka & Kastner)					
		Pi = 0 kg/cm^2		Pi = 0 kg/cm^2		Pi = 1.2kg/cm^2		Pi = 2.4 kg/cm^2	
		Elasto-Plastic Boundary (m)	Displacement (mm)	Elasto-Plastic Boundary (m)	Displacement (mm)	Elasto-Plastic Boundary (m)	Displacement (mm)	Elasto-Plastic Boundary (m)	Displacement (mm)
I (B)	Vault	3	14	1	14	1	13	-	-
	Side-Wall	1-5	38	(5)	(22)	(3)	(18)	(2)	(16)
II (C_H)		-		3	16	3	15	-	-
				(9)	(27)	(8)	(24)	(6)	(22)
III (C_M)	Vault	10	58	14	62	11	53	9	46
	Side-Wall	6-17	148						
IV	Vault	8	11						
	Side-Wall	10-17	110						

Notes IV : Anisotropic Rock (Joints Direction C_L-C_M, Cross-Direction C_H-B)
( ) : Residual Strength C = 3 kg/cm^2, ∅ = 45°

kind that had to be taken into account beforehand in the process of designing, the study involved only systematic patterns.

b. Specifications for supporting and lining
Based on the above-described calculations, actual field tests were made and the basic specifications necessary to ensure the cavern stability were determined as described below. The safety of the basic supporting pattern was also checked with respect to falling-in and slippage in relaxed zones.

a) Rock anchor
Rock anchor is the main supporting method adopted, being the most reliable method of strengthening the bedrock to ensure the cavern stability. The specifications for rock anchor are defined below.

i) The unit rock anchor design induced force is set at 96 tons, or 70 % of the yield point load of a wire strand, taking the displacement of the wall by excavation into account.

ii) As a rule, rock anchor is bonded at non-relaxed zones. Since the strand tension transmission length in the application areas, based on field tests, is in the neighborhood of 0.97 - 2.7 m, the anchor bond length is set at 4 m for safety.

iii) From Table 5 it was determined that the depth of the relaxed zone was a maximum of 8 m (Pi = 1.2 kg/cm^2) for class C_H and above, estimated to account for the greater part of bedrock at the site, and 11 m (Pi = 1.2 kg/cm^2) for class C_M; in order to be certain that even the bedrock of class CM, found locally, would be properly accounted for, the rock anchor's length was set at 15 m (including bonded length 4 m).

iv) The basic pattern for rock anchor positioning is set to range from 8 m^2 (in vault) to 10 m^2 (in side wall sections) per strand for C_H bedrock (Pi = 1.2 - 1.0 kg/cm^2) and from 4 m^2 (in vault) to 5 m^2 (in side wall sections)

per strand for C_M - C_L bedrock (Pi = 2.4 - 2.0 kg/cm^2), so as to keep the calcu- lated relaxed zones within 8 to 9 m of the wall.

v) During excavation of the cavern, rock anchor is kept within steel sheaths, except 4 m of the anchor portions, to make retensioning possible. At the wall displacement covergence stage, mortar is injected within the sheath, and ultimately the fully bonded type is taken. (Figure 7, Table 6)

b) Rock bolting and shotcreting

i) By rock bolting and shotcreting immediately onto the newly excavated walls, not only is the commencement of local degradation (such as peeling off the surface) prevented from developing, but these operations provide primary supporting until rock anchor is set. Studies into rock bolting covered supporting for relaxed zone between rock anchors, primary supporting during cutting and widening of the vault, and

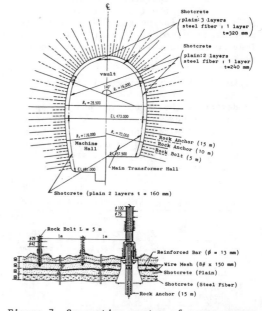

Figure 7. Supporting system of power cavern

Table 6. Mortar mixes for rock anchors

FM of Sand	Flow Value (s)	W/(C+CSA*) (%)	CSA/(C+CSA) (%)	Quantity per Cubic Meter					
				Water W(kg)	Cement C(kg)	CSA (kg)	Sand (kg)	NL-4000** (L)	Aluminium Powder (g)
1.3±0.1	18±2	42	11	409	864	107	730	1.94	97

* : CSA#20 (Bland Name of Expansive Cement)
** : NL-4000 (Bland Name of Non-Chloridl Water Reducing Agent)

Table 7. Properties of shotcrete

	Rebound (%)	Steel Fiber Attachment (%)	Compressive Strength (kg/cm^2) 3hrs	Compressive Strength (kg/cm^2) 24hrs	Compressive Strength (kg/cm^2) 28 days	Bending Strength (kg/cm^2)	Shearing Strength (kg/cm^2)	Compressive Toughness (kg/cm^2)	Bending Toughness (kg/cm^2)
Plain	31	-	16	130	300	50	41	1	1
Steel Fiber	29	89	-	-	350	53	50	1.8	6.4

Table 8. Shotcrete mixes

	Cement (kg/cm^2)	Max. Size of Coarse Aggregate (mm)	Water-Cement Ratio (%)	Sand Percentage (%)	Quick Setting Agent-Cement Ratio (%)	Size of Steel Fiber (mm)	Steel Fiber Percentage (°/vol)
Plain	350	15	50	70	5	-	-
Steel Fiber	350	15	50	70	5	0.5x0.5x30	1

effectiveness of rock bolting within plastic zones. Studies into shotcreting covered effectiveness of lining against shearing, bending and compressive fracture.

ii) Rock bolts are 5 m long, one bolt being placed per 5 tons of design induced force, and one bolt is located every two square meters.

iii) Shotcreting, in consideration of its role in lining and in evening out irregularities of the walls of the excavation, is made 32 cm thick in vault (through the application of four 8 cm layers) and 24 cm thick (three 8 cm layers) on walls. Steel fiber reinforced concrete (SFRC) is used for the surface layer in order to increase resistance to local fracture and prevent rock falls. In between each layer of plain shotcrete, was decided to install wire netting (#8, 150 mm wire mesh).
As for the mixing of the shotcrete, quality and workability tests were run (Table 7) and the basic mix was determined, as shown in Table 8, so that design standard strength σ ck = 200 kg/cm^2 and target mixture strength = 250 kg/cm^2.

c) Study on safety for falling-in and sliding of the relaxed zones
A study was made into the safety of the resistance of the above-described supporting and lining under the assumption of an extreme case, where the bedrock surrounding the cavern had loosened, losing its resistance, so that the vault had fallen in and the walls had slid by its weight.
With regard to the extent of the relaxed zone, the results obtained from calculations by FEM were used and the design

horizontal seismic coefficient of 0.065 was adopted.

d) Study into PC wire strand breaking strain
Since relaxation occurs due to the tension to which the PC wire strands are subject, it is necessary to observe not only stress, but strain as well.
Tests results showed that breaking strain for PC wire strands is 5.5 %.

Breaking strain, free length 11 m x 0.055 = 60 cm
Stretch caused by induced force (96 tons) = 7 cm
Maximum assumed wall displacement = 5 cm
Margin of safety for breaking strain (60 cm – 7 cm – 5 cm) = 48 cm

Even should the assumed value for wall displacement during excavation be greatly exceeded, there is an ample margin against PC wire strand breaking.

2.6 Planning of measurements

a. Measurement items
The design calculations for behavior analysis of the bedrock and supporting and lining were based on the properties of the test sites and the assumptions introduced into the calculations. In the light of the nonhomogeneity of the bedrock, it is necessary to have control through detailed measurements to ensure the permanent stability of structures and stability during construction work.
In establishing the measurement scheme, the following points were considered.

i) The principal measurements taken during excavation are convergence, bedrock displacement and stress change in

Table 9. Measurements

Measurements	Instruments	Location
Displacements	Multi-Stage Extensometer L=20-30m (4 or 5 steps) L=5m (3 steps)	7 Sections (B-H) 49 Lines 7 Sections (B-H) 31 Lines
Convergence	Tape Extensometer Theodolite	8 Sections (A-H) 6 Lines/Section 8 Sections (A-H) 9 Lines/Section
Force Induced by Rock Anchor	Center-Hole Type Load Cell (30 Ton and 120 Ton)	200 Pieces, 1 Piece/8-10 Anchors
Leakage	Pore Pressure Meter	5 Bore Holes, 390m
Joints	Permeability Tester Bore Hole TV	Mainly C Section 7 Holes, L=187m
Seismic Wave	Discharge Type	C Section, 4 Lines, 93m
Shotcrete Stress	Reinforced Bar Stress Meter, Thermometer	C and F Sections, 22 Points
Rock Stress	Multi-Axial Strain Meter	C Section, 6 Points

rock anchor, since these are the most direct and accurate measurements in terms of stability control.

ii) Since the vault lining by reinforced concrete is not placed, measurements of the vault sections are stressed even more than usual.

iii) As a supplement to the above, pore pressure and quantitative changes in seepage water which have a great influence on the cavern stability are measured. The number and items of measurement based on these factors are shown in Table 9.

b. Arrangement of measuring instruments
The eight measurement sections were set up, numbered A through H, at nearly equal distances along the central axis of the cavern, and between these, another seven

auxiary measuring sections. In measuring sections C and F, the behavior of bedrock during excavation from the initial period can be picked up by installing extensometers beforehand, utilizing exploratory tunnel (EL. 522 m).
An example of the arrangement of extensometers is shown in Figure 8.
It was also sought to make the measurements automatic by using the strain gages. This ultimately made it possible to use up to 800 gages for daily control of work progress.

3 CONSTRUCTION OF THE POWER PLANT CAVERN

3.1 Construction Program

The following basic program is used for the construction of the power plant cavern.

1) Excavation begins with the vault and proceeds downwards.

2) Horizontal drilling holes are made in alignment with the central axis of the power plant when excavation reached the vicinity of the finishing surface; and smooth blasting method is used to reduce damage.

3) The finishing surface is quickly supported and lines to confine the displacement of rock surface.

4) Various measurements are made to get an accurate grasp of the surrounding rock behavior.

5) Large-scale machinery and robots are used to minimize the time required for mucking, shotcreting, and inserting wire strands of rock anchor.

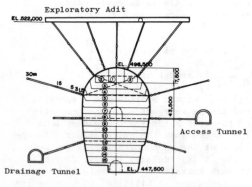

Notes

━○━ Multi-Stage Extensometers
---- Measuring Line of Convergence
○ Openning Stages

Figure 8. Arrangement of multi-stage extensometers and measuring line of convergence

356

3.2 Procedure and Methods Used in the Cavern Opening

First the vault is completed over its entire length of 160 m, height of 7.5 m, and maximum width of 22 m. Bench cutting method is then used to progressively deepen and widen the main part of the cavern.

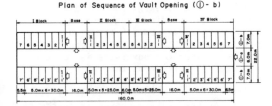

Plan of Sequence of Vault Opening (①- b)

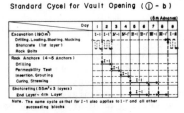

Standard Cycel for Vault Opening (①- b)

Figure 9. Sequence of vault opening

a. Excavation of the vault (EL.498.50-491.00)
In excavating the vault, a central heading 7.5 m in height, 8 m in width is first dug over the entire length. Then at two points in this heading (at 1/4 and 3/4 of its length) an enlargement base is established from which widening excavations are made successively in four directions, each covering an area of 120 m² (Figure 9). Except the enlargement base itself, excavation is made in the direction of the center axis of the power plant, and 2.5 to 3.0 m progress is made with each blasting. Smooth blasting method is then used at the finishing surface.

b. Excavation of the main part of the cavern (below EL.491.00)
Two methods are used to excavate the main part of the cavern: bench cutting for the central part and finishing excavation for the side walls. In the finishing excavation of the side walls, drilling is done in the direction of the central axis of the power plant to obtain a smooth finishing surface.
The mucking out is done as shown in Fig. 10, by means of the slide mucking method and the glory hole method. A layer of shotcrete was applied and rock bolting is

Cross Section   Standard Cycle for Bench Excavation (② and below)

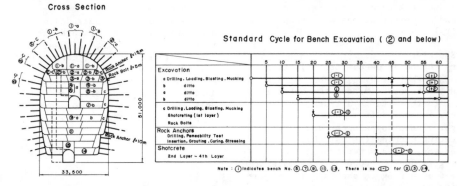

Longitudinal Section

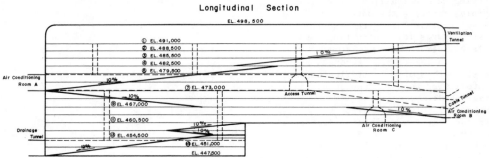

Figure 10. Sequence of bench excavation

357

carried out as soon as a rock wall is excavated. In consideration of the space between machines, drilling and inserting of rock anchor is carried out 20 m apart from the face. Tensioning wires is completed within 40 m of the face.

3.3 Supporting and Lining

   a. Rock bolting

Immediately after excavation, the walls are given a layer of shotcrete (t=8 cm) and a hydraulic wheel jumbo drills a hole 42 mm in diameter and 5 m deep. Full-surface adhesion rock bolt is then inserted with an epoxy resin filler. After hardening, a tensile force of 5 tons is induced using an impact wrench.

   b. Rock anchoring

Upward rock anchoring in a vault has never been done in Japan. Manual rod extending in the drilled holes was neither safe nor efficient, by the results of execution test. So an upward drilling machine with a rod changer was developed and put into operation. Manual cable inserting was also difficult, unsafe, and extremely in inefficient, so a pinch-roller cable inserter was also developed.

The wires are tensioned after the mortar material reaches a compressive strength of 250 kg/cm^2 three days after grouting. Some 1,200 rock anchors have already been set, and met expectations with respect to quality.

   c. Shotcreting

The dry method is used. Briefly, this means that the batching is done with a continuous concrete mixer, the batch is brought to the site in a truck, and the concrete is loaded from the truck into hoppers. These hoppers carry a shotcreting machine (ALIVA 260), accelerator, and a water tank. The spraying is done by robot. Materials are supplied according to the capacity of the spraying machine: a flow meter, for example, controls the water content of the shotcrete. There are also three 80 m^3 stock yards for controlling sand surface water.

In order to ensure high strength and quality with a minimum of fluctuation, the following work control standards are established:
- Sand surface water: 5+1%
- Pressure driven horizontal distance: 20-60 m
- Discharge pressure: 3.0-3.5 kg/cm^2
- Nozzle control: Maintained at a perpendicular 1.0 to 1.5 m

from the spray surface

The results of strength tests on panel specimens show that the mean compressive strength for plain concrete is σ_{28} = 319 kg/cm^2 with a coefficient of variation of 15 percent (test performed 44 times on 3 specimens each time). In the case of steel fiber reinforced concrete (SFRC), the mean compressive strength is σ_{28}=340 kg/cm^2 with a coefficient of variation of 15 percent; the bending strength is 59 kg/cm^2 with a coefficient of variation of 12 percent, and the mean bending toughness is 6 kg/cm^2 (test performed 6 times on 3 specimens each time). The strength of the cores from the work site is, on the average, 90 percent of that of panel cores; no porous specimens are found, which shows the high impermeability of the concrete. Water content is in the 44 to 47 percent range.

4 INSTEAD OF CONCLUSION

Excavation on the power plant cavern began at the end of July 1980. The vault was completed at the beginning of February 1981 and immediately thereafter began the cutting down of the main part of the cavern. At present (end of December 1981), approximately 150,000 m^3 of the planned total of 200,000 m^3 have been excavated.

The behavior of the surrounding bedrock accompanying the cavern excavation result, on the whole, in lower figures for displacement, etc., than calculated. Wall displacement of around 20 mm has occured, however, in some places. Additional rock anchoring and rock bolting have been used to counter displacement in these cross sections.

STUDIES OF STRENGTH AND STABILITY OF ROCK MASS AROUND LARGE UNDERGROUND MACHINE HALLS OF HYDRO POWER AND PUMPED STORAGE PLANTS

Untersuchung der Festigkeit und Standsicherheit des Felsverbandes in der Umgebung von grossen unterirdischen Maschinenkavernen von Wasserkraftwerken und Pumpspeicherwerken

Étude de la résistance et de la stabilité du massif rocheux autour des grandes cavernes souterraines des centrales hydroélectriques et des usines de pompage

V.M.MOSTKOV & R.A.REZNIKOV
Scientific Research Centre of the 'Hydroprojekt' Institute, Moscow, USSR

SUMMARY:
The underground position of the hydroelectric and pumped storage power plants has become considerably widespread, mainly in the rock. The paper presents a brief description of a number of existing, under construction and planned underground power plants in the USSR. The sizes and significance of such structures demand a complex analysis which involves a-nalytical technique, modelling, in-situ investigations, and which takes into consideration the experience gained in construction and operation. Principal requirements are for-mulated for the components and the precision of the geological survey which should pro-vide information on the strength and deformability of the rocks, the systems of joints (special attention should be paid to the tectonic joints adjacent to the cavern), and of the initial state of stress of the rock mass. The final stage of the studies is both the in-situ measurements of the cavern contour displacements and of the anchor forces, and the analysis. The statements mentioned in the paper are illustrated with specific examples of the powerhouse caverns investigation.

ZUSAMMENFASSUNG:
Die unterirdische Anordnung der Maschinenkavernen für Wasserkraftwerke und Pumpspeicher-werke hat sich hauptsächlich in Felsgesteinen immer stärker durchgesetzt. Im vorliegenden Bericht werden einige in der UdSSR im Betrieb stehende, im Bau befindliche und projektier-te unterirdische Maschinenkavernen kurz beschrieben. Wegen der grossen Dimensionen und der wirtschaftlichen Bedeutung solcher Bauwerke ist eine komplexe Betrachtungsweise unter An-wendung von Berechnungsverfahren, Modellierung, in-situ-Versuchen und unter Berücksichti-gung der langjährigen Erfahrungen im Bau und Betrieb erforderlich. Es werden grundsätzliche Forderungen an die Zusammensetzung und Genauigkeit der ingenieurgeologischen Erkundungen zusammengefasst, die über die Festigkeits- und Deformations-eigenschaften der Gesteine, Kluftsysteme (unter besonderer Beachtung der tektonischen Klüfte in der Nähe der Maschi-nenkaverne), den natürlichen Spannungszustand des Felsverbandes Aufschluss geben müssen. Der Sachverhalt des Berichtes wird an einigen konkreten Beispielen der Untersuchung der Maschinenkavernen für die Wasserkraftwerke klargelegt.

RESUME:
Une disposition souterraine des centrales hydroélectriques et des centrales à accumula-tion par pompage s'est répandue largement, surtout quand il s'agit des terrains rocheux. Dans le rapport les auteurs donnent une brève description de quelques usines souterraines, déjà mises en service, à construire et à projeter en URSS. De grandes dimensions et l'im-portance de tels ouvrages demandent une analyse complexe, qui comporte des méthodes thé-oriques, modélisation et investigations in situ et qui tient compte de l'expérience, ac-quise pendant la construction et l'exploitation. Les auteurs formulent des exigences es-sentielles, concernant la composition et la précision de la reconnaissance du terrain qui doit aussurer l'information sur la résistance et la déformabilité des terrains, sur le système de joints (une attention essentielle doit être prêtée aux fussures tectoniques à proximité des cavernes), sur l'état de contrainte initial du massif rocheux. L'exposé est illustré par d'exemples concrets relatifs aux études des cavernes.

A number of various large underground workings intended for accomodation of machine halls, transformer halls as well as of gate chambers of hydroelectric power plants in a variety of geological conditions has been constructed or is at present under construction in the USSR.

Recently the underground machine hall of the Inguri hydroelectric power plant, 127 m long, 22 m wide and 51 m high, has been put into service (Maysuradze & Potskhoveria 1977, 1978). The machine hall is situated in jointed water-bearing limestone and covered with a reinforced concrete vault, 1 m thick, on which crane beams are suspended.

In the diversion and spillway tunnels of the Nurek hydroelectric power plant large underground gate chambers (for permanent, emergency and repair gates) are provided (Iliushin 1977; Gurtovnik, Shutenkov, Mel'nikov 1980). The chambers are 25 m high, 14 m wide and 45 m long and are spaced at 52 m intervals between centre-lines. The chambers are situated in interbedding sandstones and aleurolites of medium hardness and the rock mass around the chambers is rock-bolted.

The underground machine hall of the Ust-Khantaisk hydroelectric power plant was built under severe climatic conditions of the North, in dolerite of large-block structure (Kelmi & Vittenberg 1975). The clear span of the machine room is 24 m, the maximum height - 48 m, the length - 148 m. The working walls are rock-anchored, the vault is of reinforced concrete.

The underground machine hall of the Zhinvali hydroelectric power plant (Gvelessiani & Eliava 1975) is now under construction. The rocks are conglomerates, the machine room is 37 m high, the clear span is 14 m, the length - 52 m. The vault is of reinforced concrete, 0.6 m thick, the walls are rock-anchored, with anchors 9 m long, and covered with shotcrete over a steel mesh.

The construction of a large underground machine hall of the Kolyma hydroelectric power plant in a permafrost area (Glusskin et al. 1974) is nearing completion. The rock anchors are 9 and 12 m long.

Construction is started of the largest underground Rogun hydroelectric power plant (Ossadchii et al. 1975, 1980) in sedimentary rocks. The mountain mass is under the action of tectonic stresses; the seismic shocks intensity in the area is 9, MSK scale. The maximum width of the machine hall is 28 m, the height - 68 m, the length - 200 m. At the distance of 40 m from the machine hall the transformer room will be located, 18 m wide, 40 m high and about 200 m long. The vaults of both workings will be lined with reinforced concrete, the walls will be rock-bolted with deep anchors of high bearing capacity (the anchors length is 16 to 22 m).

As the above incomplete enumeration shows, the dimensions and conditions of siting of underground chamber workings are essentially different and the results obtained in investigation of one working cannot be applied directly to other workings.

The importance of such structures necessitates thorough investigations of their behaviour in each individual case, with detailed consideration of numerous natural and engineering factors. Below is described the complex method used in the USSR of researching the state-of-stress-and-strain in a rock mass around large underground hydrotechnical installations and estimating the underground workings strength and stability. The fundamentals of the method, including 10 following stages, has been published earlier (Mostkov & Reznikov 1979).

The first stage - the determination of the field of stresses by the finite elements method or using other numerical methods of the mechanics of deformable solid. The accuracy, sufficient for practical purposes, is in a number of cases achievable with the help of computational model of a piecewise homogeneous isotropic linearly-elastic medium under conditions of two-dimensional strain. Other computational models were used too for estimation of errors of such a simplified approach and for consideration of some individual features of underground structures (relating to their design or specific engineering-geologic conditions).

Of all the non-linear computational models the elastic-plastic medium (provided the Coulomb-Mohr criterion is used to establish a line of demarcation between the elastic and plastic zones) the no-tension material (Zienkiewicz 1971) are applicable to the solution of problems in question. As a rule, the underground machine halls of hydro power plants are sited in strong rocks at relatively small depth (ranging from tens to some hundreds of meters) and due to this - as the analytical studies performed in the Research Centre of the "Hydroproject" Institute have demonstrated - the nonlinear effects play no decisive role at this stage of analysis; the influence of these effects is usually limited by small zones of stress concentration near the corners of the underground workings. The allowance for the nonlinear behaviour results in attenuation of the stress concentration.

The anisotropic computational model allows not only for the real anisotropy of rocks but also for the fictitious (reduced, structural) anisotropy which reflects the deformability of the rock mass composed of alternating thin layers of various rocks, or of a jointed rock mass dissected by sets of dense parallel joints. The anisotropy can exert a substantial influence on the state of stress in the immediate surrounding of the underground excavation as well as on the forces in the reinforced concrete vault.

The stressed state of the reinforced concrete vault is determined on the first stage too. Though this problem is beyond the scope of this paper, it should be noted that the allowance for the sequence of the underground machine hall construction is of a special importance for the vault design. First the space under the vault is excavated and the vault is constructed, then the excavation proceeds down to the design floor elevation. The excavation brings about the stresses re-distribution and development of compressive forces in the reinforced concrete vault. Besides, it should sustain the weight of rock inrushes that may occur above the vault.

The experience gained in researches and construction demonstrated the importance of individual consideration of the influence of large tectonic fractures and of properties of the fracture fill material, since they can significantly affect the stresses in the rock mass and especially in the reinforced concrete vault.

Three-dimensional computational models are to be used for the places where the tunnels adjoin the underground machine hall. The calculations performed by the method of boundary integral equations of the theory of elasticity have shown that the effects of the three-dimensional state of stress are telling only at small distances (of about the tunnel diameter) from the point of tunnel adjoining.

The above statical analysis is to be supplemented by determination of stresses arising from seismic shocks when siting the structures in seismic areas. The studies (in particular, by Matrossov, Reznikov & Tsukermann 1979) have shown that the quasi-statical computational model (Napetvaridze 1959; Fotieva 1980) may be used in designing underground machine halls; in this model the seismic effects are substituted by applying to the boundaries of the zone under consideration the static stresses equalling the stresses which arise in the homogeneous medium with a seismic wave going through.

It is obvious that to carry out the first stage one should know the results of engineering-geological investigation which are to ensure the information on the strength and deformability of rocks, on sets of joints and on seismological characteristics. Particular attention should be paid to the rock mass natural state of stress, which existed in the rock mass prior to the underground excavation execution. The simplest theoretical assumption that at the depth H the following stresses are developing in the rock mass:

$$\sigma_y = \delta H, \quad \sigma_x = \lambda \delta H, \quad \lambda = \frac{\gamma}{1-\gamma} \quad (1)$$

is far from being always confirmed in field tests; especially frequent and substantial are the deviations of the value of λ from the formula (1). In this formula δ is the average rock density, ν is the Poisson's ratio for the rock, λ is the coefficient of the lateral thrust.

Though various methods of determining natural stresses in the rock mass, and the relevant apparatus (Turchaninov et al. 1977) require further improvement, they have found already practical application in investigation and in design studies of a number of underground structures.

In case the data on the value of λ are lacking, or they are inadequately accurate, several versions of computing are usually made, assuming different values of λ (within the prescribed range of values), and the engineering conclusions are made basing on the worst (from the standpoint of stages II-IV) version. In case of indeterminacy of other initial parameters the similar procedure may be adopted.

Second stage - revealing (based on the results of the first stage) the zones of tension around the underground excavations. The dimensions of these zones are the first approximation (as a rule, with a considerable underestimation) to the required lengths of rock anchors. It is advisable to assume for safety in zones, where both the principal stresses are tension ones, the rock being disturbed and to consider its weight as the load on the main struc tural elements (the vault and anchors).

Third stage - comparison of principal compressive stresses in the rock mass around the working against the design compressive strength R of the rock mass. The value of R may be determined from the strength R_0 of rock as found from uniaxial compression tests on rock specimens, using the formula:

$$R = K_{sw} \cdot R_0 \qquad (2)$$

where the coefficient of structural weakening K_{sw} is assuming the values from 0.2 to 0.9, depending on the number of sets of joints and on the distance between the joints. For instance, with two sets of joints and the distance between the joints ranging from 1.0 to 1.5 m, $K_{sw} = 0.7$; with 3 to 4 sets of joints and the distance between the joints 0.5 to 1 m, $K_{sw} = 0.5$; the number

of sets of joints being over six and the distance between the joints being less than 0.3 m, $K_{sw} = 0.2$.

The zones around the working, for which the condition $\sigma \leqslant R$ is not obeyed or is fulfilled with a small only margin of safety ($R/\sigma < 1.25$), require rock bolting. However, since the value of R is a conditional one, the estimation made at this stage should be considered a preliminary one only.

Fourth stage - estimation of the rock strength using the Coulomb-Mohr criterion. In the opinion of the majority of authors, the most adequate theory of strength for rocks is the Coulomb-Mohr theory, according to which the strength is retained if the actual Mohr circle for the point in question lies within the envelope of the limiting Mohr circles, as shown in Fig. 1. Various versions of estimation of the rock strength using the Coulomb-Mohr criterion in the shape of the limiting circles envelope and in methods of evaluation of the mutual position of the actual circle and the envelope.

The ratio of lengths of intercepts DA and EA in Fig. 1:

$$K = DA/EA \qquad (3)$$

may be termed the local factor of safety. EA is the radius of the actual Mohr circle; DE is the minimum distance between this circle and the envelope. The equation of the envelope being known:

$$\tau = f(\sigma) \qquad (4)$$

the value of K may be expressed by the formula:

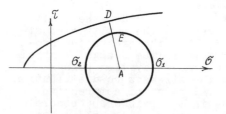

Fig. 1. To estimation of rock strength from Coulomb-Mohr criterion: 1 - envelope of limiting Mohr circles.

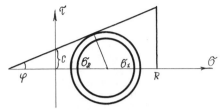

Fig. 2. Linearized envelope of Mohr limiting circles.

$$K = \frac{\sqrt{[\sigma^* - 0.5(\sigma_1+\sigma_2)]^2+f^2(\sigma^*)}}{0.5(\sigma_1-\sigma_2)} \quad (5)$$

where σ^* is the root of the equation:

$$2[\sigma - 0.5(\sigma_1+\sigma_2)] +2f(\sigma)\cdot f'(\sigma)=0 \quad (6)$$

In the particular case when the envelope of the Mohr circles is assumed to be rectilinear (Fig. 2) and

$$f(\sigma) = C + \sigma \, tg\varphi \quad (7)$$

the expression (5) assumes a more simple form:

$$K = \frac{0.5(\sigma_1+\sigma_2)\sin\varphi + C\cdot\cos\varphi}{0.5(\sigma_1-\sigma_2)} \quad (8)$$

which can be obtained directly from the consideration of Fig. 2.

The parameters of cohesion and friction C and tan used here are determined with an adequate degree of reliability for most of important constructions from in-situ tests. These data being absent (in early phases of design studies), the characteristics given in the "СНиП (Building Norms and Rules) II-16-76" ("Foundations of hydrotechnical structures") can be used in designs. It is advisable to supplement the inclined rectilinear envelope in Fig. 2 by a vertical straight line $\sigma = R$, which is equivalent to a check by the third stage.

Similarly to (8), the local coefficients of safety in the direction of sets of joints can be determined:

$$K = \frac{C_j + Ntg\varphi_j}{T} \quad (9)$$

where N and T are the stresses in the elementary area parallel to the planes of the set of joints under consideration; N is the normal stress; T is the shearing stress or projection of its vector on the line formed by intersection of the joint plane with the plane of the machine hall cross-section (in the last case the possibility of the shear only under condition of a two-dimensional strain has been taken into account); the C_j and φ_j parameters are similar to C and φ parameters, but are characteristic of joints and not of rock mass. It is obvious that $\tan\varphi_j < \tan\varphi$; $C_j < C$. Computing the K_j value from formula (9) for different sets of joints, the minimum values of the K coefficient can be found. The joints planes may be oriented in space arbitrarily in respect to the machine hall centre line.

The zones where the local factors of safety as determined from formulae (8) and (9) are less than 1.25 (and, consequently, the rock mass in these zones is nearing its limit state) are to be rock-bolted. The value 1.25 is adopted by analogy with the factor of safety for the Ist category hydrotechnical structures prescribed by the Soviet Standards.

Fifth stage – estimation of stability of individual large rock blocks around the working.

Analysis of the experience gained in underground construction shows that the possible movements of individual rock blocks, limited by large fissures, are the source of the maximum danger for the stability of the rock mass around the underground working. Thus, the revealing of such presumably hazardous blocks, the check of their stability and additional stabilization in case of necessity are extremely important.

The preliminary geomechanical analysis of rock blocks stability may be carried out using the methods developed at the "Orgenergostroy" Institute (Mostkov 1974). In accordance with these methods, the loss of stability of the rock mass in the working wall may occur by shifting along the certain sliding plane under the combined action of the following forces: the weight of an unstable rock mass in the working

wall, limited by the sliding planes
and the boundary of the zone found
in the fourth stage; the surcharge
of the sliding rock mass by the
weight of inrushing rock from the
working roof; the outward thrust
and the weight of the reinforced
concrete vault. The holding forces
are the friction and the cohesion
forces in the sliding planes as
well as the forces in rock bolts.

The possible integration of the
first stage with this (fifth) stage
shall be based in future on detailed nonlinear analysis of the
processes of deformation and failure.

Sixth stage - fixing the parameters of rock bolting on the basis
of results of the analysis made in
the fourth and fifth stages, taking
into account the technical potenti-
alities and the experience gained
previously in construction of
similar structures.

Seventh stage - tests of models of
equivalent materials. In order to
check the pattern and the main parameters of rock bolting of underground machine halls the models
scale 1:50 - 1:200 are tested; these
models reflect factors hardly amen-
able to considering by computation,
in particular, the jointing of the
rock mass, the nature of rock bedding, the properties of the joints
fill material, etc. (Mostkov, Kha-
chaturian, Stepanov & Belkin 1972).
Of a great interest are the three-
dimensional models; however due to
complicacy and the labour input required for these tests only solita-
ry cases of such models of underground machine halls are known (Mostkov 1974).

Eighth stage - tests on photoelastic models (Khessin, Ed. 1975). This
stage is not obligatory for two-dimensional problems of statics, as
it is duplicating the first stage

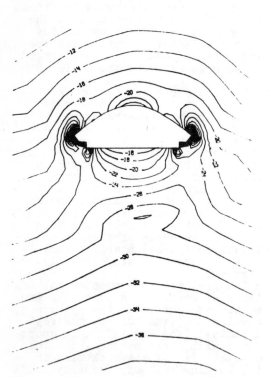

Fig. 3. Isolines of principal stresses σ_2 after excavating the under-
the roof-space (compression-
negative).

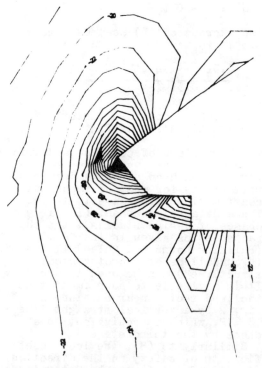

Fig. 4. Fragment of field of isolines of principal stresses σ_2
after excavating the under-the roof-
space (compression - negative).

364

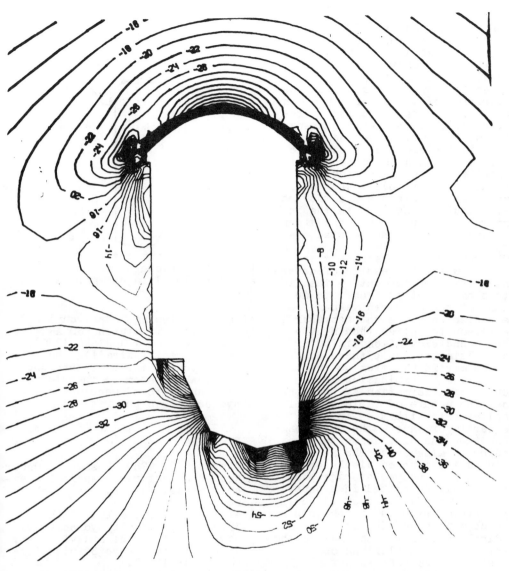

Fig. 5. Isolines of principal stresses σ_2 after finishing the power house cavern excavation (compression — negative).

studies (analysis by the finite elements method) and is useful only as a tool of check. While analysing the seismic effects the modelling by the method of dynamic photoelasticity may give a substantial supplement to results of computing.

The results of studies of three-dimensional photoelastic models, with consideration of effects of tunnels adjoining the machine hall, the medium heterogeneity and the proper-

ties of the joint filler, are of a great value.

Ninth stage - refinement of initial data in the process of engineering-geological investigations and in-situ tests during the construction period, following which the repetition of stages 1 to 7 may be necessary.

Tenth stage - measurements of displacements of the underground excavation outline and of forces in an-

365

chors and the analysis of the measurements results. Such measurements do not enter as a rule the complex of surface structures design studies and investigations to ground the design. However, one of the peculiarities of the underground constructions is the necessity of refining and correcting (in some cases - considerably) the design solution in the process of construction, as the data on geotechnical properties of the rock mass are accumulated. For this reason this stage (see the ninth stage too) may be rightfully grouped with the investigations carried out for grounding and checking the adopted design.

The measured displacements are compared with the results of determining the displacement by the finite element method. Moderate deviations of the measured values from the design ones are not necessarily the reason for strengthening the underground excavation lining or rock bolting, because these discrepancies may result from an inaccuracy in the determination of the modulus of deformation of the rock mass. The nature of variations of displacements with time is of a greater importance - the question is whether the displacements are tending to attenuate. The results of investigations of displacements of walls of a pumped storage plant machine hall described in a paper by Mostkov and Vinogradov (1978), may serve an example of analysis of such a process. The attenuation of displacements for several months after completing blasting operations may be considered normal.

The empirical formula given below (Mostkov & Grossman 1973) may serve as another tool for approximate estimation of maximum displacements:

$$\delta = 4.5H^{1.5}f^{-2} \qquad (10)$$

where δ is the maximum displacement, mm; H - height of the wall, m; f - the coefficient of the rock hardness (after Protodiakonov), $f \approx 0.01R$, where R - compressive strength, kgf/cm^2.

All the computation stages of the complex procedure, briefly outlined above, are implemented in the system of the complex automa-

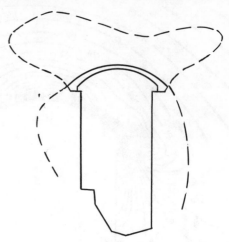

Fig. 6. Envelope of zones with inadequate local safety margin.

tion of analysing underground hydrotechnical structures "SONAR" (Zolotov, Reznikov & Rodinko 1980). Figs 3-6 are illustrating the application of the procedure and the "SONAR" system to the studies of the underground machine hall of a hydroelectric power plant.

REFERENCES

Fotieva, N.N. 1980, Design of underground structures support in seismic areas. Moscow, Nedra Publishers.
Gvelessiani, L.G. & L.A. Eliava 1975, The Zhinvali hydroelectric power plant on the Aragvi River, Gidrotekhnicheskoye Stroitel'stvo, N° 4: 13-17.
Glusskin, Ya.E. et al. 1974, The Kolyma hydroelectric power plant, Gidrotekhnicheskoye Stroitel'stvo, N° 8: 20-21.
Gurtovnik, F.I., Shutenkov, S.V. & A.K. Mel'nikov 1980, Construction of the permanent gates chamber on the bottom spillway tunnel of the Nurek Dam, Gidrotekhnicheskoye Stroitel'stvo, N° 6: 9-12.
Iliushin, V.F. 1977, New design solutions in underground structures of the Nurek hydroelectric power plant, Gidrotekhnicheskoye Stroitel'stvo, N° 3: 2-7.
Kelmi, A.M. & B.A.Vittenberg 1975, Construction of underground structures of the Ust-Khantaisk hydro-

electric power plant, Energeticheskoye Stroitel'stvo, N° 9: 49-
53.

Khessin, G.L. (ed.) 1975, Photoelasticity method. Moscow, Stroyizdat
Publishers.

Maissuradze,I.I. & G.A.Potskhoveria
1977, Construction of the Inguri
hydroelectric power plant underground machine hall, Energeticheskoye Stroitel'stvo, N° 4: 43-47.

Maissuradze, I.I. & G.A.Potskhove -
ria 1978, Construction of underground chambers, Energeticheskoye
Stroitel'stvo, N° 4: 36-39.

Matrossov, V.V., Reznikov, R.A. &
Ya.A.Tsukerman 1979, Comparative
analysis of seismically-induced
state of stress of underground
structures of the Rogun hydro project by the dynamic photoelasticity method and by the method of finite elements. Proceedings of the
VIIIth All-Union Conference on
Photoelasticity, v.3, Tallin: 56-
58.

Mostkov, V.M. 1974, Underground
structures of large cross-sections.
Moscow, Nedra Publishers.

Mostkov, V.M. & V.M.Vinogradov 1978,
Studies of deformations of walls
of the underground machine room of
a pumped storage plant during construction, Gidrotekhnicheskoye
Stroitel'stvo, N° 9.

Mostkov, V.M. & R.A. Reznikov 1979,
On the procedure of statical analysis of underground machine halls
of hydroelectric power and pumped
storage plants, Gidrotekhnicheskoye Stroitel'stvo, N° 1: 20-23.

Mostkov, W.M. und I.I. Grossmann
1973, Eine Methode zur Bestimmung
Kritischer Verschiebungen und Verformungen des Gebirges im Bereich
von untertäglichen Hohlräumen mit
grofsem Querschnitt, Neue Bergbautechnik, H. 9.

Mostkov, W.M., Chatschaturjan, N.S.,
Stepanov, P.D. und M.N.Belkin
1979, Untersuchung Unterirdischer
Wassertechnischer Bauwerke au Mo-
dellen aus äquivalenten Stoffen,
Der 4 Internationale Kongress für
Felsmechanik, Schweiz, Montreux.

Napetvaridze, Sh.G. 1959, Seismic
stability of hydraulic structures,
Gosstroyizdat Publishers.

Ossadchii, L.G. & R.I.Bakhtiarov
1975, The Rogun hydro project on
the Vakhsh River, Gidrotekhnicheskoye Stroitel'stvo, N° 4: 10-13.

Ossadchii, L.G., Iliushin, V.F. &

I.S. Bubman 1980, New design solutions in underground structures
of the Rogun hydroelectric power
plant, Gidrotekhnicheskoye Stroitel'stvo, N° 6: 3-8.

СНиП (Building Norms and Rules) II-
-16-76, 1977, Foundations of hydrotechnical structures. Moscow,
Stroyizdat Publishers.

Turchaninov, I.A., Yofiss, M.A. &
E.V. Kasparian 1977, Fundamentals
of rock mechanics. Leningrad, Nedra Publishers.

Zienkiewicz, O.C. 1971, The finite
element method in engineering
science. London McGraw-Hill.

Zolotov, O.N., Reznikov, R.A. & O.N.
Rodinko 1980, System of combined
automation of statical analysis
of underground hydrotechnical
structures. Sbornik nauchnykh tru-
dov Gidroproyekta, N° 74: 99-110.

MINING CHAMBERS WITH LARGE SPANS
Abbaukammern mit grosser Spannweite
Chambres d'exploitation de grandes portées

A.M.MYRVANG
Norwegian Institute of Technology, Trondheim

SUMMARY:
In the Norwegian mining industry very large, stable caverns have been and are excavated.
This paper gives case histories from mines present in operation. Examples of seemingly
stable spans up to 80 meters are given. The use of rock stress measurements and other
rock mechanical investigations connected to the chambers is described.

ZUSAMMENFASSUNG:
In den Norwegischen Bergbauindustrie wird sehr grosse stabile Kavernen abgebaut. In
dieser Publikation wird 'Case histories' von Gruben heute in Betrieb beschreiben.
Felsmechanische Untersuchungen in Zusammenhang mit den Abbau wird vorgestellt.

RESUMÉ:
Dans le mine norwègienne des cavernes de très grand postees sont creusé. Cet article
présente des études de cas de mines a présent à opération. Des mesures de la
contrainte et des déformation sont exposées.

1 INTRODUCTION

In Norway, as in many other countries, there is a strongly increasing interest for underground caverns in connection with non-mining activities. This may be due to several factors among which energy considerations, lack of building grounds in urban areas and safety reasons (bomb shelters) may be the most important. Traditionally, underground situation of hydroelectric power plants, defence constructions and storage plants for oil and other products has a strong position in Norway. The span of the chambers used for those purposes has usually been in the range of 10-20 m. During the recent years, however, demand for larger spans has arisen. One of the reasons for that is favourable government support to the construction of municipal bomb shelters. This has led to the idea of combining the construction underground in rock. Until now, at least 5 sport halls or swimming halls has been constructed with spans up to 27 m, and several others are planned.

While 27 m is regarded as a very large span in civil inegineering practice, much larger spans are known from mining engineer-ing. In many Norwegian mines very large caverns have been and are excavated as s part of the mining methods. The majority of these chambers are completely without support or lining, but have neverthless in some cases been stable for centuries. Many of the chambers are flat-roofed as the ore excavations has followed the bedding or foliation planes of the rock.

2 FACTORS DETERMINING THE POSSIBILITY OF CONSTRUCTING STABLE LARGE SPANS

Several factors will influence the possibility of constructing stable large spans. The most important may perhaps be:

a) The geological conditions i.e. rock type and composition, strike and dip, orientation and properties of joints, cracks and faults, mechanical properties of the rock and rock mass.

b) The geometry of the opening i.e. span width, height/width ratio, radius of curvature.

c) The virgin stress conditions. At shallow depth the existence of horizontal stresses in excess of the gravimetric stresses is particularly important.

In several Norwegian mines it has been observed that mine openings with surprisingly
large spans have been stable for very long
periods of time. Spans of 50 m and more
with almost completely flat roofs have
been reported in areas with not too favourable geological conditions. As stress measurements became usual, it seemed evident
that these openings were usually situated
in areas with favourable stress conditions.
A usual picture is that the major principal
stress is approximately parallell to the
roof, giving a 'prestress' effect of the
immediate roof. Direct measurements of this
effect will consequently give valuable in-
formations about the general stability of
a roof. The Rock Mechanics Laboratory of
the Mining Division, the Norwegian Institute of Technology, has for many years
performed such measurements. In this case
the doorstopper is the common method, as
the stress acting parallell to the measuring hole at or near the surface of the roof
is zero or very small. A light-weight compressed air driven diamond drill machine
is mounted to a tripod steel frame which
is bolted to the roof with rock bolts.
Thus the feed thrust is transferred to the
roof, making it possible to operate the
machine and the measuring equipment from a
light-weight scaling platform or similar.
This makes measurements quite easy up to
any height covered by the platform. Fig. 1
shows the result of a roof measurement in
a 20 m flat span.

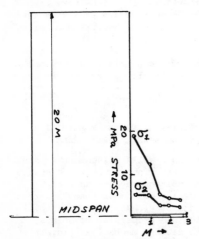

Fig. 1. Roof stresses measured in a 20 m
span.

The decreasing tendency with depth indicates that the stresses are due to an external stress field (residual or tectonic
stresses) and not internal (or remanent)
stresses. Based on the measuring results

and geological data this particular mine
has increased the span from 20 m til 25 m.
Similar measurements from many mines and
other large underground openings show similar patterns.
The stress conditions are emphasized in
this connection, as it is felt that these
often are underestimated when large spans
are discussed. The other factors mentioned
above are of course as important in many
cases.

3 CASE HISTORIES FROM NORWEGIAN MINES

3.1 The Skorovas Mine

The Skorovas deposit is situated in Middle
Norway and consists simplified of two more
or less cigar shaped main orebodies of
copper-pyrite. The surrounding rocks consist mainly of rather massive greenstones,
but parts of them may be more scistous. Both
the orebody and the greenstones are moderately jointed. The orebody has been mined by
so called transverse sublevel stoping,
leaving transverse pillars as indicated on
fig. 2.

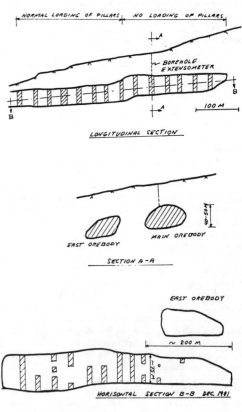

Fig. 2. Simplified lay-out Skorovas Mine.

The roof of the chambers are completely without support. About 30% of the orebody was originally left as pillars, and the mine management was very much interested in recovering at least parts of the pillars. In 1972 a rock mechanics investigation started including:

1) Three dimensional measurements to determine the virgin stresses.

2) Stress measurements in selected pillars with doorstoppers.

3) Photoelastic model studies to determine the stress distribution around the stopes (based upon the three dimensional stress measurements).

4) Control of the hanging wall (roof) subsidence by means of borehole extensometer measurements.

5) Classification (RQD) of the hanging wall rock based upon available diamond drill cores.

The pillar measurements showed that while the outermost pillars had a normal stress level according to overburden, the inner pillars had no stress at all i.e. these pillars did not seem to carry any load.

The three dimensional stress measurements showed no high stress values, but the photoelastic model studies showed that the horizontal stresses were high enough to create compressive stresses in the roof of the chambers in the inner part of the orebody. This, combined with a natural arching of the hanging wall, results in a stable self-supporting roof. Hence, the pillars are not necessary from a stability point of view. It was therefore decided to remove the central part of a pillar as indicated on fig. 2. To record the movement of the hanging wall a stringtype multiple position borehole extensometer was installed in a 55 m vertical diamond borehole drilled from the surface above the pillar in question. In the autumn 1973 the pillar was blasted in steps, and readings were taken on the extensometer after each blast until the final opening was established. The only movement recorded was in fact a slight upward movement of the lower anchors. Visual control from available openings showed only minor outfalls from the roof. During the years after 1973 most of the pillars in the inner part of the mine has been removed, and in addition the so called 'east' orebody has been mined out. In December 1981 the situation was as indicated on fig. 2, i.e. the main chamber has a span up to 75 m, a height up to 45 m and a length of approximately 200 m along the axis. Extensometer readings have been taken regularly during the whole periode, showing only minor fluctuations probably

due to temperature changes throughout the year. The east chamber has about the same span and height and has a length of about 150 m. Thoroughly visual inspections each year have shown no sign of instability. This mine will be mined out in 1983, but has during its periode of operation had a remarkable total recovery of ore due to the pillar extraction.

3.2 The Joma Copper Mine

The Joma copper-pyrite deposit is also situated in Middle Norway about 60 km NE from the Skorovas deposit. The orebody is more or less shaped like a double curved bowl. The strike, dip and thickness of the orebody is variable, and different types of mining methods are used. The mining operations started in 1972 and in the years 1972 and 1974 rock mechanics investigations were performed. Rock stress measurements showed that the major principal stress was horizontal and parallell to the strike of rocks. The surrounding rocks are also here mainly greenstones and greenscists. While the ore itself may be very jointed, the greenstones are moderately jointed.

During the last three years the mining of a rather flat-dipping part of the orebody has opened very large spans. In March 1981 the situation was as indicated to the left of the dotted line on fig. 3.

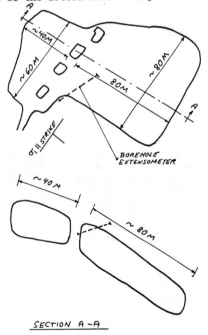

Fig. 3. Simplified lay-out Joma Mine.

A chamber approximately 30-40 m x 80 m
with height 20 m had been excavated leaving a row of pillars as indicated. Stress
measurements in the pillars showed moderate stresses, and repeated three dimensional measurements in undisturbed rock in the
neighbourhood verified earlier measurements
i.e. the major principal stress is horizontal and about 10 MPa in magnitude. The
overburden at the measuring site is about
100 m giving theoretical (and also measured) vertical stresses of about 2,7 MPa.

The mining company wanted to extend the
excavation further down (right on fig. 3)
with the highest possible recovery. A rod
type single point borehole extensometer
was installed in a 30 m borehole, drilled
from a stable position out over the future
span as indicated on fig. 3. Even if the
borehole makes only an angle of 30° with
the roof, the extensometer will give some
indication if subsidence of importance is
happening. Today (January 1982) the mining
of this section has just been completed
giving a chamber with an area of approximately 80 m x 80 m and a height of 20 m.
The roof is approximately flat and completely without support. Extensometer readings
have been taken after every major blast,
but practically no movement has been recording to this date. Visual inspections
show only minor downfalls from the roof.
The blasting hole pattern is longhole fan
drilling, with the end of the holes perpendicular to the roof. This is a very unfavourable blasting pattern from a stability point of view, but this does not seem
to influence the general stability in this
case.

3.3 The Norsk Nefelin nephelin-syenite mine

This deposit is situated on the Stjernøy
island in the northermost part of Norway
(slightly north of the 70°N parallell).
The deposit is huge, and the mining method
is large scale so called sublevel stoping.
Fig. 4 shows a simplified picture of the
method. The mine is situated in a 700 m
high mountain, and the mining is going from
200 m above sealevel and upwards. The rock
is massive nephelin-syenite with very little
jointing and has generally excellent properties from a stability point of view.

Every 40 m vertical distance a blasting
level is established. The rooms are opened
up to full width and length as indicated
on fig. 4. The slab between two levels are
then blasted in steps with blasting holes
parallell to the dip ($\simeq 70^\circ$). This has
created rooms with a length of 50 m, width
of 25 m and height up to 200 m, with

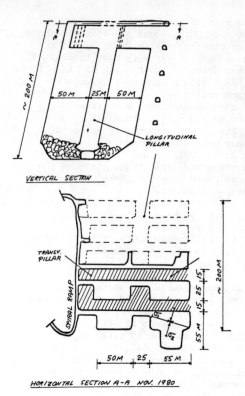

Fig. 4. Simplified lay-out Norsk Nefelin
Mine.

12-15 m pillar between the rooms. Two rows
of such rooms are divided by a 25 m longitudinal pillar.

In 1973 (after about 10 years of operation) a rock mechanics investigation was
started to get more information for future
planning. The stress measurements showed
also here horizontal stresses much in excess
of the gravimetric horizontal stresses.
Direct measurements in the roof of the rooms
showed considerable compressive stresses
even midspan (fig. 1). Based on these measurements and measurements in the pillars
and geological data it was decided to increase the span in the rooms from 20 m to
25 m. Control measurements in the roofs and
pillars are taken on every new blasting
level i.e. approximately once a year. Rod
type two-point borehole extensometers are
installed in two pillars. One of these has
a total length of 140 m. The general tendency after 8 years of measurements is that
the 'prestress' in the roof remains virtu-
ally constant while the pillar stress decrease as the mining proceeds upwards. In
one of the pillars a movement of 8 mm has
been recorded by the extensometer. The latest roof stress measurements were taken in

November 1980. Due to special conditions
the room had a shape as indicated on fig.
4. The roof is completely flat without rock
bolts or other support. In the middle of
the roof the average stresses over 3,0 m
hole depth was 10,2 MPa and 5,3 MPa as indicated.

4 CONCLUSION

Based on the experiences gained from mining
it is the author's opinion that underground
chambers with spans of 50 m and more can
safely be constructed under proper geological and rock mechanical conditions. A
very important parameter seems to be the
existence of a sufficient horizontal stress-
field to create proper compressive stresses
in the roof of the chamber.

5 ACKNOWLEDGEMENT

The author wants to thank the Elkem A/S,
Skorovas Mine and Norsk Nefelin Mine, and
Grong Gruber A/S, Joma Mine, for the kind
permission to publish data concerning the
mines mentioned above.

EFFECTS OF FLATTENING THE ROOF OF CAVERNS - A CASE STUDY
Auswirkungen der Firstabflachung in einer Kaverne - Eine Fallstudie
Effets de l'aplatissement du toit des cavernes - Un exemple

B.NILSEN
Norsk Teknisk Byggekontroll A/S, Norway

SUMMARY:

In northern Norway construction of an underground installation is being planned. A cavern with length 100 m, width 17 m and height approx. 12 m is required. The surrounding topography has such a character that existence of high topographical gravitation stresses in the rock mass is unlikely. High tectonic stresses are also unlikely. Traditionally, caverns in Norway are often constructed with arched roof, the height of arch corresponding to 20-25% of the span. For the planned cavern a "traditional" height of arch thus would be approx. 4 m. For the intended purpose such an upper, arched part, however, would represent a volume of no value. Giving the cavern a "traditional", arched roof rather than an alternative, flat roof is estimated to represent higher construction costs amounting to approx. US $ 65,000 (NOK 350.000). Where the geological conditions are favourable flattening the roof of caverns therefore opens the possibility of considerable cost reductions. Flattening the roof on the other hand may have an unfavourable influence on the interlocking. For a closer study of this, two-dimensional finite element analyses have been carried out. The analyses have included a cavern with a height of arch of 4 m and a cavern with a flat roof.

ZUSAMMENFASSUNG:

In Nordnorwegen ist der Bau einer unterirdischen Anlage geplant. Ein Hohlraum von 100 m Lange, 17 m Breite und ca. 12 m Höhe ist dazu notwendig. Das Gebiet wo die Anlage liegen soll schliesst starke topografische Gravitationsspannungen im Erdbereich aus. Starke tektonische Spannungen sind auch unwahrscheinlich. In Norwegen sind traditionell Berghallen oft mit gewölbtem Dach gebaut. Die Wölbung entspricht 20-25% von der Spannweite. Die Bogenhöhe des geplanten Hohlraumes wird also ca. 4m. Für den zugedachten Verwendungszweck ist das Volumen des oberen gewölbten Teils ohne Wert. Ein traditionell gebogenes Dach im Bergraum, anstatt ein flaches Dach, hat US $65,000 (NOK 350.000) höhere Konstruktionskosten. Eine wesentliche Kosteneinschränkung kann deshalb, bei günstigen geologischen Verhältnissen durch eine Abflachung des Daches, erreicht werden. Auf der anderen Seite kann ein flaches Dach eine ungünstige Wirkung auf die Steineinspannung haben. Eine nähere Studie darüber wurde mit zweidimensionalen Elementanalyser durchgeführt. Die Analyse behaltet ein Bergraum mit einer Bogenhöhe von 4 m und einem Bergraume mit flachem Dach.

RESUME:

Dans le nord de la Norvège la construction d'une installation souterraine est projetée. Une caverne ayant une longueur de 100 m, une largeur de 17 m et une hauteur de 12 m est requisée. La topographie des environs a un tel caractère que l'existence des contraintes topographique élevées est peu probable. Des contraintes tectoniques élevées sont aussi peu probables. Traditionellement les cavernes en Norvège sont fréquemment construit avec un toit vouté, la hauteur de la voute correspondant à 20-25% de la portée. Pour la caverne projetée une hauteur de la voute "traditionelle" serait donc à-peu-près 4 m. Cependant, pour le but projeté, une telle partie supérieure voutée représenterait un volume n'ayant aucune valeur. On estime q'en donnant un toit vouté "traditionel" à la caverne plutôt que un toit plat on augmenterait les frais de construction d'à-peu-près US $ 65,000 (NOK

350.000). Là où les conditions géologiques sont favorables, l'aplatissement des toits des cavernes donnent par consequent la possibilité d'obtenir une réduction considérable des frais. D'autre part l'aplatissement du toit peut avoir une influence défavorable sur l'enclenchement. Pour étudier ceci de plus près, des analyses d'éléments finis à deux dimensions ont été réalisées. Les analyses ont compris une caverne ayant une hauteur de vouté de 4 m, et une caverne ayant un toit plat.

1 INTRODUCTION

In northern Norway construction of an underground installation is beeing planned. A cavern with length 100 m, width 17 m and height approx. 12 m is required.

Traditionally, caverns in Norway are often constructed with arched roof, the height of arch corresponding to 20-25% of the span. This is based on the assumption that an arched roof generally is causing evenly distributed compressive stresses along the whole periphery of the opening, and hence the best stability. For the cavern in question, however, such an upper, arched part would represent a volume of no value.

In horizontally bedded rocks it has earlier been shown possible in Norway to make caverns with flat roofs along the bedding planes (Selmer-Olsen & Broch 1977). From Norwegian mines at present in operation, seemingly stable flat-roofed spans up to 75 m have been reported (Myrvang 1982).

For the underground opening in question a flat roof opens the possibility of considerable cost reductions compared to a traditional design. For a closer investigation of the effect that flattening of the roof may have upon stability, finite element analyses have been carried out.

2 TOPOGRAPHICAL AND GEOLOGICAL CONDITIONS

The proposed site of the underground opening is the protruding "nose" shown in fig. 1. Just above the planned cavern the maximum height of the mountain is approx. 100 m.a.s.l. 300 m further north-east the mountains are reaching heights of 160 m.a.s.l. With a few minor exceptions the bedrock is exposed all over the area.

Caledonian micaschists are predominant within the area. In the western part the schists are intersected by numerous, thin veins of hydrothermal quartz and wider, pegmatitic zones rich in quartz.

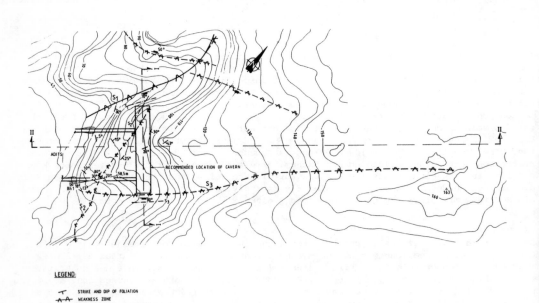

LEGEND:

⊥ STRIKE AND DIP OF FOLIATION
A-A WEAKNESS ZONE
A-A WEAKNESS ZONE, APPROXIMATE LOCATION
⊿ STRIKE AND DIP OF JOINTS AND WEAKNESS ZONES
----- ESTIMATED LOCATION OF WEAKNESS ZONE AT 38 m.a.s.l.
⊕ 58.5m/18° CORE DRILLING WITH LENGTH AND INCLINATION

Fig. 1 Map showing topography, tectonics and recommended location of cavern

The schists have a distinct, relatively flatlying foliation, with dip angle varying between 5° and 30°. Compared to other Scandinavian rocks, the micaschists have a relatively low mechanical strength (uniaxial compressive strength σc = 55 MPa measured on 32 mm, water saturated drill cores).

The tectonics are rather complex including smooth, regional folding as well as intense, small scale folding. As a result of folding, the strike direction varies considerably, see fig. 1.

The orientation of joints appears from the joint rosette, fig. 2. It follows that strike joints and a system of steep cross joints are predominant. For strike joints as well as for cross joints average joint spacing normally exceeds 1,0 m.

Core drillings have indicated that the RQD-index with few exceptions is exceeding 80 (corresponding to "good" and "excellent" rock quality).

Three weakness zones have been observed having such a location and character that they represent a potential threat to the stability of the underground opening, see fig. 1. The steeply dipping zones designated S_1 and S_3 are well exposed, and undoubtedly they are the major ones.

The weakness zone S_2 is considerably less exposed. With the proposed location of the cavern this is, however, the zone with which it will be most difficult to avoid intersection. For a more precise indentification of the location and character of this zone, core drillings have been performed. The drillings have confirmed that the zone is a minor one. Its dip angle has been found to be steeply towards west, see fig. 1.

3 ORIENTATION OF LENGTH AXIS

When orientating underground openings a general rule is to strive for the largest possible angle between its length axis and the strike directions of major joint sets and weakness zones. An angle smaller than approx. 20° is generally considered as very unfavourable with respect to stability. Often particularly important is the intersection angle with the foliation.

The assumed optimum orientation of the cavern in question appears from fig. 2.

4 LOCATION OF CAVERN

Considerations of outdoor installations, location of portals and the desire for

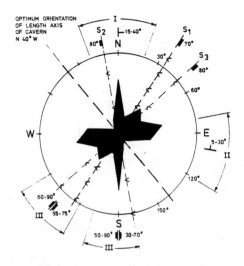

LEGEND:

I. Strike joints in the northeastern part of the area
II. Strike joints in the southern and western part of the area.
III. Cross joints.
S_1, S_2 S_3: Weakness zones (cfr. fig. 1)

Fig. 2 Joint rosette

avoiding descending adits indicate an optimum floor level of the cavern at 38 m.a.s.l.

The core drillings indicate that the surface weathering reaches depths of approx. 10 m. Based on experience the planned cavern with span 17 m is presumed to demand a minimum rock cover of 15 m. With floor level at 38 m.a.s.l., height of walls 12 m and height of arch 4 m this means that the cavern has to be located beyond the contour line corresponding to 69 m.a.s.l.

In addition to rock cover, considerations have to be taken for the three weakness zones which may intersect the cavern if unfavourably located. The locations of the zones are indicated in fig. 1.

The recommended location of the cavern appears from fig. 1. This location makes intersection by any of the major weakness zones S_1 and S_3 very unlikely. The minor weakness zone S_2, however, will probably intersect the north-western corner of the cavern with an intersection angle of approx. 30°. The locations of the weakness zones also appear from fig. 3, which is a cross-section following the length axis of the cavern.

By locating the cavern approx. 10 m

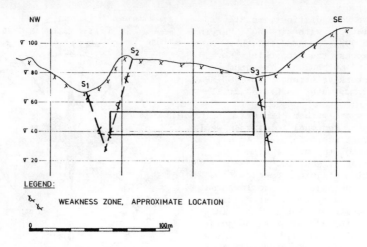

NW   SE

∇ 100

∇ 80   S₂   S₃

S₁

∇ 60

∇ 40

∇ 20

LEGEND:

WEAKNESS ZONE, APPROXIMATE LOCATION

0   100m

Fig. 3 Cross section along profile I-I showing recommended
location of cavern (cfr. fig. 1)

further to the northeast, intersection with
the weakness zone S₂ also would be unlikely.
Such a location, however, would increase
the total length of adit tunnels with
approx.20 m. As zone S₂ seems to be a minor
one, which is not anticipated to demand
comprehensive reinforcement, such an
alternative location is not presumed to be
economical.

5 SHAPING OF CAVERN

The surrounding topography has such a
character that existence of high topographical gravitation stresses in the rock
mass is unlikely. Previous experience
has indicated that high tectonic horizontal
stresses may exist in this particular area.
The cavern, however, is planned at a level
probably too shallow for tectonic stresses
to affect stability.

Potential problems due to stresses in the
rock mass will therefore be caused by too
low stresses in the roof of the cavern
rather than by too high ones. Too low
stresses may cause poor interlocking, and
consequently increase the possibility of
rockfall.

Flattening the roof of the cavern instead
of constructing a "traditional" arched roof
with a height of arch of 4 m, opens the
possibility of considerable cost reductions.
Such a flattening may on the other hand
have an unfavourable influence on the interlocking, and hence on stability. For a
closer study of this relationship, two-
dimensional finite element analyses have
been carried out.

The finite element model is shown in

fig. 4. The model, which is homogeneous
and isotropical, is representing a cross
section perpendicular to the length axis
of the cavern, following profile II-II in
fig. 1. The mechanical parametres are also
given in fig. 4, i.e. spesific gravity (γ),
modulus of elasticity (E) and Poissons
ratio (ν). The parameters are based on
testing of Ø 32 mm, water saturated drill
cores.

As can be seen, the size of the elements
gets smaller close to the roof of the
cavern. This has been done in order to get
the best possible information about stresses
in this area. The model, which is a plane
strain model, is divided into three sub-
structures containing all together 83
elements (260 nodal points).

The model allows excavation of the elements in the roof, thus permitting analyses
for a cavern with a height of arch of 4 m
as well as for a flat roofed one. For both
cases the width of the cavern is 17 m, the
heights of the walls are 12 m and the level
of the floor is 38 m.a.s.l. The finite
element mesh close to the cavern follows
from fig. 5, so does the numbering of the
nodal points.

The nodal points at the bottom of the
model in fig. 4 are free to move horizontally only, while the nodal points at the
left hand side are free to move vertically
only. Vertically the model is loaded with
gravity forces, γ.h. Horizontal load is
applied on the right hand side of the model,
and is given as K·γ·h. This is including
forces resulting from elastic deformations
as well as tectonic forces.

The finite element analyses were carried
out before it was possible to do any stress

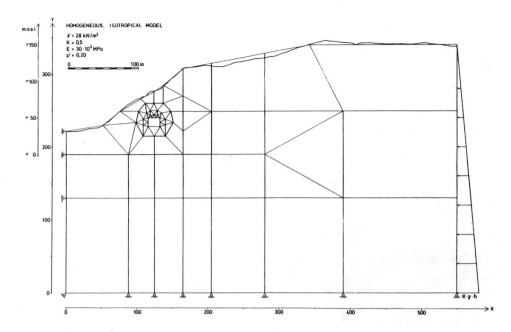

HOMOGENEOUS, ISOTROPICAL MODEL
γ = 28 kN/m³
K = 0,5
E = 30·10³ MPa
ν = 0,20

Fig. 4 Finite element model

measurements (no underground access). A K-value therefore had to be estimated. According to previous experience, a K-value of 0,5 has been found to be fairly common in Norway (Selmer-Olsen 1974, Broch & Nilsen 1979). Hence, this value has been used for the analyses. Potential minor errors in the input-parameters will not change the main conclusions of this analysis, as the primary purpose is to analyze the changes of stresses for two different geometries, not very accurately to calculate the values of the stresses.

The finite element calculations give the dimensions and directions of stresses in all nodal points. The main results from the analyses appear from fig. 6. Estimated directions and values of major and minor principal stresses (σ_1 and σ_3, respectively) close to the roof are plotted for a cavern with flat roof and a height of arch of 4 m respectively. The values of the principal stresses are indicated as well as the numbers of the belonging nodal points (cfr. fig. 5).

In the roof of the cavern the major principal stress (σ_1) approximately equals the tangential stress. Hence the size of σ_1 is governing the degree of interlocking between individual blocks in the roof. From fig. 6 it follows that for the central part of the roof σ_1 is only slightly higher for an arched roof than for the alternative flat roof (1,5 MPa respectively 1,4 MPa). As an average for

the three central nodal points in the roof, σ_1 is approx. 20% higher for an arched roof than it is for a flat one.

On this basis a completely flat roof compared to a "traditional" roof with a height of arch of 4 m is presumed to cause

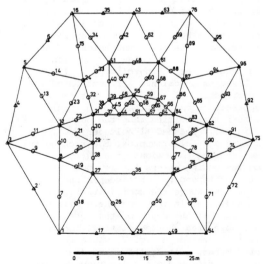

Fig. 5 Mesh of elements and numbering of nodal points close to cavern

379

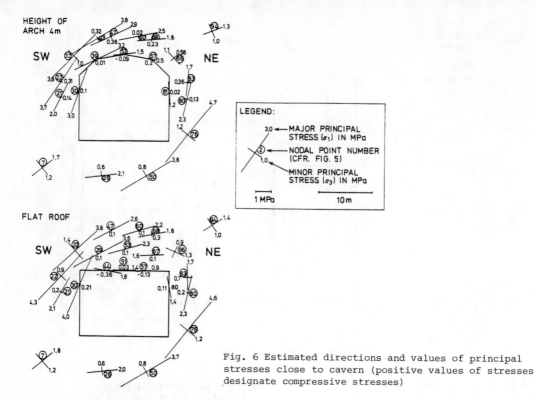

Fig. 6 Estimated directions and values of principal stresses close to cavern (positive values of stresses designate compressive stresses)

a reduction of the roof interlocking of approx. 20%.

In this particular case, however, a completely flat roof is not desirable. Because of the need for having a certain inclination of the roof of a planned inside building, a height of arch of approx. 1 m is required. Reducing the height of arch from 4 to 1 m will cause a reduction of the roof interlocking of approx. 15%.

Based on experience a reduction of the interlocking of only 15% is not to any appreciable extent presumed to require closer rock bolting than the pattern originally planned (1 bolt per 2 m^2, making a total of approx. 850 rock bolts). By reducing the height of arch the corresponding stress levels, however, will be forced somewhat deeper into the rock mass above the roof (cfr. fig. 6). In addition, in the roof there will be an increase in the depth of the potential unstable area due to jointing. The latter is illustrated in fig. 7, where the two predominant joint systems are sketched for height of arch 4 m and 1 m respectively.

A height of arch of 1 m consequently will require somewhat longer rock bolts than a "traditional" height of arch of 4 m.

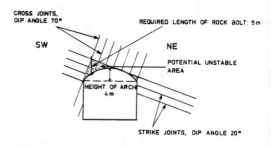

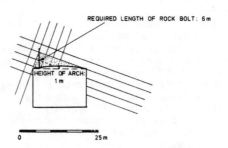

Fig. 7 The effect of flattening the roof on required length of rock bolts.

This in particular applies to the south-western part of the roof, where a reduction of the height of arch will require an increase in length of bolts of 1-2 m. For the north-eastern part of the roof an increase in length of bolts of approx. 1 m is presumed to be required.

6 CONCLUSION

For the cavern in question finite element analyses have indicated that a reduction of the height of arch from 4 m to 1 m will only reduce the roof interlocking with approx. 15%. The number of rock bolts required in the roof was originally estimated to 850 (systematical bolting with an average of approx. 1 bolt per 2 m^2). It is assumed that the roof flattening will not to any appreciable extent necessitate closer bolting. However, the average length of bolts in the roof will have to be increased with approx. 1,5 m. This will cause excessive expences of approx. US $ 15.000 (NOK 85.000).

The estimated reduction in construction costs by flattening the roof is consider-ably higher (US $ 65.000, or NOK 350.000, i.e. NOK 100 per m^3). Consequently, the cavern has been recommended to be constructed with a height of arch of only 1 m.

This example from northern Norway is illustrating that where the geological conditions are favourable, flattening the roof of caverns opens the possibility of considerable cost reductions. In each individual case, however, careful attention has to be paid to the effects that a flattening may have on stability.

7 REFERENCES

Broch, E. & B. Nilsen 1979, Comparison of calculated, measured and observed stresses at the Ørtfjell open pit, Proc. 4th Int. ISRM-Congress, Montreux, vol. 2: 49-56.
Myrvang, A. 1982, Mining chambers with large span, Proc. Symp. on Rock Mechanics related to Caverns and Pressure Shafts, Aachen 1982 (in print).
Selmer-Olsen, R. 1974, Underground openings filled with high-pressure water or air, Bull. Int. Ass. Eng. Geol., no. 9: 91-95.
Selmer-Olsen, R. & E. Broch 1977, General design procedure for underground openings in Norway, Proc. Rock Store 1977, Stockholm, vol. 2: 219-226.

DESIGN OF ROCK REINFORCEMENT AND ASSESSMENT OF STABILITY ON THE EXCAVATION OF THE SHIMOGO UNDERGROUND POWER STATION

Entwurf von Gebirgsverstärkungen und Abschätzung der Stabilität beim Bau des
unterirdischen Kraftwerkes Shimogo

Dimensionnement du renforcement de la roche et évaluation de la stabilité de l'excavation
de la centrale électrique souterraine de Shimogo

TSUTOMU NISHIDA, YOSHIAKI MATSUMURA & MASAYUKI HORI
Electric Power Development Co.Ltd., Tokyo, Japan

SUMMARY:
The dimension of the underground power station in Shimogo pumped storage
hydro plant project is 171 m in length, 45.5 m in height and 22 m in
width. The rock surrounding this cavern is consisted mainly of diorite,
and partly of the formation of sandstone and shale lying underneath the
diorite deposit.
This paper is mainly undertaken to introduce a rational design procedure
of the rock reinforcement which was successfully accepted for the
present case.
The paper also describes a mechanism of rock movement and its relation
to the stability of the cavern. A detail observation of the rock movement gives an interesting fact that the movement induced by the stress
relief due to the excavation consists both of elastic and plastic one,
and that these two components can be separated phenomenologically from
the obtained deformation curve.

ZUSAMMENFASSUNG:
Die Ausmaße der unterirdischen Kammer in dem Shimogo Pumpspeicher-Wasser-
kraft-Projekt sind 171 Meter Länge, 45,5 Meter Höhe und 22 Meter Breite.
Das Gestein, welches diesen Hohlraum umlagert, besteht hauptsächlich aus
Diorit, sowie teilweise aus Sandsteinformationen und Schiefer welche
unter dem Dioritlager liegen.
Dieser Bericht soll in der Hauptsache einen rationalen Vorgang zur Ausführung von Gesteinsverstärkung vorstellen, welcher in dem vorliegenden
Fall erfolgreich angewendet wurde.
Dieser Bericht befaßt sich ebenfalls mit dem Mechanismus der Gesteinsbewegung im Zusammenhang mit der Stabilität der Aushöhlung. Eine detaillier-
te Beobachtung der Gesteinsbewegung ergibt die interessante Tatsache,
daß die Bewegung, hervorgerufen durch den Spannungsnachlaß infolge des
Aushöhlens, elastischer wie auch plastischer Art ist. Es zeigt sich
ferner, daß diese beiden Komponente phänomenalisch von der gewonnenen
Deformationskurve getrennt werden können.

RESUME:
Les dimensions de la centrale électrique souterraine du projet de centrale hydro-électrique à accumulation par pompes de Shimogo sont les
suivantes: 171 m de long, 45,5 m de haut et 22 m de large.
La roche qui entoure l'abri se compose principalement de diorite, et
partiellement d'une formation de grès et de schiste située sous la couche
de diorite.
Ce document vise principalement à présenter une procédure d'étude
rationnelle de renforcement de la roche qui a été un succès en la
situation présente.

Ce document s'efforce également de décrire le mécanisme du mouvement de
la roche et sa relation avec la stabilité de l'abri. Une observation
détaillée du mouvement de la roche révèle des faits intéressants, à
savoir que le mouvement occasionné par la réduction de la contrainte due
à l'excavation est à la fois élastique et de qualité plastique, et que
ces deux composantes peuvent être séparées phénoménologiquement à partir
de la courbe de déformation obtenue.

1 INTRODUCTION

In excavating a large cavern, a great attention must be paid on its stability
during and after the construction period.
In general, rock reinforcement of large
cavern is conducted by means of reinforced
shotcrete and anchoring with use of pre-
stressing steel wire and/or rock bolt. However, design procedure concerning the reinforcement has not definitely established
yet. This paper is undertaken to introduce
a rational design procedure of rock reinforcement by means of pre-stressing steel
wire, which was successfully accepted in a
construction of the underground power station
of the hydropower plant at Shimogo, Japan.
To accomplish this procedure, characteristics of joint sets existing in rock were
geologically investigated in detail, and
they were·taken into account in the stress
and deformation analysis by means of finite
element method.

The paper also deals with a mechanism
concerning about rock movement measured
during the excavation period, and shows its
correlation to the stability of the cavern.
A detailed observation of the rock movement
gives an interesting fact that the movement
induced by the stress relief due to the excavation consists both of elastic and plastic one. It was also found out that concerning the plastic movement, a rate of
movement is closely related to amount of
pre-stressing force applied to the steel
wire. This quantitative evaluation will be
an important design criterion on the reinforcement by the steel wire when assessing
a stability of large cavern.

2 UNDERGROUND POWER STATION IN SHIMOGO
   PUMPED STORAGE HYDRO PLANT PROJECT

A pumped storage hydro plant project is being promoted at Shimogo, Fukushima Prefecture, located at about 200 km north of
Tokyo, Japan. A total length of waterway in
between upper and lower reservoirs is approximately 3.5 km. The obtained effective
head is about 400 m at maximum. The elec-

tric power to be expected is 1,000 MW. The
construction of the project has begun in
April, 1978, and the start of electric
generation will be scheduled for July,
1984.

Four generating units with a power of 250
MW each and two transformers should be installed in the power station. As shown in
the longitudinal section and the cross section of generator room, Figs. 1 and 2, respectively, the dimension of the station
is 171 m in length, 45.5 m in height and
22 m in width. The total volume of the
space is about 130,000 cubic meter.

3 GEOLOGICAL INVESTIGATION

3.1 Geology

As shown in Fig. 3, the base rock lying in
a region around the underground power station consists mainly of diorite and sedimentary rocks which are called Ohto formation, the Mesozoic (detailed age is not
confirmed), consisting of alternative
layers of fine grained sandstone and shale.
The rocks of Ohto formation are generally
brittle and have relatively low uniaxial
compressive strength, ranging from 150 to
500 kgf/cm^2. Interval of joints is short,
in general. RQD is less than 20%. On the
other hand, the formation of diorite,
which has been formed by a geological
process of penetration into the Ohto formation, is rather competent and less fractured. In this formation, porphyrite is also
observed as a seam in some places. These
igneous rocks exhibit mediumly high
strength ranging from 800 to 1,400 kgf/cm^2.
RQD in these rocks is 50% in average.

3.2 Investigation of joint set

A detailed observation concerning about
existing joints which appeared on excavated
surface of the rock, was carried out in an
early stage of the excavation of the power
station. Strike and dip of major joint were
mainly taken measurements, and they were

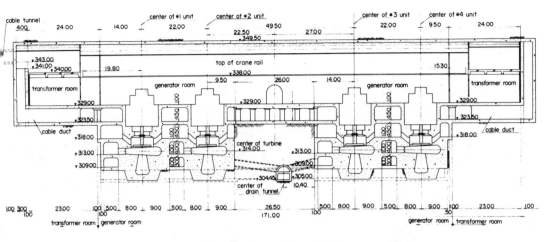

Fig. 1   Longitudinal section of the power station

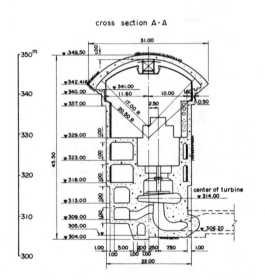

Fig. 2   Cross section of the power station

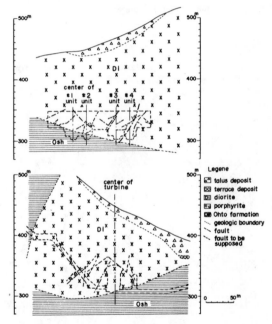

Fig. 3   Geological formations in a region around the power station

plotted on Schmidt net as shown in Fig. 4(a). Totally, ninety joints were picked up and plotted. Furthermore a density distribution was obtained to represent a degree of concentration of the results and find out predominant joint sets distributing in the rock mass, as shown in Fig. 4(b). According to this, it is noted that the predominant joint sets are expressed representatively as N35°E80°SE and N40°W60°SW. A

geometric relation in a plan between the position of the power station and the predominant joint sets is illustrated in Fig. 5(a), and while, the projection on the cross section is shown in Fig. 5(b).

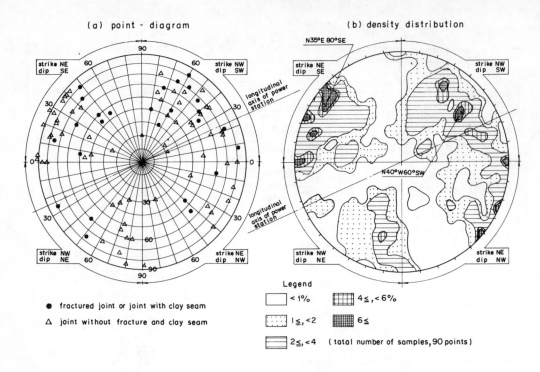

(a) point - diagram   (b) density distribution

Legend

☐ < 1% ▦ 4≤,< 6%

▥ 1≤,<2 ▦ 6≤

▤ 2≤,<4 (total number of samples, 90 points)

● fractured joint or joint with clay seam

△ joint without fracture and clay seam

Fig. 4   Determination of predominant joint sets

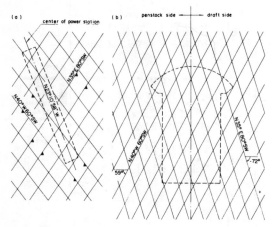

Fig. 5   Aspect of the predominant joint sets

3.3 Insitu stress

In the present project, a stress measurement was carried out by so-called overcoring method in an inspection adit to be placed in the power station prior to its excavation. A representative stress state determined by the stress measurements is that the major principal stress is in the order of 95 kgf/cm^2 in the magnitude and acts in the direction almost normal to the longitudinal axis of the power station. The minor principal stress is about 20 kgf/cm^2 in the magnitude and its direction is sub-parallel to the axis of the station. On the other hand, the intermediate principal stress is in the order of 30 kgf/cm^2 which is equivalent to the overburden pressure at this depth.

For a numerical analysis described in the following section, the three-dimensional stress state is projected on a cross section of the power station on which two-dimensional analysis is conducted by the finite element method. The appropriately modified stress state on this plane is shown in Fig. 6. Accordingly, the major principal stress becomes to be 90 kgf/cm^2 in the magnitude, and the minor principal stress is 30 kgf/cm^2. The former acts in direction sub-parallel to the ground surface of which inclination is relatively gentle. The latter is consequently acting in direction almost normal to the ground surface. As the state of in-

386

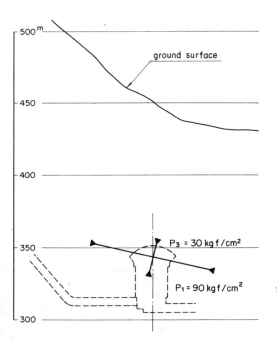

Fig. 6   In-situ principal stresses
existing in the rock

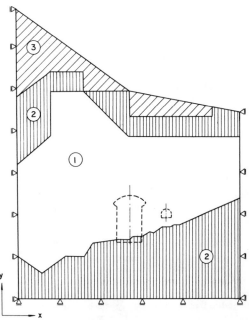

Fig. 7   Region and zoning of rock formation
for the numerical analysis

situ stress concerned, the obvious characteristic is firstly that a considerably
high stress exists in the rock formation
with almost horizontal direction. In addition to this, the horizontal stress is
three times the overburden pressure.

4 ANALYTICAL DESIGN OF ROCK REINFORCEMENT

4.1 Numerical analysis on the cavern by
    finite element method

A numerical analysis on the cavern was conducted by means of finite element method
to predict deformation of the surrounding
base rock and stress changes induced by
the excavation, and also to assess a stability of the cavern during and after the
excavation period. The obtained results
were also provided for a design of rock
reinforcement.

The analysis was performed on the assumptions of two-dimensional plane strain condition on a cross section of the cavern
and a linear elasticity of the rock materials. The analytical region in consideration is taken as shown in Fig. 7, and is
devided into triangle meshes with number
of 776 elements. Simulating the actual
schedule on excavation process of the power
station and the draft gate chamber, de-

formation and stress were obtained at each
stage of the excavation.

The analytical region was devided into
three zones according to the rock formations from a geological viewpoint. Zone 1
in Fig. 7 represents the formation composed of diolite and porphyrite, zone 2
Ohto formation of fine grained sandstone
and shale. Zone 3 represents talus deposit
in the surface layer. Physical properties
of each rock zone to be taken in the
analysis are listed in Table 1, which have
been determined from test results of plate
loading test and block shear test performed
at the site.

As for the initial stress in the medium,
concerned, an assumption has been made that
a magnitude of both major and minor principal stresses, changes linearly with depth,
on the basis of the stress state as shown
in Fig. 6. Moreover, it is also assumed
that a direction of the major principal
stress is to be parallel to the ground surface at the corresponding position.

Meanwhile, it is well known that rocks in
a circumferential area surrounding the
cavern will be failed in some extent due to
stress relief and vibration and/or shock
induced by blasting for the excavation. As
a result, the rocks in this region will be
fractured and loosened depending on a magnitude of the stress relief and an inten-

387

sity of the blasting as well as strength of the rocks. This phenomenon is referred as loosening, and such region where the rock is fractured and/or loosened is called a loosening zone. It is most important in designing rock reinforcement to predict accurately how much the loosening zone extends in the rock medium.

Generally speaking, failure mechanism of rock mass is classified into two categories. The first one is shear failure. The second one is slip failure along joints. The latter case will be more realistic, because shear strength along a joint may be much lower than a strength of the intact rock. In the present analysis, both types of failure were analysed, and those failure zone were obtained individually for a comparison.

As described in the previous section 3.2, two representative joint sets (see Fig. 5(b)) were taken into account to determine a loosening zone caused by the slip failure. Whether a slip failure occurs or not, is judged numerically by such a way as explained in Fig. 8. In the analysis, the strength parameters of the joint are taken as zero for c_j and 45° for the friction angle, ϕ_j.

Main results obtained by the numerical analysis are described below. Fig. 9 shows the lateral movement of the excavated surface on side wall of the cavern with a process of the excavation. The following conclusions may be drawn;

1. A lateral movement is very large, and the magnitude is about 50 mm at maximum. The movement on the penstock side is slightly larger than the other side.

2. The maximum displacement appears at the mid height of the side wall.

3. Due to the large movement induced by the excavation of the power station, the draft gate chamber is strongly influenced and displaces toward the station with amount of 40 mm at maximum.

The occurrence of such this large amount of movement is owing to a reason that there exists high horizontal stress remaining in the rock as previously described.

Fig. 10 represents an extent of loosening zone, in which three cases of failure, shear failure, slip failure on the joint with an inclination angle of -72° made at horizontal plane and another slip failure on the joint with 59° of an inclination angle, are shown all together.

Table 1 Elastic constants and strength constants used in the numerical analysis

Zone	Type of rock	Modulus of elasticity kgf/cm²	Poisson's ratio	Strength constants c (kgf/cm²)	ϕ
1	Diorite Porphyrite	60,000	0.25	15	55°
2	Ohto formation	Fine graind sandstone Shale	40,000	0.20	0	50°
3	Surface layer	10,000	0.20	0	45°

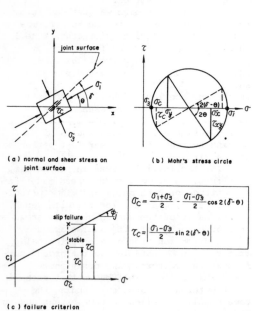

(a) normal and shear stress on joint surface

(b) Mohr's stress circle

(c) failure criterion

$$\sigma_c = \frac{\sigma_1 + \sigma_3}{2} - \frac{\sigma_1 - \sigma_3}{2} \cos 2(\delta - \theta)$$

$$\tau_c = \left| \frac{\sigma_1 - \sigma_3}{2} \sin 2(\delta - \theta) \right|$$

Fig. 8 Failure criterion for slip failure on a joint surface numerical analysis

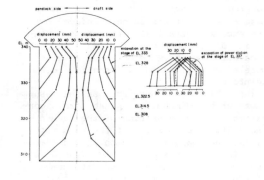

Fig. 9 Numerical result of lateral movement on the side wall of the cavern

388

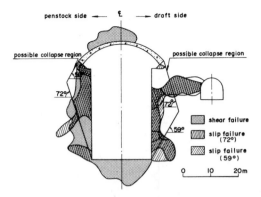

penstock side ⟶ ℓ ⟶ draft side

possible collapse region   possible collapse region

72°

72°

59°

▨ shear failure

▨ slip failure (72°)

▨ slip failure (59°)

0   10   20m

Fig. 10 Numerical result of loosening zone and determination of possible collapse region

4.2 Design procedure of rock reinforcement

A purpose of rock reinforcement in large cavern is to prevent the surrounding rock from collapsing, and to ensure a stability of the cavern during and after excavation. Rock bolts and/or steel wires are usually employed to apply a pre-stressing force to the rock. The surrounding rock which has been loosened by stress relief due to excavation, is tightened by the application of the force, and as a result, a shear resistance of the rock increases depending on the magnitude of the pre-stressing force. In the practice of the construction, immediately after a blasting was finished, a shotcrete with 10 cm of the thickness was conducted on the excavated surface for a protection of the loosening of the rock. Then, a temporary rock reinforcement was conducted by driving rock bolts of 3 or 5 m in length into the rock. Finally, a pre-stressing steel wire was then driven and a pre-stressing force was applied for a permanent rock reinforcement.

A design procedure to determine rationally a pre-stressing force required for the reinforcement is here introduced. At first, we must define a term, possible collapse region, which implies a region that would possibly collapse, unless rock reinforcement is treated. It might be corresponding to a loosening zone which can be obtained from the numerical analysis as previously described. In most cases of collapse of side wall in a cavern previously experienced, however, it arises generally along major joints. And the collapse region is not necessarily identical with the loosening zone obtained by the analysis. In the present study, taking into account the analytical result of the loosening zone and also the major joint

sets determined from geological investigation, a possible collapse region is decided as represented in Fig. 10.

The possible collapse region would be considered to change with an excavation process, but its shape would be similar in each stage as illustrated in Fig. 11. Furthermore, for simplicity of the calculation later on, a shape of the region is replaced by an appropreate circular arc as shown in the figure. Now, we consider a phenomenon of collapse more in detail. Fig. 12 represents a failure mechanism of a block. The block can be devided into two portions, primary and secondary collapse regions, from a phenomenological viewpoint of the collapse. The primary collapse is caused by a slip failure along the joint. On the other hand, in the secondary collapse region, a "falling down" will rather take place by an influence of the primary collapse. If the primary collapse is prevented from arising, however, the secondary collapse will not occur. Therefore, only a region of the primary collapse is treated in this design procedure. The region in consideration is therefore limited in the shaded area as shown in Fig. 13.

As shown in Fig. 14, a possible collapse region in each stage of the excavation is

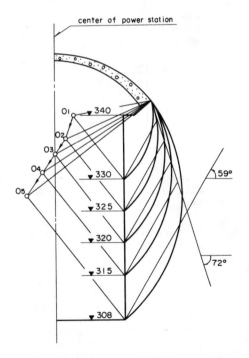

center of power station

O1 ▽ 340

O2

O3

O4 ▽ 330

O5

▽ 325

59°

▽ 320

▽ 315

72°

▽ 308

Fig. 11 Expansion of the possible collapse region corresponding to a stage of the excavation

389

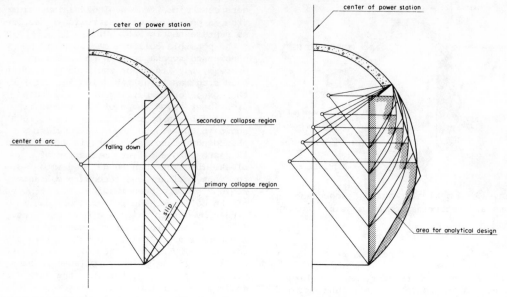

Fig. 12　Failure mechanism in the possible collapse region

Fig. 13　Analytical region considered in the design of rock reinforcement

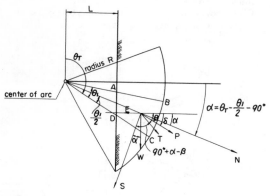

$$\alpha = \theta_r - \frac{\theta_l}{2} - 90°$$

Fig. 14　Forces acting to an arbitrary block to be considered in the design of rock reinforcement

devided into appropriate number of blocks. The forces subjecting to an arbitrary block to be taken into account are as follows;

1. Self weight of the block, W (in vertical direction): $W = W' \times (1+k)$, where W' denotes the self weight of the rock per unit thickness and k the coefficient of vibration intensity. Namely, an additional inertia force induced by vibration or shock of blasting is taken into account.

2. horizontal inertia force due to vibration or shock of blasting, E: $E = kW'$

3. thrust force as a reaction force,

transmitting from the arch concrete lining, T (with angle of β from horizontal): This force is only taken in the block adjacent to the arch abutment.

4. pre-stressing force of the steel wire to be required for rock reinforcement, P (with angle of δ from horizontal)

Assuming cohesion along slip surface to be zero, a resultant force in a tangential direction of the slip surface is given by

$$S = W \cos\alpha + E \sin\alpha + P \sin(\delta-\alpha) + T \sin(\beta-\alpha) \qquad (1)$$

where, α is expressed in terms of the angles θ_T and θ_1 shown in Fig. 14 as follows;

$$\alpha = \theta_T - \frac{1}{2} \theta_1 - 90° \qquad (2)$$

While, a resultant force in radial direction is given by

$$N = W \sin\alpha - E \cos\alpha + P \cos(\delta-\alpha) + T \cos(\beta-\alpha) \qquad (3)$$

Expressing factor of safety with a notation Fs, it can be given as

$$F_s = \frac{N \tan\phi}{S} \qquad (4)$$

where, φ means the friction angle on the slip surface.

Putting Eqs. (1) and (3) into Eq. (4), the equation to determine the pre-stressing force, P, can be deduced as follows;

390

$$P = \{ W(F_S \cos\alpha - \sin\alpha \tan\phi) + E(F_S \sin\alpha$$
$$+ \cos\alpha \tan\phi) + T(F_S \sin(\beta-\alpha)$$
$$- \cos(\beta-\alpha) \tan\phi)\}/\{ \cos(\delta-\alpha) \tan\phi$$
$$- F_S \sin(\delta-\alpha)\} \qquad (5)$$

4.3 Initial design of rock reinforcement

The pre-stressing force to be requaired to support the possible collapse region defined in Fig. 11 was calculated for each phase of excavation with Eq. (5). Numerical conditions to be employed in the calculation were determined based on the actual design conditions. They are listed in Table 2. Deviding the calculated pre-stressing force by its applied area, it is expressed in terms of pressure; the force per unit area. The result is shown in Fig. 15, in which the analytical design value implies a line connecting the maximum value obtained in the calculation for each phase of excavation. It is noted that at about mid-height of the cavern, a maximum pre-stressing force is required and its value

is about 17 tf/m². Nevertheless, supposing that the design must be decided based on the observation of actural rock behavior during the excavation period, an initial design was consciously taken as shown in the figure.

Arrangement of the pre-stressing steel wire corresponding to the distribution of pre-stressing force decided as the initial design, is represented in Fig. 16. A design value of the pre-stressing force applied to the steel wire in one position is to be 40 ton. The length of the wire was determined according to a depth of the possible collapse region.

Table 2 Numerical conditions employed in the design of rock reinforcement

Cohesion along slip surface c	0 t/m²
Friction angle on slip surface ϕ	55°
Density of rock γ	2.5 t/m³
Coefficient of vibration intensity k	0.1
Thrust force transmitting from the arch concrete lining T	300 t
Angle of the thrust force β	56°
Angle of pre-stressing force δ	10°
Factor of safety	1.1

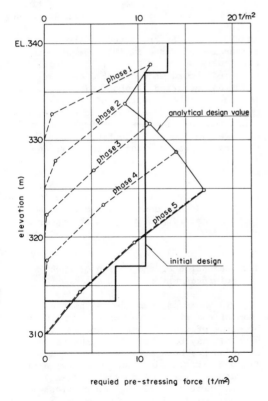

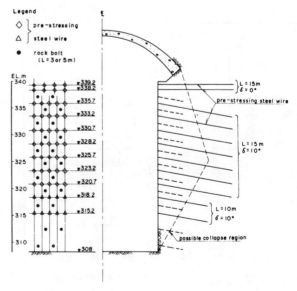

Fig. 15 Analytical design value of the pre-stressing force and initial design for rock reinforcement

Fig. 16 Arrangement of pre-stressing steel wire for the initial design of rock reinforcement

5 ASSESSMENT OF STABILITY OF THE CAVERN

5.1 Field measurement

To observe rock behavior and to confirm a stability of the cavern during the excavation, a series of field measurements was systematically carried out by means of measuring instruments. The following measurements have been taken; convergence of the span in the cavern, inward movement of the excavated rock surface, change of the applied tension load in the pre-stressing steel wire and, stress and strain in arch concrete lining. In this paper, representative data is only described in relation to the design of reinforcement.

A measurement of the convergence was taken in a cross section on the center of the generating unit from No. 1 to No. 4 unit at a few representative elevations. The obtained data is plotted in Fig. 17 which is a typical result measured at EL. 333 m, and is compared with the numerical value predicted by the finite element analysis. It is noted that the convergence

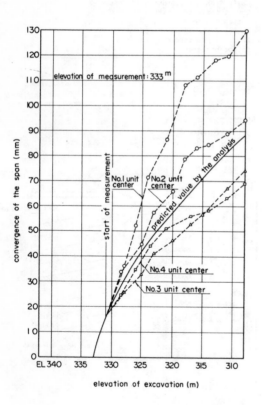

Fig. 17 Convergence of the span of the cavern and comparison between the analytically predicted value and the measured values

in No. 1 unit cross section was considerably larger compared with those in other sections. It became to be 130 mm in magnitude when the cavern has been completed in the excavation. The result in No. 2 unit cross section was 95 mm, and about 70 mm in No. 3 and 4 unit sections. It is also known from the figure that the prediction by the numerical analysis is quite good both in quantitative evaluation and tendency of increase in the convergence.

A lateral movement in the side wall of the cavern was taken measurement by an extensometer which was instrumented in a drill hole, and was anchored independently at the depth of 5, 10 and 20 m from the surface of the rock wall. The obtained result was therefore able to be evaluated as a relative displacement of the surface against a position of the anchor. The measurement was taken at appropreate elevations in both penstock and draft sides.

Fig. 18 is a representative record of the displacement which has been observed at the elevation of 333 m in the penstock side in the section of No. 1 unit center. A final displacement recorded at the time when the excavation of the cavern has been finished is 37 mm for the anchor of 20 m in the depth. As predicted by the numerical analysis of the finite element method previously shown in Fig. 9, the actually observed record showed that a maximum displacement occurred at about mid-height of the cavern. The magnitude of the displacement, however, was slightly lower than the predicted one. The maximum displacement observed in the cross section of No. 1 unit center was between 30 to 40 mm appearing at EL. 333 m, 20 to 30 mm in the section of No. 2 unit center which appeared at EL. 333 ∿ 329 m. On the other hand, it was relatively small in the sections of No. 3 and 4 unit center, 10 to 20 mm and 15 to 25 mm, respectively, both appearing at EL. 326 m.

5.2 Evaluation of the design of rock reinforcement

Fig. 19 shows an increase in the tension load of the steel wire which was measured by means of a load cell installed to the wire. It may be noted that since the excavation has been attained down to below EL. 328, tension load and also the lateral movement of the rock in the side wall began to increase rapidly with progress of the excavation in both sections of No. 1 and No. 2 unit centers. On the contrary, the increase was very small in the middle section between No. 3 and No. 4 unit centers.

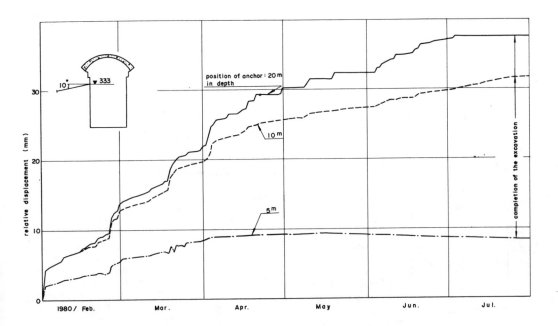

Fig. 18   Representative record of the relative displacement
on the side wall of the cavern

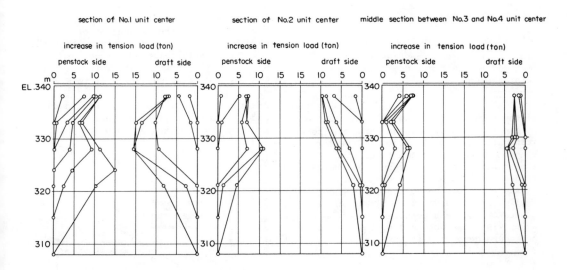

Fig. 19   Change in the tension load applied to the steel wire

   With reference to these observations by
the field measurements, it was judged
from engineering sence that such a rapid
increase in the tension load and the
movement of the rock would be probably
caused by a lack of rock reinforcement.
Therefore, the initial design of the rock
reinforcement was re-examined since then

and, the magnitude of the pre-stressing
force was increased by adding extra number
of pre-stressing steel wires in the side
of No. 1 and No. 2 generator room, as shown
in Fig. 20. On the other hand, in the side
of No. 3 and No. 4 generator room, it was
rather decreased, since the increase in
the tension load and the lateral movement

393

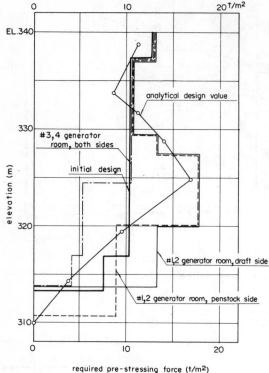

required pre-stressing force (t/m²)

Fig. 20 Required pre-stressing force employed in the final design of rock reinforcement

of the rock was comparatively small. Due to the re-examination concerning the rock reinforcement, the behavior of the surrounding rock has become to be stable and, the stability of the cavern could be maintained until it has been completed. The final design of the rock reinforcement applied in the side of No. 1 and No. 2 generator room has resultantly become to agree with that obtained by the design procedure described in this paper.

5.3 Correlation between rock movement in the cavern and rock reinforcement

As seen in a representative record of the rock displacement shown in Fig. 18, the obtained records may be generally illustrated as a schematic diagram of Fig. 21. A trace of the daily record obtained by an extensometer installed as shown in the figure exhibits a stepwise increasing curve. It is then supposed that a total displacement is composed of an instanta-

neous displacement and a retarded displacement. The former arises mainly when a blasting of the rock for bench cut is performed just under the point of the measurement. It is caused elastically by a stress relief due to the excavation and, amount of the instantaneous displacement gets smaller in general when the position of blasting is getting away from a point of the measurement. On the other hand, the latter is a displacement arising even when the excavation is at a standstill and/or a blasting is performed far away from the point of the measurement. Moreover, it has been found that this retarded displacement increases with a certain constant rate, just like a creep phenomenon of a plastic medium.

The authors paid a great attention to this fact found from the field measurement in relation to the rock reinforcement and also to a stability of the cavern. Namely, it is supposed that a rate of the retarded displacement, which may correspond to a creep velocity, is related to a degree of rock reinforcement as well as rock conditions. The rate of displacement per day was calculated from each trace of the daily record measured by the extensometer anchored at 10 m of the depth. The result is plotted in Fig. 22 in comparison with the progress of the excavation of the cavern. It is very clear to note that the rate is closely related to a performance of the rock reinforcement. Initially, it exhibited a large value of 0.1 to 0.2 mm/day. Especially, the value calculated in draft side of No. 1 unit center showed about 0.25 mm/day, which might be influenced by the excavation of the shaft

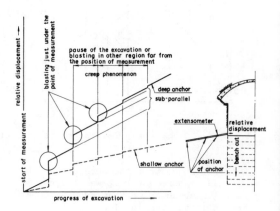

Fig. 21 Schematic diagram of the relative displacement in relation to a progress of the excavation

394

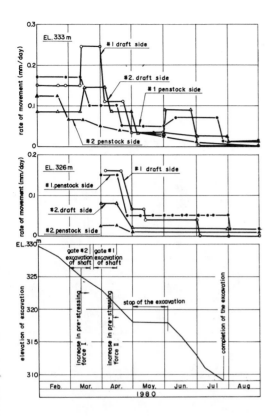

Fig. 22 Relationship between rate of rock movement and the pre-stressing force of the rock reinforcement

in the draft gate chamber locating adjacent to the power station. As a result of the increase in the pre-stressing force in accordance with re-examination of the rock reinforcement as shown in Fig. 20, however, the rate decreased gradually in magnitude. It became finally to be less than 0.1 mm/day.

The idea of the rate of displacement is a first attempt which correlates the rock movement to the design of rock reinforcement. To confirm this idea more in detail, we have to gather a lot of data. However, it is expected that this idea is one of

indices to evaluate a rock reinforcement and/or stability of a cavern.

6 CONCLUSIONS

Main conclusions obtained throughout the investigations in this project are as follows:

1. A possible collapse region was defined for a purpose of economical and realistic rock reinforcement, which could be determined from the extent of the loosening zone obtained by the numerical analysis and the characteristics of the predoninant joint sets. Based on this, a rational design procedure of rock reinforcement was established. As a result of the application of this design procedure to the present case, it was confirmed that the procedure was quite reasonable to design a pre-stressing force as the rock reinforcement.

2. The lateral movement of the side wall in the cavern was very large, probably resulting from the high horizontal in-situ stress in the base rock. The convergence of the span of the cavern to be measured became to be in a range of 70 to 130 mm when the cavern has been completely excavated.

3. It was found from the field measurement of the rock movement in the side wall that the movement consists both of elastic and plastic one, and that these two components can be separated phenomenologically from the obtained curve of the daily measurement. The elastic component is induced by a stress relief due to the excavation. Whilst, the plastic one corresponds to a deformation caused by creep characteristics of the rock medium. Moreover, it was found out that a rate of the plastic movement is closely related to amount of the pre-stressing force of the rock reinforcement. In the present case, the rate of movement was fairly large with the magnitude of about 0.15 mm/day initially as for the initial design of rock reinforcement. The slight increase in the pre-stressing force, however, reduced the rate of movement correspondingly, and it became finally to be about 0.05 mm/day.

395

ZUR AUFFAHRUNG UND ZUR STANDSICHERHEITSBEURTEILUNG GROSSER KAVERNEN
Remarks on driving and on stability analysis of major caverns
Creusement et examen de la stabilité des grandes cavernes

P.W.OBENAUER, L.LIELUPS & P.RUSE
Ingenieurbüro im Bauwesen Bung, Heidelberg, Bundesrepublik Deutschland

SUMMARY:

The feasibility of immense caverns in rock mass concerning underground nuclear power plants was analysed. In the case of the axisymmetric reactor cavern of 63 m free span an adapted solution and decision on this question was required regarding the intended purpose and some particular loadings as well as that of the special shape and the unique dimensions. A novel method of driving runs under the difficult phases of driving such a cavern by treating the rock mass gently; an early worked inner concrete lining supports the rock mass in bearing its own weight and becomes by aid of the back pressure an obstacle to the spreading of radioisotopes.

The sensivity of essential parameters was analysed by a finite element program and then very improbable but not quite unrealistic parameter constellations, which lie near the designed state, were evaluated with regard to construction phases. Despite the informality of such calculations as to an appointed site without rock mechanical investigations it could be stated that such caverns are feasible.

ZUSAMMENFASSUNG:

Die felsbauliche Realisierbarkeit sehr großer Kavernen für untertägige Kernkraftwerke wurde untersucht. Im Falle der rotationssymmetrischen Reaktorkaverne von 63 m lichter Weite forderten der Verwendungszweck und spezielle Belastungen sowie besondere Form und Größe eine angepaßte Problemlösung und -beurteilung. Ein neuartiger Auffahrvorgang unterläuft die für eine Kaverne dieser Größe schwierigen Bauzustände unter Schonung des Gebirges; eine sehr frühzeitig eingebrachte Betoninnenschale unterstützt die Tragwirkung des Gebirges und wird unter dem Gebirgsdruck zu einem Hindernis für die Ausbreitung radioaktiver Stoffe.

Es wurden mit einem FEM-Programm der Einfluß wichtiger Parameter untersucht und dann Nachbarzustände mit sehr unwahrscheinlichen Parameterkonstellationen unter Berücksichtigung von Bauzuständen berechnet. Ungeachtet der Unverbindlichkeit solcher Berechnungen für einen bestimmten Ort ohne vorausgehende felsmechanische Untersuchungen an diesem Ort konnte ausgesagt werden, daß solche Kavernen realisierbar sein werden.

RÉSUMÉ:

Nous avons examiné la possibilité de réaliser la construction rocheuse de très grandes cavernes pour des centrales nucléaires souterraines. Dans le cas de la caverne de réacteur axisymétrique et dont la largeur intérieure s' élève à 63 m, le but d'utilisation et les charges spéciales aussi que la forme et la grandeur particulières demandent une solution et un examen adaptés au problème. Une nouvelle méthode de creusement escamote les conditions difficiles que représente la construction d'une caverne d'une telle dimension, tout ménageant le massif rocheux; une coquille intérieure betonnée tres tôt étaye l'effet portatif du massif rocheux et devient, par la pression du massif rocheux, un obstacle à la diffusion des radio-éléments.

A l'aide d'un programme d'éléments finis, l'influence de paramètres importants a été examiné; puis nous avons calculé les positions avoisinantes en y joignant des constellations paramètriques très improbables en tenant compte des conditions de construction. Bien que de tels calculs soient sans engagement pour un endroit sans recherches précédentes en mécanique des roches, il est possible de dire que de telles cavernes seront réalisables.

1. EINLEITUNG

1.1 Anlaß und Problemstellung

In den Jahren 1976 bis 1979 erarbeitete das Ingenieurbüro Bung für den Bundesminister des Innern der Bundesrepublik Deutschland in zwei Stufen die Studie SR 72 (Bung 1977, 1980) "Beurteilung der felsbaulichen Realisierbarkeit großer Kavernen im Fels bei unterirdischen Kernkraftwerken". Diese Beurteilung umfaßte:
- Anordnungskonzept des Kernkraftwerkes
- Bauverfahren und bauliches Konzept
- vorläufige Standsicherheitsbeurteilung
- Bauzeiten und Baukosten.
Über Teile der drei ersten Punkte soll hier berichtet werden.

Die Problemstellung war die möglichst unveränderte Unterbringung der oberirdisch üblichen Anlagenkomplexe eines Kernkraftwerkes der Kraftwerk Union mit einem 1300 MWe-Druckwasserreaktor durch Bereitstellung von Felshohlräumen für die jeweiligen Gebäude. Eine Optimierung im Hinblick auf eine möglichst gute Nutzung der felsbaulichen Möglichkeiten, z. B. hinsichtlich der Form und Höhenlage der Gebäude, wurde in dieser Bearbeitungsstufe wegen der besonderen Komplexität eines Kernkraftwerkes noch nicht angestrebt. Damit stellte sich die Frage nach der Realisierbarkeit von Langhauskavernen mit 41 m und von rotationssymmetrischen Kavernen mit 63 m lichter Weite unter deutschen Gebirgsverhältnissen. Bei der Problemlösung mußte auch das übergeordnete Ziel eines untertage mit einem verhältnismäßigen Aufwand erreichbaren Schutzes gegen natur- und zivilisationsbedingte äußere Einwirkungen und eines zusätzlichen Sicherheitseinschlusses bei hypothetischen Unfällen bei allenbaulichen Überlegungen beachtet werden.

1.2 Vorgaben

Auf die Vorgaben bezüglich des Betriebes und der nuklearen Sicherheit sei in diesem Rahmen nicht tiefer eingegangen.

Es waren drei typische Gebirgsarten, nämlich Sandstein, Schiefer und Quarzit vorgegeben, die jeweils auch stellvertretend für solche mit ähnlichen felsmechanischen Eigenschaften standen. In jeder dieser Gebirgsarten war auch eine wirkliche Geländeform und eine zugehörige Raumstellung der hauptsächlichen regelmäßigen Trennflächen gegeben. Weitere Trennflächen, Nebentrennflächen genannt, wurden gleichmäßig verteilt, aber ganz beliebig ausgerichtet angenommen und bestimmten mit ihren Eigenschaften als unterer Abschätzung alle anderen möglichen Raumstellungen eines Bruches.

Die Festigkeitsparameter waren unabhängig vom angenommenen Ort als typisch für die Gebirgsart vorgegeben und für die Parameteruntersuchungen der Reaktorkaverne wurden sogar für alle drei Gebirgsklassen gemeinsame Mittelwerte und Grenzen dieser Parameter angegeben (Tabelle 1). Die angegebenen Mittelwerte (jeweils dritte Zeile) sind zugleich die wahrscheinlichen Werte der "mittleren" Gebirgsart Schiefer, also jene Werte, die in etwa zur Berechnung des Gebrauchszustandes oder des Vergleichszustandes in Bezug zu Messungen zu benutzen wären; die jeweils erste und vierte Zeile geben die Grenzen des Bereichs für die Parameteruntersuchung an.

Unabhängig von der Gebirgsklasse wurden auch die Überlagerung (180 m oder 270 m über Kugelmittelpunkt Kavernenkuppel) und der Seitendruckbeiwert (0,2;0,5;0,93;1,50) variiert. Die Wichte (0,027 MN/m³) und die Querdehnzahl (0,25) wurden nicht variiert. Das elastische Verhalten von Sandstein und Quarzit wurde als isotrop angenommen, so daß der einzige Unterschied zwischen beiden im Rahmen der Parameteruntersuchung der Elastizitätsmodul war (Variation 10000 MPa und 35000 MPa). Schiefer wurde transversal anisotrop mit $E_{\parallel}$= 20000 MPa und $E_{\perp}$= 7500 MPa gerechnet und zwar so, als sei er abwechselnd aus dünnen Schichten zweier isotroper Materialien aufgebaut (z. B. 98 % der Dicke E = 20404 MPa und auf 2 % der Dicke E = 196 MPa).

Großklüfte wurden für die wesentlichen Bereiche der Anlage ausgeschlossen, d.h. daß hohe Anforderungen an den Standort gestellt werden auch auf die Gefahr hin, auf einige

Tafel 1.Festigkeitskennwerte für Parameteruntersuchungen und Nachbarzustand Schiefer

Felskennwerte untere Grenze sicherer Wert wahrscheinl.W. obere Grenze	Grundmaterial einschl. Nebentrennfl.		Haupttrennflächen	
	vor Bruch	nach Bruch	vor Bruch	nach Bruch
Kohäsion MPa c	5,0	0,10	1,0	0,02
	2,5	0,05	1,25	0,025
	5,0	0,10	2,5	0,05
	10,0	0,20	5,0	0,10
Reibungs- Grad winkel ρ	25,0	20,0	20,0	20,0
	27,6	22,5	22,5	22,5
	30,0	25,0	25,0	25,0
	35,0	25,0	25,0	25,0
Zug- MPa festigkeit	0,4	0,0	0,05	0,0
	0,2	0,0	0,10	0,0
	0,4	0,0	0,20	0,0
	0,8	0,0	0,40	0,0

Standorte verzichten zu müssen. In weniger wesentlichen Bereichen, und zwar mit jeweils angemessenen Sanierungsmaßnahmen, können auch große Klüfte ertragen werden.

2 GESAMTANORDNUNG DER UNTERTAGEANLAGE

Die ungefähre Größe und Form der Kavernen ergab sich aus dem Ziel, nachzuweisen, daß die Gebäudekomplexe eines oberirdischen KKW notfalls auch nahezu unverändert untertage unterzubringen wären. Die gewählte Größe und Form berücksichtigt unter Inkaufnahme von Mehrausbruch Aspekte wie Standsicherheit der Kavernen, Bauverfahren und Raumbedarf für Zugänglichkeit sowohl im Betrieb als auch im Bauzustand und bei der Montage vieler, z. T. sehr großer Komponenten. Es ergaben sich 3 Kavernen mit großer Spannweite und großem Volumen (je etwa 180000 m³) sowie 7 kleinere Kavernen (zusammen 75000 m³).

Die ungefähre Anordnung der Kavernen ergab sich durch die Forderung, möglichst geringe Abstände im Zuge der zahlreichen Leitungsverbindungen und Verbindungswege zu erzielen. Es wurde angenommen, daß im Kavernenbereich eine Trennflächenschar, die relativ gleichmäßig hinsichtlich Neigung und Bruchverhalten ist, im Hinblick auf die Standsicherheit dominiert. Dies bedingte eine Ausrichtung der Langhauskavernen und vieler wichtiger Stollen normal zur Streichrichtung.

Anstelle einer Abhängigkeit des Abstandes der Kavernen von deren Spannweite wurde in Anbetracht der sehr verschiedenen Größen, Formen und der versetzten Anordnung davon ausgegangen, daß jede Kaverne exklusiv eine auf ihre Grundfläche bezogene Fläche des Gebirges von 4-facher Größe bei geometrischer Ähnlichkeit und gleichem Schwerpunkt entspricht. Bei langen Langhauskavernen allein entspräche dies einem Felspfeiler von 3 Spannweiten, bei rotationssymmetrischen Kavernen allein entspräche dies einem Mindestabstand von etwa 0,9 Durchmessern.

Stollen in verschiedener Höhenlage und Größe (etwa 5,0 km) sowie Schächte von insgesamt etwa 1,5 km Höhe sind aus betrieblichen, Sicherheits- (Redundanz-) und auffahrtechnischen Gründen zusätzlich in diesen Sicherheitspfeilern oder deren näherer Umgebung aufzufahren. Die Länge der 6 horizontalen Stollen aus diesem Bereich zum Vorland und zum Vorfluter betrug je nach Standort zusammen zusätzlich zwischen 2,5 und 5,0 km.

Die Anordnung der 3 großen und von 4 der 7 kleinen Kavernen wurde unabhängig von Gebirgsklasse und Geländeform stets beibehalten. Die 3 restlichen Kavernen wurden je nach Lage der Untertageanlage zum Vorfluter als ganze Gruppe der erstgenannten Gruppe neu zugeordnet, nachdem diese im Hinblick auf geeignete Überlagerung, geringe Länge der Fahr- und Leitungsstollen und die Streichrichtung der Haupttrennfläche in das Gebirge am Standort eingepaßt worden waren.

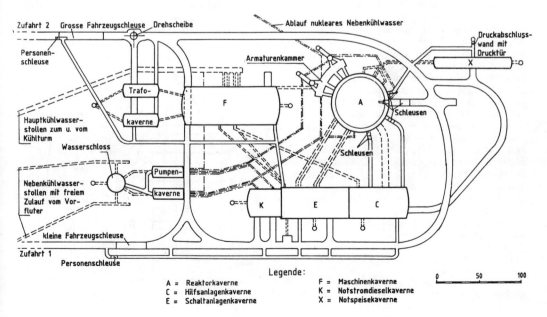

Bild 1: Grundriß Untertageanlage am Standort Schiefer

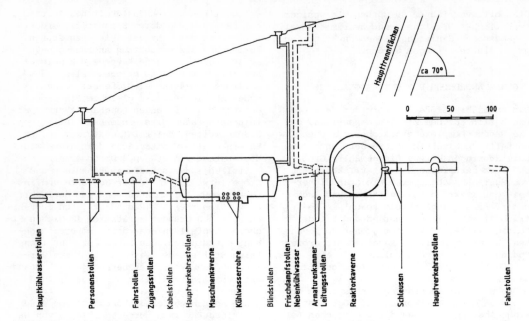

Bild 2: Schnitt durch die größten Kavernen am Standort Schiefer

Bild 1 und 2 zeigen die Anordnung am Standort Schiefer.

3 DIE REAKTORKAVERNE

3.1 Besonderheiten im Hinblick auf Zweck, Belastung, Größe und Form

Für die Reaktorkaverne war festgelegt, daß
die Anlagen, einschl. deren Anordnung und
der Verbindung nach außen, nicht verändert
werden durften. Es war allein eine Erweiterung des Raumes nach außen erlaubt, um Raum
für die Montage der Stahlhülle schaffen und
um die zum Hilfsanlagengebäude führenden
Leitungen besser bündeln zu können.

Die Form des Reaktorgebäudes (oberirdisch),
bestehend aus einer Halbkugel und einem
Stück Kreiszylinder, ist für die Untertagebauweise sehr gut geeignet und wurde deshalb
unter Schaffung eines allseitig gleichen
Montageraumes im wesentlichen beibehalten;
nur der untere Teil des Kreiszylinders wurde durch eine Kugelzone ersetzt, so daß die
ursprüngliche Grundfläche der Sohle und
eine Form mit geringeren Spannungskonzentrationen erreicht wurde. Es ergab sich dabei eine lichte Weite von 63 m und eine
lichte Höhe von 66 m.

Die Form ist für die Membranwirkung des
Ausbaus nahezu ideal; kleine Korrekturen
beim Übergang zwischen Zylinder und Kugel-
schale und Sohle sind denkbar. Dies gilt

auch für den unausgebauten Zustand bei isotrop anzunehmendem Fels. Bei geklüftet anzunehmendem Fels wäre die ideale Form von
der Raumstellung und Festigkeit der Trennflächen abhängig, was bei einem allgemein
gültigen Konzept nicht genutzt werden kann.
Die günstige Form des Endzustandes für den
Spannungszustand im Fels ist ohnehin nur
dann voll zu nutzen, wenn auch in den Bauzuständen günstige Spannungsverhältnisse
herrschen und die Entfestigung des Gebirges
möglichst auf jene Bereiche beschränkt wer-

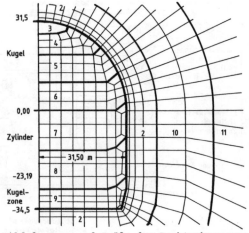

Bild 3: Form und Größe der Reaktorkaverne;
Ausbruchfolge (3 bis 9) bei Kalottenausbruch

den kann, die auch im Endzustand betroffen
wären.

Beim bestimmungsgemäßen Betrieb eines Kernkraftwerkes wird die Reaktorkaverne nur
durch eine geringfügige Anhebung der Temperatur im Innenraum und durch relativ hohe
Lasten auf die Sohle sowie gewisse Kräfte
im Zuge der Durchführungen von Rohrleitun-
gen belastet. Alle diese Beanspruchungen
erscheinen vergleichsweise gering und gut-
artig.

Im Falle schwerer hypothetischer Reaktor-
unfälle muß jedoch mit hohen Innendrücken
(bis etwa 10 bar) und Temperaturen (bis
max. 180° C) gerechnet werden. Ferner muß
ein möglichst dichter Einschluß gewährleistet werden. Zu diesem Zweck war zum einen
ein möglichst dichter innerer Ausbau und
zum anderen ein möglichst ungestörter, even-
tuell noch durch Injektionen verbesserter
Fels in der Umgebung der Kaverne erforderlich.

Die Besonderheiten von Zweck, Belastung,
Größe und Form der Reaktorkaverne machten
somit spezielle Überlegungen zum Auffahrvorgang, zum Ausbau und zur Standsicherheitsbeurteilung erforderlich.

3.2 Spezielle Auffahrmethode

In Anbetracht der besonderen Forderungen
wurden zwei Bauweisen untersucht und einander gegenübergestellt. Die eine ist die
derzeit übliche mit Ankerung zur Unterstützung der Tragfähigkeit des Gebirges und mit
Spritzbeton, angewendet auf eine Auffahrung,
die mit der Kalotte beginnt (Zone 3 in
Bild 3) und sich strossenweise bis zur Sohle
(Zone 9) fortsetzt.

Die zweite Bauweise wurde für die speziellen Bedingungen dieser Kaverne neu entwickelt und ist entgegen dem ersten An-
schein nicht eine Wiederaufnahme von Kernbauweise des Tunnelbaus und traditionellem
Stahlbetongewölbe. Anker und Spritzbeton
dienen in erster Linie als temporärer Ausbau; vor dem Einbringen der Innenschale
sind die Anker zu verpressen.

Die Auffahrung der Kaverne beginnt mit
einem Ringstollen am Umfang der Sohle
(Zone 3 in Bild 4) von einem diagonal ver-
laufenden Erschließungsstollen aus. Beide
Stollen, deren Größe weitgehend nach baubetrieblichen Gesichtspunkten gewählt werden kann, werden vorläufig verbaut und ge-
gebenenfalls geankert; im Ringstollen wird
bereits ein Teil der Innenschale betoniert.
Die Auflockerung um diesen Stollen hält sich
in engen Grenzen, wobei ein großer Teil dieser Auflockerungszone, (z. B. über der Firste) in Bereiche fällt, die später ebenfalls

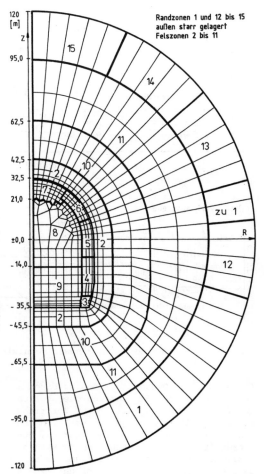

Bild 4: Auffahrfolge (3 bis 9) Schlitzbauweise

auszubrechen sind. Zugleich wird auf einer
höheren Ebene ein zweiter Diagonalstollen
aufgefahren und zwei Schächte, die der Versorgung dienen können, zum inneren Rand des
Ringstollens abgeteuft.

Alsdann wird der frische Beton im Ringstollen und die Anschlußbewehrung zum Schutz
gegen Beschädigung abgedeckt und begonnen,
den Ringstollen nach oben zu einem Ringschlitz zu erweitern. Dabei ist der bereits
aufgelockerte Fels über der Firste, der zwei
freie Oberflächen hat, zu lösen. Ein Teil
des gelösten Materials kann jeweils zur Auffüllung des Schlitzes und zur Herstellung
einer bequemen Arbeitsebene genutzt werden.
Das restliche Ausbruchmaterial kann ohne
Störung der Sicherungs- und weiterer Bohrarbeiten auf der etwas tieferliegenden Ebene geladen und zu Abwurfschächten gebracht
werden, die zusammen mit dem Schlitz aufge-

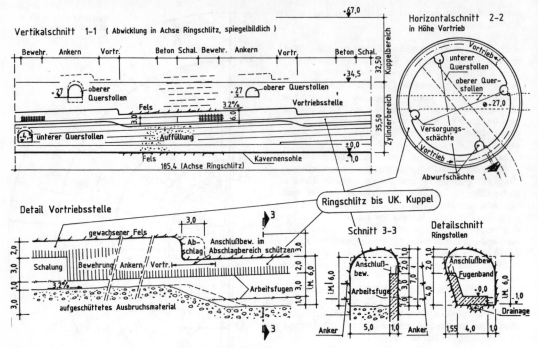

Bild 5: Schema der Auffahrung sowie Schnitte und eine Abwicklung des Schlitzes

fahren werden. Dieser Teil des Ausbruchmaterials wird über den unteren Querstollen abgefahren. Für den Fall zweier Vortriebsstellen wird die Abfolge von Vortrieb (Lösen, Spritzen und Schuttern), Ankern, Bewehren, Schalen und Betonieren in Bild 5 gezeigt. Diese Vortriebsart kann bis in den unteren Bereich der Kuppel beibehalten werden.

Eine Darstellung der Spannungen um den Ringschlitz herum (Bild 6) zeigt, wie wenig weiträumig der Spannungszustand durch das Auffahren verändert wurde. Die Firste ist durch den stehenbleibenden Kern nach wie vor gestützt; der Kern selbst kann sich in den Schlitz hinein entspannen und gibt dabei auch in vertikaler Richtung etwas nach. Der Kern wird durch das aufgeschüttete Ausbruchmaterial gestützt, so daß keine plötzliche und vollständige Entspannung zu erwarten ist. Durch den sich nach oben erweiternden Schlitz und die allmähliche Entspannung des Kernes nähert man sich dem sekundären Spannungszustand so direkt und so schonend wie möglich. Im Gegensatz zur Kernbauweise ist der Ringschluß bei der Schlitzbauweise mit 6 m Abstand (ca. 1/10 Durchmesser) zu der ringförmigen, nach oben wandernden Ortsbrust sehr frühzeitig.

Die äußerst vorteilhafte Form der Betonschale aus Zylinder und Kugelfläche erlaubt die Ausbildung eines hohen Ausbauwiderstandes im Vergleich zu den resultierenden Schalenkräften (200 % und mehr gegenüber Langhauskavernen); daher kann das Verhältnis von Schalendicke zu Spannweite mit 1 : 64 extrem gering gehalten werden.

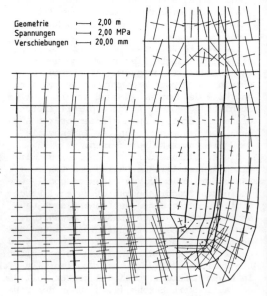

Bild 6: Spannung in Umgebung des Schlitzes

Die Freisetzung der Firste kann, wie in
SR 72 vorgeschlagen, durch im Grundriß diagonal im Aufriß kreisförmige Stollen erfolgen, die sich im Scheitel treffen oder,
was als Alternative zu untersuchen wäre,
durch einen Kalottenraum, ähnlich wie bei
der ersten Auffahrmethode, wobei dieser
Raum jedoch in den schon weitgehend ent-
spannten Fels vorgetrieben und ebenfalls
direkt in den Endzustand übergehen könnte.

Nach Erreichen der Firste und Schließen
der Betonkuppel kann der Kern im Steinbruch-
betrieb von oben nach unten abgebrochen werden, wobei der verfüllte Ringschlitz die Betonschale schützt. Die große Menge des Ausbruchmaterials kann durch verbesserte Trans-
portmöglichkeiten nunmehr leicht abtranspor-
tiert werden. Zuletzt kann die Betonschale
eingebracht und sofort mit der Ausführung
der inneren Betoneinbauten begonnen werden.

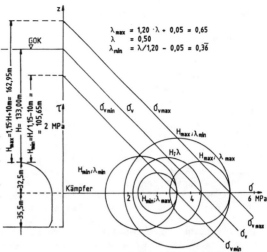

Bild 7: Nachbarzustände und Sicherheitsbei-
werte des Primärspannungszustandes für den
Kämpfer am Standort Schiefer

3.3 Methode des Standsicherheitsnachweises und gewählte Sicherheitsabstände

Bei unterirdischen Kernkraftwerken kommt
dem Standsicherheitsnachweis aus drei Gründen besondere Bedeutung zu:
- eine Gefährdung der nuklearen Anlagen und
  zugehöriger Sicherheitssysteme muß wegen
  der schwer absehbaren Folgen ausgeschlossen werden;
- nachträgliche Änderungen und Verstärkungen im Rahmen einer Langzeitbeobachtung
  (observational method) sind durch die
  Enge vieler Räume und Strahlenschutzauf-
  lagen erschwert und bedingen ein hohes
  finanzielles Risiko (Stillstandszeiten);
- bei den hypothetischen inneren Störfällen
  können Innendrücke und -temperaturen auftreten, deren Einfluß auf die Standsicherheit weder aus Erfahrung noch aus Beobachtung zu beurteilen ist und daher einer
  Prognose bedarf.

Die Sicherheitsanalyse erfordert die Kenntnis des Einflusses einzelner Parameter auf
das jeweilige Sicherheitskriterium bei den
gegebenen Verhältnissen hinsichtlich Geometrie, Werkstoffen (Spannungs-Dehnungsgeset-
ze und Festigkeit), Belastung (Primärspannungszustand, spätere Lastfälle) und Bauverfahren (Bauzustände und Art des Ausbaues).
Diese Kenntnis ist in die deterministische
Untersuchung von charakteristischen Nach-
barzuständen in der Form verteilter Sicher-
heitsbeiwerte einzubringen. Die Nachbarzustände entstehen aus mittleren Zuständen
(z. B. Gebrauchszustand) durch "kombinierte
Veränderung mehrerer verallgemeinerter Parameter" (Duddeck 1980). Diese Sicherheits-
beiwerte sind so zu wählen, daß das Auftreten der Nachbarzustände am Bauwerk mit sehr

hoher Wahrscheinlichkeit ausgeschlossen werden kann.

Als Sicherheitskriterium für mehr als lokales Versagen der Standsicherheit wurde die
Konvergenz bei der nichtelastischen Berechnung angenommen. Gegen lokales Versagen sind
konstruktive Maßnahmen vorgesehen. Die Si-
cherheitsbeiwerte wurden in drei Gruppen
eingeteilt; sie betreffen die Ungewißheiten
- bei der Annahme oder Bestimmung des primären Spannungszustandes (oder anderer
  Lasten);
- bei der Geometrie (Bautoleranzen) sowie
  bei dem Spannungs-Dehnungsverhalten und
  dem zugehörigen Rechenverfahren (Differenz zwischen primärem und sekundärem
  Spannungszustand) und
- bei den Festigkeiten und deren Anwendung
  auf den sekundären Spannungszustand.
In der ersten Gruppe wurden die Überdeckung
der Kaverne und der Seitendruckbeiwert als
maßgeblich gewählt. In der zweiten Gruppe
wäre von der Berechnung her nur eine Veränderung der Steifigkeitsverhältnisse prakti-
kabel gewesen, hätte jedoch doppelten Aufwand benötigt, weshalb davon abgesehen wurde. Außerdem betreffen diese Sicherheits-
werte den Übergang (Differenz) vom primären
zum sekundären Spannungszustand und beide
Zustände können ihrerseits mit etwas höheren
Sicherheitsbeiwerten versehen werden.

In der ersten Gruppe mußten Sicherheits-
abstände nach beiden Seiten vorgegeben werden, weil, z. B. bei Innendruck, eine geringere Überdeckung ungünstiger als eine
höhere sein kann. Bild 7 zeigt die für diese Studie gewählten Nachbarwerte zur Über-

deckung H, zum Seitendruckbeiwert λ und die Mohr'schen Kreise des Primärspannungszustandes und der 4 Nachbarzustände in Höhe des Kämpfers.

Bei den Festigkeiten sind nur Abminderungen vorzusehen. Für den Fall Schiefer sind die Nachbarwerte in Tafel 1 jeweils in der zweiten Zeile eines Blockes als "sichere Werte" angegeben. Das gleiche ist in Bild 8 unten dargestellt, nur die Linie "sichere Restfestigkeit" (etwa 90 % Restfestigkeit) fehlt. Im gleichen Bild oben sind die entsprechenden Angaben für Beton und Betonstahl gemacht. Da die Rechenfestigkeiten bei beiden Werkstoffen schon versteckte Sicherheiten enthalten und da die Eigenschaften dieser Werkstoffe geringeren Streuungen unterliegen, wurden die Sicherheitsabschläge mit 30 % statt 50 % bei Fels angesetzt. In einachsiger Druckfestigkeit ausgedrückt ergeben sich beim Beton (B 25) eine Anfangsfestigkeit von 16,46 MPa, eine sichere Festigkeit von 8,87 MPa = $\beta_R/1{,}97$, also ein Sicherheitsbeiwert von 1,97 und eine Restfestigkeit von 0,22 MPa.

Auf eine Schwierigkeit sei hier schon hingewiesen: Liegt der Reibungswinkel ρ unter dem Wert arcsin $[(1-\lambda)/(1+\lambda)]$ beim Grundmaterial und arcsin $[(1-\lambda)/\sqrt{1/\sin^2\alpha+\lambda^2/\cos^2\alpha}]$ bei mit dem Winkel α einfallenden Trennflächen, so ist ab einer bestimmten Tiefe schon der angenommene Primärzustand evtl. nicht möglich und ein höherer Seitendruckbeiwert erforderlich. Mit den Werten λ und ρ des Nachbarzustandes liegt diese Grenze schon bei geringer Tiefe. Am Standort Quarzit bei sehr kleinem Seitendruckbeiwert (λ_{min} = 0,2) und Haupttrennflächen in ungünstigster Stellung lag diese Umlagerungsgrenze nur 8 m unter der Sohle der Kaverne.

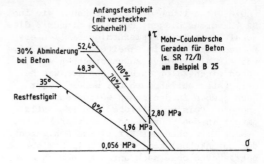

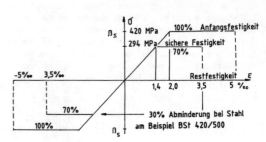

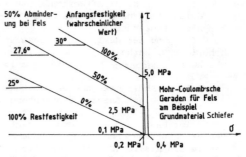

Bild 8: Anfangs-, "sichere" und Restfestigkeiten für Beton, Betonstahl und Schiefer

3.4 Berechnungsverfahren

Als Berechnungsverfahren für eine nach Sicherheitsanforderungen, Größe und Belastung neuartige Kaverne zur Untersuchung des Einflusses vieler Parameter kam nur die Finite-Element-Methode (FEM) in Frage. Auch für die Berechnung der Nachbarzustände, die in vielen Fällen hochgradig nichtlinear sind, waren Berechnungen eines Abbildungsmodelles nach diesem Verfahren erforderlich. Dies schließt jedoch nicht aus, daß viele Erkenntnisse schneller, übersichtlicher und billiger bereits durch Anwendung fertiger Lösungen der Elastizitätstheorie, einfache Rechnungen und Überlegungen zu finden und bei der Wahl der Kavernenform und der Ausbaumittel und -abmessungen anzuwenden waren. Die aufwendige FEM dient dann der notwendigen Nachrechnung des vorgegebenen Systems als Abbildungsmodell, da kein anerkanntes technisches Ersatzmodell zur Verfügung steht. Auf die Grenzen der Anwendung, auch der FEM speziell im Felshohlraumbau wurde an anderer Stelle (Lielups u. Obenauer 1979) ausführlich hingewiesen.

3.4.1 Einfache Abschätzungen und Berechnungen

Die richtige Wahl und Reihenfolge der Anwendung einfacher Abschätzungen ist problemabhängig und daher nur bedingt übertragbar. Die erste Abschätzung könnte die "Verträglichkeit des anzunehmenden Primärspannungszustandes mit den anzunehmenden Festigkeiten" (Abschnitt 3.3) betreffen; hierbei wird in etwa der Spielraum angedeutet, den man für die Störung des Primärzustandes zur Verfügung hat.

Die zweite Abschätzung ergibt sich, wenn

man eine ein- oder zweiachsig freie Quer-
dehnung zuläßt. In beiden Fällen können
sowohl die Gesteinsfestigkeit als auch die
Festigkeit bekannter oder vermuteter Trennflächen in der jeweiligen Raumstellung getrennt berücksichtigt werden. Da die Fest-
igkeitsüberschreitung in den Haupttrennflächen von den Raumstellungen des Primärspannungszustandes und der Trennflächen
zueinander in hohem Maße abhängt, ist eine
Abschätzung der Hauptspannungsrichtungen,
z. B. unter einem mit dem Winkel α einfallenden Hang, angezeigt. Nach Bung 1977
(Anlage A) neigt sich die absolut größere
Druckspannung um $\alpha_O = 0,5 \cdot \arctan |2 \cdot \lambda \cdot tg\alpha/(1-\lambda)|$
in Richtung auf die Fallinie. Bei der Hang-
neigung von 11,5° am Standort Schiefer er-
gab sich beim $\lambda_{min} = 0,3\overline{6}$ nur 6,6° Winkelab-
weichung, was für die unter 70° einfallende
Haupttrennfläche (Bild 2) eine unbegrenzte,
gleichmäßige Heraufsetzung aller Komponenten
des Spannungszustandes ohne Bruch erlaubt.
Die Erkenntnis lautet, daß
- der Primärzustand in diesem Fall außer-
ordentlich günstig ist, daß aber
- eine große Empfindlichkeit des Spannungszustandes und der Haupttrennflächen hinsichtlich Abweichungen besteht. Solche
Abweichungen sind für den Spannungszustand in Hohlraumnähe unvermeidbar und
können für die Haupttrennflächen im Ge-
birgskomplex durchaus vorkommen.
Daher wäre bei manchen Standorten ein Sicherheitsbeiwert hinsichtlich der Raumstellung der Haupttrennflächen angezeigt.

Zur Abschätzung des Sekundärspannungszu-
standes, insbesondere des Spannungsverlau-
fes an der Kavernenleibung kann oft eine
Lösung aus der Elastizitätstheorie (z.B. für
zweidimensionale Probleme aus Sawin 1956
oder für dreidimensionale Probleme aus
Lurje 1963) angewendet werden. Dabei müssen
der Spannungszustand, die Form des Hohlraumes und die Randbedingungen möglichst gut
passen, was beim Endzustand manchmal, aber
bei Bauzuständen selten gegeben sein wird.
Man kann versuchen, für jede Hauptspannung
getrennt näherungsweise eine Hohlraumform
zu finden, die, in Richtung dieser Spannung
gesehen, die gleiche Ansichtsfläche und am
betrachteten Ort die gleiche Krümmung wie
der planmäßige Hohlraum hat.
Im vorliegenden Fall konnte für den oberen
Kavernenbereich im Endzustand der sphärische
Hohlraum genutzt werden. Ist r der Radius,
σ_v die Vertikalspannung in der Höhe des Mit-
telpunktes, λ der Seitendruckbeiwert (beide
Richtungen), p die Summe aus Innendruck und
konstantem Ausbauwiderstand aus Betonschale
und q der konstante Ausbauwiderstand aus
Ankerung sowie a die Ankerlänge, so ergibt
sich mit θ = 0 im Scheitel und μ = 0,25:

$$\sigma_\theta = \sigma_v \{23,25-30 \cos^2\theta + \lambda (-6+30 \cos^2\theta)\}/11,5 \\ -0,5(p+q)+5 \ qr^2/6/(r+a)^2$$

$$\sigma_\phi = \sigma_v \{0,75-7,5 \cos^2\theta + \lambda (16,5+7,5 \cos^2\theta)\}/11,5 \\ -0,5(p+q)+5qr^2/6/(r+a)^2$$

$$\sigma_n = p+q$$

Voraussetzung ist die Konstanz der primären
Vertikalspannung über den ganzen Raum und
der Ausbauwiderstände über die ganze Kugelfläche. Wie FE-Berechnungen zeigten, kann
man für jeden untersuchten Punkt näherungsweise die Vertikalspannung dieses Punktes
in die Formeln einsetzen, um dann die Span-
nungen σ_θ und σ_ϕ dieses Punktes zu berechnen
(Bild 9).
   Den obigen Formeln kann man den Unterschied
zwischen beiden Ausbauwiderstandsarten ent-
nehmen. Bei Innendruck und Widerstand einer
Schale entsteht in Normalenrichtung Druck,
aber in der Tangentialebene Zug der halben
Größe, was z. B. im Scheitel unerwünscht
sein kann. Anders bei kurzen Ankern; im vorliegenden Fall mit einem Radius von 32,5 m
tritt bis zu 9,5 m wirksamer Ankerlänge in
der Tangentialebene Druck auf.
   Der Berechnung der Spannungen muß der Vergleich mit den Festigkeiten folgen. Gegebe-
nenfalls muß zuvor für jeden Punkt (φ;θ)
die Transformation in ein trennflächenbezoge-
nes Koordinatensystem erfolgen. Die Beurteilung der Entfernung des Spannungszustandes
vom Bruchkriterium (Sicherheitsabstand)

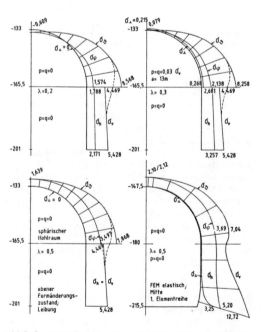

Bild 9: Vergleich von Spannungsabschätzung
(elastisch) und FEM-Berechnung (unten rechts)

405

setzt Annahmen über Art und Umfang der möglichen Abweichungen des grob berechneten Spannungszustandes voraus und kann sich an dieser Stelle schon einmal zu einer kleinen Parameterstudie ausweiten.

3.4.2 Methode der finiten Elemente anhand des verwendeten Programmes

Das Programm PAM-GEOM (Program in Applied Mechanics/Geomechanical Analyses) der Firma ESI (Dubois, Bianchini, Locci 1978) soll der physikalisch nichtlinearen, statischen, aber auch zeitabhängigen Berechnung von Baukörpern nach der Methode der Finiten Elemente dienen. Das Programm arbeitet nach der Formänderungsgrößenmethode und verwendet je ein isoparametrisches, rotationssymmetrisches 4-Knoten-Körperelement, 2-Knoten-Kluftelement und 2-Knoten-Schalenelement. Das Programm wurde vorzugsweise zur Berechnung von Baukörpern entwickelt, die teils oder ganz aus Boden oder Fels bestehen. Sie müssen in ihrer Geometrie und in ihren elastischen Eigenschaften rotationssymmetrisch sein (Reaktorkaverne, Schächte) oder sich näherungsweise über einen ebenen Formänderungszustand darstellen lassen (Maschinenkaverne, Stollen), wobei der Berechnungsausschnitt sehr weit von der Rotationsachse entfernt liegt.

Die elastischen Eigenschaften können meist isotrop und teils auch orthotrop sein, wobei zwei Orthotropieachsen in der Meridianebene liegen müssen.

Die Belastung und die Spannungen können entweder rotationssymmetrisch oder einfachsymmetrisch zu einem ausgezeichneten Meridianschnitt sein; im letzteren Falle ist die Eingabe über Fourierkoeffizienten möglich. Die Eingabe von Primärspannungen kann als lineare Funktion der Koordinaten angegeben werden. Volumenkräfte (bereichsweise), Flächenbelastung (knotenweise normal zu Elementgrenzen), Linienlasten, Verschiebungen und evtl. Verdrehungen (alle knotenweise) sowie Temperatur (knotenweise, auf benachbarte Elemente ausstrahlend) können über eine fiktive Zeitachse veränderlich vorgegeben werden; bei jeder Teilberechnung, die stets einer Zeit zugeordnet ist, wird die zugehörige Belastung interpoliert. Die Flächenbelastung wurde z. B. zur Realisierung der Vorspannung durch Anker benutzt, die Temperaturbelastung z. B. zur Darstellung des Schwindens.

Es ist nur die Erstellung eines ebenen Netzes (Meridianschnitt) erforderlich. Als Randbedingung sind freie Knoten und starre Festhaltungen in den Achsenrichtungen möglich. Elastische Festhaltungen, z. B. auch der Fels außerhalb des Berechnungsausschnittes, wurden durch Randelemente (s. Bild 4) mit entsprechend abgestimmten Eigenschaften modelliert. Die Materialparameter, nicht jedoch die Materialgesetze, können zwischen den Teilberechnungen eines Problemes verändert werden; so können z. B. das Altern des Betons und felsverbessernde Maßnahmen erfaßt werden. Von Beginn an definierte Zonen können auch zwischen den Teilberechnungen entfernt oder hinzugefügt werden, z. B. zur Darstellung der Bauzustände.

Für die Schalenelemente besteht nur ein linearelastisches Materialgesetz.

Für die Kluftelemente besteht ein linearelastisch-plastisches Materialgesetz.

Für die 4-Knoten-Elemente stehen 7 Materialgesetze zur Verfügung, davon zwei rein elastische, eines mit den vier alternativ zu wählenden, allgemeinen Plastizitätsgesetzen v. Mises, Drucker-Prager, Tresca und Mohr-Coulomb und vier mit jeweils sehr speziellen Gesetzen für Beton, Fels und Bewehrung oder Felsanker.

Die volle Dilatanz führte bei dem assoziierten Fließgesetz der allgemeinen Plastizitätsgesetze zu Schwierigkeiten bei Elementen am Ausbruchrand, weil ein brechendes Element sich nicht durch ein Ausweichen oder Ausbauchen zwischen den Knotenlinien entspannen kann und das ungebrochene Nachbarelement sprengt, so daß der Bruch sich ungerechtfertigterweise ausdehnt.

Das Materialgesetz Stahl erlaubt die Modellierung dreier gleichmäßig über das Volumen verteilter, rechtwinklig zueinander angeordneter, ansonsten voneinander unabhängiger Bewehrungsscharen (im Beton oder als Anker im Fels) mit idealelastisch - idealplastischem Verhalten und Bruch.

Das eine Werkstoffgesetz für Fels als plastisches Material mit gleichzeitig überall anzutreffender Klüftung (Dubois, Obenauer 1979) wurde für klüftigen Fels mit Schieferung oder einer vorherrschenden Schar von Klüften entwickelt. Es wird unterschieden zwischen Eigenschaften für das Grundmaterial, wobei hier auch die Eigenschaften untergeordneter Kluftsysteme berücksichtigt werden müssen und den Eigenschaften der Haupttrennflächen. Bei den plastischen Eigenschaften wird sowohl für das Grundmaterial wie für die Haupttrennflächen unterschieden zwischen einem Schubbruch (Mohr-Coulomb) mit Vorgabemöglichkeit für den Grad der Dilatanz, für Restkohäsion und Restreibungswinkel und einem Trennbruch bei Überschreiten der Zugfestigkeit (Restfestigkeit null).

Die plastische Dehnung, die einer Öffnung der Haupttrennflächen entspricht, wird ihrer Größe nach verfolgt; die Spannungen in der Haupttrennfläche werden bei geöffneter Haupt

trennfläche gleich null gesetzt und nach
Schließen des Spaltes wieder zugelassen. Im
Grundmaterial selbst wird die Raumstellung
sowie das Öffnen und Schließen der Brüche
nicht verfolgt.

Das zweite Werkstoffgesetz für Fels ist
thermo-visco-elasto-plastisch und wurde
wegen vernachlässigbaren zeitabhängigen
Verhaltens nicht benötigt.

Das Materialgesetz für Beton umfaßt drei
Brucharten und benötigt versuchsmäßig zu
ermittelnde Werte, die nicht vorlagen. Es
wurde daher auf dieses Gesetz verzichtet
und mit dem einfachen Mohr-Coulomb-Gesetz
gerechnet, das einfacher und schneller arbeitet.

Die Rechenläufe sind rein elastische Teilberechnungen mit nachträglicher Abfrage auf
Überschreitung der jeweils material- und
zustandsspezifischen Bruchbedingungen an
den Integrationspunkten und anschließender
Spannungsumlagerung bei eingefrorenem Deh-
nungszustand. Die durch Spannungsumlagerung
aus dem Gleichgewicht geratenen Knotenkräfte gehen bei der folgenden Teilberechnung
neben Veränderungen äußerer Belastungen in
die Belastung des Systemes ein. Die neu berechneten Verschiebungen und Spannungen werden den gespeicherten Verschiebungen und
Spannungen hinzugefügt. Ähnliches gilt bei
Wegnahme von Zonen.

Bei der Berechnung einfach symmetrischer
Zustände mittels Fourierzerlegung müssen
die Knotenkräfte zur entkoppelten elastischen Berechnung jeweils zerlegt und zur
Abfrage der Spannungsüberschreitung jeweils
wieder superponiert werden.

3.5 Rechenergebnisse und Schlußfolgerungen

Bei den Parameteruntersuchungen mittels der
FE-Berechnung ergab sich vor allem, wie auch
schon gemäß Bild 9 zu erwarten war, der
überragende Einfluß des Seitendruckbeiwer-
tes. Der zweite überragende Einfluß, nämlich die Raumstellung der Haupttrennflächen
bei großen Unterschieden zwischen der Festigkeit der Haupttrennflächen und des
Grundmaterials, konnte im Rahmen der Para-
untersuchungen nicht nachvollzogen werden,
da der hierfür notwendige Rechenaufwand
wegen der erforderlichen Fourierzerlegung
in jedem Einzelfall etwa 8fach und wegen
der erforderlichen Schrittweite bei der Variation des Fallwinkels (z. B. alle 10 Grad)
in etwa 80-fach gegenüber einer der anderen
Variationen eines Parameters angewachsen
wäre. Es wurde daher bei allen Variationen
mit horizontalen Haupttrennflächen gerechnet. Ein bemerkenswertes Ergebnis war auch,
daß bei höherem Elastizitätsmodul des Felses

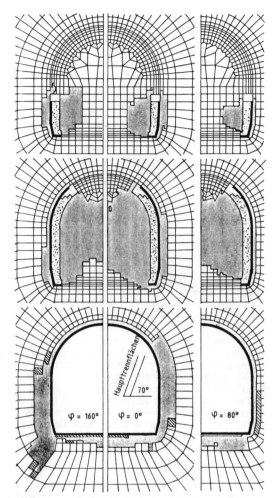

Bild 10: Überbeanspruchte Bereiche Nachbarzustand Standort Schiefer in 3 Radialebenen

und gleicher Festigkeit wegen der geringeren Verschiebungen in den Hohlraum hinein
eine geringere Reaktion der Betonschale
(Ausbauwiderstand) geweckt und somit der
Fels weniger gestützt wurde, was im steife-
ren (besseren?) Fels größere Bruchzonen als
im weicheren Fels verursachte. Da in den Parameteruntersuchungen die Bauzustände sehr
stark abgekürzt berechnet wurden, kam bei
diesen Berechnungen allerdings der Vorteil
des frühzeitigen Einbringens der Betonschale nicht voll zum Tragen. Der Einfluß des
Ausbauwiderstandes und auch der Einfluß der
Ankerlänge erwies sich bei dem noch weitgehend elastischen Verhalten des Gesamtsystems
als von geringem Einfluß. Bei den Parameteruntersuchungen wurden Lastfälle mit Innendruck berechnet.

407

Auch die Untersuchung der Nachbarzustände mußte bei diesen Untersuchungen unvollständig bleiben. Es wurde jeweils nur ein Nachbarzustand mit H_{max} und λ_{min} berechnet. Für jede der drei Gebirgsarten wurde eine Berechnung mit den 7 Ausbruchzonen und 6 Betonierzonen der Schlitzbauweise (Bild 4) und für den Standort Sandstein zusätzlich eine Berechnung mit den 7 Ausbruchzonen (Bild 3) der Kalotten-Strossenbauweise durchgeführt. Im Bild 10 sind für den Standort Schiefer für 2 Bauzustände und den Endzustand in je 3 Radialschnitten die überanspruchten Zonen des Felses dargestellt. Der jeweilige Bauzustand mit der entsprechenden Betonschale und der Auffüllung mit Ausbruchmaterial sowie dem Luftraum darüber ist jeweils zu erkennen. Zum ersten dieser Zustände gehört als Spannungs- und Verformungsbild Bild 6.

Da die Berechnung den Nachbarzustand und nicht den Gebrauchszustand betrifft, ist die Größe der überanspruchten Zonen nicht die zu erwartende Größe, sondern eine mit höchster Wahrscheinlichkeit nicht auftretende. Das gleiche gilt für Spannungszustand und Verformungen. Man sieht, daß der größte Teil der überanspruchten Zonen in jenen Bereich fällt, der später ausgebrochen wird, und daß sich aufgrund des Einfallens der Haupttrennflächen und der Schrägstellung des Primärspannungszustandes deutliche Unterschiede in den Bruchzonen in den drei Richtungen ergeben. Die Überbeanspruchungen außerhalb des späteren Kavernenraumes ereignen sich überwiegend erst beim Abbruch des Kernes und in den gesondert gekennzeichneten Elementen nach Auffahren der Kaverne unter der Annahme des Schwindens der Betonschale und des vollständigen Ausfalls der Ankerung, was einen zusätzlichen Sicherheitsabstand bringt; man sieht also, daß die Überbeanspruchung außerhalb im wesentlichen erst dann erfolgt, wenn bereits die Innenschale vorhanden ist und insgesamt ein günstiger und im wesentlichen endgültiger Spannungszustand herrscht. Es sind somit die Erwartungen an die Schlitzbauweise rechnerisch bestätigt worden; eine praktische Erprobung steht freilich noch aus. Zum Aufwand für die Berechnung eines solchen Nachbarzustandes ist kurz zu erwähnen, daß für jedes der 5 Fourierglieder 1590 Freiheitsgrade vorliegen und daß diese 5 Systeme in 41 Grundschritten und weiteren 141 Iterationsschritten zu berechnen waren.

Die beiden anderen Standorte waren gekennzeichnet durch einen ungünstigen Seitendruckbeiwert ($\lambda = 0,3$) sowie im Falle Quarzit durch sehr ungünstiges Einfallen der Haupttrennflächen und im Falle Sandstein durch geringe Festigkeit des Grundmaterials bei günstig liegenden Haupttrennflächen. In beiden Fällen ergaben sich wesentlich größere überbeanspruchte Zonen für den Nachbarzustand, wobei im Falle Quarzit der ganze untere Bereich schon vor Auffahren der Kaverne gebrochen war. Anstelle der 182 Rechenschritte beim Standort Schiefer wurden beim Standort Sandstein bei Schlitzausbruch 262 Rechenschritte benötigt, letztlich aber doch, wie auch im Falle Quarzit, Konvergenz festgestellt. Allein im Falle des Kalotten-Strossenausbruchs am Standort Sandstein schnellte die Zahl der Rechenschritte auf 835 in die Höhe und die Konvergenz war doch erst in geringerem Maße ausgebildet als bei der Schlitzbauweise. Man steht hiermit vor dem Dilemma, zu einem weiteren Vorgehen entweder die erprobtere Kalottenbauweise oder die sich rechnerisch als vorteilhafter darstellende Schlitzbauweise zu empfehlen.

Ebenso wie bei der Reaktorkaverne in der Kalotten-Strossenbauweise am Standort Sandstein kam man auch bei der Maschinenkaverne, die ebenfalls in der Kalotten-Strossenbauweise aufgefahren und ausschließlich mit Ankerung und Spritzbeton ausgebaut werden sollte, im Falle des Standortes Sandstein an die Grenzen der nachweisbaren Standsicherheit. Im Gegensatz zur Reaktorkaverne kann hier die Schlitzbauweise aufgrund der anderen Kavernenform nicht angewendet werden, wohl aber Vorschläge von Rotter 1970 sowie Stephansson und Stillborg 1977.

Die Untersuchung großer Kavernen für unterirdische Kernkraftwerke zeigt, daß solche Kavernen unter deutschen Gebirgsverhältnissen grundsätzlich machbar sind; es ist selbstverständlich, daß eine solche Aussage für einen bestimmten Standort sehr intensive ingenieurgeologisch-felsmechanische Voruntersuchungen erfordert, daß in endgültiger Standsicherheitsnachweis aufgrund der Ergebnisse dieser Voruntersuchungen in verfeinerter Form zu führen ist, ehe eine solche Aussage standortgebunden gemacht werden kann.

4. ANMERKUNG

Für die freundliche Genehmigung zur Veröffentlichung der Ergebnisse sei dem Bundesminister des Innern an dieser Stelle gedankt.

5. LITERATUR

Bung, Ingenieurbüro im Bauwesen, Teil I 1977
    Teil II (2 vol.) 1980, Beurteilung der
    felsbaulichen Realisierbarkeit großer Ka-

vernen im Fels bei unterirdischen Kernkraftwerken, Studie SR 72 im Auftrag des
Bundesministers des Innern.

Dubois J., Bianchini J. C., Locci J. M.
1978, User and theoretical manuals of
PAM-GEOM, Engineering System International, Rungis (Paris).

Dubois J., Obenauer P.W. 1979, Efficient
three dimensional finite element analysis of stratified rocks in W. Wittke
(ed.) Numerical Methods in Geomechanics
Aachen 1979 Proc. 3rd Int. Conf. Num.
Meth. Geomech., Vol. 2, p. 515-522,
A.A. Balkema, Rotterdam.

Duddeck H. 1980, Sicherheitsanalyse und
Nachweise der Standsicherheit von Fels-
gebirge bei unterirdischen Kernkraftwerken, Studie SR 65 im Auftrag des Bundesministers des Innern, Bericht Nr. 80-34,
Institut für Statik, TU Braunschweig.

Lielups L., Obenauer P.W. 1979, Kritische
Betrachtung der Anwendungsmöglichkeiten
von Finite-Element-Berechnungen im Felshohlraumbau, Rock Mechanics, Suppl. 8,
p. 43-57, Springer, Wien.

Lurje A.I. 1963, Räumliche Probleme der
Elastizitätstheorie, Akademie-Verlag,
Berlin (Ost).

Müller-Salzburg L. 1979, Die Bedeutung
der Ringschlußlänge und Ringschlußzeit
im Tunnelbau in Proc. 4th Int. Cong.
Rock Mech. Montreux, Vol. 1, p. 511-519,
A.A. Balkema, Rotterdam.

Pahl A., Schneider H.J., Wallner M. 1978,
Ingenieurgeologisch-felsmechanische Kriterien und Möglichkeiten des Großkaver-
nenbaues für die unterirdische Anordnung eines Reaktors im Fels, in O. Natau,
E. Fecker, G. Reik, (eds.) Grundlagen
und Anwendung der Felsmechanik, Felsmechanik Kolloquium Karlsruhe 1978,
p. 217-232, Trans Tech Publications,
Clausthal.

Sawin, G.N. 1956, Spannungserhöhung am
Rande von Löchern, VEB Verlag Technik,
Berlin (Ost).

Stephansson O., Stillborg B. 1977, Theo-
retical and experimental study of
"rib-in-roc" for large underground ope-
nings in M. Bergman (ed.) Storage in
Excavated Rock Caverns, Proc. 1st
Int. Symp. Rockstore 77, Stockholm,
Vol. 2, p. 253-258, Pergamon Press,
Oxford.

UNTERIRDISCHE BAUWEISE VON KERNKRAFTWERKEN – EIN RESÜMEE ÜBER DAS INTERNATIONALE SYMPOSIUM IN HANNOVER 1981

Underground construction methods for nuclear power plants – A review of the international symposium held in Hannover 1981

La construction souterraine de centrales nucléaires – Un résumé du symposium international de Hannovre en 1981

A.PAHL & H.J.SCHNEIDER
Bundesanstalt für Geowissenschaften und Rohstoffe, Hannover, Bundesrepublik Deutschland

SUMMARY:
In March 1981, a Symposium on underground construction methods for nuclear power plants was held in Hannover. In all, 36 papers were presented on current research activities in the field of underground construction. All papers were followed by discussion. The advantages of building underground were seen to be, firstly that added protection is afforded to the plant itself, and conversely to the population, by a thick shield of rock, and secondly that the choice of possible sites is considerably broadened. Speakers gave their accounts of the current state-of-the-art in different countries and the feasibility of employing either the cavern or the cut-and-cover method of underground construction. In addition to the increased degree of protection afforded to underground nuclear power stations, certain financial and technical aspects concerning the operation of the plant would also be advantageous. A review of papers given at the Symposium is presented and particular attention is paid to the geotechnical aspects of construction.

ZUSAMMENFASSUNG:
Im März 1981 fand ein Symposium über die unterirdische Bauweise von Kernkraftwerken statt, bei welchem in 36 Vorträgen über die derzeitigen Aktivitäten auf dem Gebiet der unterirdischen Bauweise zusammenfassend berichtet und diskutiert wurde. Hierbei wurden die Beweggründe, d.h. Schutzziele, Schutzwirkung, Erweiterung des Standortangebotes u.a., für das untertägige Bauen dargelegt. Im einzelnen wurde über den Stand der Technik und die Realisierbarkeit der verschiedenen Bauweisen - Grubenbauweise, Kavernenbauweise - in verschiedenen Ländern informiert. Neben der Erhöhung des Schutzgrades von Kernkraftwerken durch die unterirdische Bauweise wurden auch finanzielle und betriebstechnische Aspekte erörtert. Im folgenden wird ein Resümee unter besonderer Berücksichtigung der geotechnischen Aspekte aus den Symposiumsbeiträgen gezogen.

RESUME:
En Mars 1981 eut lieu un symposium sur la construction souterraine des centrales nucléaires, au cours duquel 36 exposés sur les activités actuelles dans la domaine de la construction souterraine fournirent un résumé et firent l'objet de discussions. Ainsi furent expliqués les motifs de la construction souterraine, c'est à dire entre autres les buts de sécurité, l'effet de sécurité, extension des possibilités données par la localité. En détail, on fut informé du niveau de la technique et de la possibilité de réalisation des différentes facons de construire les mines et les cavernes - dans différents pays. En plus du rehaussement du dégré de sécurité des centrales nucléaire par la construction souterraine, il fut discuté les aspects financiers et de ceux de marche d'une entreprise. Suit, un résumé des rapports du sympo-

sium, tenant particulièrement compte des aspects géotechniques des fondations.

1 EINLEITUNG

Das Symposium "Unterirdische Bauweise von Kernkraftwerken, sicherheitstechnisches Potential und ingenieurmäßige Realisierung" fand vom 16.3.81 - 20.3.81 in der Bundesanstalt für Geowissenschaften u. Rohstoffe, Hannover, statt. Insgesamt nahmen an der fünftägigen Veranstaltung 241 Fachleute, davon 49 Teilnehmer als ausländische Gäste aus den Staaten USA, Italien, Frankreich, Belgien, Schweden, Österreich, Schweiz, Japan, Großbritannien, Canada, Norwegen und Dänemark teil.

Das Symposium wurde mit dem Ziel durchgeführt, einen internationalen Meinungsaustausch über Ergebnisse in- und ausländischer Untersuchungen zur Untertagebauweise herbeizuführen. Die Vor- und Nachteile der U-Bauweise gegenüber der oberirdischen Bauweise sollten vorgetragen und diskutiert werden, um die unterirdische Bauweise besser bewerten zu können.

Zu folgenden Themenkreisen wurden Vorträge gehalten:
"Überblick über internationale Aktivitäten zur unterirdischen Bauweise von Kernkraftwerken"
"Konzept für unterirdische Kernkraftwerke"
"Standortspezifische Probleme von unterirdischen Kernkraftwerken"
"Beurteilung des Sicherheitspotentials von unterirdischen Kernkraftwerken"
"Oberirdische alternative Containmentkonzepte"
"Methoden zur Gesamtbewertung der unterirdischen Bauweise und alternativer oberirdischer Containmentkonzepte"

Eine Exkursion mit ca. 50 Teilnehmern nach Hemfurth/Edersee, wo die Kaverne des PSW Waldeck II mit einem Querschnitt von 106 m x 33,5m x 52 m als der größte ingenieurmäßig erstellte Hohlraum im Fels steht, beendete das Symposium am 20.3.81.

Das folgende Resümee soll im Hinblick auf felsmechanische Probleme vor allem Beiträge zu internationalen Aktivitäten, Konzepte für unterirdische Kernkraftwerke (UKKW), standortspezifische Probleme und Sicherheitspotential von UKKW beinhalten.

2 INTERNATIONALE AKTIVITÄTEN ZUR UNTERIRDISCHEN BAUWEISE VON KERN_KRAFTWERKEN

Seit 1965 werden in der Bundesrepublik Deutschland Kernkraftwerke für die Stromversorgung gebaut. Der Energiebedarf unseres Industriestaates erfordert den Einsatz von Kernenergie, weil die fossilen Energierohstoffe wie Erdöl und Kohle nur begrenzt zur Verfügung stehen und außerdem auch als Rohstoff für Industrieprodukte zunehmend Verwendung finden.

Die Planung von Kernkraftwerken wurde, besonders in der dichtbesiedelten Bundesrepublik, aber auch in den USA, z.B. in Kalifornien, durch das Umweltbewußtsein der Bevölkerung zu neuen Überlegungen angeregt. Dazu wird gefragt, ob Kernkraftwerke unterirdisch gebaut werden können und welche Vorteile, vielleicht auch Nachteile verglichen mit der bisherigen oberirdischen Bauweise zu erwarten sind.

Im ersten Themenkreis wurde über internationale Aktivitäten zur Untersuchung der unterirdischen Bauweise von Kernkraftwerken berichtet. Ontario Hydro, eine große kanadische Elektrizitätsgesellschaft, hat eine Studie über die technische Ausführbarkeit und die Wirtschaftlichkeit einer unterirdischen CANDU - Kernkraftanlage mit 4 Einheiten à 850 MW durchgeführt. OBERTH teilte dazu mit, daß grundsätzlich davon ausgegangen wurde, das obertägige Referenzkraftwerk für die unterirdische Bauweise in Kavernen zu modifizieren. Als Ergebnis der untertägigen Anordnung sind 4 Hauptkavernen vorgesehen, deren Abmessungen 35 m Spannweite, 60 m Höhe und 100 m Länge betragen. Zwischen den Kavernen wurden Felspfeiler von 20 m gefordert. Die Kavernen können in 400 m Tiefe durch Schächte erschlossen werden und liegen im Granit. Diese tiefe Anordnung in Granit-Kavernen erfordert eine um 16 Monate längere Bauzeit und um 31 - 36 % höhere Kosten als die oberirdische Bauweise. Die geologische Situation in der Umgebung von Toronto würde die Planung solcher Kavernen in 400 m Tiefe zulassen.

Aus Japan berichtet Y. ICHIKAWA, daß eine wesentliche Motivation für die Kavernenbauweise aus der großen Bevölkerungsdichte resultiert. Die dichte Besiedelung des Flachlandes, das nur 30 % der Gesamtfläche ausmacht, läßt kaum neue Kraftwerkstandorte zu. Deshalb ist 1977 ein Komitée vom Ministerium für Handel und Industrie gegründet worden, um die Möglichkeiten der unterirdischen Bauweise eines 1100 MW Kernkraftwerk-Types in bergmännisch aufgefahrenen Kavernen im Fels an der Küste zu untersuchen. Bis 1981 wurden einige Tests insitu und im Labor durchgeführt, außerdem Erfahrungen aus Kavernen für Wasserkraftwerke, besonders in Bezug auf Erdbebenerschütterungen, zusammengetragen.

Umfangreiche Untersuchungen sind in den USA ausgeführt worden, worüber FINLAYSON berichtete. 1976 verlangte der Staat Kalifornien die Durchführung einer Studie über die Notwendigkeit, Wirksamkeit und wirtschaftliche Ausführbarkeit für den Bau unterirdischer Kernkraftwerke. In die zu betrachtenden Unfälle war die Kernschmelze mit einzubeziehen. Grundsätzlich wurde die Grubenbauweise mit Überdeckung und die Bauweise in bergmännisch aufgefahrenen Kavernen untersucht. Die Reaktorkaverne sollte in einem für Kalifornien typischen Berggebiet liegen mit einem Stollenzugang von 240 m Länge und einer Überdeckung von 100 m Fels. In den Studien konnte die Ausführbarkeit und der Gewinn an Sicherheit nachgewiesen werden, allerdings unter erheblichen Mehrkosten und Bauzeitverlängerung. Der kalifornische Staat beschloß daraufhin die Untergrund-Bauweise gesetzlich nicht zu verlangen da es technische Alternativen über Tage gibt, die weniger aufwendig sind.

Um fundierte Antworten auf die Fragen zu bekommen, ob Kernkraftwerke unterirdisch gebaut werden können und welche Vorteile und Nachteile gegenüber der oberirdischen Bauweise zu erwarten sind, sind im Auftrage des Bundesinnenministeriums in der Bundesrepublik Deutschland von mehreren Institu-

tionen und Firmen eine Reihe von Studien durchgeführt worden. Diese Studien, die 1974 begannen, sollten das sicherheitstechnische Potential der unterirdischen Bauweise untersuchen, unter Einbeziehung extremer Belastungen. BACHUS berichtete darüber.

Abb. 1 zeigt die untersuchten Möglichkeiten der unterirdischen Bauweise eines Kernkraftwerkes, und zwar Grubenbauweise und Hangbauweise mit Überschüttung sowie Kavernenbauweise.

Referenzkraftwerk für die Untersuchungen war ein Druckwasserreaktor des 1.300 MW-Types, der möglichst unverändert unter Tage gebaut werden sollte. Die Standorteigenschaften des Gebirges wurden von der Bundesanstalt für Geowissenschaften und Rohstoffe angegeben, wie sie für bestimmte Gebirgsarten der Bundesrepublik typisch sind. Die Randbedingung, das Anlagenkonzept möglichst unverändert zu übernehmen, führte zu sehr großen Abmessungen für die Reaktorkaverne, die mit 65 m Durchmesser nicht Stand der Bautechnik für Kavernen im Fels sind. Folgende Ergebnisse lassen die Studien, die zum Teil noch nicht abgeschlossen sind, in der Tendenz erkennen:
- Zusätzlicher Schutz gegen äußere Einwirkungen, insbesondere Waffenwirkung,
- Reduzierung der hochradioaktiven Auswirkung von Unfällen auf die Umgebung
- Zeitliche Verzögerung von Freisetzungen bei Unfällen
- Problematik der großen Abmessungen: z.B. Spannweite der Kaverne von 65 m bisher nicht gebaut, wird aber bei geeigneter Felsqualität für möglich gehalten. Zur Klärung sind umfangreiche Standortuntersuchungen und eine Probekaverne nötig.
- Mehrkosten bei Kavernenbau von 14 - 17 %
- Bauzeitverlängerung (ca. 5 %)
- Einige Betriebsvorgänge werden bei unterirdischer Bauweise schwieriger (z. B. Transporte).

Das Studienprojekt des Bundesinnenministeriums soll mit einer Kosten-Nutzen-Untersuchung abschließen.

3 KONZEPTE FÜR UNTERIRDISCHE KERNKRAFTWERKE

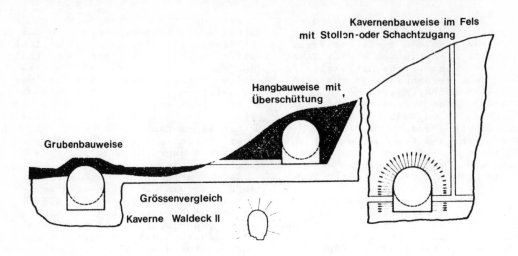

Abb. 1: Unterirdische Bauweisen für Kernkraftwerke

In Abb. 1 sind die Bauweisen dargestellt, und zwar in Gruben, am Hang,
und in Kavernen. SCHETELIG hat in
einem Beitrag zusammen mit BRÄUER &
HEIGL die Vor- und Nachteile einzelner Varianten gegenübergestellt.
Das Konzept der Langhauskaverne mit
ca. 40 m Spannweite wurde in den
letzten Jahren nicht weiter untersucht, weil unter der Vorgabe einer
möglichst unveränderten Übernahme
des oberirdischen Kernkraftwerk-
types eine Großkaverne von mindestens 60 m Durchmesser für das Re-
aktorbauwerk gefordert war. Die
technische und wirtschaftliche Ausführung dieser Großkaverne untersuchte das Ing.-Büro Bung in einer
Studie für das Bundesinnenministe-
rium. Abb. 2. und 3 zeigen einen
Schnitt durch die Reaktorkaverne
sowie das untertägige Anlagenkonzept. Die Realisierbarkeit der
Reaktorkaverne konnte für verschiedene Gebirgstypen unter bestimmten
Annahmen für das Gebirge, den Ausbau und die Auffahrungsmethode
nachgewiesen werden. Das Konzept
eines Kernkraftwerks in einer tiefen Felsbaugrube mit Lockergesteinsüberdeckung in einem Plateau hat
OBENAUER beschrieben. Diese Fels-
bauweise setzt eine spezielle Ge-
ländesituation voraus, wo es neben
einem Vorfluter ein Felsplateau in
etwa 50 bis 110 m Höhe über dem

Vorfluter in günstiger Entfernung
gibt. Der seitlich umgebende Fels
und die Überschüttung bieten Schutz
gegen äußere Einwirkungen und können
der Druckaufnahme sowie der Wärme-
speicherung zur Verzögerung von Auswirkungen bei hypothetischen Störfällen dienen.

4 STANDORTSPEZIFISCHE PROBLEME VON
UNTERIRDISCHEN KERNKRAFTWERKEN

Über Standortmöglichkeiten für unterirdische Kernkraftwerke im Fels
berichteten PAHL & SCHNEIDER. Aus
ingenieurgeologisch-felsmechanischer
Sicht muß die technische Realisierbarkeit der Felsbauten und die
Schutzwirkung von Fels bei innerer
und äußerer Beanspruchung beurteilt
werden. Erfahrungen und Stand der
Felsbautechnik wurden im Hinblick
auf die unterirdische Anordnung
eines Druckwasserreaktor-Kernkraft-
werks mit einer Reaktorkaverne von
ca. 65 m Durchmesser erläutert.

Die Beurteilung eines unterirdischen Gebietes für die Standortwahl erfordert ingenieurgeologisch-
felsmechanische Grundlagen. Danach
lassen die in der Bundesrepublik
Deutschland anzutreffenden Felsar-
ten eine Unterscheidung von 3 Basis-
Gebirgstypen zu, nämlich Typ 1
"Quarzit", Typ 2 "Schiefer" und Typ
3 "Buntsandstein".

414

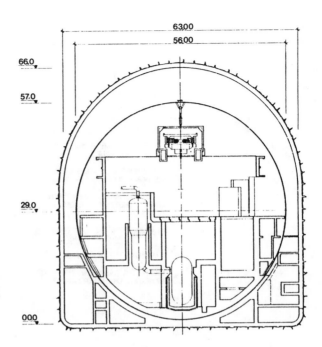

Übersichtsskizze

Abb. 2: Querschnitt und Grundriß der Reaktorkaverne (aus d. Studie des Ing.-Büro Bung)

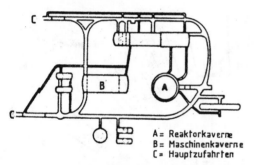

A = Reaktorkaverne
B = Maschinenkaverne
C = Hauptzufahrten

Abb. 3: Anordnung einer Kernkraftanlage in Kavernenbauweise (aus d. Studie des Ing.-Büro Bung)

Für die vorläufige Beurteilung von Standorten sind von der Bundesanstalt für Geowissenschaften und Rohstoffe (BGR) ingenieurgeologisch-felsmechanische Kriterien erarbeitet worden, nach denen dem Gebirge 3 Klassen zugeordnet werden (Abb. 4).

Aufgrund der bisher durchgeführten Standorttypisierung und ingenieurgeologisch-felsmechanischen Vorerkundungen konnte eine grobe Selek-

GEBIRGS-KLASSE / BEWER-TUNGSKRIT.		GEBIRGS-KLASSE I	GEBIRGS-KLASSE II	GEBIRGS-KLASSE III
STANDSICHERHEIT	GEBIRGSFESTIGK. / GESTEINSFESTIGK.	-1	$-\frac{1}{2}$	$-\frac{1}{5}$
	AUFLOCKERUNG	TIEFE ≤ 2 m / δ_{versch} ≤ 30 mm	TIEFE ≤ 5 m / δ_{versch} ≤ 60 mm	TIEFE ≤ 10 m / δ_{versch} ≤ 100 mm
	RHEOLOGISCHES VERHALTEN	KEINE ZEITABHÄN-GIGEN VERFORMUNGEN	ÖRTLICH PLASTISCHE BEREICHE; ZEITABHÄN-GIGE VERFORMUNGEN WÄHREND DES AUSBRUCHS	PLASTISCHE UND VISKO-SE VERFORMUNGEN SIND DURCH BAUMAS-NAHMEN ZU BEGRENZEN
	PRIMÄRSPG.	0,7 ≤ λ ≤ 1,5	0,3 ≤ λ ≤ 0,7	λ { < 0,3 / > 1,5
AUSBRUCH		PROFILGENAU; GROßER QUERSCHNITT	PROFILGENAU; FREISTEHENDE ABBAU-HÖHE U. -TIEFE BEGRENZT	MEHRAUSBRUCH; GERINGE ABBAUHÖHEN UND -TIEFEN
AUSBAU		SPRITZBETON; LEICHTE FLÄCHENANKERUNG AUSBAUWIDERSTAND: W < 0,5 BAR	BEWEHRTER SPRITZBE-TON; SYSTEMANKERUNG FREISPIELANKER BIS 25m 0,5 < W < 1,5 BAR	STARK BEWEHRTER SPRITZ-BETON; SCHWERE SYSTEM-ANKERUNG; FREISPIELANKER > 25m; 1,5 < W < 2,5 BAR
BERGWASSER		< 200 l/MIN	< 500 l/MIN	> 500 l/MIN VORTRIEB UND SICHE-RUNG DURCH WASSER - ANDRANG BEHINDERT
ERDBEBENZONE		0	I und II	III
BEEINFLUSSUNG DER OBERFLÄCHE		KEINE BEEINFLUSSUNG	SETZUNGEN UND GRUND-WASSERENTZUG OHNE SCHÄDLICHE AUS- UND NACHWIRKUNGEN	SETZUNGEN UND GRUND-WASSERENTZUG; DURCH VORSORGENDE TECHNISCHE MASSNAHMEN KÖNNEN SCHÄ-DEN VERMIEDEN BZW. EIN-GEGRENZT WERDEN
EIGNUNG DES AUSBRUCH MAT.		FÜR BAUTECHNISCHE ZWECKE GEEIGNET	FÜR BAUTECHNISCHE ZWECKE BEDINGT GE-EIGNET; KLASSIERUNGS-VERFAHREN	FÜR AUFSCHÜTTUNGEN GEEIGNET

Abb. 4: Ingenieurgeologische Kriterien zur Gebirgsklassifizierung

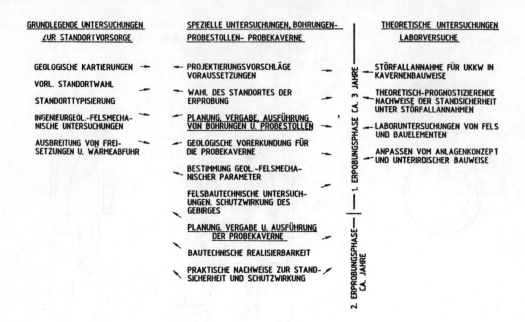

Abb. 5: Rahmenprogramm für UKKW in Kavernenbauweise

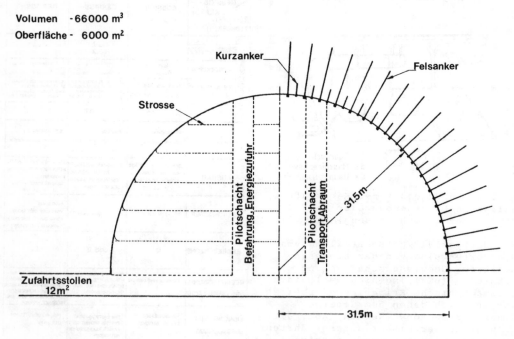

Abb. 6: Probekaverne mit Auffahrungsschema nach dem Strossenabbauverfahren

416

tion von grundsätzlich in Frage kommenden Standorten in der Bundesrepublik Deutschland vorgenommen werden, und zwar über 50 Standorte für Kavernenbauweise mit Stollenzugang über Flußniveau und etwa 140 m Überdeckung und über 20 Standorte für Hangbauweise im Fels. ebenfalls über Flußniveau. Danach ergeben sich also zusätzlich Standortmöglichkeiten für Kernkraftwerke und letztlich auch eine Reduzierung von Standortrestriktionen, die für übertägige Kernkraftwerke ausgelegt sind.

Die bisher durchgeführten theoretischen Studien, die im ganzen gesehen zu positiven Ergebnissen geführt haben, müssen jetzt, insbesondere im Hinblick auf die Kavernenbauweise und die Schutzwirkung von Fels, durch praktische Untersuchungen in-situ ergänzt werden. Hierfür ist von der BGR gemeinsam mit dem Institut für Statik, Braunschweig, ein Rahmenprogramm entwickelt worden, das in Abb. 5 zusammengefaßt ist und die nötigen Erprobungen und Untersuchungen zeigt.

Abb. 6 soll einen Eindruck von der zu planenden Probekaverne geben.

Die felsmechanischen Aspekte in Bezug auf die Planung und den Bau von großen Hohlräumen im Fels wurden von WITTKE behandelt. Das mechanische Verhalten von Fels wird wesentlich von Klüften, Störungen und Gebirgsspannungen bestimmt. An vier Bei-

spielen, den Kavernen Wehr/Schwarzwald, Turlough Hill/Irland, Bremm/Eifel und Estangento Sallente/Spanien werden die felsmechanischen Probleme und die Anwendung eines bereits erfolgreich angewendeten Modelles beschrieben. Den Einfluß von Klüftung, Störungen und in-situ Spannungen zeigt die Abb. 7.

Abschließend kommt WITTKE zu dem Ergebnis, daß Felskavernen mit Durchmessern und Höhen von rund 60 m durchführbar sein werden. Allerdings weist er auf Einschränkungen bei der Standortwahl hin und auf die Notwendigkeit eines umfangreichen Untersuchungsprogrammes.

5 SICHERHEITSPOTENTIAL VON UNTERIRDISCHEN KERNKRAFTWERKEN

In einem 4. Themenkreis wurde das Sicherheitspotential von unterirdischen Kernkraftwerken beurteilt und alternative Ertüchtigungsmaßnahmen für oberirdische Anlagen diskutiert.

Für eine unterirdische Anordnung eines Kernkraftwerkes nach dem "cut and cover" Prinzip wurde von KELLER die Ausbreitung der kontaminierten Wasserdampf-Gas Atmosphäre bei einem inneren Störfall mit einer Leckage des Reaktorcontainments in der Überlagerung des umgebenden Gebirges rechnerisch simuliert.

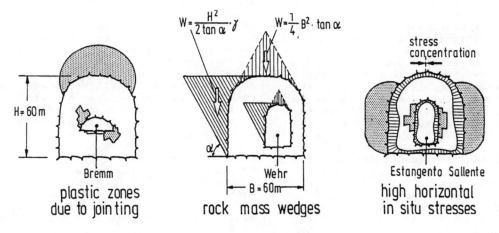

Abb. 7: Einfluß von Klüftung, Störungen und in-situ Spannungen beim Großkavernenbau (nach WITTKE)

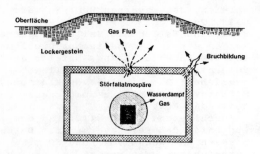

Abb. 8: Freisetzungspfade der Störfallatmosphäre in der Überdeckung der Reaktorkaverne (nach KELLER)

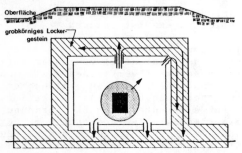

Abb. 9: Freisetzungspfade der Störfallatmosphäre in die Kondensationsschicht (nach KELLER)

Die Freisetzung der Störfallatmosphäre erfolgt in bindigen Materialien durch Bruchbildung, die sich sukzessiv zur Oberfläche fortsetzt und in stark porösem Lockergestein als Wasserdampf-Gasblase, die bei geringer Überlagerung zu Einbruchschloten in der Überlagerung führen kann.

Durch eine zusätzliche Kondensationsschicht aus grobklastischem Material, die zur Umgebung mit bindigem Material abgedichtet wird, kann das Sicherheitspotential dieser Bauweise beträchtlich gesteigert werden, da hier bei ausreichendem Porenvolumen die Störfallatmospäre auskühlt und aufgefangen wird. Durch vorgesehene Schleusen in Decke und Boden des Reaktorgebäudes wird das Wasserdampf-Gasgemisch gleichmäßig in die Kondensationsschicht freigesetzt.

Die Ausbreitung von radioaktiven Stoffen aus erdversenkten Kernkraftwerken und die Kontamination des Grundwassers sowie die Bewältigung der Störfallfolgen werden von

SCHWILLE untersucht. Die Standorte von Kernkraftwerken in Grubenbauweise liegen im Bereich bewegten Grundwassers. Bei den Zerfallzeiten der radioaktiven Stoffe und der Fließgeschwindigkeit des Grundwassers reicht das Selbstreinigungsvermögen des Untergrundes bei einem Störfall nicht aus, um nicht große Grundwasservorkommen zu gefährden. Bei der zu erwartenden Breite der kontaminierten Grundwasseraureole von ca. 50 m reicht eine Brunnenanordnung von 1-2 Brunnen in einer Entfernung von 100 m vom Reaktorgebäude aus um das kontaminierte Grundwasser vollständig aufzufangen. Die anfallenden Wassermengen, die zu dekontaminieren sind, überschreiten die technischen und wirtschaftlichen Möglichkeiten, so daß eine technische Variante mit Dichtungswänden um das Reaktorgebäude vorschlagen wird. Die austretende Störfallatmosphäre wird hierbei im Aufschüttungsmaterial zwischen Dichtungswand und Reaktorgebäude gesammelt und kann mit einer vorab installierten Absenkanlage in überschaubarer Menge gewonnen und dekontaminiert werden.

Für denselben Störfall wurden von H.J. SCHNEIDER die Ergebnisse einer experimentellen Studie zur Ausbreitung kontaminierter Wasser im Fels für Kernkraftwerke in Felskavernen vorgetragen. Aufgrund der besonderen Wasserwegigkeit von Fels in Klüften lassen sich die Ausbreitungsvorgänge nicht mit derselben Verläßlichkeit wie im Lockermaterial abschätzen. Die Klüftung des Gebirges bewirkt inhomogene und anisotrope Durchlässigkeitseigenschaften. Die Durchlässigkeit der einzelnen Kluft ist in der Regel um 1-2 Zehnerpotenzen größer gegenüber der Gesamtdurchlässigkeit des Gebirges, so daß einzelne Großklüfte in kurzer Zeit eine Freisetzung der Störfallatmosphäre über große Entfernungen ermöglichen. In Feldversuchen wurden hierbei Tracerlaufzeiten von 1 - 4 Stunden für eine Entfernung von 50 m gemessen. Technische Lösungen durch Abwehrbrunnen wie in Lockermaterial zur Entnahme des kontaminierten Grundwassers bringen aufgrund der inhomogenen Durchströmung nicht den gewünschten Erfolg, so daß die Ausbreitung der kontaminierten Stoffe im Fels wirksam nur durch eine Dichtung des Gebirges

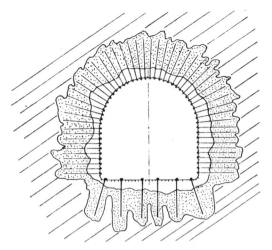

Abb. 10: Injektionsmaßnahmen zur Abdichtung der Reaktorkaverne (nach H.J. SCHNEIDER)

durch Injektion verhindert werden kann. Mit diesen Maßnahmen können neben der Erhöhung des Schutzpotentials das Bergwasser von der Kavernenauskleidung ferngehalten und die Ausbauelemente durch zirkulierende Wasser vor Korosion geschützt werden.

BOWMAN, WATLING & Mc CAULEY stellen ein Konzept eines untertägigen Kernkraftwerkes in Grubenbauweise vor, das für alle Typen von Leichtwasserreaktoren geeignet ist.

Die Studie weist am Beispiel eines 1100 MW Kernkraftwerks nach, daß die Technologie der obertägigen Anlagen

übernommen werden können. Die Freisetzung kontaminierter Stoffe bei inneren Störfällen kann durch Wahl geeigneter Schüttmaterialien verhindert werden. Baumaßnahmen der oberirdischen Anlage gegen Einwirkungen von außen werden reduziert, da die Überdeckung diese Schutzfunktionen übernimmt und somit eine Kostenersparnis und Verkürzung der Bauzeit ermöglicht wird. Nach dieser Studie sind die Gesamtkosten dieser Bauweise gegenüber der obertägigen Anlage vernachlässigbar klein. Bei der unterirdischen Anlage entfallen gewisse Standortrestriktionen für obertägige Kernkraftwerke, was sich in einem erweiterten Standortangebot und kürzeren Bewilligungszeiten niederschlägt. Nach Ansicht der Autoren stellt dieses untertägige Baukonzept eine gleichwertige Alternative zu obertägigen Kernkraftwer-

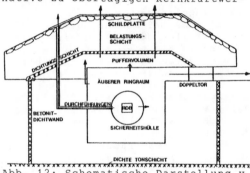

Abb. 12: Schematische Darstellung v. Überschüttung und Freisetzungspfaden (nach HOFMANN et al.)

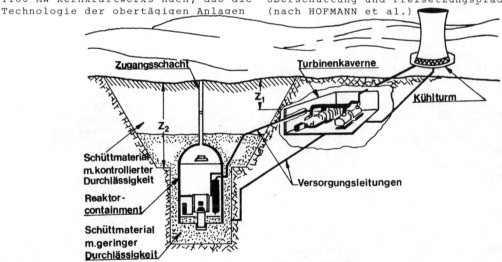

Abb. 11: Konzept einer untertägigen Kernkraftanlage in Grubenbauweise
(nach BOWMAN et al.)

419

ken dar.

Der Feisetzungsverlauf der Störfallatmospäre wird von HOFMANN et
al. für ein Kernkraftwerk in Grubenbauweise untersucht und ein Konzept
der Erdüberschüttung entwickelt.

Die Erdüberschüttung hat 3 verschiedene Funktionen zu übernehmen:
1. Die erste Schicht aus Grobkies
dient als Puffer für die aus dem
äußeren Ringraum austretende Störfallatmosphäre.
2. Die darüber liegende 2. Schicht
übernimmt die eigentliche Dichtung
und besteht aus verdichteten Fein-
sanden. Am Übergang zur dritten
Schicht kann alternativ eine Abdichtung gegen Gas mit Folie oder Bi-
tumen eingesetzt werden.
3. Die oberste Schicht ist eine Be-
lastungsschicht aus dem Bodenaus-
hub. In diese ist eine Schildplatte
zum Schutz gegen Waffeneinwirkung
o.ä. eingelassen.

Sollte es bei dieser Überdeckung
in Störfällen dennoch zu einer Frei-
setzung in die Atmosphäre kommen,
so wird diese um mehrere Tage bis
Wochen gegenüber der obertägigen
Bauweise verzögert, wo Schutz- und
Gegenmaßnahmen auf die potentielle
Dosis von 7 Tagen abzustimmen sind.

HEIERLEI & KESSLER untersuchen
das Schutzpotential von Kernkraftwerken bei gewaltsamer Sabotage
und Kriegseinwirkungen. Ein Voll-
schutz der Reaktoranlage gegen kon-
ventionelle Waffeneinwirkungen kann
bei untertägiger Bauweise durch eine
Lockergesteinsüberdeckung mit Schutz-
platte von 20 m Mächtigkeit oder
durch eine Felsüberlagerung von 10 m
Mächtigkeit erreicht werden. Die
oberirdische Anlage besitzt bei ge-
waltsamen Einwirkungen von außen
nur ein begrenztes Schutzpotential.

6 ERGEBNISSE

In dem Symposium konnten die deutschen und auch ausländischen Konzepte der unterirdischen Bauweise
vorgestellt und diskutiert werden.

Grundsätzlich lassen sich zwei
unterirdische Bauweisen unterscheiden, und zwar in Gruben und in Felskavernen. Bei beiden ergaben sich
bauliche Probleme, die das Anord-
nungs- und Baukonzept beeinflussen.
Das deutsche Konzept geht von einer
möglichst wenig veränderten Anordnung und Größe der obertägigen An-

lage aus, während ausländische
Studien größere Veränderungen im
Hinblick auf die unterirdische Bauweise in Betracht ziehen. Als Vorteile der unterirdischen Bauweise
werden genannt:
- Größerer Schutz bei äußeren Einwirkungen auf die Anlage.
- Bei Störfällen erfolgt eine ver-
zögerte Freisetzung von Spaltpro-
dukten bei funktionierenden Ab-
schlüssen an die Umwelt.
Als Nachteile werden angesehen:
- Mehrkosten für die unterirdische
Bauweise.
- Notwendige Erstellung eines Proto-
typs, Erprobung und Überwindung von
technischen Problemen der einzelnen Bauweisen (tiefe Baugruben im
Fels, am Hang und im Lockergestein
sowie bei sehr großen Kavernen).
- Zusätzliche Sicherheitsnachweise
(standortbezogen) für das Genehmi-
gungsverfahren.
- Beschränkung auf Standortregionen
mit geeigneten Boden- und Felsei-
genschaften wegen der geotechnischen
Durchführbarkeit.
Eine abschließende Gesamtbewertung
der aufgeführten Vor- und Nachteile
unterblieb.

Einigkeit erzielte man in der
Forderung, daß vertiefte Baugrund-
untersuchungen am vorgeschlagenen
Standort im Einzelfall notwendig
sind und die technischen Einzel-
probleme der vorgesehenen Bauweise
örtlich betrachtet werden müssen.
Dies gilt auch für das quantitative
Spaltprodukt-Rückhaltevermögen der
überdeckenden Fels- oder Bodenschichten.

7 LITERATUR

Zur weiteren Information sind die
Arbeiten nach Themenkreisen zusammengestellt, die im Frühjahr 1982
von F. BENDER als Herausgeber, bei
der Schweizerbart'schen Verlagsbuch-
handlung Stuttgart veröffentlicht
werden.

Sahl, W.: Einleitungsworte
Bender, F.: Vorwort

Überblick über internationale Aktivitäten zur unterirdischen Bauweise von Kernkraftwerken

Oberth, R.C., The canadian study of
underground nuclear power plants

Reaktorgebäude im Vergleich zur
unterirdischen Bauweise

Methoden zur Gesamtbewertung der
unterirdischen Bauweise und alternativer oder irdischer Containmentkonzepte

ANALYSIS OF A SHALLOW CHAMBER EXCAVATED IN JOINTED ROCK
Berechnung eines oberflächennahen Hohlraums in geklüftetem Fels
Analyse d'une cavité peu profonde creusée dans une roche à diaclases

CARLOS E.RODRIGUEZ
University of Puerto Rico, Mayaguez

SUMMARY:

The analysis of a shallow opening in jointed rock is described by studying the rock movements and loads developed around the opening during excavation. The study was conducted by applying the finite element method to typical geologic cross-sections of the opening. The finite element model included joint (slip) elements to explicitly consider the major geologic discontinuities of the rock mass. Shear zones were modeled by quadrilateral elements bounded by slip elements since field observations showed that most of the zone movements were produced by sliding. The effects that inward wall movements exerted on the chamber behavior were also studied. A scheme was developed to obtain pressure-displacement relationships to analyze the opening behavior. The patterns of rock displacements in the rock mass were also studied and related to the wall movements. The analysis results were briefly compared to measurements obtained in the field.

ZUSAMMENFASSUNG:

Die Berechnung eines oberflächennahen Hohlraums in geklüftetem Fels wird anhand der Untersuchung von Felsverformungen und -spannungen beschrieben, die während des Ausbruchs auftreten. Die Untersuchung wurde mit der Finite-Element-Methode bei üblichen geologischen Öffnungsquerschnitten durchgeführt. Das Finite-Element-Modell beinhaltete Kluftelemente um die wesentlichen geologischen Diskontinuitäten untersuchen zu können. Scherzonen wurden mit vierseitigen Elementen verbunden mit Gleitelementen nachmodelliert, da Feldbeobachtungen zeigten, daß die meisten Bewegungen aufgrund von Gleitvorgängen entstehen. Die Auswirkungen von Auskleidungsverschiebungen auf das Verhalten des Hohlraums wurden ebenfalls untersucht. Es wurde ein Schema entwickelt, mit dem die Spannungs-Dehnungs-Beziehungen zur Berechnung des Hohlraumverhaltens ermittelt werden können. Die Verteilung der Gebirgsverschiebungen wurden ebenfalls untersucht und mit den Auskleidungsbewegungen in Verbindung gesetzt. Die Berechnungsergebnisse wurden kurz mit den Feldmessungen verglichen.

RESUME:

L'analyse d'une ouverture peu profonde dans une roche à diaclases est faite au moyen de l'étude des mouvements de la roche et des charges développées autour de l'ouverture durant l'excavation. L'étude s'est effectuée en appliquant la méthode des éléments finis à des sections transversales gé-

ologiques typiques de la cavité. Le modèle des éléments finis comprenait
des éléments à diaclases (glissement) qui permettaient de considérer
explicitement les principales discontinuités géologiques de la masse
rocheuse. Les zones de cisaillement ont été représentées par des éléments
quadrilatéraux limités par des éléments de glissement, puisque les observations effectuées sur place avaient montré que la majorité des mouvements de zone étaient dus à des glissements. Les effets produits par les
mouvements de la paroi intérieure sur le comportement de la cavité ont
été également étudiés. Pour analyser le comportement de l'ouverture, un
schéma permettant d'obtenir le rapport pression-déplacement a été conçu.
Les modèles des déplacements des roches de la masse rocheuse ont été
aussi étudiés et reliés aux mouvements de la paroi. Les résultats de l'analyse ont été brièvement comparés aux mesures faites sur place.

1 INTRODUCTION

The Dupont Circle Station of the Washington
Metro System is a large underground chamber
excavated in jointed rock. The station is
724 ft. long, 76 ft. wide and 44 ft. high
and it is located 65 ft. below the ground
surface with an average rock cover of 30 ft.
and 35 ft. of soil. The station was excavated in five stages as shown in Figure 1.
Stage 1 involved an enlargement of a previously excavated pilot tunnel to an
approximately 20 ft. wide by 26 ft. high
opening. Stage 2 included the driving of
two lateral drifts. Stage 3 called for the
complete removal of the station top heading
and immediate installation of a permanent
lining. Stages 4 and 5 involved the
excavation of the opening bench. After
each stage of excavation, initial support
in the form of rock bolts, steel ribs and
shotcrete, was installed incrementally to
provide for greater stability of the
opening as subsequent stages were open.
The permanent lining installed in Stage 3
consisted of steel ribs embedded in a
shotcrete layer whose average thickness was
30 in. A detailed description of the actual
construction of the station is given by
Brierley (1975) and Mahar (1977).

Field data in the form of extensometer
and support strain measurements were made
at the chamber site to monitor the behavior
of the opening during construction. The
availability of these data provided the
opportunity to study through the finite
element method the rock movements and loads
developed around the chamber to better
understand the causes that contributed to
loads and opening stability.

2 SITE GEOLOGY

Cording and Mahar (1974), Brierley (1975),
and Mahar (1977) describe in detail the site
geology encountered in the Dupont Circle
Station. The chamber was driven in foliated
metamorphic rock whose primary features
consisted of joints, shears and shear zones.
The rock encountered was primarily unweathered to slightly weathered schist and gneiss
with pronounced North-South foliation and
RQD values ranging from 50 to 100%, except
in the shear zones where RQD values were
typically less than 50%. The joints were
highly continuous, smooth, and planar,
usually tight but occasionally opened and
weathered near the surface. The shears
consisted of slickensided joints containing
gauge filling of clay and chlorite. They
were commonly spaced 4 to 10 ft apart,
except in the shear zones where they were
more closely spaced. The shear zones consisted of fractured rock containing several
parallel shears and one or more gauge zones
with thickness ranging from 1/4 to 12 in.
Eight major shear zones intersected the
station. They were generally 1 to 10 ft
wide and spaced 10 to 50 ft apart. The
zones were sub-parallel to the rock foliation, striked within 10° of the chamber axis
and dipped 50 to 60° to the west. Typical
geological cross-sections of the site are
given in Figure 2. The combination of
joints, shears and shear zones led to form
a blocky and seamy condition of the rock
mass at the site.

3 FINITE ELEMENT IDEALIZATION

The station was studied by applying the
finite element method to typical geological
cross-sections of the chamber during excavation. Analysis of Stages (1), (2), (4),
and (5) has been described elsewhere
(Rodríguez 1980, 1982). The analysis
results of Stage (3) are described herein.

The station finite element model included
joint (slip) elements of the type described

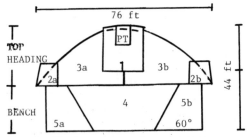

Fig. 1 Chamber excavation sequence

by Goodman et al. (1968) to explicity
consider the major geologic discontinuities
of the rock mass. The shear zones were
modeled by quadrilateral elements bounded
by slip elements, and the remaining rock or
"intact" rock by quadrilateral elements
(Fig. 3). Incorporation of slip elements
in the shear zones was necesary since field
observations showed that most of the zone
movements were produced by sliding.

The chamber excavation process was modeled
by sequentially removing the rock elements
belonging to every stage of excavation.
Although the real conditions of the problem
were not symmetrical about a vertical plane
through the opening axis, symmetry about
this plane was assumed for Stages (3), (4),
and (5) in order to simplify the analysis.
In addition, field observations showed that
installation of the lining in Stage (3)
helped in smoothing the non-symmetrical
condition of the rock mass observed during
excavation of Stage (1) (Rodríguez 1980,
1982). On the basis of this assumption
only half of the region under consideration
was modeled.

Analysis of Stage (3) also incorporated
the lining installation. Since in the
field the lining was installed near the
heading, excavation and lining placement
were performed in this analysis as
simultaneous events.

It has been indicated elsewhere (Rodríguez
1980) that rock loads imposed on the support
of openings in jointed rock vary with the
displacements taking place at the opening
walls. The effect of these inward displacements was studied by analyzing Stage (3)
with linings of different stiffness. Softer
linings than those installed in the field
were used to study the influence of
displacements that occurred prior to as well
as after the installation of the actual
stiffer lining. The contact between the
rock and lining was modeled by slip elements
to allow separation and full slippage of the
linings from the surrounding rock mass and
obtain rock loads carried entirely by the
support. Under this scheme, pressure-
displacement relationships were obtained
and used to study the chamber behavior when

subjected to several values of wall
displacements.

The material properties used in the
finite element model were selected from
either the project test data when available,
or from available summaries of rock and
discontinuity properties in the literature
from which reasonable estimates could be
made for the properties at the chamber site.
These values are shown in Table 1.

4 OPENING DISPLACEMENTS

Brierley (1975) gives a detailed description
of the measurements taken in the field.
The displacements in the crown and opening
walls were measured by extensometers installed during the chamber excavation.
Most of these extensometers had multiple
heads and extended 20 to 30 ft from the
edge of the opening. Rodríguez (1980)
describes in detail the comparison between
the measured and calculated rock movements.
A summary of this comparison is given for
Stage (3) in Fig. 4 where rock movements
measured at two lined sections of the
chamber are compared with those obtained in
the finite element analysis for an actual
lining. Despite small differences, a close
agreement exist between the measured and
calculated rock movements. As indicated by
Rodríguez (1980), this good agreement helped
in using the finite element analysis to

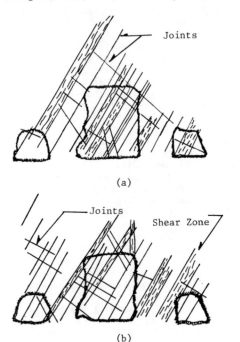

Fig. 2 Typical geologic conditions at the
site

425

Table 1. Material properties

Rock between joints					Shear zones					Joints			
E psi	ν	c psi	ϕ deg	γ pcf	E psi	ν	c psi	ϕ deg	γ pcf	K_n pci	K_s pci	c_j psi	ϕ deg
1×10^6	.15	5000	45	165	$.5 \times 10^6$	.3	0.	35	165	10000	500	0.0	15

E = modulus of deformation
ν = Poisson's ratio
c = cohesion
ϕ = angle of friction
γ = unit weigth
K_n = normal stiffness of joints
K_s = shear stiffness of joints
c_j = cohesion of joints

further study the opening behavior during excavation. The results of this study are given below.

Figure 5 shows the rock mass movements obtained in the finite element analysis of Stage (3) when displacements of different magnitude take place at the opening crown. These results show how the rock mass discontinuities introduce planes of weakness that strongly orient the preferred patterns of displacement of the medium. For crown displacements greater than 0.7 in, which can be reached soon after the excavation is opened, separation and sliding of large deep wedges occur at the opening crown and sidewalls which may fall into the excavation if proper support is not given. Figure 5 also indicate that most of the rock movements are due to the blocky condition of the rock mass since block deformation results minimum. This was confirmed by comparing these results to values obtained by assuming the rock mass without discontinuities. The sole presence of joints in the rock mass increases the displacements that take place when the excavation is performed.

The results of Figure 5 give the progression of movements in the rock mass. As more displacements take place at the opening walls, more movements are transmitted into the surrounding rock mass by the rock joints. These movements reach the top of rock and yield the settlement trough shown in Fig. 6.

The zone of loosening given by the finite element analysis of Stage (3) is shown in Fig. 6 when large wall displacements are allowed to take place. The zone extends from the opening walls to the soil-rock contact encompassing the complete rock

cover above the opening. Development of a zone like this indicates that the complete rock cover may collapse into the opening if proper support is not given to the rock blocks and wedges developed at the opening walls.

5 ROCK MASS STRESSES

The finite element analysis helped in providing an overall picture of the redistribution of stresses developed around the opening during construction. This redistribution of stresses varied with the amount of inward displacements taking place at the opening walls. Figure 7 shows the stress distributions in the rock mass during excavation of Stage (3) for two values of the crown displacements. For small displacements, the configuration of the stress distribution roughly conforms the shape of an arch. By means of this arching action, the rock mass acquires certain ability to transfer most of the overburden loads to the opening abutments. When larger displacements take place, the stresses around the crown rotate slightly decreasing the arching capacity of the rock above the crown. As a result, more overburden pressure is transferred directly to the support at the crown. Also, at larger displacements, high concentration of stresses occur in a narrow region at the opening abutments. In a real situation, this concentration may cause crushing of the rock block corners that may affect the behavior of the rock mass.

From the stress distribution point of view, the orientation of the joint sets plays an important role in the opening stability. At the opening abutments, a

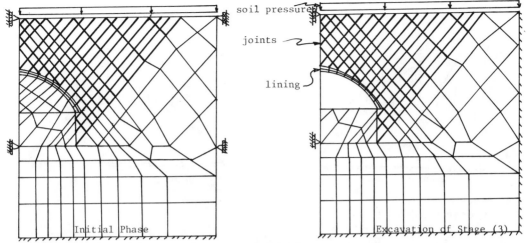

soil pressure

joints

lining

Initial Phase

Excavation of Stage (3)

Fig. 3 Finite element idealization of Stage (3) of excavation

strengthening effect results due to an increase in the joint normal stresses. At the crown, a weakening effect occurs due to an increase in the joint shear stresses which carries some discontinuities to failure. The balance between these two effects influences the opening stability.

6 DISTRIBUTION OF PRESSURES IMPOSED BY THE ROCK MASS

The scheme developed for Stage (3) helped in estimating the rock pressures imposed on the support with respect to the movements taking place in the rock mass surrounding the opening. The results of the finite element analysis (Fig. 8) show that excavation of Stage (3) provokes a complex distribution of radial active and passive rock pressures on the support that vary in magnitude and shape with respect to the wall displacements. The variation is such that as more movement takes place, the pressure distribution becomes largely non-uniform involving high load concentrations in some sections of the opening arch and zero loading in others. The high concentrations of load are largely a result of the weight of loosened rock blocks.

The pressure distributions of Fig. 8 suggest that lining design methods of shallow openings in jointed rock considering a uniform vertical pressure over the entire upper half of the lining may lead to estimates of lining thrust and bending moments that can be quite different from those given by the rock mass, especially when large displacements are allowed to take place at the opening walls. However, many of these design methods of easy application assume large factors of safety in their design that may overcome the differences given by their assumptions.

The pressure-displacement relationships (or ground reaction curves) obtained to study the opening behavior at Stage (3) are given in Fig. 9 for several arch sections of the opening. The curves were obtained by averaging the rock pressures of Fig. 8 over the section of the arch and plotting them versus the crown displacements. The results of Fig. 9 indicate that for a given rock condition, the opening ground reaction curve is not unique and depends on the section under consideration. At the crown (curve c), the curve shows a trend of declining rock pressures during the initial stage of deformation. As larger displacements take place, the pressures increase mainly as a result of a large volume of loosened rock developed at this location. The minimum pressures of curve c largely agree with the pressures required to support the critical rock wedges indentified at the crown (Rodríguez 1980). Previous identification of these wedges will give, then, an indication of the magnitude of the minimum rock pressures to be expected. The results of curve c also enhance the importance of the initial support in holding the critical wedges in place and maintaining the integrity of the rock mass. Early installation of this support will reduce the chances of possible fallouts and collapse of the rock cover above the opening.

Figure 9 also shows the ground reaction curve for the complete arch (curve a). Consideration of only this curve to analyze the opening can be misleading since it underestimates the pressures on some arch sections and overestimates them in others. Therefore, ground reaction curves for several arch sections of the opening should be considered in the analysis of loads imposed by jointed rock masses.

The results of Fig. 9 indicate that for a

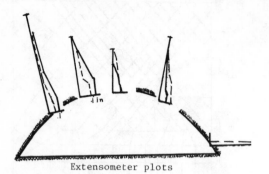

Extensometer plots

Test Section 1

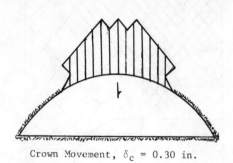

Crown Movement, δ_c = 0.30 in.

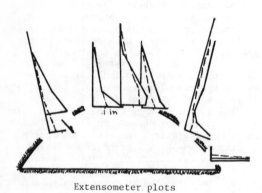

Extensometer plots

Test Section 3

— Measured
– – – FEM Results

|—————|
0   15 ft

Fig. 4   Comparison between measured and
          calculated displacements at two
          chamber sections

shallow opening in jointed rock, the
minimum rock pressures can be reached at
relatively small wall displacements, soon
after the excavation is opened. A delay in
installing the initial support will result
in rock loosening and greater support loads.
This situation contrast to the wide spread
concept applied to deep tunnels where large
displacements must occur before the rock
pressures reach a minimum value.

The ground reaction curve of the opening
springline is also shown in Fig. 9. The
curve is such that the imposed rock pressures considerably increase with crown

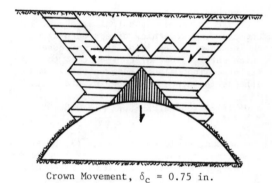

Crown Movement, δ_c = 0.75 in.

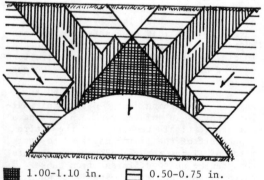

▓ 1.00–1.10 in.   ⊟ 0.50–0.75 in.
▥ 0.75–1.00 in.   ▢ 0.25–0.30 in.

Crown Movement, δ_c = 1.10 in.

Fig. 5 Rock Mass Movements

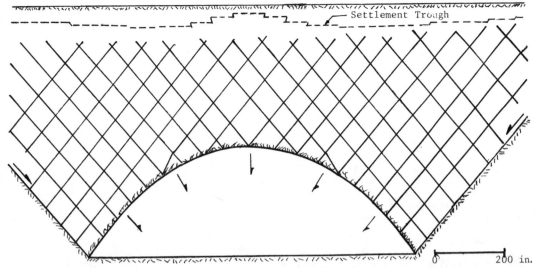

Fig. 6 Zone of loosening – Stage (3) of Excavation

displacements, reaching a maximum at displacements of 0.6 in. Further movements cause a decrease in pressure. Although the springline undergoes, at large displacements, inward movements that would dissipate some of the initial pressures, a mobilization of more rock weight to be supported also occurs, yielding curve s as the net result of these two actions.

The maximum and minimum pressures of the ground reaction curves of Fig. 9 can also be given in terms of the initial pressure p of the arch section under consideration. At the crown, the minimum pressures reach values of 55% of p, whereas at the springline they raise to values of 137% of p. The maximum pressures range from 72% of p

at the crown to 169% of p at the springline. If the ground reaction curve of the complete lining is considered, the minimum pressures account for 63% of p and the maximum pressures for 70% of p. If the rock pressures at the crown are given in terms of the hypothetical heights (H) of loosened rock, values of H that range from 40 to 53 ft are obtained. A value of H of 53 ft represents approximately 80% of the total soil-rock cover above the opening.

The stability of the chamber can also be given in terms of the ratio (n) of the height of loosened rock to the opening width (76 ft). Cording et al. (1971) have suggested that n can be considered a function of: 1) rock quality, 2) displacement along discontinuities, 3) joint strength and

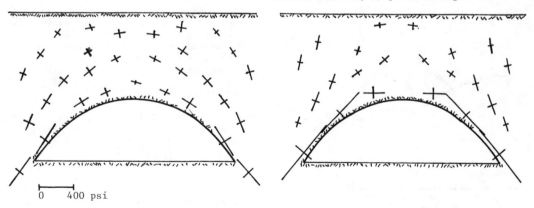

(a) Crown displacement, δ_c = 0.56 in. (b) Crown displacement, δ_c = 1.97 in.

Fig. 7 Distribution of stresses around the opening

429

orientation, and 4) the ratio of the unconfined compressive strength to the maximum natural stress, q_u/σ, when σ is large. For large chambers in rock of good quality and not heavily sheared, n values typically range from 0.1 to 0.25. The presence of shear zones and joint sets can result in higher values of n, which in this case varies from .53 to .70.

7 CONCLUSIONS

On the basis of the finite element results of Stage (3), it can be said that shallow openings in jointed rock, like the Dupont Circle Station, require initial support as soon as the excavation takes place. Any delay in support installation will result in rock loosening and geater loads since the minimum rock pressures occur at small wall displacements. An estimate of the minimum initial support can be obtained by identifying in advance the critical rock wedges that may develop around the opening. The analysis results show that the distribution of pressures imposed by the jointed rock mass is largely non-uniform and vary in magnitude and shape with the wall displacements indicating, thus, that ground reaction curves for several arch sections of the opening should be considered in the analysis of loads imposed by the jointed rock mass.

This analysis also shows, as observed in the field, that most of the rock movements

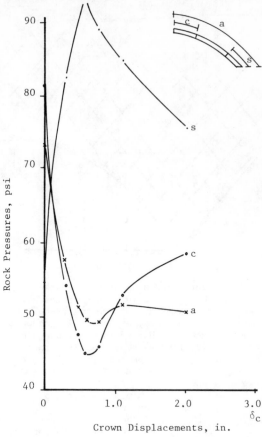

Fig. 9 Ground reaction curves for Stage (3)

are largely controlled by the rock mass discontinuitites. Most of these movements are produced by the blocky condition of the rock mass. Since the discontinuities play a significant role in the opening behavior, the jointed analysis becomes the most appropriate method that can be used to evaluate their effect.

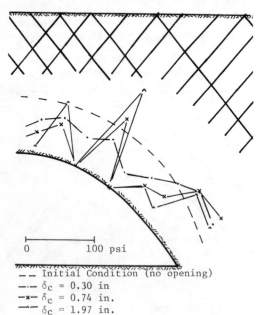

Initial Condition (no opening)
δ_c = 0.30 in
δ_c = 0.74 in.
δ_c = 1.97 in.

Fig. 8 Distribution of imposed radial pressures

8 REFERENCES

Brierley, G.S. 1975, The performance during construction of the liner for a large, shallow underground opening in rock. Ph.D. Thesis, Department of Civil Engineering, University of Illinois, Urbana.

Cording, E.J., Hendron, A.J. & D.U. Deere 1971, Rock engineering for underground caverns. Symp. on Underground Rock Chambers, ASCE, Phoenix: 567-600.

Cording, E.J. & J.W. Mahar 1974, The effects of natural geologic discontinuities on behavior of rock in tunnels. Proc. of

the Rapid Excavation and Tunneling
   Conference, AIME, San Francisco, Vol. 1:
   107-138.
Goodman, R.E., Taylor, R. & T.L. Brekke
   1968, A model for the mechanics of jointed
   rock, J. of the Soil Mech. and Found.
   Div., ASCE, Vol. 94, No. SM3: 637-659.
Mahar, J.W. 1977, The effect of geology
   and construction on behavior of a large
   shallow underground opening in rock.
   Ph.D. Thesis, Department of Geology,
   University of Illinois, Urbana.
Rodríguez, C.E. 1980, Analysis of an
   underground opening in jointed rock.
   Ph.D. Thesis, Department of Civil
   Engineering, University of Illinois,
   Urbana.
Rodríguez, C.E. 1982, Finite element
   analysis of a shallow opening in jointed
   rock. To be published.

MONITORING OF CAVERNS DURING CONSTRUCTION PERIOD
Beobachtende Überwachung von im Bau befindlichen Kavernen
Contrôle des cavernes pendant leurs périodes de construction

S.SAKURAI
Kobe University, Japan

SUMMARY:
In this paper a technique monitoring the stability of underground caverns during a construction period is described. The technique is based on displacement measurements such as convergence, borehole inclinometer and extensometer measurements. The stability of the caverns is convinced directly from strains evaluated by the measured displacements, without analyzing stress distributions around a cavern. The practical examples are shown to demonstrate an applicability of this technique. The failure criterion of rock and soil masses is also discussed in connection with the proposed monitoring technique.

ZUSAMMENFASSUNG:
In diesem Beitrag wird eine Technik vorgestellt, mit der die Standsicherheit von unterirdischen Kavernen während der Bauperiode überwacht werden kann. Die Methode beruht auf Verformungsmessungen, wie Konvergenzen, Bohrlochinklinometer und Extensometermessungen. Die Standsicherheit von Kavernen wird hauptsächlich von den Dehnungen hergeleitet, die aus den gemessenen Verformungen errechnet werden, ohne dass es notwendig ist Spannungen im Bereich der Kaverne zu berechnen. Die angeführten praktischen Beispiele sollen die Anwendbarkeit dieser Methode zeigen. Das Bruchkriterium von Fels und Boden wird ebenfalls in Verbindung mit der vorgeschlagenen Überwachungsmethode diskutiert.

RESUME:
Cet exposé décrit une technique de contrôle de la stabilité des cavernes durant leur période de construction. Cette technique est basée sur des mesures de déplacement telles que la convergence, l'inclinaison des trous de forage et la dilatation. La stabilité des cavernes est démontrée directement à partir des variations de longueur évaluées en fonction des déplacements mesurés, sans analyser les répartitions des contraintes autour de la caverne. Des exemples pratiques sont présentés pour prouver une applicabilité de cette technique. Le critère de rupture des masses de sol et de roche est aussi présenté en rapport avec la technique de contrôle proposée.

1. INTRODUCTION

Field measurements have been recognized as a potential tool for monitoring the stability of underground caverns during a construction period. Many different types of field instrumentations are now available for measuring stresses and displacements in the underground media. The most reliable and recommended monitoring system, however, must be the one which is based on the displacement measurements such as convergence and borehole extensometer measurements.

The displacement measurements are desirable because of simplicity of instrumentation and reliability of the data obtained, while the direct stress measurements are occasionally questionable and less reliable. Nevertheless, in order to give a quantitative interpretation to the results of displacement measurements, the stress distribution around caverns must be back-analyzed from the measured displacements, because the failure criterion of rocks is in general given in terms of stress. Therefore the stability of caverns can be assessed by comparing the computed stress with the failure criterion of the material. This back-analysis of stress, however, definitely depends upon the stress-strain relationship of rocks which is not easily evaluated for in-situ rock masses.

In order to overcome such a shortcoming involved in the stress analyses, the author has proposed a monitoring technique which is based on strain rather than stress, so that the stress analyses are unnecessary. Since strain is kinematically related to displacement, the proposed technique can achieve monitoring the cavern stabilities directly from the measured displacements. Accordingly it is named "Direct Strain Evaluation Technique (DSET)[1)]," which can be used in any complex geological formations because stress-strain relationship is unnecessary, and it is applicable to any three-dimentionally complex shape of caverns.

The DSET is based on convergence, borehole inclinometer and extensometer measurements performing during a construction period. The procedure of the technique is as follows. That is, when the displacements are measured at several measuring points around a cavern, a continuous displacement function is assumed so as to interpolate the measured values at the measuring points. The displacement function yields a strain distribution around the cavern by differentiating the function. If the derived strains tend to be greater than critical failure strains, then the additional supports such as shotcrete, rock bolts and steel ribs must be installed.

It is noted in the proposed technique that the most significant problem is how to evaluate the allowable strains of in-situ rock masses properly. In order to determine failure criteria in terms of strain, the author has analyzed the results of laboratory and in-situ tests, and has found out the fact that the critical failure strains obtained by laboratory tests are the same order of magnitude as those observed in in-situ tests. This shows that a failure criterion in terms of strain, which is utilized in monitoring the stability of caverns, may be determined by only the laboratory tests.

Since the DSET is simple in operation, the stability of caverns can be assessed immediately after taking the displacement measurements. In order to achieve a quick interpretation of the data, the author has developed a monitoring system by introducing a micro-computer that makes the DEST applicable to any construction sites where a big computer system is not available.

2. EVALUATION OF STRAIN FROM MEASURED DISPLACEMENT

Let us consider the displacements around cavern measured at certain points by borehole inclinometers and extensometers, as shown in Fig. 1. In the figure the points numbered 1 to 27 denote the measurement positions. In this paper the region surrounded by the measurement points is called the "element". The displacement in the elements can be interpolated in terms of the measured displacements.

The shape of element can be expressed in terms of interpolation functions and the coordinates of the measurement points, i.e.,

$$x = \sum_{i=1}^{N} P_i(\xi, \eta, \zeta) x_i$$
$$y = \sum_{i=1}^{N} P_i(\xi, \eta, \zeta) y_i \qquad (1)$$
$$z = \sum_{i=1}^{N} P_i(\xi, \eta, \zeta) z_i$$

where $P_i(\xi, \eta, \zeta)$ i = 1 to N is the interpolation function in terms of the curvilinear coordinates and x_i, y_i and z_i are, respectively, the x, y and z coordinates of measurement points i, and N is the total number of measurement points for the element.

If we assume an isoparametric element proposed by Zienkiewicz[2)] the displacements in an element are expressed in terms of the same interpolation functions as for the shape function of the element. Hence the displacement functions become as,

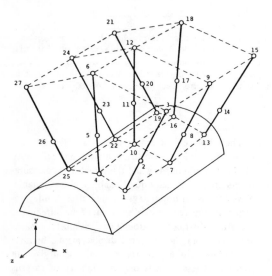

Fig. 1 Measurement points around a cavern

$$u = \sum_{i=1}^{N} Pi\,(\xi, \eta, \zeta)\,u_i$$

$$v = \sum_{i=1}^{N} Pi\,(\xi, \eta, \zeta)\,v_i \qquad (2)$$

$$w = \sum_{i=1}^{N} Pi\,(\xi, \eta, \zeta)\,w_i$$

where u_i, v_i and w_i are the measured displacements in the x, y and z directions at the measurement point i.

The kinematic relationship between displacement and strain is given as follows,

$$\{\varepsilon\} = \begin{Bmatrix} \varepsilon_x \\ \varepsilon_y \\ \varepsilon_z \\ \gamma_{xy} \\ \gamma_{yz} \\ \gamma_{zx} \end{Bmatrix} = \begin{Bmatrix} \partial u/\partial x \\ \partial v/\partial y \\ \partial w/\partial z \\ \partial u/\partial y + \partial v/\partial x \\ \partial v/\partial z + \partial w/\partial y \\ \partial w/\partial x + \partial u/\partial z \end{Bmatrix} \qquad (3)$$

Substituting Eq. (2) into Eq. (3) gives a strain distribution in an element in terms of the displacements measured at the measuring points, i.e.,

$$\{\varepsilon\} = [B]\{u\} \qquad (4)$$

where

$$\{u\} = <u_1 \ v_1 \ w_1 \ u_2 \ v_2 \ w_2 \cdots\cdots u_N \ v_N \ w_N >$$
$$[B] = [T_1(\xi, \eta, \zeta) \ T_2(\xi, \eta, \zeta) \cdots\cdots\cdots T_N(\xi, \eta, \zeta)] \qquad (5)$$

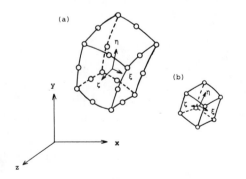

(a)

(b)

Fig. 2   Elements surrounded by measurement points

and

$$[Ti(\xi, \eta, \zeta)] = \begin{bmatrix} \dfrac{\partial Pi}{\partial x} & 0 & 0 \\[2mm] 0 & \dfrac{\partial Pi}{\partial y} & 0 \\[2mm] 0 & 0 & \dfrac{\partial Pi}{\partial z} \\[2mm] \dfrac{\partial Pi}{\partial y} & \dfrac{\partial Pi}{\partial x} & 0 \\[2mm] 0 & \dfrac{\partial Pi}{\partial z} & \dfrac{\partial Pi}{\partial y} \\[2mm] \dfrac{\partial Pi}{\partial z} & 0 & \dfrac{\partial Pi}{\partial x} \end{bmatrix} \qquad (6)$$

The interpolation functions $P_i(\xi, \eta, \zeta)$ are expressed, for instance, for a hexahedron element with 8 nodes (see Fig. 2 (a)) as,

$$Pi(\xi, \eta, \zeta) = \frac{1}{8}(1 + \xi_i\,\xi)(1 + \eta_i\,\eta)$$
$$(1 + \zeta_i\,\zeta) \qquad i = 1 \sim 8 \qquad (7)$$

and for a hexahedron element, with 20 nodes (see Fig. 2(b)) as,

$$Pi(\xi, \eta, \zeta) = \frac{1}{8}\xi_i^2\,\eta_i^2\,\zeta_i^2(1 + \xi_i\,\xi)$$
$$(1 + \eta_i\,\eta)(1 + \zeta_i\,\zeta)(\xi_i\,\xi + \eta_i\,\eta$$
$$+ \zeta_i\,\zeta - 2) + \frac{1}{4}\Big\{(1 - \xi_i^2)(1 + \eta_i\,\eta)$$
$$(1 + \zeta_i\,\zeta)(1 - \xi^2) + (1 - \eta_i^2)$$
$$(1 + \zeta_i\,\zeta)(1 + \xi_i\,\xi)(1 - \eta^2)$$
$$+ (1 - \zeta_i^2)(1 + \xi_i\,\xi)(1 + \eta_i\,\eta)$$
$$(1 - \zeta^2)\Big\} \qquad i = 1 \sim 20 \qquad (8)$$

Since the interpolation functions $Pi(\xi, \eta, \zeta)$ are given by a curvilinear coordinate system, the coordinate transformation is necessary to calculate the derivatives of Eq. (6).

The principal strains and the maximum shear strain can be easily obtained from the strain components calculated by Eq. (4).

3. PRACTICAL APPLICATION[3]

The DSET was used to assess the stability of an underground opening excavated in a weak rock formation consisting of sand stone and mud stone. The displacements around the opening were measured by the borehole extensometers, so that only the radial displacements were detected. The tangential displacements were not measured. Instead, they were estimated with the help of theoretical analyses considering the distribution of radial displacements.

In general the measurements of tangential components of displacement are difficult, although some measurement instruments are now available. Hence, the analytical method adopted here must be useful. However, in the construction of large underground caverns like power plant and storage house, the performance of field measurements could be more concentrated at one place, compared with long tunnels where the measurements must be performed at many different sections along the tunnel axis.

The radial displacements measured by the extensometers are shown in Fig. 3.

When obatining the displacements, we can calculate the strain distributions by using Eq. (4). The maximum principal strain, maximum shear strain and volumetric strain distributions are, respectively, illustrated in Fig. 4, 5 and 6. All these computations were performed by the computer YHP9825. It is seen from these figures that the largest maximum principal strain becomes more than 1% at the place near the crown, and the volumetric strain for expansion also becomes at most 1%.

4. FAILURE CRITERION IN TERMS OF STRAIN

According to the DSET, the stability of openings can be assessed by comparing the strain derived from the measurements of displacement with a given allowable strain.

The most important point in this technique is how to evaluate the allowable strain considering the failure of the material. In this section the failure criterion of rock and soil is discussed in terms of strain.

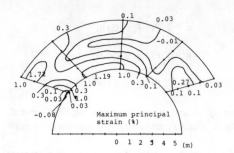

Fig. 4   Distribution of maximum principal strain (Extension is positive)

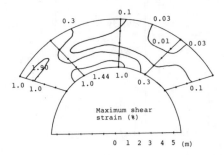

Fig. 5   Distribution of maximum shear strain

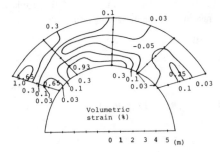

Fig. 6   Distribution of volumetric strain (Expansion is positive)

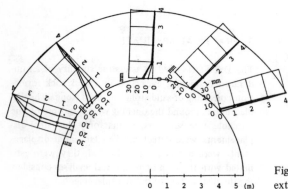

Fig. 3   Radial displacement measured by borehole extensometers

436

4-1 Failure Strain of Rock and Soil in Laboratory Experiments.

The uniaxial stress-strain relationship of rock and soil is generally expressed by the following hyperbolic function [4],

$$\sigma = \frac{\varepsilon}{b + a\varepsilon} \tag{9}$$

in which $b = 1/E_i$ and E_i is the initial modulus of elasticity.

Let us define a uniaxial compressive strength σ_c as follows;

$$\sigma_c = R_f / a \tag{10}$$

where R_f denotes a parameter representing the failure strength. From the uniaxial compressive strength σ_c and the initial modulus of elasticity E_i, we define the critical strain ε_0 as follows (See Fig. 7);

$$\varepsilon_0 = \sigma_c / E_i \tag{11}$$

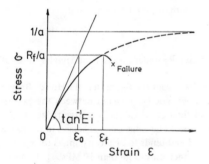

Fig. 7   Hyperbolic stress-strain relationship and definition of critical strain ε_0

It is noted that this critical strain ε_0 generally differs from strain ε_f at failure. However, for a brittle material in which the stress-strain relationship is almost linear to failure, the critical strain is assumed to be approximately the same as the failure strain.

The critical strain for various rocks and soils is plotted against the uniaxial strength, and the results are as shown in Fig. 8. It is obvious from this figure that the critical strain tends to decrease with increase in uniaxial strength, and it ranges approximately from 0.1 to 1.0 % for rock and from 1.0 to 5.0 % for soil (particularly for cohesive soils). It is of interest to know that the critical strain lies in the range 0.1 - 5.0 % although the uniaxial strength varies a wide range i.e. $0.2 \sim 2000$ Kg/cm^2.

The failure strain ε_f can be given by

$$\varepsilon_f = \frac{\sigma_c / E_i}{1 - R_f} = \frac{\varepsilon_0}{1 - R_f} \tag{12}$$

The parameter R_f for various rocks and soils is plotted in Fig. 9. The figure shows that the value of R_f lies in the rather wide range between 0.05 and 0.8 and tends to decrease with increase in uniaxial strength. For engineering practices, however, we can use the smallest values for a given uniaxial strength.

Let us now consider the failure strains in a triaxial state. If we assume that the stress-strain relationship of the material is given by a hyperbolic function even under a triaxial state of stress, then the shear modulus G_t is expressed for a certain level of the stress deviator $(\sigma_1 - \sigma_3)$, as follows;

$$G_t = G_i \left\{ 1 - R_f' \frac{\sigma_1 - \sigma_3}{(\sigma_1 - \sigma_3)_f} \right\}^2 \tag{13}$$

where G_i denotes the initial value of shear modulus. R_f' is the value of R_f under a triaxial stress state. $(\sigma_1 - \sigma_3)_f$ is the stress deviator at failure.

Substituting Eg. (13) into the following equation gives the maximum shear strain γ_t.

$$\gamma_t = \int_0^{\tau_{max}} d\tau / G_t \tag{14}$$

We introduce the magnification factor M defining as the ratio of the failure maximum shear strains under uniaxial and triaxial stress states. Then, the maximum shear strain for a triaxial state are expressed as,

$$\gamma_f (\text{ triaxial }) = M \gamma_f (\text{ uniaxial }) \tag{15}$$

Let us now consider the following two different types of failure conditions.

For the Mohr - Coulomb criterion,

$$\sigma_1 - \sigma_3 = 2c \cos \phi + (\sigma_1 + \sigma_3) \sin \phi \tag{16}$$

where c and ϕ denote cohesion and friction angle, and σ_1 and σ_3 are the maximum and minimum principal stresses, respectively. Compressive stress is taken to be positive in this study.

For the Hoek - Brown criterion [5],

$$\sigma_1 - \sigma_3 = \sqrt{m\sigma_3 + n} \tag{17}$$

where m and n are the material constants.

Considering these failure criteria, we can evaluate G_t, γ_f and M given by Eqs. (13), (14) and (15), as shown in Table - 1.

The magnification factor M was determined by laboratory triaxial compression tests. The experimental

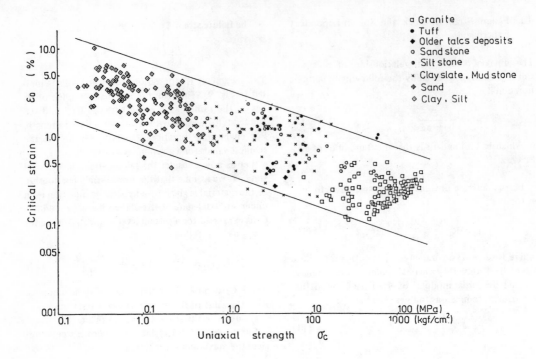

Fig. 8   Relationship between critical strain and uniaxial strength of intact rock and soil

results for sandstone are shown in Fig. 10 as a function of confining pressure. The analytical results for the two different types of failure criteria are also indicated for two different values of κ which is defined as,

$$\kappa = (1 - R_{f_1})/(1 - R_{f_3}) \qquad (18)$$

where R_{f_1} and R_{f_3} denote, respectively, the values of

the parameter R_f under uniaxial and triaxial states of stress.

It is obvious from the figure that the Hoek - Brown criterion shows good agreement between the experimental and theoretical values in a large range of confining pressure. The value of κ changes in the range of 1.0 ~ 1.3 and tends to be a constant as the confining pressure increases more than 10 MPa. This means that the value of R_{f_3} becomes a constant under a certain level of confining pressure.

Tabl - 1   Shear modulus, failure maximum shear strain and magnification factor

Failure Criterion	Shear Modulus G_t	Failure Maximum Shear Strain γ_f	Magnification Factor M
Mohr-Coulomb	$G_i \left\{ 1 - \dfrac{R_f (\sigma_1 - \sigma_3)(1 - \sin\phi)}{2\sigma_3 \sin\phi + 2c\cos\phi} \right\}^2$	$\dfrac{C\sqrt{\dfrac{1 + \sin\phi}{1 - \sin\phi}} + \dfrac{\sin\phi}{1 - \sin\phi}\sigma_3}{G_i (1 - R_f)}$	$\kappa\left(1 + \dfrac{\sigma_3}{c}\tan\phi \right)$
Hoek-Brown	$G_i \left\{ 1 - \dfrac{R_f (\sigma_1 - \sigma_3)}{(\sqrt{m\sigma_3 + n})_f} \right\}^2$	$\dfrac{\sqrt{m\sigma_3 + n}}{2 G_i (1 - R_f)}$	$\kappa\sqrt{\dfrac{m}{n}\sigma_3 + 1}$

438

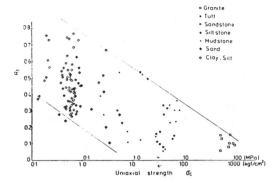

Fig. 9 Parameter R_f in relation with uniaxial strength of intact rock and soil

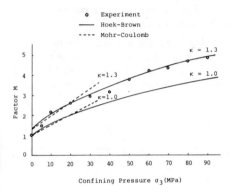

Fig. 10 Variation of magnification factor M with increasing confining pressure

When we determine the factor M, the maximum shear strain at failure under a triaxial state of stress can be evaluated from the failure strain obtained by uniaxial tests. In general, however, the shear strains are difficult to measure even in laboratory tests. Therefore, the maximum principal strain may be a better index in engineering practices, although the materials fail by shear. In this case, of course, the confining pressure must be known.

If we assume that the same magnification factor M is valid for normal strains, then the maximum principal strain at failure under a triaxial state of stress is also evaluated by the similar equation to Eq. (15).

$$\varepsilon_f(\text{ triaxial }) = M\varepsilon_f(\text{uniaxial }) \qquad (19)$$

4-2 Failure Strain of In-Situ Rock Mass

There are many different types of exploration methods now available to investigate the mechanical characteristics of in-situ rock masses. Among the methods are a plate bearing test for determining deformability, and a shear test for determining the strength of rock masses (see Fig. 11 and 12). Those are the tests most commonly used at construction sites where rock mechanics becomes an important consideration. From these tests, we can determine the modulus of elasticity, cohesion and the friction angle of the rock masses.

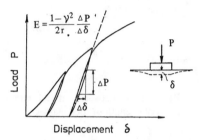

Fig. 11 Load-displacement curve obtained by in-situ plate bearing test

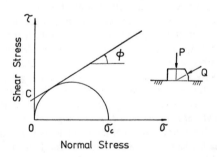

Fig. 12 Failure envelope obtained by in-situ shear test

The uniaxial strength σ_c of the rock mass may be obtained from the following equation.

$$\sigma_c = 2c \cos \phi / (1 - \sin \phi) \qquad (20)$$

where c is the cohesion and O is the friction angle. Hence the critical strain ε_0 for in-situ rock masses can be calculated from

$$\varepsilon_0 = \sigma_c / E. \qquad (21)$$

The data from in-situ tests performed mainly at dam construction sites are analyzed to evaluate the critical strain. Fig. 13 shows relationship between the critical strain and the uniaxial strength of in-situ rook masses.

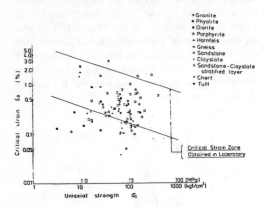

Fig. 13   Relationship between critical strain and uniaxial strength of rock masses

It is seen from the figure that the critical strain for rock masses ranges approximately from 0.1 to 1.0 %. The two solid lines indicate the range of the critical strain for intack rocks obtained from laboratory tests. It is obvious that the critical strain for in-situ rock masses is almost the same order of magnitude as the one for intact rocks. This may be due to the fact that the strength of rock masses decreases with increase of a number of cracks and joints, while the modulus of elasticity also decreases in the same amount, so that the ratio of these two quantities, i.e., the critical strain becomes a constant. This gives an explanation to scattering of the data shown in Fig. 13. That is, the critical strain is a constant, while the uniaxial strength decreases because of cracks and joints (see Fig. 14).

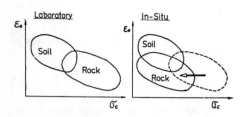

Fig. 14   Schematic diagram for relationship between crifical strain and uniaxial strength in laboratory and in-situ tests

It is understood that the critical strain may be independent of cracks, joints and other discontinuities, and it is considered to be an inherent material property. Considering this fact, it may be concluded that we can determine the critical strain of in-situ rock masses from laboratory experiments on small sized specimen.

When obtaining the critical strain of in-situ rock masses, we can determine the failure strain, provided that the parameter R_f is evaluated. It may be possible to evaluate R_f from the load-displacement relationship obtained by plate bearing tests (see Fig. 15)

$$R_f = \sigma_{cs} \, Aa \qquad (22)$$

where σ_{cs} denotes the uniaxial strength of rock masses. A is the area of loading plate. a is a parameter of hyperbolic function. One example for obtaining R_f for in-situ rock masses is shown in Fig. 16, where R_f becomes 0.381.

By considering many different data of plate bearing tests, it seems that the parameter R_f ranges from 0.3 to 0.5. This means that the value of R_f for in-situ rock masses may be smaller than the one for intact

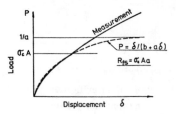

Fig. 15   Hyperbolic load-displacement curve fitting with measurement of plate bearing test

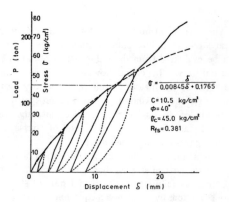

Fig. 16   Example of evaluating parameter R_f for in-situ rock masses

440

rocks. Therefore, we can use the value of R_f obtained from laboratory tests for the engineering practices, because the smaller values give a safe side for monitoring the stability of caverns.

Assuming that the magnification factor M is the same as the one obtained from laboratory tests, the maximum principal strain ε_F at failure under a tri-axial state is expressed as follows,

$$\varepsilon_F \ (\text{triaxial}) = M \ \varepsilon_F (\text{uniaxial})$$
$$= M \ \varepsilon_0 \ / \ (1 - R_f) \tag{23}$$

This may be used as the maximum allowable strain for monitoring the stability of caverns.

5. CONCLUSIONS

In this paper the Direct Strain Evaluation Technique (DSET) assuring the stability of the underground caverns during a construction period, is described. According to the technique, the stability of the caverns can be assessed directly from measured displacements without performing any stress analyses. That is, the existing strains around the caverns are calcutated from the measured displacements by considering kinematic relationships between displacement and strain. And the strains are compared with the allowable strains which are determined by laboratory compression tests. If the existing strain is still smaller than the allowable strain, then the stability of the caverns is verified.

6. REFERENCES

1) Sakurai, S., "Direct Strain Evaluation Technique in Construction of Underground Opening", Proc. 22nd U.S. Sympo. Rock Mech., MIT, pp. 278 ~ 282, 1981.
2) Zienkiewicz, O.C., The Finite Element Method in Engineering Science, McGraw Hill, 1971.
3) Yoshimura, H . et. al., "Utlization of Displacement Measurement Results in Tunnel Excavation (in Japanese)", Proc. Sympo. GENBA KEISOKU (Field Measurement Method), Japanese Soc. Soil Mech. & Foundation Eng., Osaka, Japan pp. 209 ~ 214, 1981.
4) Kondner, R.L. "Hyperbolic Stress - strain Res-Ponse: Cohesive Soils", Proc. ASCE, SM1, pp. 115 ~ 143, 1963.
5) Hoek, E. and E.T. Brown, "Empirical Strength Criterion for Rock Masses", Proc. ASCE, Vol. 109, No. GT9, pp. 1013 ~ 1035, 1980.

PLANNING AND CONSTRUCTION OF THE BEDROCK SHELTER OF HERVANTA
Planung und Bau des Gebirgsschutzraums in Hervanta
Planification et construction de l'ouvrage de protection à Hervanta

P.S.SÄRKKÄ
Helsinki University of Technology, Espoo, Finland

SUMMARY:
In Tampere, an underground air-raid shelter is being built where two ice-hockey rinks
will be placed for civilian use. It consists of a single hall with a span width of 32 m,
a maximum height of 9.2 m and a length of 134 m.
The site investigations included different types of geological mapping, diamond core
drilling and rock stress measurements. The final cross-sectional profile was chosen on
the basis of BEM and FEM calculations.
The need for strengthening was mainly determined by the shelter specifications. The
strengthening consists of a combination of rock bolts, steel net and shotcrete. Rock
mass conditions are followed with precise levellings and extensometers during and after
the construction stage.

ZUSAMMENFASSUNG:
In Tampere baut man eine Gebirgsschutzraum, wo zwei Eishockeybahnen für Zivilgebrauch
liegen werden. Sie ist eine Einzelhalle mit einer Spannweite von 32 m, einer Höhe von
9.2 m und einer Länge von 134 m.
Die Platzuntersuchungen enthielten geologische Kartierung auf verschiedenen Weisen, Kern-
bohrungen und Gebirgsspannungsmessungen. Der endgültige Querdurchschnitt war auf der
Grunde der Grenzelement- und Finite-elementberechnungen gewählt.
Das Befestigungsbedürfnis war hauptsächlich von Schutzraumgebrauch festgesetzt. Die Be-
festigung besteht aus einer Kombination von Felsankern, Stahlnetz und Spritzbeton. Die
Gebirgsmassenverhältnisse sind mit genauen Abwägungen und Extensometern unter und nach
Abbau gefolgt.

RESUME:
A Tampere on est en train de construire un abri souterrain contenant deux patinoires
pour le hockey sur glace. Il embrasse une simple halle avec une portée de 32 m, une hauteur de 9.2 m et une longueur de 134 m.
Les investigations in situ embrassont des etudes géologiques variées, des forations au
diamant pour le carottage et des mesures de l'état de contrainte des roches. La section
transversale finale a été choisie sur la base de calculations par les methodes des éléments de bord et finis.
Le besoin de renforcer était principalement déterminé par l'usage d'abri. Le renforcement consiste en boulons, en filet d'acier et en béton projété combiné. Les conditions
dans le massif rocheux sont observées par les mesures géodétiques et par les extensomètres pendant et après la construction.

1 CIVILIAN USE FOR AIR-RAID SHELTERS

According to the Finnish legislation a
town district of 10 to 30 thousand inhabitants has to have air-raid shelters from 1
to 3 hectares (30 000 m²) altogether. Today this is an investment of up to 100 million Finnish marks (25 million USD), only
for exceptional use. To utilize these investments more effectively a civilian use
is always tried to find for these spaces.
In larger spaces one has of course more alternatives to choose.

1.1 Alternative uses

Nearby all of the larger air-raid shelters have been built in rock since the beginning of the 1960´es (Vuorela and Tervilä, 1980). The Finnish bedrock is usually of good quality and the soil cover is thin.

The first bedrock shelters were mainly used for storages or car parking. Today there are much more possibilities, e.g. gymnastics and tennis halls, running tracks, swimming halls, cinemas, bowling halls etc., not to speak of training rooms for pop groups.

The most important restriction to the civilian use is the demand that the shelter has to be able to be changed to its original purpose in 24 hours.

2 PRELIMINARY INVESTIGATIONS

At the middle of the 1970´es such good experiences had been obtained on bedrock shelters that an idea was arisen to place an ice-hockey rink underground into a bedrock air-raid shelter. After some discussions with the Finnish Ice-hockey Association it was found out that the minimum acceptable width for an ice-hockey rink was 28.5 m. This again supposed a bedrock shelter with a span width of minimum 32 m.

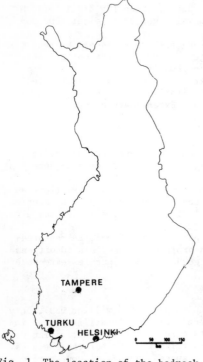

Fig. 1. The location of the bedrock shelter of Hervanta.

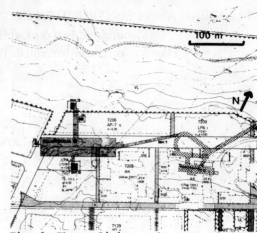

Fig. 2. The preliminary placement of the bedrock shelter of Hervanta. Cross-lined area is the crushing plant, shadowed area the bedrock shelter.

The planning of the first bedrock shelter with a span width of 32 m was started in 1977 in the town of Turku (Holopainen and Oksanen, 1980). The second one was started a year later in Hervanta, in the town of Tampere (Fig. 1). This one is discussed in more details here. The third one will probably be started this year in the vicinity of Helsinki.

The capacity planned for the bedrock shelter of Hervanta is 3 000 persons, which means a hall area of 134 x 32 m in a single hall (Fig. 2).

2.1 Geological investigations

The investigations in Hervanta were started with aerial photogeological mapping and surface geological mapping in summer 1978. On the basis of the information obtained from these the shelter was preliminary placed in a larger block in the bedrock (Fig. 2). The shortest distance to the nearest fault zone was about 250 m (N-NW from the shelter). The shelter axis was in the direction of the bedrock block.

The rock type in the block was homogeneous, coarse-grained, unaltered porphyric granite. In summer 1980 two diamond drill holes were made, one in both ends of the planned shelter. The information obtained from these holes supported earlier knowledge. Rock was found to be homogeneous and unaltered at the depth of the planned shelter. Fracture spacing was in average over 1 m. The dominating fracture directions were found to be $280 - 330^g/50 - 90^g$ and $150 - 200^g/20^g$ (dip direction/dip).

444

Table 1. The physical characteristics of
the Hervanta porphyric granite.

	mean	std.dev.
Compressive strength	105 MPa	10 MPa
Tensile strength	7.5 MPa	1.4 MPa
Young's modulus	64 GPa	5 GPa
Poisson's ratio	0.29	0.05
Density	2760 kg/m^3	60 kg/m^3

2.2 Rock mechanics investigations

The physical characteristics of the rock
type were determined according to the ISRM
recommendations (1981) from 9 specimens.
The results are presented in Table 1.

In water pressure tests water loss was
observed only temporarily and the amounts
were minimal, maximum 0.007 1/m/min/kPa.
According to Hoek & Bray (1981) this gives
a coefficient of permeability k maximum
9 x 10^{-5} cm/s. With the fracture spacing
obtained this means a maximum fracture
opening of 0.07 mm, i.e. the fractures are
practically closed.

The rock mass was also classified according to the NGI-system. Q-values were found
to vary between 8 and 25.

2.3 State of stress

Ten years earlier a crushing plant (Fig. 2)
had been established underground with a
span width of 12 m about 150 m from the
planned location of the shelter. From the
crushing plant a rock stress measurement
was made by Suomen Malmi Oy Finnexploration with the Leeman-NTH method (1, Fig.
12). This measurement gave a horizontal
state of stress with a compressive stress
of 5.8 MPa in the direction of the shelter
hall and 4.3 MPa transversely to the hall.
In vertical direction a small tensile
stress of -1.1 MPa was found. This may,
however, be due to the measuring errors.

3 PLANNING

According to the Technical Specifications
(1977) a bedrock shelter has to have a
roof thickness

$T \geq L/2 + 3$ m, and at least 6 m, (1)

where L is the span width,

and an arrow height

$P \geq L/5$. (2)

All the Finnish civilian shelters are di-
mensioned for conventional weapons only.

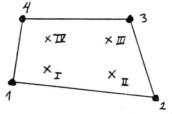

Fig. 3. The element of JTROCK (Hittinger
and Goodman, 1978).

3.1 Stability calculations

Because the rock mass was generally seen
homogeneous and its physical characteristics were known quite well (Table 1), the
dimensioning was made with element methods.
Both boundary and finite element methods
were used.

The program most used was a modified
JTROCK (Hittinger and Goodman, 1978), a
FEM program which uses isoparametric elements with four nodal points and linear
shape functions (Fig. 3). The principal
stresses are calculated in the integral
points of the elements (Roman numbers).
Then they are smoothed to the nodal points
(Arabic numbers) by the method of least
squares (Fig. 4). Finally the state of the
stress of the element is calculated as an
average of the nodal point stresses.

In the dimensioning we have mostly used
factors of safety according to the failure
criterions of both Mohr-Coulomb (Fig. 5)
and Hoek-Brown (Fig. 6). These criterions
consider both tensile and shear failures.

The tensile side of the former has been
modified a little. In our opinion this modification makes the use of experimental data easier in the determination of the criterion parameters.

In the latter criterion it is even possible to consider the scale effect quite
easily. If Q-values are determined for u-

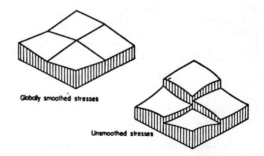

Globally smoothed stresses

Unsmoothed stresses

Fig. 4. The effect of smoothing to the element stresses (Hinton and Campbell, 1974).

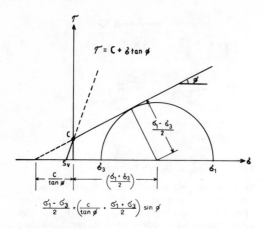

$$\frac{\sigma_1 - \sigma_3}{2} = \left(\frac{c}{\tan\phi} \cdot \frac{\sigma_1 + \sigma_3}{2}\right)\sin\phi$$

Fig. 5. The modified failure criterion of Mohr-Coulomb.

nit cells of a certain size in the rock mass, their dispersion is the greater the larger the rock mass is. Consequently reasonable minimum values of Q can be used when determining the parameters m and s.

In the following figures (Figs. 7 to 10) these parameters respond to a Q-value of 10 in a granitic rock.

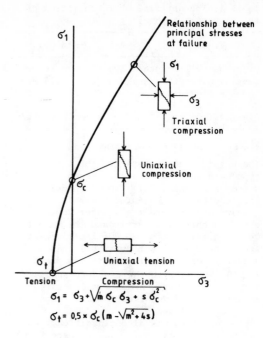

$$\sigma_1 = \sigma_3 + \sqrt{m\,\sigma_c\,\sigma_3 + s\,\sigma_c^2}$$
$$\sigma_t = 0.5 \times \sigma_c\left(m - \sqrt{m^2 + 4s}\right)$$

Fig. 6. The failure criterion of Hoek-Brown (Hoek and Brown, 1980).

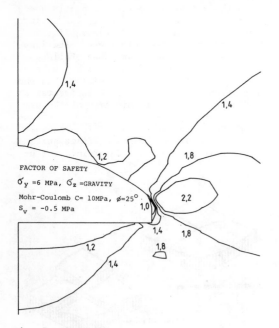

FACTOR OF SAFETY

σ_y =6 MPa, σ_z =GRAVITY

Mohr-Coulomb C= 10MPa, ϕ=25°

S_v = -0.5 MPa

Fig. 7. The safety factors in horizontal state of stress according to the failure criterion of Mohr-Coulomb.

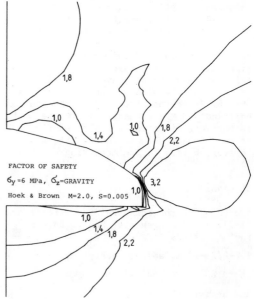

FACTOR OF SAFETY

σ_y =6 MPa, σ_z=GRAVITY

Hoek & Brown M=2.0, S=0.005

Fig. 8. The safety factors in horizontal state of stress according to the failure criterion of Hoek-Brown.

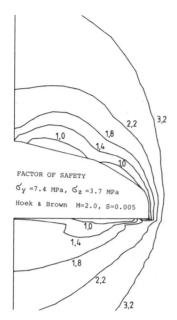

FACTOR OF SAFETY

σ_y =7.4 MPa, σ_z =3.7 MPa

Hoek & Brown M=2.0, S=0.005

Fig. 9. The factors of safety in the lower profile with σ_h/σ_v = 2.

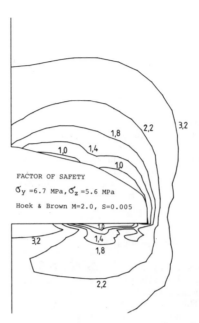

FACTOR OF SAFETY

σ_y =6.7 MPa, σ_z =5.6 MPa

Hoek & Brown M=2.0, S=0.005

Fig. 10. The factors of safety in the lower profile with σ_h/σ_v = 1.2.

The behaviour of these two failure criterions was studied in the known state of stress and with the known characteristics of the rock mass (Figs. 7 and 8). The different rock mass parameters used were matched to be as realistic as possible.

No major differences were found between the behaviour of these criterions. The criterion of Hoek-Brown seems to have a somewhat steeper gradient, i.e. in the probable safe areas it gives higher factor of safety values and again larger failed areas near to the openings. This criterion was chosen for the final calculations, mainly because it was easier to take into account the different rock mass conditions in it.

The final choice of shape was made between two profiles, one with an arrow height of 6.4 m and another with an arrow height of 8.0 m. The latter had a year earlier been chosen for a similar bedrock shelter in Turku (Holopainen and Oksanen, 1980).

In the preliminary calculations the planned shelter shape had been found feasible. To compare the effect of a change in arrow height a sensibility analysis of both profiles was performed in relation to the state of stress and to the condition of the rock mass. This effect was found to be nearly negligible in the probable range of variation of these parameters.

The failure criterion was exceeded both in the floor and in the roof of both profiles but the thickness of broken area was not more than 1.5 m at worst (Figs. 9 and 10). The final decision was made to the advantage of the lower profile, because the excavated masses and thus the stoping costs, too, were smaller.

4 CONSTRUCTION

4.1 Stoping

The stoping order is presented in Fig. 11. The middle part (1) of the profile was stoped first to a width of 19 m and a height of 4.5 m by first drifting and then slashing from both sides. The last layer of 1 –

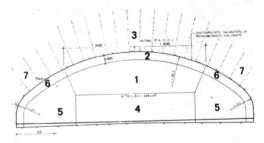

Fig. 11. The stoping order of the Hervanta bedrock shelter.

447

1.5 m (2) against the final roof line was taken with cautious blasting so that the broken zone was limited to 0.4 m. After this the final roof area was bolted (3).

The middle part was then benched down (4) 4 m to the final floor line, the side parts (5) were slashed to final width, the last layer (6) again with cautious blasting, and the yet unbolted part of the roof and wall area was bolted (7).

Stoping was carried out completely according to the timetable. No surprises were met anywhere. All the stoping phases (1 - 7) were performed during six months, i.e. in two three month's periods interrupted by a four month's summer break (see Fig. 14).

4.2 Control measurements

During the stoping phase 1 two additional rock stress measurements were performed (2 and 3, Fig. 12). This was done to confirm that there do not exist tensile stresses in the rock mass. These were not found and the state of stress in the rock mass was well in the limits of the sensibility analysis.

Three REX rod extensometers were installed in the beginning of construction from the surface to the roof area of the shelter. Their purpose was to control the depth of the possible loosening arch area and to measure the amount of loosening. Their base plates were precise-levelled, too, to control the amount of subsidence. The places of the extensometers (D, F and E) are presented in Fig. 12 and their anchoring points in relation to the shelter roof in Fig. 13.

The extensometer results up to the end of January 1982 are presented in Fig. 14

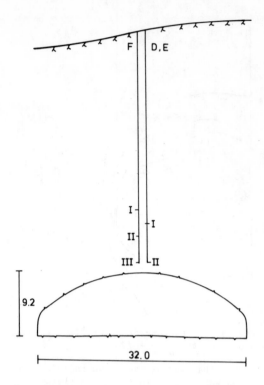

Fig. 13. The positions of extensometer anchoring points in relation to the shelter.

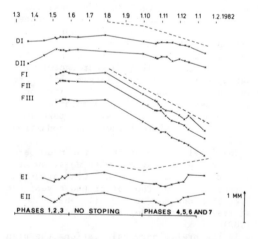

Fig. 14. The results of extensometer and subsidence measurements.

together with the subsidence measurement results. Anything unexpected has not taken place in the roof area. The possible loosened volume has not exceeded the prognosed depth, 1.5 m, in the area of any of the extensometers.

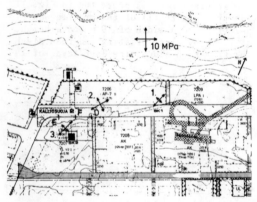

Fig. 12. The horizontal state of stress in the area of Hervanta bedrock shelter and the places of control extensometers.

448

The subsidence measurements show, however, that the roof has as an entity behaved as a plate. It has bent downwards but this bending suits well to the values obtained in the planning calculations, 2.5 mm. However, the situation had not been totally stabilized at the moment of writing.

In the original plans of control measurements there were convergence measurements, too, to control the inside deformation of the shelter. In this case they were found inadequate, mainly because a standard convergence over 30 m of length was not found. Because the expected deformations were quite small, of the order of some millimeters, there was no reason to buy some special pieces of equipment.

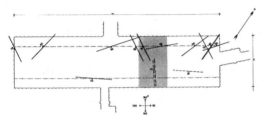

Fig. 15. A map of the structural features in the Hervanta bedrock shelter.

During the summer break, after the completion of the stoping phase 3, mapping of structural features on the exposed surfaces of the shelter was performed (Fig. 15). The linear features were continued to the final wall lines to give a prognose on the possible difficult areas for stoping. The rock mass was more broken in the shadowed area, and the only rock falls took place in this area in stoping phase 5, especially in the upper left part of the area (see Fig. 15). The amount of fallen rock was some tens of tonnes, and the situation was got into control with local bolting.

5 STRENGTHENING

The Technical Specifications (1977) give following limit values to the strengthening of bedrock shelters:

$$A_b \geq 0.0002 \times A_r, \text{ if } 2L \geq T \geq L/2 + 3m, \quad (3)$$

where A_b is the total cross-sectional area
 of rock bolts,
 A_r is the roof area,
 T is the roof thickness and
 L is the span width.
The quality of rock bolt steel has to be at least A 400 H (400 N/mm^2, weldable).

The shotcrete thickness has to be at least 60 mm in the roof.

The steel net reinforcement has to have a wire diameter of at least 3 - 5 mm and a mesh size of 100 - 150 mm at most.

5.1 Bolting

The preliminarily planned rock bolts were ribbed steel rods, 25 mm in diameter, untensioned and grouted. In the stoping phase 3 their spacing was 1.5 x 1.5 m and length 5.6 m. In the stoping phase 7 spacing was 1.5 x 1.75 m and length 4.0 m.

On the basis of planning calculations the bolt length could have been reduced to 2.4 m, including a grouting length of 0.8 m in sound rock. However, this would have presupposed a bolt spacing of 0.8 x 0.8 m and given a possibility to diminish the bolt diameter down to 12 mm.

This approach was rejected, mainly because of the increased drilling and installation work. Instead the bolt length was unified to 4.5 m overall in the shelter to ease bolting work and to give some extra safety against possible variations in rock quality.

5.2 Weapon effect

According to Vähäsarja (1976) the safe roof thickness with no formation of inverted cone can be estimated in crystalline metamorphosed Precambrian bedrock from

$$T_s = 0.54 \times W^{1/3} \quad (4)$$

where T_s is the safe roof thickness (m)
 and
 W is the amount of explosive (kg).
 T_s has to be multiplied by a factor increasing from 1 to 1.6 when the roof thickness/span width - ratio diminishes from 10 to 1.

According to Eq. (4) the bedrock shelter of Hervanta will tolerate surface explosions up to 50 tons, i.e. all the known conventional weapons.

On the other hand, to be safe against nuclear weapons the shelter ought to be placed remarkedly deeper in the rock, to a depth of about 150 m for tactical weapons and about 350 m for strategic weapons. This would cause extreme difficulties in ventilation and in construction of safe roadways. That has not been regarded appropriate for civilian purposes, because the shelter area is not expected to be a target, and it does give shelter for secondary effects.

449

6 CONCLUSIONS

Bedrock shelters with span widths of 30 – 35 m can be technically and economically feasibly constructed in Finnish bedrock with standard methods of excavation. A major part of the feasibility comes from the multipurpose use of the shelter.

Usual control methods (rod extensometers, precise levelling) are in most cases adequate. However, if it has not been succeeded to place the shelter in a homogeneous block of bedrock, there are reasons to be reserved to some extraordinary methods.

Resistance against the weapon effects can be obtained cheapest and easiest by leaving the roof thick enough, i.e. by taking advantage of the strength of rock instead of the extra reinforcement. The strengthening needed for civilian use has to be done in any case.

ACKNOWLEDGEMENTS

The Technical Bureau of the City of Tampere is acknowledged for the permission to use their material and for their kindly co-operation in the preparation of this paper.

I am indebted to Kontio and Anttila Engineers, especially Mr. J. Koskento, MSc(C. Engn.), for their co-operation during this project, and to Suomen Malmi Oy Finnexploration, especially Mr. E. With, MSc(Geol.), for a possibility to work as their consultant.

I am also indebted to the personnel of our laboratory for their computational help.

The Academy of Finland is appreciated its financial support.

Finally, I thank Mr. A. Öhberg, MSc(Min.), for correcting the English text.

REFERENCES

Hinton, E and Campbell, J. 1974. Local and global smoothing of discontinuous finite element functions using a least squares method. Int. J. Num. Meth. Eng. 8:461-480.

Hittinger, M. and Goodman, R. 1978. JTROCK, a computer program for stress analysis of two-dimensional, discontinuous rock masses. Report No. UCB/6T/78-04, Dept. Civ. Engn., Univ. of California.

Hoek, E. and Bray, J. 1981. Rock slope engineering, 3rd ed.. IMM, London. 358 p.

Hoek, E. and Bray, J. 1980. Underground excavations in rock. IMM, London. 527 p.

Holopainen, P. and Oksanen, J. 1980. The use of an underground bomb shelter as ice-hockey rinks. Subsurface Space 1:137-140, Pergamon Press, London.

International Society for Rock Mechanics 1981. Rock characterization, testing and monitoring, ISRM suggested methods. Pergamon Press, London.

Vuorela, M. and Tervilä, K. 1980. Peacetime use of subsurface air-raid shelters in Finland. Subsurface Space 1:237-242, Pergamon Press, London.

Vähäsarja, P. 1976. Sotilasgeologia II (Military Geology II). Central Headquarters, Helsinki. 153 p.

Technical Specifications of S3 and S6 class Air-raid Shelters 1977. Ministry of the Interior, Rescue Department, Helsinki. 54 p.

'RIB-IN-ROC' PRE-REINFORCEMENT SYSTEM FOR LARGE CAVERNS

'Rib-in-roc' ('Rippen im Gestein') – Eine Methode zur Vorspannung grosser Hohlräume
'Rib-in-roc', une méthode de précontrainte des grandes cavernes

OVE STEPHANSSON
University of Luleå, Sweden
BENGT STILLBORG
Swedish Mining Research Foundation, Kiruna

SUMMARY:
This paper summarises the result of a research programme, the objective of which was to develop the understanding of the Rib-in-Roc method. Through dimensional analysis and two- and three-dimensional physical model experiments it has been possible to establish the contribution to both permanent and immediate stabilisation of a large cavern pre-reinforced by the Rib-in-Roc method. Theoretical work also has demonstrated that the Rib-in-Roc method is a working system of pre-reinforcement. The theoretical and experimental work was conducted during 1975-1979. Since then the Rib-in-Roc method has been suggested for a number of applications, e.g. underground caverns for nuclear power reactors. The present situation, where the system has not been applied, indicates the need of a demonstration cavern. A conceivable test cavern for later oil storage has been suggested to be located at an oil storage plant in southwestern Sweden.

ZUSAMMENFASSUNG:
In diesem Artikel werden die Ergebnisse eines Forschungsprogramm zusammengestellt, das mit dem Zweck durchgeführt wurde, die 'Rib-in-Roc'-Methode zu entwickeln. Durch Dimensions- analyse und mit Hilfe von Experimente an zwei- und dreidimensionalen Modellen konnten die stabilisierende Effekte der Vorverstärkung nach der 'Rib-in-Roc'-Methode sowohl während des Baus wie während der Anwendung von unteriridischen Hohlräume festgestellt werden. Die Anvendbarkeit dieser Methode als Vorverstärkungssystem wurde auch theoretisch nach- gewiesen. Die theoretische und experimentelle Untersuchungen wurden 1975-1979 duchgeführt. Seitdem ist die 'Rib-in-Roc'-Methode für eine Reihe von Anwendungen – u.a. für Hohlräume als unteriridische Verlegung von Kernkraftwerke – vorgeschlagen worden. Die Methode kam bisher noch nicht zur praktischen Anwendung; dies deutet den Bedarf an, eine Vorführungs- anlage zu bauen. Es wird deshalb vorgeschlagen, im südwestlichen Teil Schwedens eine Versuchsanlage zu bauen, die später als Erdöllager angewendet werden kann.

RESUME:
Dans l´article présenté ci-dessus, on a résumé les résultats d´un programme de recherches exécuté dans le but d´étudier et de développer la méthode 'Rib-in-Roc'. Grâce à l´analyse dimensionelle et grâce à des expériences sur des modèles physiques à deux ou trois dimensions, il a été possible de démontrer, aussi bien au stade de la construction qu´à celui de l´utilisation, les effets stabilisateurs que la méthode Rib-in-Roc apportait dans le pré-reinforcement des grandes salles creusées dans le roc. La possibilité d´utiliser la méthode comme système pratique de pré-renforcement a aussi été démontrée théoriquement. Les travaux théoriques et expérimentaux ont été exécutés durant la période de 1975 à 1979. Depuis, la méthode Rib-in-Roc a été proposée pour la réalisation d´un certain nombre de projets, en particulier pour les espaces souterrains nécessaires aux réacteurs nucléaires. Mais jusqu´à présent, elle n´a pas encore été mise en application, ce qui montre la nécessité d´en faire une première démonstration. C´est pourquoi, il est proposé qu´une salle qui pourrait être ensuite affectée à léntrepôt de produits pétroliers soit creusée à proximité d´un dépôt de pétrole dans le sud-ouest de la Suède.

DESCRIPTION OF THE RIB-IN-ROC SYSTEM

An isometric view of the Rib-in-Roc pre-reinforcement system is presented in fig. 1. Before any full-scale excavation takes place, an entry is made in the host rock and rib raises are driven around the proposed opening. These raises are spaced at intervals dependent upon rock quality; an opening in poor rock needs more ribs per length of opening. As the ribs are driven they are used as a site from which

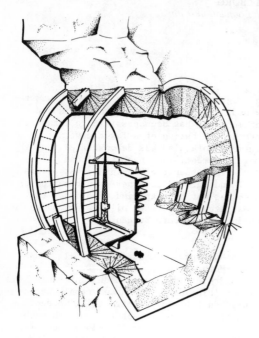

Fig. 1 Isometric view of the Rib-in-Roc system

competent cable bolting can be carried out. As a rib is excavated, it is filled with reinforced concrete. Finally, after the proposed opening has been reinforced, the displacements are automatically controlled as the opening is being excavated. Using this method, openings with a span of 50-60 m and a height of 60-80 m can be achieved. This should be compared with the largest man-made openings in rock for permanent installations which have spans in the order of 35 m.

The maintenance of a stable opening depends on restricting displacements by using reinforcement around the opening. Improvement in the behaviour of the rock mass results from restrained displacements, additional confinement and arch continuity. Once excessive displacements have occurred,

no amount of rock bolt tensioning or additional steel sets is going to bring back the lost strength. The key to the most effective reinforcement or support is to restrain displacements, within certain limits, as soon as possible. The Rib-in-Roc system, being a pre-reinforcement system, is most effective in this case.

The Rib-in-Roc method will be examined step by step through all stages of performance. Modifications according to rock mass quality, inherent state of stress and span width have to be made. The opening envisaged has a span of 50 m, a height of 60 m and a length of 100 m and is excavated in massive, moderately jointed, major igneous rock, subjected to a stress field where the horizontal stress component is three times the vertical. This corresponds to the case studied in the physical model investigation as described later.

EXCAVATION OF THE RIB TUNNELS

The side elevation of the rib tunnel may be excavated to either rectangular or elliptical form. The latter (fig. 1) is to be preferred where horizontal stresses are greater than the vertical ones. A technique applicable to the excavation of elliptical form rib tunnels is illustrated schematically in fig. 2. This technique employs raise climbers such as are commonly used to excavate advanced raise forms in the mining industry (vein mining). In the case of rectangular form ribs, the raises may be excavated using raise borers, while

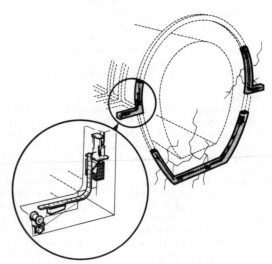

Fig. 2 Excavation of curved rib tunnels using raise climbers

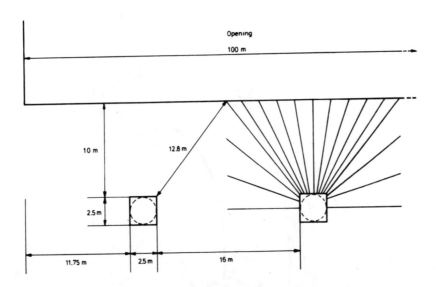

Fig. 3 Suggested layout for a cavern with length 100 m, height 60 m
and span 50 m in a moderately jointed granitic rock

conventional drill-and-blast tunnel drifting
would be applicable to the roof section.
The cross-sectional area should be the
smallest possible, while making allowance
for the drilling of cable holes. This
would suggest an area of the order of
2.5 x 2.5 m², which makes it possible to
use 1.2 m drill rods and still have access
for a powerful drilling machine. The ribs
should be placed approximately 10 m
(measured from the inside wall) from the
proposed wall of the opening. A rib spacing
of 16 m is suggested, based upon a nominal
bolt hole length of 12.5 m. Although this
length may be greater than 12.8 m at the
ends of the opening for example (fig. 3),
the practicality of drill rod coupling will
in fact limit the length.

When the ribs are excavated there will be
a stress redistribution around the rib.
This is in fact favourable to the proposed
opening (Stephansson and Stillborg, 1977).
As the rib is excavated, it may be
exploited as a site in which to perform an
investigation leading to input data for an
optimum rock bolting layout. Loose parts of
the rock mass and zones of ground water
seepage may be grouted from the rib tunnels.
Such grouting can effectively increase
friction in major joint systems and even
prohibit water inflow to the opening during
excavation.

ROCK BOLTING

Rock bolting is carried out from the rib

tunnels (fig. 3). The main contribution to
the reinforcement is made by the cables.
They, together with the strength of the rock
mass form a rock arch around the proposed
opening. Their action is to 'sew' the
jointed rock mass together so that, as the
opening is excavated, the rock mass tends
more readily toward self-stabilisation.
This follows because of the prevention of
gross shearing, translation, rotation and
opening of joints (fig. 4).

Since the major disturbances during
excavation of the opening will take place
inside the volume confined by the ribs and
the opening, the cables should be placed
towards the opening and between the ribs.
Apart from preventing gross sources of
displacement, the cables will create a
certain confinement to the concrete filled
rib. In order to avoid too high stresses
being 'built in' and for the sake of overall
economy, the cables should not be prestressed. Instead of having pre-stressed,
high-quality hoist cables it would seem
altogether wiser to employ cheap, flexible
old ropes, ungreased. They should be fully
grouted in order to optimise their effect
and for protection against rust. The
spacing and the detailed setting of cables
should be based upon the in-situ rib tunnel
investigation.

RIBS OF REINFORCED CONCRETE

The rib-tunnels could, after the completion
of the bolting, but not necessarily before

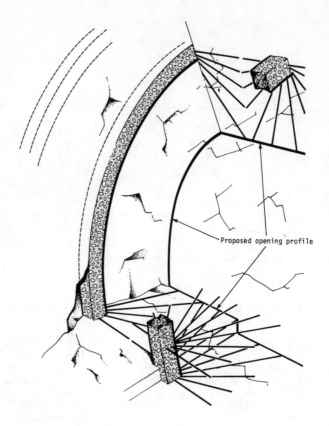

Fig. 4 The supporting system of cable bolts and reinforced
concrete as ribs before excavation of the opening

excavation of the opening, be filled with
reinforced concrete. Even though it has
been shown by Åkesson (1977) that the
reinforced rib itself gives only negligible
support to the rock mass (the major
contribution is created by the reinforced
rock arch) the ribs could be filled, under
certain conditions. One reason for filling
the ribs would be to achieve a shear
reinforcement, which could conceivably serve
to prevent collapse of the opening in the
case of earthquakes or displacements along
a large fault zone. However, a significant
reason for not filling would be to make it
possible to gain access to the tunnels and
apply additional spot bolting if necessary.
In a less competent rock mass the ribs
should be filled, so contributing to the
available rock strength.

THEORETICAL ANALYSIS AND PHYSICAL MODELS

Theoretical analysis of the behaviour of the
reinforced arch was presented by Stephansson

and Stillborg (1977) and Stillborg and
Stephansson (1978). They applied the theory
of the New Austrian Tunneling Method to the
overall stability of the cavern and to the
stress drops obtained in supports with
different yielding properties. They concluded that a system of fully grouted non-
tensioned cables and reinforced concrete
ribs would give a yielding support of the
arch and a stable cavern.

Åkesson (1977) applied a static mode of
action to the structure and calculated the
number of pre-stressed cables needed and the
properties of the reinforced concrete for
the ribs according to traditional concepts
of civil engineering.

Stillborg and Stephansson (1978) made
two-dimensional physical models of plaster
of paris and ribs made of reinforced
concrete. The models were loaded bi-axially
to determine the fracture development around
the opening and the overall stability. The
models were semi-quantitative and gave
information about the increase in strength
as a function of the number of ribs that

454

Fig. 5 Model test chamber and recording units for testing Rib-in-Roc pre-reinforcement in sand-wax models

were employed and the distance from the edge of the rib to the surface of the cavern.

Stillborg et al (1979) also introduced a new three-dimensional modelling technique and this was applied to the Rib-in-Roc method. The test chamber of steel which allows for triaxial loading of 1 m³ blocks of hard model material is shown in fig. 5.

A sand-wax mixture was used as model material and joints were simulated by means of thin teflon sheets. The displacement was monitored continously with a high degree of accuracy during the test, by means of electromagnetic sensors.

Dimensional analysis was applied and the properties of the model material, the model boundary conditions and dimensions were properly scaled. Nine dimensionless π-numbers were used in the dimensional analysis and displacements in the field can be obtained from the recorded displacements in the model for a given rock type and stress conditions along the boundary. For more details the reader is referred to the original paper by Stillborg et al (1979).

DESIGN CRITERIA

In order to create an appropriate design for the Rib-in-Roc method to be applied to a specific site, an extensive pre-investigation programme must be performed. The programme envisaged can be divided into three steps:

1. Site investigation (field tests)
2. Rock mechanics test (laboratory tests)
3. Testing of proposed layout (physical modelling)

Site investigation

The investigation should focus upon the following activities, each in order of importance:

a) Geological surveying: all survey material available should be collected and interpreted, together with results from a detailed geological survey of the area.

b) Stress measurements: the in-situ stress field should be investigated. The three principal stresses and their directions should be determined at locations bounding the opening.

c) Diamond drilling: core samples and joint samples should be collected from different levels. The diamond drilling programme should be so extensive as to detect major fault zones and joint planes.

d) Hydro-geological surveying: detection of water table, permeable zones in the area, complete with water loss measurements of major fault zones.

Rock mechanics tests

The material to be used in the rock mechanics tests comprises that collected in the site investigation. The following parameters should be determined in the laboratory:

- joint roughness
- joint filling properties (mineralogical properties)
- Young's modulus of the different rock types
- Poisson's ratio of the different rock types
- critical energy release rate of the different rock types

Testing of proposed layout

On the basis of the results from the site investigation and rock mechanics tests it becomes possible to create a three-dimensional model of the site considered. The optimum position and orientation of the opening in relation to major structures and with respect to the stress field is then established. This model, together with the reinforcement should then be tested. Three-dimensional physical models can be built and geological structures can be simulated as demonstrated by Stillborg and Stephansson (1978).

PROPOSAL OF A RIB-IN-ROC TEST CAVERN FOR OIL STORAGE

Since the Rib-in-Roc method was invented in the mid-seventies by Ivar Sagefors, WP-System, Sweden, the method has been suggested for a number of applications, e.g. oil storage, nuclear power plant, gymnastic halls, swimming-halls etc. The present situation where the method has not been applied to any cavern or chamber indicates the need of a demonstration cavern. A concievable test cavern for later oil storage is suggested to be located at an existing oil storage plant in Brofjorden, Sothwestern Sweden.

Brofjorden is one of the three oil refining plants in Sweden with extensive oil storage in unlined rock caverns. In 1979 a 2.6 milj m^3 depot for crude oil was completed for the Swedish Government and its Board for Economic Defence.

The storage consists of three 600 m^2 twin-tunnels with a length of 600 to 900 m. Nearby, an additional storage for 1.4 milj m^3 crude oil is planned to be built, fig. 6. The test cavern for the Rib-in-Roc method is suggested to be located at the northeastern end of the planned oil storage.

A comprehensive site investigation has been conducted for the whole area and it covers most of the activities listed under the heading Design Criteria in this paper. The rock of the site area is dominated by a homogeneous, medium-grained granite with a RQD-value in the range of 0.9-1.0. Major discontinuities of faults and shear zones are steep dipping and oriented NE-SW and WNW-ESE bounding large rock plinths with the dimension of kilometers where the oil storage tunnels are located. The rock mass has three sets of joints

1. N20°-40°E, 60°-80°NW
2. N50°-60°W, vertical
3. subhorizontal jointing and/or banking

Stress measurements with over-coring technique in four 70 m deep boreholes in the area indicate an excess of horizontal stresses. The average components of the stresses in the horizontal plane are shown in fig. 6. With respect to the quality of the rocks, the directions of discontinuities and the state of stress the test cavern with preference should be oriented with the long axis parallel with the direction of the maximum principal stress and one of the directions of the major discontinuities (N50°-60°W) as indicated in fig. 6. With respect to the rock burst phenomena developed during construction of the 2.6 milj m^3 storage as reported by Bergman and Jansson (1981), the roof of the test cavern should be designed with a large curvature and a low arch. The results of the three-dimensional physical models reported by Stillborg et al (1979) are relevant to the situation for the suggested test cavern.

By locating the test cavern for Rib-in-Roc to the area of Brofjorden one would gain a lot from the existing knowledge about the geology and rock mechanics and the experience in blasting and rock reinforcement. However, it should be emphasiced that the proposal is not yet approved by the Board of Economic Defence and the research foundations in Sweden.

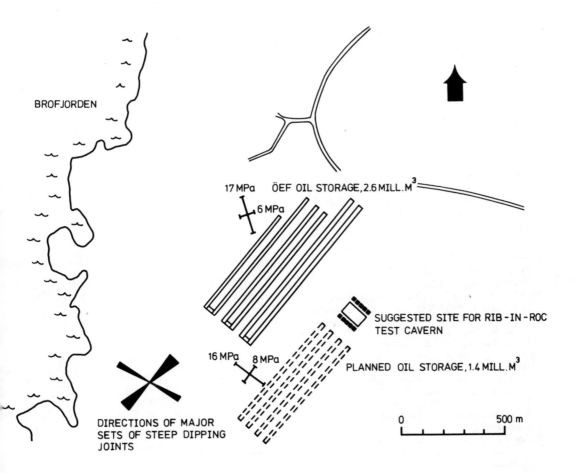

BROFJORDEN

17 MPa   ÖEF OIL STORAGE, 2.6 MILL. M^3

6 MPa

SUGGESTED SITE FOR RIB-IN-ROC TEST CAVERN

16 MPa   8 MPa

PLANNED OIL STORAGE, 1.4 MILL. M^3

DIRECTIONS OF MAJOR SETS OF STEEP DIPPING JOINTS

0   500 m

Fig. 6 Suggested site for Rib-in-Roc test cavern at the oil storage plant of Brofjorden, Southwestern Sweden

COST ESTIMATES

The Rib-in-Roc method has earlier received critisism for being too expensive. In reply Stillborg (1979, 1980) gave cost estimates which will be reproduced here.

Referring to the opening mentioned earlier in this paper, length 100 m, 50 m span and height 60 m requiring five ribs plus bolts with additional cross cuts access and communication between ribs the total cost is approximately $ US 4 million. This is close to the cost of excavating the opening and corresponds to a total unit cost, including reinforcement arrangements and opening excavation, of $ US 32 per m^3 of effective opening volume. This is, however, less than 0.4 per cent of the cost of, for example, a 1000 MW nuclear power plan. The latter is given in this cost comparison since such an application is already envisaged. Further applications that have been suggested for the Rib-in-Roc method are underground hydro-electric stations and any other installations needing a large span or a small span in bad rock.

ACKNOWLEDGEMENTS

All research in connection with the Rib-in-Roc pre-reinforcement method has been sponsored by WP-System AB, Stockholm. The help of its Managing Director T. Hallenius and of Mr L. Hellberg and Mr I. Sagefors, all at WP-System, is gratefully acknowledged. Research support from the Swedish Board for Technical Development is also acknowledged.

REFERENCES

Bergman, S.G.A. and Johnsson, N.-E. 1981, Rock burst problems in ÖEF 600 m^2

tunnels in Brofjorden, Sweden. In Rock
Mechanics Meeting in Stockholm, January
28, 1981. Franzén, T. (ed), Swedish Rock
Mechanics Research Foundation, Stockholm,
p. 121-147.
Stephansson, O. and Stillborg, B. 1977,
Theoretical and experimental study of
Rib-in-Roc for large underground openings. In Proc. of Rock Store 77. Berg-
man, M. (ed), Stockholm 1977, Sweden,
p. 253-258.
Stillborg, B. 1979, The Rib-in-Roc pre-
reinforcement system for large under-
ground openings. In Maevis, A. and Hust-
rulid, B. (ed) Proceedings 1979 Rapid
Excavation and Tunneling Conference,
Atlanta, Georgia, June 18-21, 1979.
p. 1372-1385.
Stillborg, B. 1980, 'Rib-in-Roc' pre-
reinforcement system for large under-
ground openings. Tunnels and tunneling,
October, p. 23-27.
Stillborg, B. and Stephansson, O. 1978,
Model study of Rib-in-Roc pre-reinforcement for large underground openings.
Research Report TULEA 1978:07. University of Luleå, Luleå, Sweden.
Stillborg, B. and Stephansson, O. and
Swan, G. 1979, Three-dimensional
physical model technology applicable to
the scaling of underground structures.
In Proc. of 4th Cong. Int. Soc. Rock
Mech. Montreux, Swizerland, 1979, Part 2,
p. 655-662.
Åkesson, B. 1977, Reinforcement of large
rock caverns using Rib-in-Roc: Statical
mode of action. In Proc. of Rock Store
77, Bergman, M. (ed), Stockholm 1977,
Sweden, p. 383-389.

ROCK MECHANICAL MEASUREMENTS AT THE EXCAVATION OF THE UNDERGROUND STATION HUVUDSTA OF STOCKHOLM'S METRO

Felsmechanische Messungen beim Auffahren der U-Bahn Station Huvudsta der Stockholmer Metro

Mesurages de mécanique des roches durant l'excavation de la station souterraine du métro Huvudsta de Stockholm

HÅKAN STILLE & LARS OLSSON
Royal Institute of Technology, Stockholm, Sweden

SUMMARY:
The station had a large span of 16-22 m without any pillar. At both ends of the station the overburden was only 6-8 m of partly poor rock. In order to achieve a safe construction of the cavern an observation system based on deformation measurement was installed. The results from the measurements and finite element calculations were the base for the choice of support. The measured high horizontal stress field around 10 times higher than the vertical overburden was found to have a stabilizing effect of the cavern. The deformation pattern showed an uplift of the roof and inward movements of the walls of around 1 mm. The results indicated that the rock mass behaviour could be interpreted as an elastic response. The rock support was therefore carried out with single bolts and a 10 cm layer of shotcrete instead of the planned concrete arches.

ZUSAMMENFASSUNG:
Die U-Bahn Station hat eine Spannweite von 16-22 m ohne Zwischenpfeiler. An beiden Enden der Station betrug die Überdeckung aus teilweise schlechtem Fels nur 6-8 m. Um einen sicheren Bau der Kaverne zu gewährleisten, wurde ein Messprogramm auf der Grundlage von **Verformungsmessungen eingerichtet**. Die Ergebnisse der Messungen und einer FEM Berechnung wurden der Wahl der Sicherungen zugrundegelegt. Das gemessene horizontale Spannungsfeld, das den 10 fachen vertikalen Spannungen entsprach, hatte einen stabilisierenden Effekt auf die Kaverne. Das Verformungsbild zeigte eine Hebung der Firste und eine nach innen gerichtete Verformung der Ulmen von ungefähr 1mm. Die Ergebnisse zeigten, dass das Gebirgsverhalten als elastisch angesehen werden konnte. Infolgedessen wurde die Gebirgssicherung mit Einzelankern und einer 10 cm dicken Spritzbetonschale durchgeführt anstatt der geplanten Betonbögen.

RESUME:
Sans les piliers, la station a une grande portée de 16 à 22m. Aux deux extrémités de la station le terrain de recouvrement, constitué de roche en partie pauvre, était seulement de 6 à 8 m. Afin de procéder à une construction sûre de la caverne, un système d'observation basé sur le mesurage de la déformation y était installé. Les résultats des mesurages et des calculs d'éléments finis étaient à la base du choix du renforcement. Le champ d'une haute contrainte horizontale mesuré, environ 10 fois plus élevé que le terrain de recouvrement vertical, a été adopté pour produire un effet de stabilisation de la caverne. Le modèle de la déformation montrait une élévation du toit et des déplacements internes de 1 mm environ. Les résultats indiquaient que le comportement de la masse rocheuse pourrait être interprété comme une réaction élastique. Par conséquent, au lieu des arches prévues, le renforcement de la roche a été exécuté à l'aide de simples boulons et d'une couche de 10 cm de béton projeté.

1 INTRODUCTION AND BACKGROUND

One part of the Stockholms Metro system called "Järvabanans södra gren" is recent-ly built with underground stations in rock with a single cavern with a span between 16-22 m and without any pillar. The older stations were built with twin cavern with a row of pillars between (Benedik 1982).

The stations are built as close as possible to the rock surface in order to reduce the cost for the elevator shafts.

The rock mechanics problem is the stability of a tunnel with a large span in a jointed hard rock with a small rock overburden. At one of the stations, Huvudsta, the rock overburden was only 6-8 m and the rock was also poor in some parts of station.

The Stockholms City Streets and Traffic Administration had two choices in handling the routine way of using the problem. One was more or less heavy concrete arches immediately following after the blasting and the other one was to install an observation system in order to guide the choice of the rock support and, if possible, reduce the support to bolting and shotcreting.

The last system was chosen and the measuring system and the measurement results with the rock mechanical discussions will be presented here. A more detailed report will be found in Stille, Olsson, Delin (1981).

2 STATION HUVUDSTA

The underground station Huvudsta had a "trumpet" shape with a span of 14 to 22 m narrowing to the east. The rock overburden is small, around 8 m at the both ends of the station. At the eastern part there is a gas station with tanks buried in the soil and vulnerable to settlements and at the western part there is a road bridge founded on the rock surface (see fig. 1).

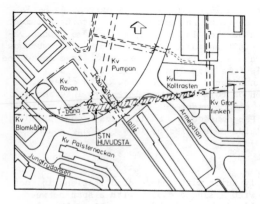

Fig. 1 Plan of station Huvudsta.

The rock overburden in the middle of the station was around 15-20 m.

3 PREINVESTIGATIONS AND ESTIMATED ROCK CONDITIONS

The preinvestigation with 37 percussion drilled holes and 3 core drill holes was concentrated to the eastern and western part of the station since the rock surface was visible from surface in the middle of the station.

The preinvestigation showed the following.

. The rock is a grey granite with small grains

. The joints are often filled with a thin layer of calcite

. Fracture zones with alterated rock material were also found

The RQD-value of the core hole BH 156 was 67%. The corresponding value of the core hole BH 143 was total 51%. Just above the tunnel roof a 5 m wide fracture zone was found in BH 143 with a RQD-value of 43%. The core loss was here 0.6 m. The expected geological conditions are shown on fig. 2 together with the station.

The rock mass classification according to the RMR-system (Bieniawski 1978) was the following:

The rock mass in the western part had a RMR-value of 35, i.e. poor rock, and for the rest of the station the RMR-value was 70 corresponding to good rock.

The strength of the rock tested on small samples in the laboratory gave the following results:

Unconfined compression strength	110 MPa
Modulus of elasticity	69 GPa
Poisson Ratio	0.18

The general question about the roof stability of such a cavern was so interesting that the Swedish Foundation of Rock Research (BeFo) payed for further investigation and more extensive measurement than was planned.

The initial stress field was therefore measured using an overcoring technique (see for example Scherman, Hiltscher and Martnar 1980).
Three measurements at two different levels were carried out in the middle part of the station at the depth of 10 and 17 m.

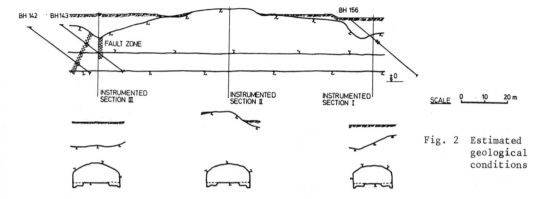

Fig. 2 Estimated geological conditions

The horizontal stress was around 6.5 MPa in north-south and 5.0 MPa in east-west. The vertical pressure was found to be around 2.6 MPa and much higher than the overburden pressure of 0.3-0.4 MPa. One explanation is that the residual stress in the granite was high, around 2 MPa.

4 MEASUREMENT SYSTEM

In order to achieve a safe construction of the cavern an observation system based on deformation measurement was installed. It was decided that one measurement section should be installed in the critical parts at the ends of the station.

In order to compare the results with more normal condition a section should also be installed in the middle of the station where the rock overburden was much higher (see fig. 2).

In each measurement section principle the following measurements should be done

. Convergence measurement with Distometer

. Extensometer measurement with multirod-extensometer from the surface

. Measurement with singlerod extensometer from the tunnel

. Rock bolt load measurement

The multirod extensometer was installed before the blasting of the tunnel and the other systems were installed just after the blasting of the measurement section.

5 ROCK MECHANICAL CALCULATION

In order to predict the behaviour of the cavern finite element calculations were

carried out. Two possible models of rock behaviour were investigated.

In the first model, the rock mass was assumed to be homogeneous. The question was how large movements could be expected with the rock still behaving elastically.

In the second model, the rock mass was considered to consist of jointed blocks with the joints governing the behaviour. In this case the question was to estimate the deformations in a discontinuous rock mass that could appear with the rock mass still "safe", i.e. with some strength margin left.

The elastic response was calculated for different values of the deformation modulus and horizontal stress.

Table 1

Case	I	II	III	VI
Structure	Homogeneous			Blocky
Modulus GPa	60	10	40	40
Horizontal stress field, MPa	6.5	6.5	4.0	4.0
Joint friction angle	–	–	–	30°
Calculated deformation				
Vertical movement in the roof (+upwards) mm	0.3	2.0	0.5	-1.0
Horizontal movement in the walls (+inwards) mm	1.0	6.2	0.8	1.0

461

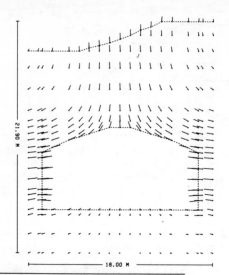

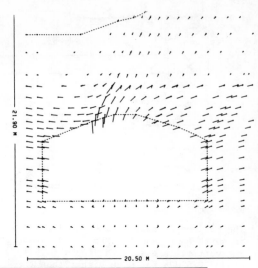

ACKUM. DISPLACEMENTS IN THE STRUCTURE

HUVUDSTA-TUNNELN -- CASE B3: EXCAVATION WITH E=40 GPA AND HÖR.SP.= 4MPA
SEQUENCE NO. 2 -- LOADSTEP NO. 1 -- ITER. NO. 1 -- PART NO.1
DISP.SCALE 0 ⊢━━┥ 0.5 MM   PLOTTED DISP.: 0.05 - 0.83 MM
GEOM.SCALE 0 ⊢━━┥ 1.0 M

ACKUM. DISPLACEMENTS IN THE STRUCTURE

HUVUDSTA-TUNNELN -- CASE C1: EXCAVATION IN JOINTED ROCK
SEQUENCE NO. 2 -- LOADSTEP NO. 1 -- ITER. NO. 5 -- PART NO.1
DISP.SCALE 0 ⊢━━┥ 2.0 MM   PLOTTED DISP.: 0.12 - 2.05 MM
GEOM.SCALE 0 ⊢━━┥ 2.0 M

Fig. 3 FEM-calculation, homogeneous conditions.

Fig. 4 FEM-calculation. Blocky conditions.

Based on empirical relations between RQD-value, RMR-value and the deformation modulus the deformation modulus of the rock mass was estimated (Bieniawski 1976 and 1978).

For the good rock (RMR=70) the deformation modulus of the rock will be about 40 GPa and for the poor rock about 10 GPa.

The results of the calculations are presented in Figs 3 and 4 and in table 1.

Based on the calculation it was decided that in the good rock an upwards movement in the roof and inwards in the wall around 1 mm could be interprete as being an elastic deformation which would require only minimal support. A blocky structure of the rock mass could also give deformation of around 1 mm (but with a deformation pattern differing from the elastic movements) and still be quite stable.

6 INTERPRETATION OF MEASUREMENT

The interpretation of the measurements would therefore take into consideration both the movement pattern and the size of the movements.

It was tentatively agreed that with movements less than one millimeter and no evidence of a "jointed- block behaviour" the

excavation would proceed with careful blasting and a minimal support system.

The permanent support was to consist of 3 m long grouted rock bolts with a distance of about 2-4 m and with a shotcrete layer of 15-10 cm.

It was also decided that a local movement pattern or movement values that did not fit in with the assumption of a homogeneous elastic behaviour would not necessarily call for a heavy support. One must obviously take into consideration the possibility of one single block moving and thus causing this reading with the rest of the rock mass still behaving elastically. In such a case the correct solution is to identify the mechanism by inspection and to put in rock bolts to anchor the specific block.

It is thus obvious that an instrument system cannot be used to determine all details of the movement. It can, however, give a good picture of the general trend and thereby help in identifying the deformation mechanism and be a guide in choosing the overall reinforement requirements.

7 RESULTS OF THE MEASUREMENT

The observation results are shown below in Figs 5, 6 and 7 for each of the three in-

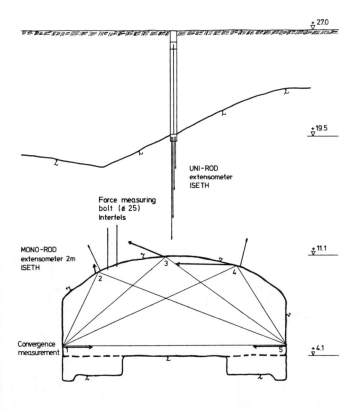

± 27.0

∇ +19.5

UNI-ROD
extensometer
ISETH

Force measuring
bolt (ø 25)
Interfels

∇ +11.1

MONO-ROD
extensometer 2m
ISETH

Convergence
measurement

∇ +4.1

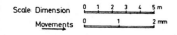

Scale Dimension 0 1 2 3 4 5 m

Movements 0 1 2 mm

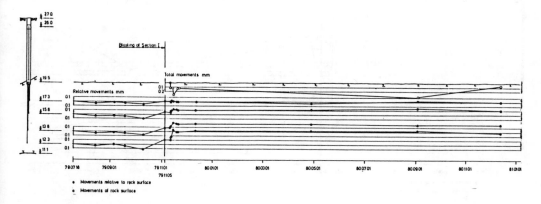

Fig. 5 Instrumented section I with results
of the measurement.

463

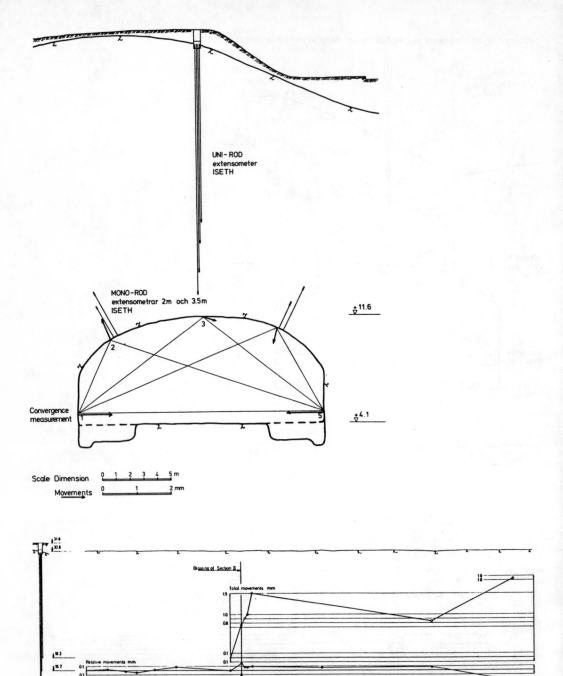

Fig. 6 Instrumented section II with results
of the measurement.

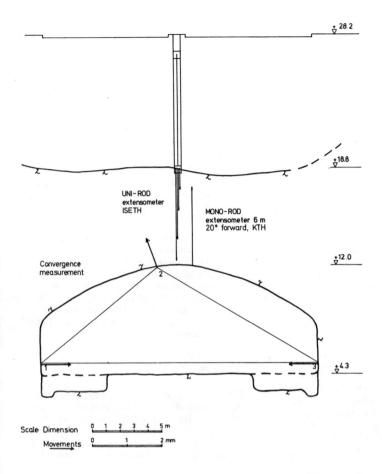

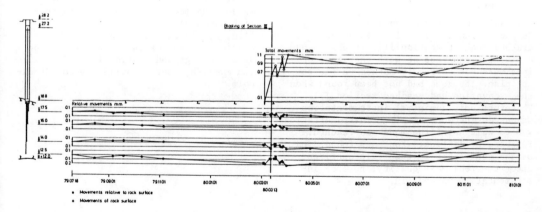

Fig. 7 Instrumented section III with results of the measurements.

strumented sections. For each section is
shown the position of the instruments and
for each observation point a vector showing its movement. Also shown is a time-
deformation diagram for the multiple rod
extensometers, which were placed before
the excavation started.

Some comments to the obtained results:

. Force measuring bolts, Interfels type:
Very low forces were registered which was
in accordance with the small deformations
measured by extensometers. No further measuring bolts were placed as no large deformations were observed in later construction stages.

. Exceeding of the threshold limit. As
was mentioned above, a tentative threshold
value of 1 mm was decided upon. In some
points this value was slightly exceeded
as can be seen from the figures
As there was no general trend in this, it
was judged that the rock mass was in a
safe state and that further reinforcement
was not necessary.

. Erratic behaviour of multirod extensometer in section II (fig. 6). The UNI-ROD
extensometer in section II gave very erratic readings, especially when the readings
were correlated to the measuring head i.e.
the rock surface. The possible cause might
be some movement of the head relative to
the rock surface or seasonal movements of
the rock surface itself. We therefore
choose to relate the movements to the up-
most anchor, i.e. we considered that anchor
to be fixed. This interpretation gave results that coincide better with the other
measurements which indicate an elastic
behaviour.

. Fault zone at section III. According
to the boring there would exist a zone of
crushed rock at section III. It was found
during the progress of work that the borings were not correctly marked on the boring plan. The zone had not been found when
the excavation had reached section III.
Therefore only a minimal instrumentation
was used. The more complete instrumentation
was to wait until the zone was reached.
However, no difficult zone was found, and
as the contractor by then felt confident
about the rock mass quality, no more instrumentation was put in.

The rock mass was jointed but not so much
as to explain the core loss of 0.6 m in
borehole 143.

8 CONCLUSIONS

The following conclusions can be drawn from
the work at Huvudsta metro station.

. The rock could for design purposes be
considered to deform elastically and with
small movements.

. The very small and even upwards movements of the roof are mostly depending on
the stabilizing effect of the large horizontal in situ stresses in the rock mass.

. The deformation calculations can predict the overall pattern of movements, but
not local deviations caused by e.g. a single block moving.

. The instrumentation system can give
misleading readings, as it only observes
movements in a small number of points.
Measurements must therefore be supplemented
by other observations in order that a
correct interpretation be made. It is therefore valuable to have different and independent systems so a more balanced picture of the movements is obtained.

9 REFERENCES

Benedik, R, Rock mechanics studies for new
    trumpet shaped underground stations in
    Stockholm. Tunnelling 82, Brighton (in
    printing 1982).
Bieniawski, Z.I, Determining rock mass de-
    formability: Experiences from case his-
    tories, J. Rock Mech. Mining Sc, Perga-
    mon Press, Vol. 15, No. 5 (1978).
Scherman, K-A, Hiltscher, R, Martna, J,
    Erfarenheter från 15 års bergspännings-
    mätningar vid Vattenfall. BeFo:s Berg-
    mekanikdag (BeFo, Stockholm, with Eng-
    lish summary).
Stille, H, Olsson, L, Delin, P, Rock me-
    chanical measurements at the excavation
    of an underground station in hard rock
    (in Swedish), BeFo -48:1/81, BeFo, Stock-
    holm.

TESTING PARAMETER WITH FINITE ELEMENT ANALYSIS
FOR DETERMINING THE OPTIMUM SUPPORT DIMENSIONS

Überprüfung der Berechnungsparameter mit einer Finite-Element-Berechnung
zur Optimierung der Sicherungsmassnahmen

Paramètres d'essai de l'analyse par les éléments finis pour la détermination des dimensions
optimales d'un blindage

G.SZIVÓS
Central Institute for the Development of Mining, Budapest, Hungary

SUMMARY:
The material constants do not participate equally in developing the
stress-, strain- and displacement stage generated when installing the
support in underground openings, and excavations. The paper describes
a method taking into calculation also the uncertainty of surrounding
rocks with assigning the standard deviation of the different data of
the final result to the standard deviation of the initial data.

ZUSAMMENFASSUNG:
Die Materialkonstanten beteiligen sich nicht mit gleichem Gewicht in der
Ausbildung der Spannungs-, Verformungs- und Verschiebungszustände. Der
Vortrag gibt eine Methode, die auch die Ungewissheit der Gebirgsumgebung
in Betracht zieht, die Standarddeviation der einzigen Daten des Ender-
gebnisses der Standarddeviation den Ausgangsdaten zuordnend.

RESUME:
Les constantes du matérial ne participent pas également au développement
de la situation des tensions, déformations et déplacements qui se
forment quand le soutènement des galeries et des cavités des mines est
effectué. L'auteur donne la description d'une méthode prenant en calculation aussi l'incertitude du terrain enveloppe, assignant la déviation des différents données a la déviation des données initiales.

When designing the support of underground roadways and openings there
occurs generally an oversizing not
to be determined that can not be
justified by aiming at safety. This
results on one hand from the fact
that there is an uncertainty in
the number of the nature parameters
used for design, in the way of measuring them and in the reliability
of the data obtained. On the other
hand the design methods used do not
adequately describe the behaviour
of support with unduly idealizing
the environment and using algorithms
excessively simplifying and without
considering exactly all boundary
conditions. In order to increase reliability and economic efficiency

some processes correct the support
parameters based on the high number
of measurements and investigations
carried out during execution with
extrapolating the subsequent construction phases not known primarily.
The rock mechanical parameters
can be detected by investigation results obtained by means of borings
and samplings. These characteristics
can show significant dispersion. In
developing the arising stress, strain
and displacement condition the material properties do not participate
equally. We show a method which by
taking into calculation also the
uncertainty of the surrounding rocks
tries to represent the environment
in the most adequate way with il-

lustrating the support method enabling the coaction of rock and support. Based on the parameter testing by the finite element method /FEM/ there can be established which data prove to be important from the point of view of the support design.

In the practice spatial problems are encountered both in mining and tunelling. The three dimensional testings of a given range requires one order higher computer capacity, calculating time /cpu/ and very sophisticated data preparation also a Hookean elasticity model compared to the plain /two dimensional/ testing. Therefore where it is not absolutely necessary using spatial programs is generrly avoided.

For the overwhelming majority of the cases occuring in pactice the plain testings are sufficient. However for special cases, e.g. the immediate surrounding of junctions, longwalls, parts near the face and very frequently changing soil and ground conditions, the three dimensional calculations prove to be indispensable.

The real situation can be well approximated by plain strain and therfore this model gives a good solution at an approximate distance of one and half road diameter from the face.

In order to investigate into the plain problems arising in our Institute isoparametric elements are used. The corresponding spatial element is the isoparametric hexahedron with 10 junctions applied for our spatial programs. Thus a high calculation accuracy can be reached with a relatively small number of elements andjunctions. For their employing we have well composed and proved programs. The FEM computation is based on continuum mechanical approach and therefore our loadings and boundary conditions have to be fixed in compliance with it.

When in the design period we have not sufficiently detailed in situ survey data we start generally from the stress condition of the homogenous isotrop elastic dead load half space in which – as admitted by us – already all geological and tectonic processes have been ended for the geological ages. Dividing the range tested is made so that the element sides coincide with the rock or soil stratum sides. The sufficiently large rectangle shaped

range taken is divided into parcels.

Correctly selecting the range sizes is important as taking too small ones can result in erroneous solutions and taking too large ones unnecessarily increases the degree of freedom of the system.

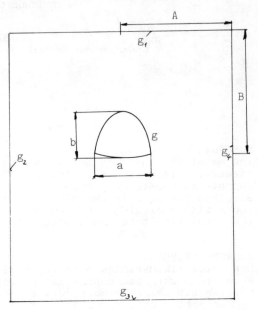

Fig. 1.

The sizes A and B of the range visible in Fig. have to be taken that the interfering effect of cave opening should decay in the surroundings i.e. along the distant boundary the stage of primary stress and displacement has to be obtained. According to the experiences this distance is larger in vertical direction than in the horizontal one.

$A \geqslant 3\ a$

$B \geqslant 4\ b.$

Our kinematic boundary conditions are as follows: normal support is applied in horizontal direction along the g_2 and g_3 sides and in vertical direction along g_3. On the side g_1 the weight of the rock mass being behind has to be operated as distributed load thus the testing range load being the dead load of every strata. This stress condition is considered as primary stage. In using quadratic isoparametric elements the exact solution is reobtained because the stress distribution and quadratic displacement stage can be exactly followed linearly by the element model. In knowledge of the primary stress stage there can be determined the internal distribution force system transmitted from the range to be removed into the remaining range along the surface of the excavation to be driven. If being satisfied by the linear elasticity solution so using the law of superposition the negative value of the internal force system is prescribed along the curve g_o, when the real stresses are so obtained that the primary stresses are superposed on the results obtained.

When not a material in the range of Hooke's law on the linear elasticity but e.g. a linearly elastic hardening plastic material is used, the principles of superposition can not be applied, i.e. the calculation have to be started by determining the loads resulting from initial primary stress field + dead load in which case no dynamic boundary conditions for the curve g_o are prescribed but its unloaded condition is obtained as the result of the program simultaneously being one of the possibilities of checking the degree of accuracy of the calculations.

THE PARAMETER TESTINGS PERFORMED AND THEIR EVALUATION

In examining the samples obtained from in situ borings /drill cores/ the rock properties have to be evaluated by statistic method because there are principally erronous the measurement protocols having one single value as result /e.g. the value given for the elastic constant E = 3872 MPa/. Here from the beginning this value has to be considered as questionable, since also the uncertainty of measurement is greatly higher than the numerical error of this numerical value and also the surrounding rocks are not homogenous and therefore from the point of view of design there is considerably righter and more reliable the following solution: e.g. E = 4000 MPa with a standard deviation of $\bar{6}$ = 180 MPa. It means E is a value between 3460 and 4540 MPa.

Similarly to the elastic constant /modulus of elasticity/ also the values of Poisson's ratio, yield and failure stress limits, internal friction angle and cohesion are subjected to standard deviations. Consequently it is not allowed to consider the initial data as accurate, thus the apparently accurate result consisting of several figures /digits/ being only misleading.

It is of significance only when testing the programme but then it is important since from it the numerical uncertainty can be evaluated.

The following results are obtained from evaluating a concrete calculation sequence performed but the conclusions drawn from it are more general. The progrem examined concerned a drift with horizontal axis having an invert arched gate cross-section. In supporting underground openings I considered as base a shotcrete support of given thickness with the wet-mix process, resulting in a high quality grip of concrete upon the rock. When using this process the co-action of the binary system of rock and support is implemented thus being faced by a typical problem of the continuum mechanics. The calculations covered also the effect of modifying the geometry of support and drift in smaller degree upon the stress and displacement field of support. From measurement results we knew the mean and standard deviation values of the mechanical properties in the surrounding rocks. By using the mean values of rock properties FEM program running was performed being considered later as the basis for the investigations. As next step a material constant was selected the value of which is gradually changed with leaving the other data unchanged. The FEM program runnings are repeatedly performed with comparing the results to the basis of the investigations. This algorithm is used for every material constants. One part of the investigations is demonstrated in the Figures enclosed.

In Fig. 2-3. the change in displacement belonging to the percentage-change in the initial data of the quasi-Poisson's ratio and elastic constant /modulus of elasticity/ is represented in two characteristic points of the range /roof and floor/ with moving the origin into the point 110%. The convergence is practically insensible to Poisson's rati. It is remarkable due to the ra-

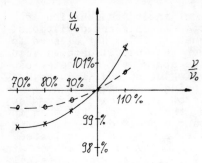

— roof point
— flat poin
$N= 0.12$

Fig. 2.

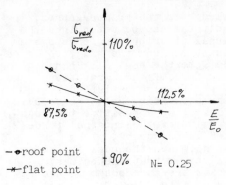

— roof point
— flat point
90% $N= 0.25$

Fig. 5.

remarkable what is not so important for drifting as for tunelling where the surface movement and damage is always prohibited being one of the most important requirements.

In order to make easier the evaluation and to compare the figures a magnification number "N" was introduced showing the uncertainty caused by the uncertainty of the given rock mechanical data and the lack of the due knowledge in surrounding rocks when loading the support installed.

From Fig. 3. it can be seen that correlated with the displacement the change in the modulus of elasticity is more important.

When we examine the reduced stresses generated in the support /because we are interested first of all in the ability of the support to bear the loading/ we experience that the uncertainty of Poisson's ratio significantly influences the stresses reduced in contrast with the elastic constant represented in Fig. 5.

After performing the parameter testings it is known which overloads of the support can be experienced in the given surrounding rocks as a result of the initial data uncertainty and what change in loading has to be taken into calculation for the support.

This design method can be used for expressing the numerical value of the uncertainties thus avoiding oversizing supports.

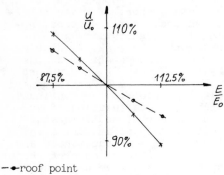

— roof point
— flat point
$N= 0.5$

Fig. 3.

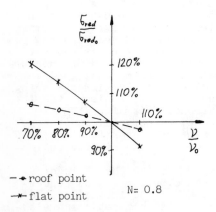

— roof point
— flat point
$N= 0.8$

Fig. 4.

tio of primary stresses being determined by the convergence.

Of the two curves evidently the change in roof convergence is more

A NEW APPROACH TO QUANTITATIVELY EVALUATE THE EXCAVATION
OF ROCK MASSES

Ein neuer Weg zur Bestimmung der Gebirgsausbruchsmengen

Un nouveau procédé pour l'évaluation quantative de l'excavation des masses rocheuses

TAO ZHEN-YU & PENG ZU-ZENG
Wuhan Institute of Hydraulic & Electric Engineering, China
YANG ZI-WEN
Chengdu Designing Institute of Hydroelectric Power, China

SUMMARY:

This paper is divided into two parts. The first, engineering quality index of rock mass M to evaluate its quality is suggested. The second, a new classification system of rock masses is proposed on the basis of the concept of the fuzzy sets, because the uncertainty of physicomechanical parameters is characteristic of rocks.

ZUSAMMENFASSUNG:

Die vorliegende Arbeit besteht aus zwei Teilen. Im ersten Teil wird der Qualitätsindex für den Gebirgskörper vorgeschlagen, um dessen Qualität zu beurteilen. Im zweiten Teil wird ein neues Klassifizierungssystem auf der Basis der Fuzzy-Mathematik aufgestellt, da die physikalischen und mechanischen Parameter des Gesteins eine unbestimmte Charakteristik besitzen.

RESUME:

L'article est divisé en deux parties. La première partie, nous suggérons que la qualité de roche massive soit évaluée par le qualitatif index M des travaux aux roches massives. La deuxième partie, un nouveau système de classification de roches massives est proposé basé sur la notion de la fuzzy-mathématiques parce que l'incertitude des paramètres physicomécaniques est une caractéristique des roches.

1. INTRODUCTION

There are two conditions in the underground construction: the first, it is carried out construction under given conditions, for which there are geological factors of all kinds and under the necessity of doing engineering treatment for unhealthy geological factors; the second, it is engineering site of underground construction which is selected, therefore, there is a problem of quantitative evaluation of quality for rock masses. This condition is discussed in this paper.

But this problem is associated with excavation of dam foundations also. This is a important problem, because it involve the limit of time of construction which is also a problem of economy.

In fact, the more cubic metres of rock to be excavated, the larger the filled concrete volume and the larger the limit of time of construction will be; on the other hand, the depth of excavation depends also upon the strength, deformation and stability of the rock masses.

2. ENGINEERING QUALITY INDEX OF ROCK MASS M.

Engineering quality of rock mass depends on weathered, fractured and condlitions of ground water et al. Yang Zi-wen (1980) Suggested by "Engineering Quality Index of Rock Mass M" to express its quality:

$$M = S \cdot k_y \cdot k_R \cdot k_v$$

where $S = (R_{fd} \cdot E_d/20 \times 10^6)^{1/2}$

$k_y = R_{ad}/R_d$

$k_R = R_{aw}/R_{ad}$

$k_i = (V_P/v_P)^2$

and   R—uniaxial compressive strength of intact
rock material (kg/cm²)

E—mudulus of elasticity of intact rock
material (kg/cm²)

V_P, v_P—Velocity of longitudinal wave of
rock mass in situ measurement and
rock material in laboratory respectively (km/sec).

a, f and w,d—foot marks, indicating weathered and fresh, satu-
rated and dry condition
respectively.

When   M$>$3, excellent quality of rock mass;

M$=$1$\sim$3, good quality of rock mass;

M$=$1.0—0.12, fair quality of rock mass ;

M$=$0.01$\sim$0.12, Poor quality of rock mass;

Table 1.   Application of Engineering Quality
Index of Rock Mass M.

Sites	Rocks	S	k_y	k_R	k_v	M
Tunnel at left bank, No.1	Syenite	5.48	0.71	1.00	0.50	1.95
Tunnel at right bank, No.14	Syenite	5.48	0.73	1.00	0.53	2.12
No.6	Basalt	7.07	0.67	0.99	0.45	2.13
No.30	Basalt	7.07	0.65	1.005	0.42	1.94

M$<$0.01, very poor quality of rock mass.
In general, when M$>$3, the rock masses may
be directly utilization; when M$=$1$\sim$3, it is necessitated to make a partial engineering treaments only.

Its application in a certain project is shown
in Table 1.

3.   METHOD OF FUZZY SETS (MFS).

Another approach to engineering comprehensive
evaluation for rock masses is method of fuzzy
sets (MFS) which was proposed by Tao Zhen-yu
and Peng Zu-zeng (1981) and is based on the
concept of the fuzzy sets (Zadeh, L. A, 1956),
because the uncertainty of physicomechanical parameters is characteristic of rocks.

This paper is with the purpose that we shall
be to improve and make further explonations of
MFS.

3.1   Any classification is always based on the
evaluations of every single factor such as uniaxial
compressive strength,velocity of longitudinal wave
et al, which are obtained from investigations and
measurements.Perhaps,these factors are more or
less the same, but they can be basically divided
into two groups. The first grpup of parameters
of rock masses can be symbolized through real
mumbers of certain interval[a,b], it is called
interval parameter, such as uniaxial compressive

Table 2.   The Conditions of Nominal Parameters

Class	I	II	III	IV	V
Condition of discontinuities	Closed joint or not continuous unweathered wall rock	Closed joint, slightly weathered walls	Weathered walls	Highly weathered walls	Weak filling (gouge) in joint
Groind water	Completely dry	Damp	Wet	Dripping	Flowing
Strike and dip orientation of joints	Very favourable	Favourable	Fair	Unfavourable	Very unfavourable
Stand-up of rock mass itself	Long term stand-up	Stand-up	Short term stand-up	Unstable	Very unstable

strength, velocity of longitudinal wave, RQD, separation of discontinuities, plane fissure rate and Lugeon coefficient etc; The second group of parameters of rock masses is called nominal parameter, its class is only determinated by means of qualitative analysis, such as condition of discontinuities, ground water, strike and dip orientation of joints, stand-up of rock mass itself etc.

As authors mentioned on a previous occasion, we still divide rock into five classes, i. e., excellent, good, fair, poor and very poor. Because this concepts are fuzzy for interval parameters, they correspond with five fyzzy sets in[a,b]which

are symbolled: I, II, III, IV and V. The membership functions are shown in Fig.1. For nominal parameter, it is suggested that the classification is shown in Table 2.

For practical rock mass in engineering, its fuzzy sets is based on information which is obtained from exploration of engineering geology and testing of rock mechanics. For example, let uniaxial compressive strength which lies between a and b corresponds to subset A. Let $n-1$ bound points, i. e. $a = a_0 < a_1 < \cdots\cdots < a_{n-1} < a_n = b$, are inserted in interval [a, b] which is divided in n small intervals. If $[a_{i-1}, a_i]$, for uniaxial compressive strength, have m_i specimens, $m = \max m_i$,

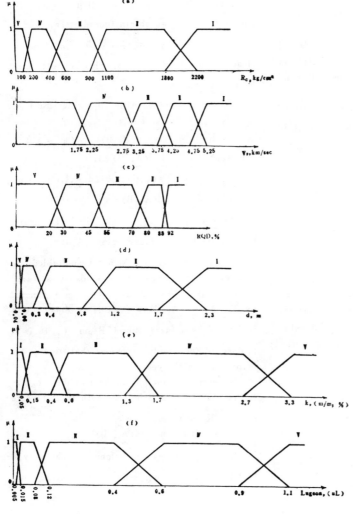

Fig.1. Fuzzy Sets of Intervallic Parameters.
(a) Uniaxial Compressive strength (Rc, kg/cm²)
(b) Velocity of longitudinal wave (Vp, km/sec)
(c) RQD (%)
(d) Separation of discontinuities (d, m)
(e) fissure rate of two dimensions (k, m/m or %)
(f) Lugeon coefficient (uL)

473

let $\mu_A\left(\frac{a_{-1}+a_i}{2}\right) = \frac{m_i}{m}$ and when $X \neq \frac{a_{-1}+a_i}{2}$, it is linear insertion, then, it is obtained mapping $\mu_A\colon [a, b] \to [0, 1]$, here μ_A is membership function of $\underset{\sim}{A}$. And fuzzy sets which correspond with other interval parameters are similarly obtained.

For nominal parameters, its values are taken in variant conditions and fuzzy sets of a few finite conditions are obtained according to observation and measurement. For example, let ground water corresponds to fuzzy subset $\underset{\sim}{B}$, according to investigation at 12 sites, in which ten sites are wet, one site is damp and one site is dripping, thus, fuzzy subset $\underset{\sim}{B}$ is

$$\underset{\sim}{B} = \frac{0.1}{I} + \frac{1}{II} + \frac{0.1}{IV}$$

3.2. *The mould recognizing and the synthesis evaluation in MFS.*

Now a neartude principle is extensively adopted to recognizing the mould in MFS. The definition of a neartude degree is given and the following is discussed.

Suppose X is an universe, $\underset{\sim}{A}$ and $\underset{\sim}{B}$ are two fuzzy subsets on X and, μ_A and μ_B are their membership functions respectively.

Let
$$\overline{\mu}_{\underset{\sim}{A}} = \underset{x \in X}{V} \mu_A(x),$$
$$\underline{\mu}_{\underset{\sim}{A}} = \underset{x \in X}{\Lambda} \mu_A(x)$$

where, $\overline{\mu}_{\underset{\sim}{A}}$ and $\underline{\mu}_{\underset{\sim}{A}}$ are called the upper norm and the lower norm of $\underset{\sim}{A}$ respectively.

Let
$$\mu_{\underset{\sim}{A} \cap \underset{\sim}{B}} = \underset{x \in X}{V} [\mu_A(x) \Lambda \mu_B(x)]$$
$$\mu_{\underset{\sim}{A} \oplus \underset{\sim}{B}} = \underset{x \in X}{\Lambda} [\mu_A(x) V \mu_B(x)]$$

They are called the interior product and the exterior product of $\underset{\sim}{A}$ and $\underset{\sim}{B}$ respectively. Notations V and Λ are used to express the maximal value ⟨or supremum⟩ and the minimal value ⟨or infimum⟩ respectively.

Let's consider
$$d(\underset{\sim}{A}, \underset{\sim}{B}) = 1 - (\overline{\mu}_{\underset{\sim}{A}} - \underline{\mu}_{\underset{\sim}{A}}) + (\mu_{\underset{\sim}{A} \cap \underset{\sim}{B}} - \mu_{\underset{\sim}{A} \oplus \underset{\sim}{B}})$$

$1°$, Since $\underset{x \in X}{V} \mu_A(x) \geqslant \underset{x \in X}{V} [\mu_A(x) \Lambda \mu_B(x)]$

$\underset{x \in X}{\Lambda} \mu_A(x) \leqslant \underset{x \in X}{\Lambda} [\mu_A(x) V \mu_B(x)]$

We have $\overline{\mu}_{\underset{\sim}{A}} \geqslant \mu_{\underset{\sim}{A} \cap \underset{\sim}{B}}$, $\underline{\mu}_{\underset{\sim}{A}} \leqslant \mu_{\underset{\sim}{A} \oplus \underset{\sim}{B}}$, that is

$$\overline{\mu}_{\underset{\sim}{A}} - \underline{\mu}_{\underset{\sim}{A}} \geqslant \mu_{\underset{\sim}{A} \cap \underset{\sim}{B}} - \mu_{\underset{\sim}{A} \oplus \underset{\sim}{B}}$$

If $(\overline{\mu}_{\underset{\sim}{A}} - \mu_{\underset{\sim}{A} \cap \underset{\sim}{B}}) + (\mu_{\underset{\sim}{A} \oplus \underset{\sim}{B}} - \underline{\mu}_{\underset{\sim}{A}}) \leqslant 1$,

then $0 \leqslant (\overline{\mu}_{\underset{\sim}{A}} - \underline{\mu}_{\underset{\sim}{A}}) - (\mu_{\underset{\sim}{A} \cap \underset{\sim}{B}} - \mu_{\underset{\sim}{B} \cap \underset{\sim}{A}}) \leqslant 1$

So that $0 \leqslant d(\underset{\sim}{A}, \underset{\sim}{B}) \leqslant 1$

$2°$, If $\underset{\sim}{B} \subseteq \underset{\sim}{A}$, then

$\mu_{\underset{\sim}{A} \cap \underset{\sim}{B}} = \underset{x \in X}{V} \lceil \mu_A(x) \Lambda \mu_B(x) \rceil = \underset{x \in X}{V} u_B(x) = \overline{\mu}_{\underset{\sim}{B}}$

$\mu_{\underset{\sim}{A} \oplus \underset{\sim}{B}} = \underset{x \in X}{\Lambda} \lceil \mu_{\underset{\sim}{A}}(x) V \mu_{B}(x) \rceil = \underset{x \in X}{\Lambda} \mu_A(x) = \underline{\mu}_{\underset{\sim}{A}}$

Thus $d(\underset{\sim}{A}, \underset{\sim}{B}) = 1 - (\overline{\mu}_{\underset{\sim}{A}} - \overline{\mu}_{\underset{\sim}{B}})$

In particular, when $\overline{\mu}_{\underset{\sim}{A}} = \overline{\mu}_{\underset{\sim}{B}}$, we have $d(\underset{\sim}{A}, \underset{\sim}{B}) = 1$

$3°$, If $\underset{\sim}{A} \cap \underset{\sim}{B} = \phi$ and $\underset{\sim}{A} \neq \phi$

(i) Suppose $\underset{\sim}{B} = \phi$, then there is bound to be $\mu_{\underset{\sim}{A} \cap \underset{\sim}{B}} = 0$, $\mu_{\underset{\sim}{A} \oplus \underset{\sim}{B}} = \underline{\mu}_{\underset{\sim}{A}}$. Thus $d(\underset{\sim}{A}, \underset{\sim}{B}) = 1 - \overline{\mu}_{\underset{\sim}{A}}$.

(ii) Suppose $\underset{\sim}{B} \neq \phi$, then there is bound to be $x_1 \in X$, such that $\mu_A(x_1) = 0$. Thus $\underline{\mu}_{\underset{\sim}{A}} = 0$.

Since $\underset{\sim}{A} \cap \underset{\sim}{B} = \phi$, we have still $\mu_{\underset{\sim}{A} \cap \underset{\sim}{B}} = 0$,

Notice $\mu_{\underset{\sim}{A} \oplus \underset{\sim}{B}} \geqslant 0$, we obtain immediately

$$0 \leqslant d(\underset{\sim}{A}, \underset{\sim}{B}) \leqslant 1 - \overline{\mu}_{\underset{\sim}{A}}$$

Hence, either $\underset{\sim}{B} = \phi$ or $\underset{\sim}{B} \neq \phi$, when $\mu_{\underset{\sim}{A}} = 1$, we have $d(\underset{\sim}{A}, \underset{\sim}{B}) = 0$.

To sum up, we have the following results.

$1°$, $0 \leqslant d(\underset{\sim}{A}, \underset{\sim}{B}) \leqslant 1$

$2°$, If $\underset{\sim}{B} \subset \underset{\sim}{A}$, then $d(\underset{\sim}{A}, \underset{\sim}{B}) = 1 - (\overline{\mu}_{\underset{\sim}{A}} - \overline{\mu}_{\underset{\sim}{B}})$,

and when $\overline{\mu}_{\underset{\sim}{A}} = \overline{\mu}_{\underset{\sim}{B}}$, $d(\underset{\sim}{A}, \underset{\sim}{B}) = 1$.

$3.$ If $\underset{\sim}{A} \cap \underset{\sim}{B} = \phi$, then $0 \leqslant d(\underset{\sim}{A}, \underset{\sim}{B}) \leqslant 1 - \overline{\mu}_{\underset{\sim}{A}}$,

and when $\overline{\mu}_{\underset{\sim}{A}} = 1$, $d(\underset{\sim}{A}, \underset{\sim}{B}) = 0$.

As above, $d(\underset{\sim}{A}, \underset{\sim}{B})$ is called the neartude degree between fuzzy subset $\underset{\sim}{A}$ and $\underset{\sim}{B}$.

Suppose the universe X has been divided into n types and each type corresponds to a fuzzy subset on X. These fuzzy subsets are denoted by $\underset{\sim}{A}_1, \underset{\sim}{A}_2, \cdots \cdots \underset{\sim}{A}_n$. Now there is an object which is denoted by a fuzzy subset $\underset{\sim}{B}$ on $\underset{\sim}{X}$. It is a problem of the mould recognize that this object berongs to which type.

A neartude principle in the mould recognize is that we say that $\underset{\sim}{B}$ belongs k-th type if there exists a K such that

$$d(\underset{\sim}{A}_k, \underset{\sim}{B}) = \underset{1 \leqslant i \leqslant n}{\max} \{d(\underset{\sim}{A}_i, \underset{\sim}{B})\}.$$

In this paper that $\underset{\sim}{B}$ belong to which type is defined to be a fuzzy subset on $\{\underset{\sim}{A}_1, \underset{\sim}{A}_2 \cdots \cdots,$

$\underset{\sim}{A_n}$} and the membership degree of $\underset{\sim}{B}$ belongs to

$\underset{\sim}{A_K}$ is difined to be $d(\underset{\sim}{A_K}, \underset{\sim}{B})$ or $\overset{L}{\underset{i=1}{V}} d(\underset{\sim}{A_i}, \underset{\sim}{B})$

$(k=1,2,\cdots,n)$ (See the application in section 3.3 of this paper).

About the synthesis evaluation we only involve a particular case in this paper.

Suppose $\{b_1, b_2, \cdots, b_m\}$ is a set of factors of the evaluation. So far as our object b of the evaluation is concerned, k-th factor of the evaluation corresponds to a fuzzy subset $\underset{\sim}{B}$ on X ($k=$ $1,2,\cdots, m$). First, let's do a evaluation of single factor.

Let $\quad X_{ik} = d(\underset{\sim}{A_i}, \underset{\sim}{B_k})$

or $\quad X_K = \overset{i}{\underset{i=1}{V}} d(\underset{\sim}{A_i}, \underset{\sim}{B_i}) \quad \left(\begin{matrix} j=1, 2, \cdots, n; \\ k=1, 2, \cdots, m; \end{matrix}\right)$

The meaning of $\underset{\sim}{A_i}$ ($i=1,2,\cdots n$) see above. Then as a result of the evaluatinn of single factor the fuzzy subset on $\{\underset{\sim}{A_1}, \underset{\sim}{A_2}, \cdots, \underset{\sim}{A_n}\}$ is obtained.

Thus

$$\underset{\sim}{B_k} = \frac{x_{1k}}{\underset{\sim}{A_1}} + \frac{x_{2k}}{\underset{\sim}{A_2}} + \cdots + \frac{x_{nk}}{\underset{\sim}{A_n}} \quad (k=1,2,\cdots, m)$$

Given L serieses of weight numbers

$$w_{11}, w_{12}\cdots\cdots, w_{1m} \quad (1=1, 2, \cdots, L)$$

Where w_{11} denotes the proportion of the facfor $b_k(k=1,2, \cdots, m)$ of the evaluation in this synthesis evaluation and satisfied

$$\overset{m}{\underset{k=1}{\Sigma}} W_{1k} = 1, \quad (1=1, 2, \cdots L)$$

As knowledge of people for things will have defference with distinct conditions and places, such weighted number should not be sole. For distinct conditions and places we should work out many serieses of weighted numbers.

Suppose

$$y_{1i} = \overset{m}{\underset{k=1}{\Sigma}} W_{1k} x_{ik} \quad \left(\begin{matrix} 1=1,2,\cdots,L \\ j=1,2,\cdots n \end{matrix}\right)$$

and let

$$y_{jmin} = \overset{L}{\underset{1=1}{\Lambda}} y_{1i}$$

$$\quad (j=1, 2, \cdots, n)$$

$$y_{jmax} = \overset{L}{\underset{1=1}{V}} y_{1i}$$

then

$$\underset{\sim}{B} = \frac{[y_{1min}, y_{1max}]}{\underset{\sim}{A_1}} + \frac{[y_{2min}, y_{2max}]}{\underset{\sim}{A_2}} + \cdots$$

$$\cdots + \frac{[y_{nmin}, y_{nmax}]}{\underset{\sim}{A_n}}$$

This is the synthesis evaluation of $\underset{\sim}{B_1}$, $\underset{\sim}{B_2}\cdots$, $\underset{\sim}{B_l}$ under L serieses of weighted numbers. The membership degree of the element $\underset{\sim}{A_i}$ is the interval number $[y_{imin}, y_{imax}]$ in this formula.

3.3. Application

According to the data of limestone and marl in certain project of China we work out a living example of computation. Our aim is explaining the method of computation above—described.

Their fuzzy subsets on the basis of data of limestone and marl is given and illustrated in Fig 2. Where limestone is indicated in Fig 2 (a)and marl is indicated in Fig 2(b).

By the formula of computation of neartude degree above—given, the result of evaluation of single factor is obtained and shown in Table 3, in which the result in that culumn of the nominal

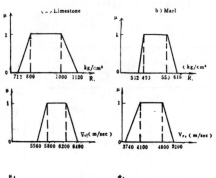

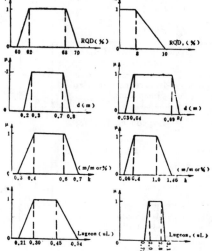

Fig.2. Fuzzy Sets of Limestone (a) and Marl (b).

Table 3. Single Factor Evaluation of Limestone and Marl

Rock		Limestone					Marl				
	Class	I	II	III	IV	V	I	II	III	IV	V
Intervallic parameters	Uniaxial compressive strength		0.688	1					0.811	1	
	Velocity of longitudinal wave	1					0·5	1	0.593		
	RQD			1							1
	Separation of discontinuities			1	0.667					1	1
	Fissure rate of two dimensions		1	1			0.205	1	1	0.176	
	Lugeon coefficient			1	0.483						1
Nominal Parameters	Condition of discontinuities		0.2	1	0.1						1
	Ground water		0.1	1					1		
	Strike and dip orientation of joints		1					1			
	Stand-up of rock mass itself	0.2	1						0.3	1	

Table 4. Single Factor Evaluation of Limestone and Marl

Rock		Limestone					Marl				
	Class	I	II	III	IV	V	I	II	III	IV	V
Intervallic parameters	Uniaxial compressive strength		0.688	1	1	1			0.811	1	1
	Velocity of longitudinal wave	1	1	1	1	1	0.5	1	1	1	1
	RQD			1	1	1					1
	Separation of discontinuities			1	1	1				1	1
	fissure rate of two dimensions		1	1	1	1	0.205	1	1	1	1
	Lugeon coefficient			1	1	1					1
Nominal parameters	Condition of discontinuities		0.2	1	1	1					1
	Ground water		0.1	1	1	1			1	1	1
	Strike and dip orientation of joints		1	1	1	1		1	1	1	1
	Stand-up of rock mass itself	0.2	1	1	1	1			0.3	1	1

parameter is obtained by measuring immediately.

We may make such understanding, in the case of k—th factor, if some rock is excellent, then it is bound to be good. In other words, in the case of k—th factor if the membership degree of some rock belongs to excellent type and good type are x_{1k} and x_{2k} respectively, then there is bound to be $x_{2k} \geqslant x_{1k}$.

Data in Table 4 is given by following formula

$$x_{jk} = \bigvee_{i=1}^{i} x_{ik} \quad \binom{k=1,2,\cdots,5}{j=1,2,\cdots,10}$$

We work out 3 serieses of weighted numbers as illustrated Table 5.

By the formula

$$y_{1j} = \sum_{k=1}^{5} W_{1k} x_{jk} \quad \binom{l=1,2,3,4}{j=1,2,\cdots,10}$$

and

$$y_{min} = \bigwedge_{l=1}^{4} y_{1j}$$

$$y_{imax} = \bigvee_{l=1}^{4} y_{1j} \qquad (j=1,2,\cdots,10)$$

Then the Table 6 is obtaind

We may see following facts immediately by the Table 6:

(i) Limestone belongs fair rock (Ⅲ—type). The degree of it belongs to good rock (Ⅱ—type) is between 0.458 and 0.575; the degree of it belongs to excellent rock is between 0.16 and 0.21.

(ii) Marl belongs very poor rock(Ⅴ—type). The degree of it belongs to poor rock(Ⅳ—type) is between 0.65 and 0.75.The degree of it belongs to Ⅰ.Ⅱ.Ⅲ—type may be consulted by the Table 6.

Table 5. Weighted Numbers of Single Factor in the Comprehensive Evaluation

Parameters	Uniaxial compressive strength	Velocity of longitudinal wave	RQD	Separation of discontinuities	Fissure rate of two dimensions	Lugeon coefficient	Condition of discontinuities	Ground water	Strike and dip crientation of joints	Stand-up of rock mass itself
1	0.20	0.15	0.20	0.05	0.05	0.10	0.05	0.10	0.05	0.05
2	0.25	0.20	0.15	0.05	0.05	0.07	0.05	0.08	0.05	0.05
3	0.30	0.15	0.10	0.05	0.05	0.10	0.05	0.10	0.05	0.05

Tabla 6. Comprehensive Evaluation for Limestone and Marl

Rock		Limestone					Marl				
Numerical groups	1	0.16	0.458	1	1	1	0.085	0.250	0.527	0.650	1
	2	0.21	0.575	1	1	1	0.110	0.300	0.598	0.730	1
	3	0.16	0.526	1	1	1	0.085	0.250	0.608	0.750	1
Y_{min}		0.16	0.458	1	1	1	0.085	0.250	0.527	0.650	1
Y_{max}		0.21	0.575	1	1	1	0.110	0.300	0.608	0.750	1

It is worth to pay attention that these computations are not complicated.

4. CONCLUSION

The new system which is based on the concept of the fuzzy sets in this paper differs with others, for example, the RSR concept by Wickham et al (1972), the geomechanics classification by Bieniawski (1973) and the Q—system by Barton et al (1974), which have been extensively employed practically in the field of tunnelling, in that it is very important how to obtain a comprehensive evaluation for rock masses in a practical engineering, although some considerations of fundamental factors of rock properties is perhaps slight difference. The authors are convinced of rationality of MFS, because the uncertainty and dispersion of physicomechanical parameters are a reflection of nature properties of rock masses.

5. REFERENCE

[1] Fu Bing-jun, Yuan Cheng-wen et al (1980), Some Developments in the Test Study of Rock Mechanics in the Conservancy Engineering Construction of China(2), Hydrogeology and Engineering Geology, NO. 5, 48—52, September (in chinese).

[2] Tao Zhen-yu and Peng Zu-zeng (1981), Application of Fuzzy Mathematics to the Engineering Classification of Rocks. Chinese Journal of Geotechnical Engineering, Vol.3, NO.1, 36—45, February (in chinese).

[3] Zadeh, L. A (1956), Fuzzy Sets, Information and Control, NO.8, 338~353.

[4] Barton, N., Lien, R., and Lunde, J, (1974), Engineering Classification of Rock Masses for the design of Tunnel Support. Rock Mechanics, Vol. 6, NO.4, 189—236.

[5] Bieniawski, Z. T. (1979), The Geomechanics Classification in Rock Engineering Applications. Proc.4th Congress of ISRM, Vol.2, 41—48.

KOMPAKTE BAUWEISE DER KAVERNENKRAFTWERKE IN NORWEGEN
Compact design of caverns for hydro power stations in Norway
Dimensionnement compact des centrales souterraines en Norvège

I.TVEITAN & B.BUEN
Ing.A.B.Berdal A/S, Norwegen

SUMMARY:
Norway relays heavily on hydro power for energy. This has made large investments necer
ssary and compact and economic design is a virtue made out of a necessity. An essential
part of the design is to determine the optimum site, and the orientation and layout of
the cavern and tunnels with respect to the geological conditions.

Compact design gives reduced excavated volume, reduced volume of construction materials
and reduced rock reinforcement. This is achieved through an arrangement of generators,
turbines, valves and transformers in a space saving way. The span width of a cavern is
usually determined by the generator shaft diameter. As a rule of thumb: span width =
generator shaft diameter + 3,0 - 3,5 m. Simple shapes of tunnels and caverns, and layout
that makes construction easy and gives low excavation costs are sought for.

Six examples of design practice covering the evolution in the period from 1945 until today are given.

ZUSAMMENFASSUNG:
Norwegen wird hauptsächlich von Wasserkraftenergie versorgt. Diese Tatsache hat grosse
Investitionen notwendig gemacht. Kompakte Bauweise und ökonomisch begründete Konstruktionen
werden immer wichtiger. Von grosser Bedeutung bei den Anlagenentwürfen ist die optimale
Festlegung des Ortes und die Positionierung und Gestaltung von Kavernen und Tunnels hin-
sichtlich der geologischen Verhältnisse.

Kompakte Konstruktionen bedeutet weniger gesprengtes Felsenvolumen und weniger Bau- und
Abstützungsmaterial. Dies wird durch eine raumbesparende Anordnung von Generatoren,
Transformatoren, Turbinen und Ventilen erreicht. Der Durchmesser des Generatorschachtes
bestimmt normalerweise die Kavernenbreite. Eine Faustregel lautet: Kavernenbreite =
Aussenmasse der Generatorschacht + 3,0 - 3,5 Meter. Vereinfachte Bauweise von Tunnels
und Kavernen die die Konstruktionen vereinfachen und niedrige Aussprengungskosten mit
sich bringen wird nachgestrebt.

Es werden 6 Beispiele von angewandten Konstruktionen gezeigt die die Entwicklung von 1945
bis heute nachspiegeln.

RESUMÉ:
La consommation d'énergie en Norvège se base lourdement sur énergie d'eau. Cela a fait
indispensable des placement important. Une composition compacte et économique est un
avantage qui est fait de nécessité.

C'est essentiel de déterminer le site et orientation optimal pour la caverne et les
tunnels par rapport aux conditions geologiques. Les volumes de l'excavation, des
matériaux pour la construction et de ferraillege de roche sont reduits avec une composition
compacte. Cela est obtenu quand on arrange les générateurs, les turbines, les vannes et
les transformateurs avec attention. La portée d'une caverne est d'habitude determinée
par le diameter du générateur. Comme une règle simple: La portée = le diameter de la

fosse du générateur. On a soin des formes simples des tunnels et des cavernes, et un
"layout" qui fait la construction simple et l'excavation moin coûteuse.

Cix exemples de pratique de compositions qui couvrent l'evolution de 1945 de 1982 ont
été donné.

1. EINLEITUNG

Die erste unterirdische Wasserkraftanlage
in Norwegen, Bjørkåsen südlich von Narvik,
wurde in den Jahren 1919-23 gebaut. Bis zu
1940 wurden nur ausnahmsweise Kraftwerke
unterirdisch gebaut und, nach heutigen
Massstäben, nur mit kleinen Leistungen.

Die meisten Kraftwerke in Norwegen, die
nach dem Kriege gebaut wurden, sind unterirdische Anlagen mit dem Krafthaus in einer
Kaverne. In den Jahren 1970-1980 sind
ungefähr 90 Kraftwerke mit einer Gesamtleistung von 6350 MW in Betrieb genommen.
60 davon sind Kavernenkraftwerke mit
einer jährlichen Produktion von 31,5 TWh.
Um diese Anlagen wirtschaftlich durch-
führen zu können, ist man gezwungen
kompakte und billige Lösungen zu finden.

2. METODEN UND MÖGLICHKEITEN IN KOMPAKTER BAUWEISE

Die topographischen Verhältnisse Norwegens
haben die Kavernenbauweise wirtschaftlich
gemacht. In erster Linie wird dadurch die
Triebwasserführung wesentlich kürzer als
diejenige, die dem Gelände angepasst ist.
Die Ersparnisse von Triebwasserleitungen
konnten die Mehrkosten bei einer unterirdischen Bauweise mehr als aufwiegen.

Anfangs war der Gewinn die Verkürzung des
Druckrohres. Später, beim einbetonieren des
Druckrohres, erhielt man grosse Stahler-
sparnisse dadurch, dass der Innerdruck sich
auf den Felsen übertragen liess. Der nächste
Schritt der Entwicklung sind Schächte mit
rohen Felswänden in denen man nur auf die
letzte 20 bis 50 M Strecke eine Druckrohr-
leitung aus Stahl verwendet.

Hinsichtlich von Platzbedarf und Umweltschutz
sind unterirdische Anlagen, soweit es die
Bauweise anbelangt, vorzuziehen. Unterirdische Anlagen haben geringere Wartungs-
und Reparaturkosten als die überirdischen
Anlagen.

Der Zweck der kompakten Bauweise von Kavern-
kraftwerken sind die reduzierten Baukosten.
Die Ersparnisse erhält man direkt bei
kleinerem Ausbruchvolumen und dadurch
weniger Baukosten und kürzere Bauzeit.
Ersparnisse bei den Abstützungsarbeiten

erhält man auch. Der Umfang der Abstützungskosten ist von Spannweite und Höhe der
Kaverne abhängig.

Für eine gegebene Felsgüte gibt es immer
eine obere Grenze der Kavernengrösse ohne
Abstützungen. Wenn die Grenze übershcritten
wird, nähern die Abstützungskosten rasch
zu.

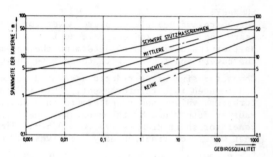

Abbildung 1.

Sicherungsmassnahmen als Funktion der
Kavernengrösse und Gebirgsqualität (BARTON
et Al. 1974).

Kompakte Bauweise der Kavernenkraftwerke
ist durch den technischen Fortschritt aller
Komponenten einer Kraftanlage möglich
geworden. Die Entwicklung gegen grössere
Einheiten, bessere Qualität des Baumaterials
und bessere Ausnützung von Möglichkeiten
haben den Platzbedarf pro installierte
Leistung ständig kleiner gemacht.

Eine ähnliche Entwicklung zeigt sich auch
bei den Kraftwerksplänen. Die Ältesten
hatten Anordnungen genau gleich den
oberirdischen Anlagen.

Nach und nach hat man erkannt, dass der
Felsen ein dreidimentionales Konstruktionsmaterial ist wo der Platzbedarf entscheident
ist für das Volumen das angebrochen werden
muss.

3. INGENIEURGEOLOGISCHE PLANUNG IM KRAFT-WERKBAU

Die Ingenieurgeologie als Fach in Norwegen
hat sich hauptsächlich als Folge des
Bedarfes in den Kraftwerksbauten entwickelt.

Bei mehreren früheren Anlagen sind Probleme auf Grund von Verwitterung, Verklüftung und Störungen des Felsens entstanden.

Heute werden immer die geologischen Verhältnisse genau registriert bevor die Pläne einer Kraftanlage ausgearbeitet werden.

Die Registrierung umfasst:

- Gesteinsart und ihre mechanische Eigenschaften.

- Trennflächenabstand,. Neigung und Richtung.

- Störmungszonen, ihre Karakter und Orientierung.

- Primäre Spannungszustand.

- Wasserverhältnisse.

Mit Rücksicht auf die Felsenverhältnisse wird eine Planlösung der Anlage gewählt, die optimal innerhalb der praktischen Grenzen des vorliegenden Fallausbaues liegt. Wenn es irgendwie möglich ist, gibt man den Kavernen, Stollen und Schächten eine Orientierung im Verhältnis zu der Klüftung und dem Gebirgsdruck die minimale Stabilitätsprobleme und Übermassen gibt. Die Querschnitte der Schächte und Kavernen erhalten eine Form, die den mechanischen Eigenschaften, der Klüftung und dem Gebirgsdruck des Felsens angepasst ist. Abhängig von den Felsenverhältnissen gibt man dem Profil ein flaches oder ein hohes First, gekrümmte Wände oder man gibt dem Profil einen asymmetrischen Form.

Wenn mehrere Stollen und Kavernen nahe an einander liegen, können sich in den Felswänden und Felspfeilern zwischen den Hohlräumen die Spannungen derart häufen das Absprengen oder Einstürtze auftreten. Der Abstand der Hohlräume muss deshalb den Felsverhältnisse genau angepasst sein.

Ein allgemein gültiges Verfahren ist von R. Selmer-Olsen & Broch (1978) klar gezeigt worden.

Der Ingenieurgeologi bestimmt in der Regel die permanente Abstützungen und Sicherungsmassnahmen. Der Felsen ist ein konstruktionsmaterial das nur dort verstärkt werden soll wo es nötig ist um die gewünschte Tragfähigkeit zu erreichen.

Es wird immer ein minimaler Aufwand zugestrebt.

Die Entwicklung des Ausbruchverfahren und der Betonteknologie hat eine günstige Einwirkung auf die Abstützungsarbeiten gehabt.

Modernes Glattsprengungsverfahren gibt eine moderate Beanspruchung der Felsenoberfläche und die notwendige Sicherungmassnahmen wird dadurch reduziert.

Glattgesprengte Felsflächen können auch ästetische Aktiva sein, und rohe Felswände werden in trockenen Kavernen oft als endgültige Wände verwendet.

Eine Felsensicherung mittels Ankerung und armierten Spritzbetons hat in vielen Fällen die früheren übliche Stahlbeton wölbe abgelöst. Die Höhe der Kraftwerkskaverne kann dadurch entsprechend reduziert werden.

4. ENTWIKLUNG DER KRAFTWERKSBAUWEISE DURCH BEISPIELE ERMITTELT

Nachfolgende Kraftwerkpläne zeigen die Entwicklung der Anordnung von Kavernenanlagen in Norwegen.

Die ersten grösseren Anlagen sind mit horizontalachsigen Peltonturbinen ausgerüstet. Um eine nicht zu grosse Spannweite der Kaverne zu erhalten, sind die Turbinen, Generatoren und Transformatoren neben einander angeordnet.

Åbjøra Kraftwerk, in den Jahren 1947-51 gebaut, hat eine solche Anordnung. Bei einer grossen Aggregatenzahl wird der Abstand zwischen Generator und Trafo gross.

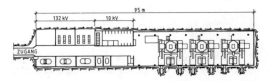

Abbildung 2. Åbjøra Kraftwerk

3 stk. horizontalachsige Peltonturbinen
mit einer Leistung von je 27 MW. Die Fallhöhe beträgt 430 Meter.

Mit vertikalachsigen Turbinen kann die
Spannweite der Kaverne reduziert werden,
und man erhält Ersparnisse im Bauvolum von
etwa 20% im Vergleich zu den horizontalachsigen Peltonturbinen.

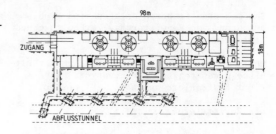

Hjartdøla Kraftverk, in den Jahren 1955-58
gebaut, zeigt eine solche Anordnung.

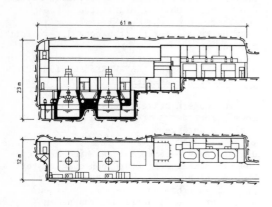

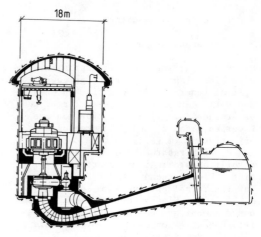

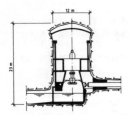

Abbildung 4. Tokke Kraftverk

Abbildung 3. Hjartdøla Kraftverk

2 stk. vertikalachsige Peltonturbinen mit
einer Leistung von je 52 MW. Die Fallhöhe
beträgt 590 Meter.

Die bei oberirdischen Kraftwerken normale
Anordnung mit den Transformatoren neben
den Generatoren ist auch in Kavernenkraft-
werken üblich. Bei grösseren Leistungen
benötigt diese Anordnung grosse Spannweiten
der Kavernen und dürfen nur bei guten
Felsenverhältnissen angewendet werden.

Tokke Kraftverk, in den Jahren 1958-62 gebaut
zeigt eine solche Anordnung.

4 stk. vertikalachsige Francisturbinen mit
einer Leistung von je 110 MW. Die Fallhöhe
beträgt 390 Meter.

Die Anordnung von Transformatoren in einer
Kaverne parallel zur Maschinenhalle hat einen
kurzen Abstand zwischen Generator und
Transformator zur Folge und reduziert damit das Risiko bei Feuer. In Bezug auf die
Stabilitätsverhältnisse ist dies
eine viel günstigere Lösung.

Brokke Kraftverk, aus den Jahren 1960-64,
zeigt eine solche Anordnung.

4 stk. vertikalachsige Francisturbinen
mit einer Leistung von je 75 MW. Die Fallhöhe ist 280 Meter.

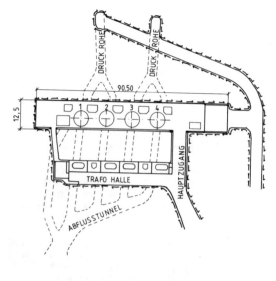

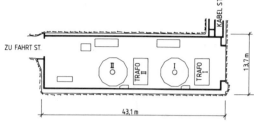

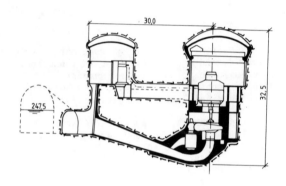

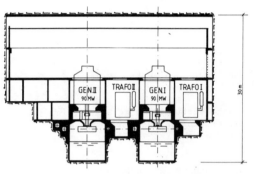

Abbildung 5. Brokke Kraftverk

Abbildung 6. Borgund Kraftverk

2 stk. vertikalachsige Peltonturbinen mit
einer Leistung von je 80 MW. Die Fallhöhe
ist 870 Meter.

Årøy Kraftverk wird im Frühjahr 1983
fertiggestellt. Statt eine Stahlbetongewölbe hat man hier eine Felsvergütung
mittels Ankerung und armierten Spritzbeton
verwendet.

Die letzte Entwicklung der Anordnung ist
die Anordnung der Transformatoren
zwischen den Aggregaten unter der Maschinen-
saaldecke. Die Abstände zwischen den
Aggregaten müssen dadurch erweitert werden.
Die Spannweite der Kaverne aber, begrenzt
sich auf ein Minimum von den übrigen
Komponenten des Aggregates bestimmt.
Die Aussenmasse der Generatorgrube und
der Ingang zu der Schieber bestimmen
die Spannweite. Die kleinste Spannweite
erreicht man wenn der Einlauf einen Winkel
von 60° zu der Hallenrichtung hat.

Borgund Kraftverk von den Jahren 1971-74
zeigt eine solche Anordnung.

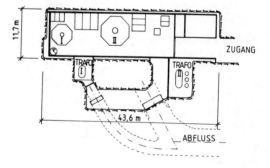

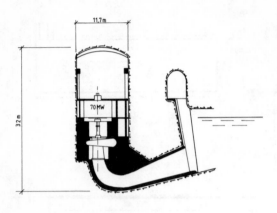

Abbildung 7. Årøy Kraftwerk

2 stk. vertikalachsige Francisturbinen
mit einer Leistung von 70 MW und 20 MW.
Die Fallhöhe ist 146 Meter.

5. SCHLUSSFOLGERUNGEN

Erfahrungen haben gezeigt, dass gute
Anpassung von Kavernen und Tunnels an die
vorhandene geologische Verhältnisse minimale Abstützungsarbeiten zur Folge haben.

Beim Anbringen mit guter Überlegung von
Turbinen, Ventilen und Transformatoren
können minimale Kavernenbreiten erreicht
werden. Die Dimension des Generatorschachtes will normalerweise bestimmend
für die Spannweite der Kaverne sein.
In den meisten Fällen wird es möglich sein,
eine Anordnung zu verschaffen wo die
Kavernenbreite etwa 3 bis 3,5 Meter
grösser ist als die Aussenmasse des
Generatorschachtes. Dabei kann allerdings
lokale Aussprengungen notwendig werden
um Platz für Ventilen etc. zu verschaffen.

In den heutigen Norwegischen Anlagen sind
Kavernenbreiten grösser als 12 Meter nur
ausnahmsweise erforderlich. Wenn die
einfachte Faustregel, Spannweite = Aussen-
mass des Generatorschachtes + 3,5 Meter,
angewandt wird, ist es einleuchtend, dass
eine Reihe Kraftwerkskavernen grösser
gebaut (geplant) als notwendig sind.

Die Höhe einer Kaverne ist durch die
technische Installationen und die Kran-
dimensionen gegeben. Etwas kann anstatt
Betongewölbe durch Anwendung von Spritz-

beton und Bolzen in den Hängen gewonnen
werden. Weiter erreicht man Ersparnisse
beim bewussten Anbringen von Hängen mit
geringer Krümmung und, als Kompensation,
die Anwendung von längeren Bolzen. Im
Übrigen muss der Platzbedarf genau ver-
angeschlagt werden, so dass nur das aller
notwendigste ausgesprengt wird. Dies
muss indessen gegen einen rationellen
Sprengungsplan für die Kaverne abgewogen
werden, da eine einfache Form eine preis-
wertere Sprengung bedeutet.

Zum Schluss soll betont werden, dass die
Planung einer Kraftwerkskaverne und des
zugehörigen Tunnelsystems als Ganzes
gesehen werden muss. Es muss grossen Wert
darauf gelegt werden, ein Lay-out zu
erstreben, dass alles in Allem eine an-
lagentechnisch einfache Arbeit hervorbringt.
Die Lösungen müssen derart sein, das notwendige Hilfs- und Transporttunnels in
die fertige Anlage grösstmöglich eingehen.
Beispielsweise kann der Transporttunnel
des Ablaufes als (Abstroms) Schwingkammer
verwendet werden.

LITERATUR

BARTON et Al. "Analysis of rock mass
quality and support practice in tunneling,
and a guide for estimating support
requirements". Report no. 54206. Norwegian
Geotechnical Institue, Oslo. 1974.

SELMER-OLSEN, R, & BROCH, E, "General
design procedure for underground openings
in Norway". Proceedings Rockstore 1977,
London, 1978.

SOLEM, A, VOIGHT, F. "Norske kraftverker"
Teknisk Ukeblads Forlag 1966.

A CUT-OFF WALL IN KARSTIC LIMESTONE WITHIN THE RIGHT ABUTMENT OF KHAO LAEM DAM

Eine Herdmauer in karstigem Kalkgestein innerhalb des rechten Widerlagers
des Khao Laem Damms

Un mur parafouille de l'appui droite du barrage Khao Laem dans une région de calcaire karstique

SOMKUAN WATAKEEKUL
Electricity Generating Authority of Thailand, Nonthaburi
C.GRATWICK & I.FREIMANIS
Snowy Mountains Engineering Corp., Cooma, Australia

SUMMARY:
Khao Laem Dam ia a 90 m high concrete faced compacted rock filled dam. The damsite is in
an area of cavernous limestone and treatment to prevent water loss through the right abutment involves the driving of six grouting galleries as the access to fill the concrete into the cavities and to execute the grouting work. Within the abutment close to the dam an
area of ungroutable microfractured limestone was encountered. A concrete diaphragm cut-
off wall was therefore required to be constructed between the galleries. Development of
the design, construction precedures, costs and program of this wall are discussed.

ZUSAMMENFASSUNG:
Der Khao Laem Damm ist ein 90 m hoher Steinschuettdamm mit einer wasserseitigen Betonmem-
brane. Die Sperrstelle liegt in einem Gebiet karstigen Kalksteines. Um Wasserverluste
durch das rechte Dammwiderlager zu vermeiden, ist der Ausbruch von 6 Galerien durch das
Massiv vorgesehen, mit der Absicht, Kavernen zu finden und mit Beton auszufuellen, oder
das Gebirge mit Zement zu injizieren. Im rechten Widerlager, unmittelbar am Anschluss des
Dammes, steht eine Zone mit uninjizierbarem, zerbrochenem Kalkstein an. Eine Betonabdich-
tungswand (Schlitzwand) ist hier zwischen den Galerien vorgesehen. Im folgenden Artikel
werden Entwicklung dieser Wand, Konstruktionsverfahren, Kostenanalyse sowie Bauprogramm
beschrieben.

RESUME:
Le Barrage de Khao Laem est une digue en enrochement avec une couche amont imperméable en
béton. Il est situé dans une région de calcaire karstique at afin d'éviter des pertes d'
eau à travers l'appui droit, on a décidé l'exécution de six galeries pour remplir des cavernes de béton et pour exécuter des injections. Une zone composée de calcaire fracturé et
non injectable se trouve dans l'appui droit en contact avec la digue. L'exécution d'un diaphragme en béton y a été choisie entre les galeries. Le développement de l'étude, les procédés de construction, les coûts et le programme de réalisation de ce diaphragme sont
discutés.

1. INTRODUCTION

The Khao Laem Project is in central west
Thailand on the Quae Noi River. The damsite was selected after study of several
alternative sites and was extensively
investigated over a period of about six
years.

The general layout of the project is
shown in Figure 1. The main features are:

A gated chute spillway at the left
abutment with a capacity of 3 200 m^3/s.

A concrete gravity intake structure
next to the spillway with three power

intakes and an irrigation outlet.

Three 6.3 m diameter, steel pressure
conduits each 240 m long.

A 300 MW capacity surface power station.

A concrete faced rockfill embankment
90 m high with a total fill volume of
about 8.0 x 10^6 m^3.

A temporary diversion channel requiring
the excavation of approximately 4 x 10^6 m^3.

A diversion tunnel of 7.0 m internal
diameter and 470 m length.

A right abutment cut-off comprising over
22 km of grouting galleries.

The development of the project has been

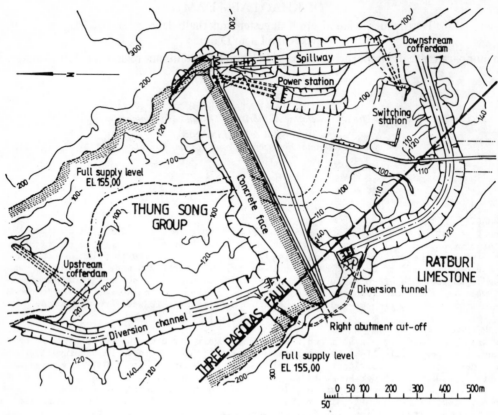

Figure 1

made very difficult by the widespread occurrence of karstic weathering in the mainly calcareous rocks of the Thung Song and Ratburi Groups which could give rise to reservoir leakage problems. In addition to conventional grouting, a 50 m deep concrete diaphragm wall is provided along part of the upstream toe of the dam.

The right abutment is composed of massive limestone of the Ratburi Group which is karstic. Treatment involves driving six grouting galleries each almost 4 km long, spaced vertically at 14 m. Between these galleries and below the bottom one, closely spaced holes are being drilled and water pressure tested to locate cavities and determine the extent of the required grouting. Cavities observed in the galleries and intersected by the drill holes will be cleaned out and filled with concrete.

The boundary between the Thung Song Group and the Ratburi Group is faulted and consists of an ungroutable microfractured limestone which includes areas of blocky material surrounded by clay filled joints. This paper discusses the treatment of this area.

2. GEOLOGY OF KHAO LAEM SITE

2.1 Topography

The Khao Laem damsite is on the Quae Noi River which flows in a valley along a regional structural feature known as the Three Pagodas Fault.

At the damsite the Quae Noi valley is about 800 m wide with a 50 m wide river channel incised approximately 20 m into the valley floor. The left side of the valley steepens gradually to form a slope of 25° above the dam crest. Between the river and the sheer limestone cliff of the right abutment is a narrow, dry valley separated from the river by a line of low hills.

The right abutment area comprises a rugged limestone range called the Khao Laem Massif which rises several hundred metres above river level. One arm of the reservoir will lap against this range which contains karstic features and a general groundwater level below full supply level. The right abutment cut-off is being constructed in this area to intersect the dry season ground

486

water level at full supply level, approximately 3.5 km south of the dam.

2.2 Rock types

The two rock formations at the damsite comprise:

Thung Song Group of probable Ordovician age consisting of interbedded shale, siltstone, limestone and sandstone, mostly in beds from 0.01 m to 0.5 m thick.

Ratburi Limestone of Permian age which is bedded to massive.

The Thung Song Group occurs on the left abutment and part of the right abutment. It has undergone complex folding with axial plane foliation trending parallel to the river in a north-south direction.

Extreme differential weathering is present in the Thung Song rocks, with weathered zones extending to 50 m below the river bed. Solution cavities, commonly infilled, persist to similar depths.

The contact between the Thung Song Group and the Ratburi Limestone is the transcurrent Three Pagodas Fault, considered to be of Tertiary age. The main fault zone dipping at 60° to 80° southwest, is about 30 m wide and consists of graphitic shale with frequent clay gouge, local overthrusts and drag folds.

A planar fault forms a prominent overhanging cliff face on the right abutment. The cliff face fault is approximately parallel to the main fault zone and is easily recognizable in all the exploratory adits, grouting galleries and diversion tunnel. A zone 70 to 80 m wide of fault altered Ratburi Limestone occurs between the main fault zone and the cliff face fault. This friable rock type, termed "microfractured" limestone, is characterized by very closely spaced (3 to 10 mm) calcite veins and clay coated fractures. The rock readily frets to sand and gravel-sized fragments. Isolated areas of foliated black graphitic limestone occur within the microfractured limestone.

Approximately 30 m west of the cliff face fault and striking parallel is a vertical faulted contact between pale grey brecciated limestone and black to dark grey, dense, crystalline limestone. This contact is the western limit of the Three Pagodas Fault Zone and is also easily recognized in the exploratory adits (where intersected), galleries and diversion tunnel. The brecciated limestone is non karstic and consists of dark grey

angular limestone fragments 3 to 10 mm size in a light grey calcareous matrix. The rock is generally dense but friable in parts. The black to dark grey, dense, crystalline limestone is typical of the Ratburi Limestone encountered in the southern drives of the six galleries.

Within the generally homogeneous, grey, crystalline limestone occur areas of limestone/calcite breccia. This distinctive rock type consists of angular fragments 10 to 200 mm size of grey to black limestone in a white crystalline calcite matrix.

Large solution cavities and other karstic features within the Ratburi Limestone have developed predominantly along steeply dipping faults and joints rather than shallow dipping bedding. Cavity dimensions and nature are variable. Some are clay and sand infilled, others are empty or coated with crystalline calcite. Only few vertical pipe-like features have been encountered.

2.3 Geology of concrete cut-off area

The right abutment concrete cut-off is to be constructed between the main fault zone and cliff face fault. A geological section through the proposed cut-off (Figure 3) shows four basic divisions within the microfractured limestone in this area:

1. A karstic weathering zone adjacent to the cliff fault, intersected in galleries E and F and the diversion tunnel consisting of in-situ microfractured limestone blocks bounded by joints infilled to 500 mm thick with firm to stiff red to orange-brown high plasticity clay. The main joints dip 10° to 20° northeast. Minor orthogonal joints produce the blocky nature of this zone which is considered unsuitable for treatment by grouting. The vertical extent of the zone below gallery F is being investigated by core drilling.

2. Light to dark grey microfractured limestone with zones of graphitic limestone with notable karstic features such as cavities and clay infilled solution enlarged joints. Cavity development is structurally controlled but irregular and discontinous. The rock is friable and easily erodible and unsuitable for treatment by grouting.

3. Grey microfractured limestone with distinctive white calcite patches has a "spotted" appearance. This rock type is non-karstic and has very low permeability but is friable and easily erodible. Closely spaced fractures (3 to 10 mm)

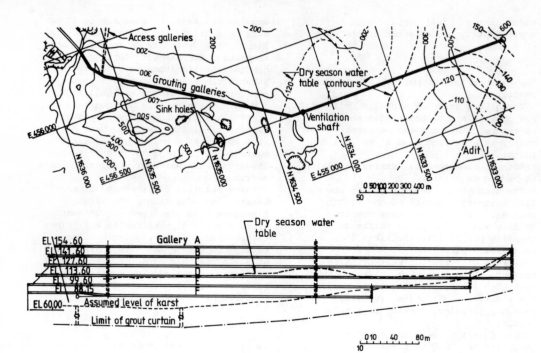

Figure 2

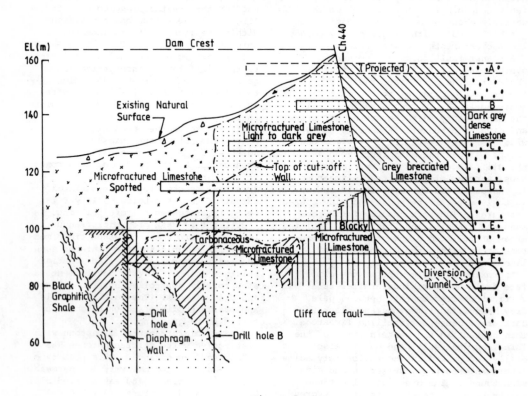

Figure 3

488

are coated with clay or amorphous calcite. A grouting trial using cement grout in this rock type showed negligible grout penetration at pressures up to 10 kg/cm^2.

4. Black carbonacious limestone has been intersected in gallery F and cored drillholes A and B (Figure 3). Grouting is not considered an effective treatment for this rock type which has very low strength, is friable and easily erodible.

The main fault zone forms a barrier to groundwater flow as evidenced by resurgence along the fault in topographically low areas. Groundwater flow through the microfractured limestone is concentrated in the zones of karstic weathering.

3. DEVELOPMENT OF DESIGN

3.1 Original design

Based on the information available at the time of the original design, it was believed that an impermeable barrier could be obtained by grouting and cavity treatment between the massive rock of the right abutment cliff (Ratburi Group) and the fault zone about 80 m to the east. It was planned that the six vertically aligned grouting galleries of the right abutment cut-off (Figure 2) would be splayed in such a way that they would line up and connect to the 1.4 to 1 plane of the upstream concrete face of the dam. Grouting between the fully pressure lined galleries would complete the water seepage barrier.

3.2 Conditions encountered

When the gallery excavation reached this area, and passed from the massive rock of the cliff into the microfractured limestone, it was found that this material contained solution and fault originated zones of variable sized rock elements, interspaced with partially to fully clay-filled seams. Minimal grout takes obtained during grouting trials in the sound microfractured limestone also indicated that the erosion potential could not be reduced by cement grouting.

As a result of these observations it was recognised that the originally proposed grouted cut-off was not feasible and other means of providing a positive water barrier were necessary.

3.3 Adopted solution

In view of these conditions it was decided to provide a continuous concrete wall between the massive rock of the right abutment cliff and the proposed concrete diaphragm wall across the fault zone, 80 m to the east of the cliff, under the plinth at the toe of the concrete face of the dam.

The problem was to design an arrangement which would allow a concrete wall to be constructed safely and economically in the difficult rock conditions. Three alternative methods of diaphragm wall construction were investigated:

1. A wall constructed in an open cut by drilling and concrete filling of overlapping 700 mm diameter holes (similar to the diaphragm wall at the upstream toe of the dam)

2. A wall constructed by raise boring and concrete filling of overlapping holes from extended galleries of the right abutment cut-off.

3. An excavated deep trench, concrete filled to provide a continuous wall, the excavation being carried out from the surface or by mining methods from extended galleries of the right abutment cut-off.

There was considerable incentive to use the overlapping pile method of wall construction as the large diameter drilling equipment (Superdrill) to do this work was on site and it had been demonstrated that it could operate successfully in the fault material. However, the Superdrill, due to its large height and weight is not suitable for drilling on a slope so that it would be necessary to excavate a horizontal base trench in the rising topography of the dam abutment right up to the cliff face. This would result in the removal of much of the microfractured limestone material supporting the toe of the overhanging massive limestone. Because of the overhanging contact between the microfractured limestone and the massive limestone and the presence of structural defects within the massive limestone itself, which could result in slope instability, it was decided to leave as much of the cliff toe material in place as possible, and thus superdrill method was abandoned.

The raise boring method of construction was rejected as it would involve significant additional capital outlay as well as time for mobilization of equipment. This mobilization time would have caused unacceptable delays to the dam construction schedule.

Consideration was also given to the construction of the wall from the surface but from contractural, programming and construction aspects it was decided that the cut-off would be excavated underground between the galleries by mining methods.

The initial proposal was to excavate and construct the wall from the original galleries which connected directly to the sloping concrete face of the dam. However, it was recognized that to excavate on a sloping plane in the poor quality material would be difficult and expensive. In the next step of the disign the galleries were therefore realigned in a vertical plane under gallery B (Figure 4) and a vertical, triangularly shaped wall under the plinth for the dam face was adopted. The extent of the wall is shown in Figure 5. The wall has a nominal thickness of 900 mm, the minimum considered - necessary for economical and practical excavation; a minimum of 600 mm was specified as the wall thickness required to resist the applied water pressure in the soft and variable material supporting it. The wall will extend between the fully pressure lined galleries to invert of the lowest grouting gallery at EL.88.15.

Diamond drilling is at present being carried out from the lowest gallery to determine the extent of the concrete cut-off required below EL.88.15.

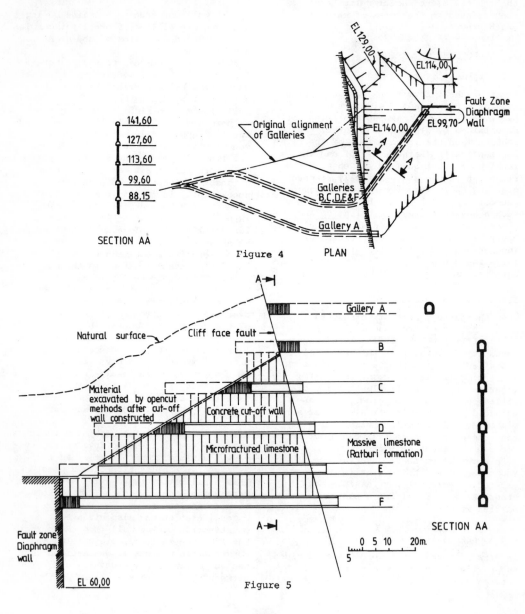

Figure 4

Figure 5

490

4. CONSTRUCTION PROCEDURES

4.1 Redriving of northern galleries

The first task to be done following the decision to go ahead with the realigned cut-off was to redrive the four lower northern galleries vertically below gallery B. This was done concurrently commencing with the uppermost gallery and maintaining where possible a minimum horizontal distance between adjacent faces of 10 m (approx 2 x Tunnel diameters).

The extension of gallery B along the new alignment was done without difficulties and after crossing the cliff face fault the blocky ground needed only a few rockbolts to pin back keystones.

After crossing the cliff face fault with gallery C and D the microfractured limestone was found to be competent and apart from isolated rock bolting where blocky ground was encountered little support was required. At a later stage, however, additional support employing pattern rock bolting, shotcrete and steel ribs had to be installed as the micro-fractured rock began to unravel; in places loss of rock occurred from the crown.

In contrast to the upper galleries, in redriving of gallery E North and later F North bad rock conditions were experienced immediately after crossing the cliff-face fault which were similar to those encountered in the original gallery E and F, the material being microfractured limestone blocks surrounded by red brown clay filled joints. These joints were in a random pattern and support of the excavation by steel ribs was necessary.

Due to excessive overbreak in the crown and shoulders and in view of the future trench blasting for the cut-off between galleries it was decided to backfill the overbreak to the back of the ribs with concrete, leaving a 1.5 m wide gap in the crown for the future cut-off trench. This method had the added advantage of containing the face while excavating the next round. Advance rates in this area averaged 75 cm/day with at times as little as 35 cm/day. After approximately 13 m of tunnel requiring this type of support the rock condition improved and the drive was continued in sound microfractured limestone requiring only shotcrete support with some bolting towards the end of the drive.

In order to improve the rate of progress in blocky ground in gallery F, the concrete backfill behind the ribs was replaced by packing with concrete filled bags, any remaining voids being filled with shotcrete. The excavation/support cycle was thus improved to above 1 m/day. The blocky, clay seam interspersed micro-fractured limestone changed to a very friable carbonacious limestone at about 20 m past the cliff face fault in gallery F. As it was not possible to drill this material, excavation by hand became necessary. Forepoling was added to the support system in addition to concrete bags to fill voids and an excavation rate of about 1.35 m per day was achieved.

4.2 Excavation and concreting

Once the realigned galleries B and C had been completed the cut-off wall

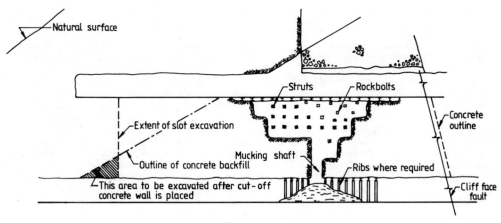

Figure 6

excavation between them was commenced. As a first step a shaft was sunk from gallery B to Gallery C at the eastern end of the cut-off wall in this section. This was done by drilling full depth holes between the galleries, with the holes then being charged in sections and the shaft excavated by raise method from gallery C to B.

With the shaft completed the cut-off wall was excavated in a step wise manner with spoil being fed down the shaft and then down the cut-off wall slot as the excavation progressed (Figure 6). The condition of the rock between these galleries was blocky but competent and the support employed in the trench consisted of short rockbolts and steel props. At the cliff face fault the trench was recessed approximately 0.5 m into massive limestone thus giving a continuous positive cut-off. Various drill patterns and depths were tried to establish a system to maintain the nominal 900 mm width of the cut-off wall. However, due to the varying nature of the rock it was found that a standard pattern produced excessive overbreak and better results were obtained by individually locating each series of small size blastholes.

The spoil was allowed to remain in the gallery below and was used as a base for the concrete placement operation, eliminating the need for formwork. The top of the spoil was levelled out about 500 mm above the crown of the lower gallery, topped up by a thin layer of sand (approx. 100 mm) and soaked by a quantity of grout prior to concreting. Concrete was then placed from the upper gallery to form the cut-off, the slump of the concrete was controlled at 100 mm to avoid excessive displacement of the unformed sloping upper cut off wall surface. Unevenness in this surface was acceptable as once the cut-off wall completed the open excavation would be continued down to this concrete and the concrete would be scabbled to achieve good bond to the dam plinth above.

It is anticipated that the cut-off wall excavation between the lower galleries will require extensive support. In addition, these walls may have to be constructed in vertical sections to maintain the stability of the ground.

Pressure lining of the galleries, tied into the concrete cut-off walls will complete the positive cut-off under the dam plinth and will allow inspection of the cut-off after the filling of the reservoir.

5. PROGRAM AND COSTS

5.1 Program

The decision to construct the cut-off from underground was influenced by program consideration. The construction of the dam embankment requires a two-stage operation with the major portion across the left part of the river valley being programmed as Stage 1 for completion by May 1983. Stage 2 across the diversion channel and up to the right abutment is programmed for completion one year later in 1984.

Due to the seasonal nature of the river flows and the complex geology of the right abutment area excavation work for the second stage of embankment construction was programmed to commence in January 1982 and to continue down to EL 100 during the 1981/82 dry season, with excavation down to the lowest foundation level being continued during the following dry season commencing November 1982, and with all foundation treatment being completed by May 1983.

Completion of the whole cut off wall by January 1982 was not possible but some delay in commencement of surface excavation could be accepted. A program was evolved based on progressive completion of the cut-off wall ensuring that it was always completed at least within 10 m of the surface works.

The program adopted was:
1. The excavation of galleries B and C and the completion of the concrete cut-off wall above gallery C by 1 March 1982.
2. The excavation of gallery D and the completion of the outer 33 m of concrete cut-off wall between gallery D and gallery C and the gallery plug in gallery C by 1 April 1982.
3. The excavation of gallery E and the completion of the outer 33 m of concrete cut-off wall gallery E and gallery D and the gallery plug in gallery D by 15 May 1982.
4. The excavation of gallery F and the completion of the outer 14 m of concrete cut-off wall between gallery F and gallery E and the lining of gallery E for a further 7 m by 1 June 1982.

An extension of the overall contract period of three months was also granted.

Due to the contractor's immediate mobilization for the additional work and commencement of construction prior to a formal agreement on costs being reached the upper parts of the cut-off were completed well ahead of this schedule.

5.2 Cost

One of the major difficulties in the establishment of an estimate for the cost of the extra work involved in this underground cut-off was the fact that although the preconstruction investigation drill holes and exploratory adits and the original gallery excavations themselves had provided very extensive information on the geological conditions to be encountered, the precise amount of the very difficult blocky ground remained unknown. Consideration was given to payment on a cost plus basis, a lump sum price and by a schedule of rates.

After much discussion between the Engineer, Client and the Contractor, it was resolved that a supplementary schedule of rates would be most appropriate, and to take into account the unknown extent of the bad ground conditions that a lump sum item would be included to cover this risk. The major cost of the cut-off wall construction was the excavation for the wall itself, amounting to almost $ US 1.5×10^6 of the $ US 3.8×10^6 total amount for the extra works involved.

6. ACKNOWLEDGEMENT

The investigation, detailed design and preparation of tender documents for Khao Laem Project were partly funded by the Australian Government under Bilateral Aid to Thailand. The owner is the Electricity Generating Authority of Thailand (EGAT). The Snowy Mountains Engineering Corporation (SMEC) has prepared the design and is supervising construction. The contractors are the Italian-Thai Development Corporation Limited in technical association with Electrowatt-Losinger and Rodio-Trevisani for the main civil works, and Italian Thai-Sheridan Joint Venture for the Right Abutment Cut-off. Vianini S.p.A carried out part of the excavation of the diversion channel in 1979 under an initial contract. EGAT's International Board of Consultants for Khao Laem comprises Mr. J. Barry Cooke (USA), Mr. I.L. Pinkerton (Aust) and Dr. J. Newbery (UK).

The authors wish to thank the Electricity Generating Authority of Thailand and the Snowy Mountains Engineering Corporation for permission to publish this paper, with particular thanks to Mr. Lek Kanchanaphol, Assistant General Manager, EGAT and John I Hilton, Chief Resident Engineer, SMEC for their valued advice, and Messrs.H.R. Bleuler (Tunnels Engineer), G. Klenowski and J.A. Gough (Geologists) for their assistance in preparing this paper.

FELSMECHANIK IM KRAFTHAUSBAU VON SPEICHERKRAFTWERKEN, DARGESTELLT AN DEN KAVERNENKRAFTHÄUSERN KOPS UND LANGENEGG UND DEN SCHACHTKRAFTHÄUSERN RODUND II, WALGAU UND AIN SUKHNA

Rockmechanics by construction of storage power plants presented at the underground powerstations
Kops and Langenegg and the shaft power stations Rodund II, Walgau and Ain Sukhna

Mécanique des roches dans la construction des usines électriques présentée aux cavernes Kops et Langenegg et les centrales énergétiques de puits Rodund II, Walgau et Ain Sukhna

E.K.R.WISSER
Vorarlberger Illwerke AG, Bregenz, Österreich

SUMMARY:
A short description of the power plants is followed by an explanation of the geological conditions; the manner of excavation and securing with bolts, steel fabric mates and gunite; the consideration to rock mechanics and their connection with the measurements in situ by calculation. The method has the following steps:
1. Based on preliminary investigations the most favourable position of the cavern or shaft is chosen.
2. A minimal securing is designed, which allows an adaption to the real behaviour of rock.
3. Measurements and comparison with calculation in the first stages of excavation give the exact values of the rock, as it is a model with scale 1:1.
4. The minimal securing is adapted to the observed values and by long-time measuring the stability of the caves is proved.

ZUSAMMENFASSUNG:
Nach einer Kurzbeschreibung der Kraftwerke werden die geologischen Verhältnisse, die Art des Ausbruches und der Sicherung mit Ankern, Baustahlgittermatten und Spritzbeton, die felsmechanischen Überlegungen und deren Verknüpfung mit den Messungen dargelegt. Die Methode hat folgende Schritte:
1. Auf Grund von Voruntersuchungen wird eine möglichst günstige Lage des Hohlraumes im Gebirge gewählt.
2. Eine Minimalsicherung wird errechnet, deren System eine Anpassung an örtliche Schwächezonen und nachträgliche Verstärkungen erlaubt.
3. Aus Messungen am Bauwerk selbst und dem Vergleich mit theoretischen Berechnungen während der ersten Ausbruchphasen werden die felsmechanischen Werte rückgerechnet (Modell im Massstab 1:1).
4. Die Minimalsicherung wird den am Bauwerk beobachteten Werten angepasst und durch Langzeitmessungen die Standsicherheit des Hohlraumes nachgewiesen.

RESUME:
Après une description brève des centrales énergétiques les conditions géologiques, la manière de percement et de renforcement de la roche au moyen d'un ancrage et de béton armé projeté, les réflexions de la mécanique des roches à relation de mesures in situ ont été décrits. Nous suivons la méthode suivante:
1. En vertu de précédents programmes de recherche une position plus favorable de la cavité a été choisie.
2. Une consolidation minime doit être projeté dont le système permet un renforcement supplémentaire.
3. Des mesures à la construction même et de la comparaison avec les calculs théoriques pendant les premières phases d'excavation les valeurs mécaniques des roches ont été recalculées (modèle en échelle 1:1)
4. La consolidation minime doit être adapté aux valeurs observées. Avec des observations pour long temps la stabilité des cavités doit être controlé.

1 EINLEITUNG

Während die älteren Krafthäuser der Vor=
arlberger Illwerke AG., wie das Vermunt=
werk (bei Inbetriebnahme 1930 mit 119 MW
leistungsstärkstes Wasserkraftwerk der
Welt) oder das Lünerseewerk (bei Inbe=
triebnahme 1958 größtes Pumpspeicherwerk
der Welt) als flach fundierte Maschinen=
blöcke mit entsprechenden Hochbauten er=
stellt wurden, können die neueren in die
zwei Typen Kavernenkrafthäuser und
Schachtkrafthäuser eingeteilt werden.
Für diese augenscheinliche Entwicklung
sind folgende Gründe maßgebend:

1.1 Bautechnische Voraussetzungen:

Spritzbeton und Anker, eingesetzt nach
der Theorie der Neuen Österreichischen
Tunnelbauweise, ermöglichen in technisch
einwandfreier und wirtschaftlicher Weise
die Schaffung großer Gebirgshohlräume.

1.2 Maschinenbauliche Bedingungen:

Leistungsstarke Turbinen mit vertikaler
Achse erfordern einen höheren Wasserge=
gendruck von der Unterwasserseite her,
um Kavitationserscheinungen zu vermei=
den. Dabei muß die Unterwasserführung
möglichst kurz sein, was meistens zu ei=
ner Kavernen- oder Schachtlösung führt.

Überdies kann bei starrer Bettung des
Maschinenblockes im Fels die bei hohen
Maschinenleistungen auftretende Schwing=
energie direkt ins Gebirge abgestrahlt
werden, sodaß ein ruhiger Maschinenlauf
erzielt wird.

1.3 Umweltgesichtspunkte:

Enge Täler, dichte Verbauung und das Be=
streben, Grundinanspruchnahme und Ein=
griffe in die Landschaft so gering wie
möglich zu halten, zwingen dazu, in den
Berg zu gehen.

1.4 Sicherheitstechnische Gründe:

Die Elektronik ermöglicht die Automati=
sierung der Kraftwerke und die Steuerung
von einer weit entfernten Zentrale. Die
Krafthäuser sind unbesetzt und lassen
sich als Kavernen gegen unbefugtes Ein=
dringen leichter schützen.

Über die infolge der Verlegung des Kraft=
hauses in eine Kaverne oder einen Fels=
schacht erforderlichen Berechnungen, Mes=
sungen und Bauverfahren wird nun anhand
der Krafthauskavernen Kops und Langenegg
sowie der Schachtkrafthäuser Rodund II,
Walgau und Ain Sukhna berichtet:

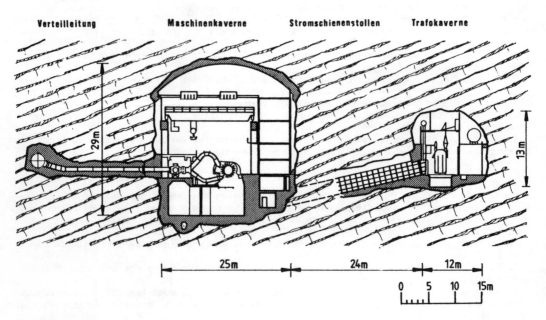

Fig.1 Querschnitt durch die Krafthauskavernenanlage des Kopswerkes der Vorarlberger Illwerke AG.

2 DAS KAVERNENKRAFTHAUS KOPS

2.1 Allgemeine Beschreibung:

Wegen Platzmangels in der Talsohle, La=
winen- und Steinschlaggefahr wurde das
Krafthaus Kops in Kavernenbauweise aus=
geführt. In der Maschinenkaverne mit den
Abmessungen LxBxH=70x25x29m sind 3 Ma=
schinensätze mit insgesamt 252 MW ein=
gebaut, im Abstand von 24m ist parallel
dazu die Trafokaverne mit LxBxH=52x12x
13m angeordnet.

2.2 Geologische Verhältnisse:

Im Bereich des Krafthauses ist die Geo=
logie sehr günstig (Loacker 1970). Das
Gebirge besteht aus großbankigem, stand=
festem Amphibolit mit vereinzelten
Schwächezonen. Die Klüftung ist stark
ausgeprägt. Durch Sondierstollen wurde
der Bereich des Kavernenkrafthauses er=
kundet und die Längsachse so festgelegt,
daß die Kluftflächen möglichst senkrecht
geschnitten werden.

2.3 Ausbruch und Sicherung:

Vom Kabelstollen aus wurde ein Quer=
schlag entlang der Stirnwand der Maschi=
nenkaverne vorgetrieben und von dort die
Kalotte aufgefahren, indem die Kämpfer
um 6m vorauseilten und der Mittelpfeiler
nachfolgte. Nach jedem Teilausbruch wur=
den Systemankerung und Spritzbeton einge=
baut, an den Ulmen Widerlagerbalken beto=
niert und im Gebirge verankert. Ca. 20m
hinter dem Abschlag wurde in Abschnitten
von 5m ein Betongewölbe eingezogen, das
auf den Auflagerbalken ruht. Der Strossen=
abtrag wurde in Stufenhöhen von 6m vorge=
nommen. Die Trafokaverne wurde ohne Beton=
gewölbe mit Systemankerung und Spritzbeton
gesichert.(Stefko 1968, Ehrle 1970)

2.4 Felsmechanische Überlegungen:

Zur Zeit des Krafthausbaues lagen keine
Erfahrungen von Kavernen ähnlicher Größe
vor. Gemäß einem Gutachten von Rabcevicz
wurde die Ankerung in der Kalotte so be=
messen, daß bei einer keilförmigen Auf=
lockerung von 7m Tiefe das Gleiten ent=
lang einer vorgegebenen Fläche durch Vor=
spannanker verhindert wird. Als zusätz=
liche Sicherung wurde ein Betongewölbe,
60cm Scheitelstärke, 80cm Kämpferstärke,
eingezogen. Für dieses wurde die Belast=
barkeit durch eine parabelförmige Auflast
und eine im Viertelpunkt angreifende Ein=

zellast für verschiedene Bettungen durch
das Gebirge nachgerechnet. In den Ulmen
wurden gemäß der Klüftung Felskeile ange=
nommen, deren Abgleiten bei Belastung
durch die Umlagerungskraft mittels vorge=
spannter Anker verhindert wird. Trotz An=
nahme hoher Reibungswinkel waren die rech=
nerisch erforderlichen Ankerkräfte so
groß, daß auf Empfehlung des Gutachters
nur die Hälfte der Anker eingebaut wurde.
(Diem, Wisser 1970)

2.5 Messungen:

Zur Kontrolle, ob die felsmechanischen
Überlegungen der Wirklichkeit entsprechen
und die Standsicherheit der Kavernen ge=
währleistet ist, wurden 85 Meßanker im
Gebirge eingebaut und das Betongewölbe
mit 17 Druckdosen bestückt. Zur Ergänzung
wurden geodätische Messungen durchgeführt.
Ein Teil der Meßeinrichtungen wird noch
heute abgelesen, um auch über das Lang=
zeitverhalten der Kavernen Aufschlüsse
zu erhalten.

2.6 Felsmechanische Erkenntnisse:

Die Auswertung der umfangreichen Messun=
gen brachte folgende Ergebnisse:
1. Die im Tunnelbau üblichen Berech=
nungsmethoden können nicht ohne weiteres
auf den Kavernenbau angewandt werden.
Der durch Systemankerung aufgebrachte
Flächendruck ist im Vergleich zu den Um=
lagerungsspannungen infolge Hohlraumaus=
bruch so gering, daß von einer Stütz=
druckwirkung oder Erhöhung der Gebirgs=
druckfestigkeit, weil die Radialspannun=
gen am Hohlraumrand nicht ganz null sind
nicht gesprochen werden kann. Mit sol=
chen Rechenansätzen ist die augenschein=
lich hervorragende Wirkungsweise der An=
ker in vollem Umfang nicht zu erklären.
2. Das tatsächliche Verhalten des Ge=
birges ist nur in beschränktem Maße vor=
aussehbar, Messungen über mehrere Jahre
sind unabdingbar. So haben die Druckdo=
sen im Betongewölbe nach Fertigstellung
des Ausbruches bis zur Inbetriebnahme
eine gleichmäßig verteilte Druckspannung
von 0,3 kN/cm^2 angezeigt. Mit Inbetrieb=
nahme der Maschinen fielen nach kurzem
Anstieg die Spannungen plötzlich ab und
das Betongewölbe wird seither von einer
über den Querschnitt gleichmäßigen Zug=
spannung im Scheitel von 0,1 kN/cm2 be=
ansprucht. Infolge der an sich gering=
fügigen Vibrationskräfte der laufenden
Maschinen wurde im Kalottenbereich die
Gebirgszugfestigkeit überwunden, das Be=
tongewölbe wirkt nun als Zugband der
flachen Felskalotte, ein Effekt, der

nicht eingeplant war, aber vom Betonge=
wölbe noch immer erfüllt wird.

3. Die Reaktion des Gebirges auf den
Ausbruch eines großen Hohlraumes er=
streckt sich auf längere Zeit. Die Um=
lagerungskräfte werden zuerst von den
hohlraumnahen Zonen aufgenommen, die un=
ter den hohen Spannungsspitzen sich ver=
formen und ein Mittragen tiefer im Ge=
birge liegender Zonen herbeiführen. Der
Prozess dauert so lange an, bis ein
Gleichgewichtszustand erreicht ist,
welcher der nach der Scheibentheorie er=
rechneten Spannungsverteilung entspricht.
Beim Kopswerk hat sich diese Erscheinung
über 3 Jahre hinweggezogen, wobei die
Beanspruchungen in der Ausbruchphase am
größten waren, da sie nur auf einen klei=
nen Bereich beschränkt sind. Im Endzu=
stand jedoch, wegen der Einbeziehung ei=
nes größeren Gebirgsbereiches, sind die
Beanspruchungen geringer, womit die
Standsicherheit der Kaverne gewährlei=
stet ist.

Wie diese Erkenntnisse in konkrete Be=
messungsregeln übergeführt wurden, wird
am Beispiel Kaverne Langenegg gezeigt:

3 DAS KAVERNENKRAFTHAUS LANGENEGG

3.1 Allgemeine Beschreibung:

Das Kraftwerk Langenegg der Vorarlberger
Kraftwerke AG wurde 1975 bis 1979 erbaut.
Planung und Bauleitung erfolgten durch
die Vorarlberger Illwerke AG. Die Kaver=
nenlösung war durch die Enge des Tales
gegeben, Form und Größe wurden durch die
geologischen Verhältnisse bestimmt. In
der Maschinenkaverne mit den Abmessungen
LxBxH=27x18x33m sind zwei stehende Ma=
schinensätze mit je 37 MW eingebaut. In
der Trafokaverne LxBxH=26x13x12m stehen
Trafos, Niederspannungs- und 30 kV-Anla=
ge. Der Felspfeiler zwischen beiden Ka=
vernen hat eine Stärke von 17 m.

3.2 Geologische Verhältnisse:

In der Molassezone des vorderen Bregen=
zerwaldes bot sich als einzige Möglich=
keit für den Bau einer Kavernenanlage
die nördliche Sandsteinrippe der Baustein=
zone an. Aus der Oberflächengeologie konn=
ten Lage und Mächtigkeit (40m) des sehr
harten Sandsteins, an den beidseitig sehr

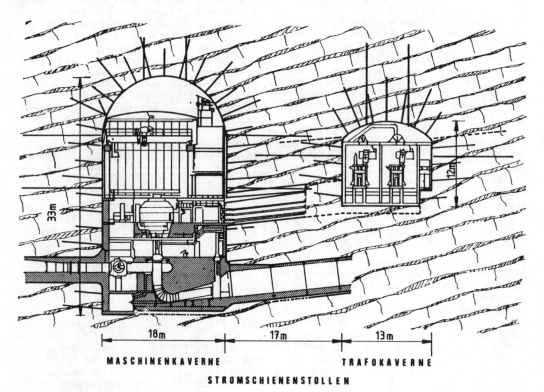

Fig.2 Querschnitt durch die Krafthauskavernenanlage Langenegg der Vorarlberger
     Kraftwerke AG.

weiche Gesteine anschließen, gut einge= messen werden. Vom Fluchtstollen aus wur= de ein Sondierstollen vorgetrieben und durch Bohrungen die Grenze der Sandstein= rippe abgetastet.

3.3 Ausbruch und Sicherung:

Vom Sondierstollen aus wurde die Kalotte der Maschinenkaverne ausgeweitet. Gleich= zeitig wurde der Zugangstunnel vorgetrie= ben und die Trafokaverne aufgefahren, so= daß abwechselnd in Maschinen- und Trafo= kaverne gesprengt, geschuttert und ge= sichert werden konnte. Der Strossenabtrag erfolgte in Tiefen von 2,4m auf gesamte Kavernenbreite. Unmittelbar nach jedem Abschlag wurde mit Stahlankern, Baustahl= gitter und Spritzbeton gesichert. (Wisser 1982)

3.4 Felsmechanische Überlegungen:

1. Allgemeine Bemessungsregeln für die Systemankerung:
Die Ankerlänge muß in Übereinstim= mung mit der Ankerbruchlast so gewählt werden, daß beim Verankerungspunkt im Gebirge sich nicht die oft zu beobach= tende Rißfläche zwischen geankertem und ungeankertem Fels ausbildet.
Die Anker sind abwechselnd mit den Längen L und 1,5 L zu versetzen, damit ein Übergang vom geankerten zum ungean= kerten Gebirge geschaffen wird.
Damit von Systemankerung gesprochen werden kann, soll der Ankerabstand 2,5/ 2,5m nicht überschreiten.
Ein Übergreifen der Ankerwirkungs= bereiche ist nur gewährleistet, wenn der Ankerabstand kleiner als die Hälfte der Ankerlänge 1,5 L gewählt wird.
2. Bemessung der Systemankerung im Felsgewölbe:
Bei Seitendruckverhältnis Horizon= tal- zu Vertikaldruck λ=0 wird die Riß= zone durch einen über dem Gewölbe aufge= setzten Rechteckwinkel begrenzt. Da der Seitendruck allgemein größer als Null ist, wird mit der Forderung, die Veran= kerung habe über den gesamten Gewölbe= bereich mindestens so lange wie der größte Abstand Gewölberand - aufgesetz= ter Rechteckwinkel zu sein, in den mei= sten Fällen der Rißbereich abgedeckt.
Die Anker haben die Reibung in be= liebig geneigten Trennflächen so zu er= höhen, daß ein nur durch sein Eigenge= wicht belastetes, sich selbst tragendes Felsgewölbe im Rißbereich gebildet wird.
Die Auflockerung wird behindert, wenn das Gewicht der unteren Hälfte des Felsgewölbes an die obere angenagelt wird.
Auf Grund dieser Bemessungsregeln wurden Dywidag-Gewindestabanker St 85/105, Ø26,5mm,4m und 6m lang, im Abstand 2,1/ 2,1m versetzt und auf 350 kN vorgespannt. Sie bilden im Verein mit Spritzbeton und Baustahlgitter die einzige Sicherung der Kalotte.
3. Bemessung der Systemankerung in den Ulmen:
Unmittelbar nach Hohlraumausbruch wirkt der Umlagerungsdruck nur auf eine schmale Laibungszone, diese deformiert sich und die Umlagerung wandert infolge= dessen tiefer ins Gebirge, bis die Gleichgewichtszustand erreicht ist. Die Ankerung hat von Anfang an einen so gro= ßen Randbereich zur Übernahme der Umla= gerungskräfte heranzuziehen, daß die Ge= birgsdruckfestigkeit nicht überschritten wird. Damit ist die erforderliche Anker= länge festgelegt.
Die Ankervorspannung ist mit 60% der Ankerbruchlast zu begrenzen. Die beim Spannen aufgebrachte Vorspannung und die infolge Gebirgsverformung einge= leitete Vorspannung dürfen zusammen die Ankerbruchlast nicht überschreiten. Die Abgrenzung zur Bruchlast ist deswegen zulässig, weil die maximale Ankerbean= spruchung im Ausbruchszustand auftritt und im Laufe der Gebirgskonsolidierung wieder abnimmt.
Die durch Vorspannen und Gebirgs= verformen erzeugte Ankerkraft soll dem Abgleiten losgelöster Felskeile, die nur durch ihr Eigengewicht belastet sind, da der Kraftfluß der Umlagerungskräfte im Zustand der Auflockerung um sie herum= geht, entgegenwirken. Wegen der Unsicher= heit der durch das Gebirge aufgebrachten Vorspannung und deren Abnahme im Laufe der Konsolidierung ist diese nur mit ei= nem Zehntel ihres Rechenwertes anzusetzen.
In den hohen, vertikalen Ulmen bil= den sich, wie man bei den Stolleneinmün= dungen sehen kann, infolge der Auflager= drücke oberflächenparallele Trennflächen aus. Dies kann durch die geringe Anker= pressung nicht unterbunden werden, die Anker haben aber ein Auskicken der so entstandenen schlanken, druckbeanspruch= ten Felswände zu verhindern.
Hiermit ergab sich eine Systemankerung von 4m und 6m langen Istorankern Ø 26 mm, im Abstand 2,3/2,3m versetzt und auf 2oo kN vorgespannt.
4. Bemessung der Spritzbetonsicherung zwischen den Felsankern im Gewölbe:
Jeder Anker erfaßt einen kegelför= migen Felsbereich mit Öffnungswinkel 2x45[o]. Die dazwischenliegenden Felspar=

tien müssen durch baustahlgitterbewehr=
ten Spritzbeton an die Felsanker ange=
hängt werden.

Die Flächenbewehrung des Baustahl=
gitters bildet die Zugbewehrung der zwi=
schen den Ankern sich bildenden Fels=
decke, die bei den Ankerköpfen punktför=
mig gelagert ist.

Im Bereich der Ankerköpfe ist eine
zusätzliche Schubsicherung und die An=
bindung des Baustahlgitters an die Anker
erforderlich.

Außerhalb dieses Bereiches übernimmt
der Spritzbeton die Schubkräfte.
Dies führte zum Einbau eines Baustahl=
gitters AQ 42 M IV, einer Schubsicherung
im Ankerkopfbereich aus 4 Torstahl 50,
Ø 1o mm und einer Spritzbetonstärke von
mindestens 10 cm.

5. Bemessung der Spritzbetonsicherung
zwischen den Felsankern in den Ulmen:
Es gelten analoge Bemessungsgrundsätze
wie für das Gewölbe, es waren Baustahl=
gitter AQ 34 M IV, 4 Ø 10 Torstahl 50
und mindestens 10 cm Spritzbeton erfor=
derlich.

3.5 Messungen

Bis Generatortischhöhe bzw. Trafogruben=
oberkante wurden die Fundamente an den
Fels anbetoniert, darüber steht der In=
nenausbau frei im Kavernenhohlraum. Sy=
stemankerung und Spritzbeton bilden in
Kalotte und Ulmen somit die einzige Si=
cherung. Um die Wirkungsweise dieses
Ausbaues überprüfen zu können und Hin=
weise auf Verhalten und Standsicherheit
des Gesamthohlraumes zu erhalten, wurden
24 Dreifachextensometer sofort nach Ab=
schlag des jeweiligen Meßstellenberei=
ches eingebaut. Damit wurden und werden
heute noch die radialen Verschiebungen
des Hohlraumrandes sowie der 4m und 8m
im Gebirge liegenden Punkte gegenüber
den 18m tief liegenden Verankerungspunk=
ten von 2 zentralen Meßstellen aus be=
obachtet. Durch Invarbandeinmessung der
Meßankerköpfe wurde die Annahme, der Ver=
ankerungspunkt bleibe in Ruhe, sicher=
gestellt. In den ersten Ausbruchsphasen
zeigten die sofort nach Abschlag einge=
bauten und beobachteten Meßanker die
Verformung fast in voller Größe. Die
Kenntnis der tatsächlichen Verschiebung
und die mehrfache Änderung des Hohlraum=
querschnittes infolge der einzelnen Aus=
bruchsphasen erlaubten es, gleichsam am
Modell im Maßstab 1:1 aus den verschie=
denen Querschnittsformen mit der bei
Wisser 1972 beschriebenen Methode die
Gebirgskennwerte zu bestimmen. So wurde

schon beim Ausbruch der Kalotte der Ma=
schinenkaverne festgestellt, daß trotz
der geringen Überlagerungshöhe von nicht
einmal 100m der Seitendruck senkrecht
zur Kavernenlängsachse nicht, wie ange=
nommen, ein Drittel, sondern das Zwei=
fache des Überlagerungsdruckes ausmacht.
(Wisser 1977). Später im Druckstollen
von anderer Seite durchgeführte Versuche
haben dies bestätigt.

3.6 Allgemeine Vorgangsweise bei der Be= messung von Kavernen:

1. Im Entwurfsstadium wird die System=
ankerung mit Baustahlgitter- und Spritz=
betonsicherung gemäß den vorhin aufge=
zeigten Grundsätzen als Minimalsicherung
gegen örtliche Auflockerung und Überbe=
anspruchung der hohlraumnahen Gebirgs=
zonen festgelegt.

2. Durch Messungen in den ersten Aus=
bruchsphasen und Vergleich mit theore=
tischen Berechnungen werden die Gebirgs=
kennwerte ermittelt. in den späteren
Ausbruchsphasen liefern die Meßanker we=
gen der vorauseilenden Vorverformungen
des Gebirges nicht mehr den vollen Wert
der Gebirgsbewegung. Außerdem führt die
Schwächung der Ulmen durch Verteillei=
tungsstollen, Zugangstunnel, Stromschie=
nenstollen und Unterwasserstollen bei
Krafthauskavernen dazu, daß eine mathe=
matische Erfassung des Systems am über=
höhten Rechenaufwand scheitert. Dennoch
sind Messungen in den Ulmen für die Be=
urteilung des Gesamtverhaltens der Ka=
verne erforderlich.

3. Die aus den Messungen rückgerechne=
ten Gebirgskennwerte werden mit den An=
sätzen für die Berechnung der Systeman=
kerung verglichen. Hier wird der Vorteil,
daß die Systemankerung jederzeit ver=
dichtet werden kann, voll ausgenützt und
durch das Herantasten von einer Minimal=
ankerung zur erforderlichen Verankerung
eine wirtschaftliche Lösung angepeilt.

4. Durch die Messungen wird die Konso=
lidierung des Gebirges und die damit
verbundene Erhöhung der Standsicherheit
sowie das Langzeitverhalten der Kaver=
nenanlagen überwacht.

Etwas anders als bei Kavernen ist die
felsmechanische Problematik bei Schacht=
kraftwerken gelagert. Auch hier soll die
Variationsbreite, die durch Wahl der Ma=
schinen, Topografie und Geologie hervor=
gerufen wird, in chronologischer Reihen=
folge dargestellt werden:

4 DAS SCHACHTKRAFTHAUS RODUND II

4.1 Allgemeine Beschreibung:

Das 1975 in Betrieb genommene Schacht=
krafthaus Rodund II besteht aus einem
56m tiefen Schacht mit 22m Ausbruchdurch=
messer, in dem eine Pumpenturbine, der
Motorgenerator und der Anwurfmotor in
vertikaler Aufstellung eingebaut sind.
Über dem Schacht steht die Montagehalle
mit den verschiedenen Betriebsgebäuden.
Die Pumpturbine mit 270 MW Turbinenlei=
stung und 256 MW Pumpleistung war zur
Zeit ihrer Inbetriebnahme die größte Eu=
ropas.(Staßko;.Innerhofer 1972)

4.2 Geologische Verhältnisse:

Durch Sondierbohrungen war die Felsober=
fläche erkundet worden; die Lage des
Krafthauses wurde so gewählt, daß die
Generatortischoberkante sicher im Fels=
bereich liegt, um die Maschinenkräfte ab=
leiten zu können. Das Gebirge besteht aus
einer steil zum Tal einfallenden Wechsel=
lagerung aus massivem bis stark geklüf=
tetem Kalk und festen bis blätterigen
Mergeln und ist stark wasserführend.
Beim Abteufen der Bohrlöcher für die
Kugelschieberverankerung auf eine Tiefe
von 10m unter Schachtsohle wurden große
Felshohlräume aufgefahren, die verfüllt
werden mußten.

4.3 Schachtaushub und Sicherung:

Vom ursprünglichen Gelände aus wurde
nach dem Humusabtrag eine kreisförmige
Schlitzwand mit Innendurchmesser 21,8m
und Wandstärke 80 cm durch die anste=
henden Bodenschichten aus Schotter,
Hangschutt, Feinsand, schluffigem Lehm,
Locker- und Grundmoräne bis zum Fels in
14m bis 26m Tiefe abgeteuft. Auf der
Schlitzwandkrone wurde bis zum 8m höher
liegenden endgültigen Vorplatzniveau
ein Ortbetonring hochbetoniert und das
Gelände ringsum eingeschüttet. Im
Schutz von Ortbetonring und Schlitzwand
wurde nun der Schacht bis zum Fels aus=
gehoben und dann in Abschlaghöhen von
2 bis 3m ein kreisrunder Felsschacht
Ø 22,2m bis zur Krafthaussohle ausge=
brochen. Die Sicherung erfolgte durch
Anker, Baustahlgitter und Spritzbeton.

4.4 Felsmechanische Überlegungen:

Nachdem mehrere Querschnittsformen wie
Rechteck, Quadrat mit und ohne abgerun=
dete Ecken untersucht worden waren, ent=
schied man sich für die statisch und
bautechnisch günstige Form des Kreises,
obwohl dadurch die Raumausnützung nicht
optimal möglich ist. Doch wegen der
Kreisform und der für das Wirksamwerden
eines hohen Horizontalgebirgsdruckes zu
geringen Tiefe des Schachtes war der
Fels infolge der schonenden Ausbruch=
weise an sich standfest. Es wurde daher
eine Minimalankerung ermittelt, welche
das Abgleiten einzelner, nur durch ihr
Eigengewicht belasteter Felskeile ver=
hindert und das Mitwirken einer genügend
tiefen Gebirgszone bei der Aufnahme der
Umlagerungsdrücke gewährleistet. Dies
führte zu einer Systemankerung Torstahl
60, Ø 26 mm, mit Perfoverankerung, auf
200 kN vorgespannt, abwechselnd 7m und
5m lang, im Abstand 2,3/2,3m versetzt.
Der Bereich zwischen den Ankern wurde
mit Baustahlgitter und mindestens 10 cm
Spritzbeton überbrückt. Der Kronenbe=
reich des Felsschachtes, in den die
Schlitzwand eingebunden ist, wurde ge=
sondert gesichert. Der Gebirgsverband
ist hier an der Felsoberfläche an sich
nicht so gut, außerdem kann sich infol=
ge des Überlagerungsdruckes ein Großkeil
lösen. Dies wird durch zwei Reihen BBRV-
Gründungsanker mit 1 MN Vorspannung ab=
wechselnd 10m und 13m lang im Abstand von
2,3/2,3m im Kronenbereich versetzt, ver=
hindert.

4.5 Messungen:

Auch hier wurden umfangreiche Messungen
durchgeführt (Diem 1981). Für die Fels=
mechanik wichtige Ergebnisse haben fol=
gende Beobachtungen erbracht:
  1. Extensometermessungen und optische
Lotmessungen:
Die 8 eingebauten Extensometer, welche
Verschiebungen des Hohlraumrandes sowie
der 5m und 10m tief im Gebirge liegenden
Punkte gegenüber einem 16m tiefen Veran=
kerungspunkt ergaben und durch optische
Loteinmessungen der Ankerköpfe gegenüber
außen liegenden Fixpunkten überprüft
wurden, haben folgendes Verhalten des
Felsschachtes aufgezeigt:
Felsankerung und Spritzbeton waren
ausreichend bemessen, denn 2 bis 3 Wochen
nach Ausbruch des beobachteten Meßhori=
zontes wurden keine nennenswerten Ver=
formungen mehr gemessen.
Die 18 m tief liegenden Verankerungs=
punkte waren nicht in Ruhe geblieben, bei
vertikalen Felsschächten gehen die Ver=
formungen sehr weit in horizontaler Rich=
tung ins Gebirge.
Da die Verformungen früh abgeklungen

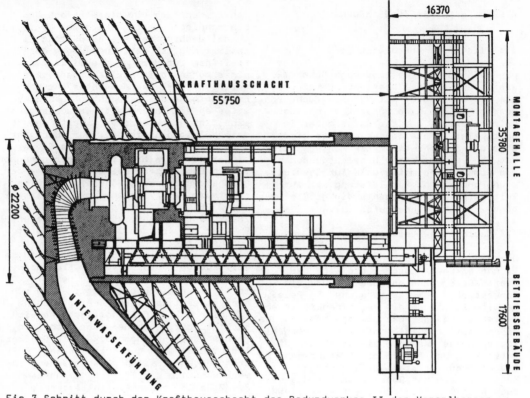

Fig.3 Schnitt durch den Krafthausschacht des Rodundwerkes II der Vorarlberger Illwerke AG.

waren, konnte der ein Jahr darnach hoch= betonierte Schachtring auf Wasseraußen= druck allein bemessen werden.

2. Teleformetermessungen:

Im Betonschachtring wurden in mehreren Horizonten innen und außen liegende hori= zontale Teleformeter eingebaut; sie haben folgende Ergebnisse geliefert:

Der Meßkurvenverlauf bildet deutlich das Baugeschehen ab. Nach dem Erstellen der Schlitzwand waren die Beanspruchungen Null, erst wenn die jeweilige Meßstelle durch den Aushub erreicht wurde, begannen die Druckspannungen anzusteigen und nah= men mit Aushubfertigstellung eine hydro- statische Verteilung an.

Am Schlitzwandfuß bildete sich eine ausgeprägte Druckspitze, die durch die Form des schräg abgeschnittenen Schlitz= wandzylinders und durch Zwängungsspannun= gen aus dem Hereindrücken der Gebirgskrone hervorgerufen wurde. Auch nach Beendigung des Schachtausbruches nahmen am Schlitz= wandfuß die Druckspannungen zu. Erst nach Ergänzung des schräg auslaufenden Schlitz= wandzylinders durch eine 30 cm starke Spritzbetonsicherung der Felskrone zu einem geraden Zylinder hörte die Span=

nungszunahme auf.

Die Bettung der Schlitzwand in der Überlagerung und des Betonschachtringes im Fels ist so gut, daß im Kreisring nur Normalkraftbeanspruchungen und keine nennenswerten Momentenbeanspruchungen gemessen wurden.

Infolge der guten Bettung bilden sich die jahreszeitlich bedingten Tem= peraturschwankungen im Spannungsbild als überlagerte Wellenlinie ab.

Die langjährigen Beobachtungen der Teleformeter, die heute noch gemessen werden, lassen erkennen, daß die Haupt= verformungen des Gebirges wohl während der Bauzeit abgeklungen waren, aber über Jahre hinaus noch Restverformungen statt= finden, welche jedoch sehr klein sind. Der als endgültiger Ausbau wirkende Be= tonschachtring ist demnach auf Wasser= außendruck und Temperaturschwankungen beansprucht, für Langzeitverformungen des Gebirges ist eine Reserve einzupla= nen.

Die gezielte Anwendung dieser Erkennt= nisse wird nun an Hand des Walgauwerkes gezeigt:

5 DAS SCHACHTKRAFTHAUS WALGAU

5.1 Allgemeine Beschreibung:

Das derzeit im Bau befindliche Schacht=
krafthaus Walgau besteht aus einem 28m
tiefen Felsschacht mit 21m Durchmesser,
einer Montagehalle und den erforderli=
chen Betriebsgebäuden. In ihm werden
zwei Maschinensätze zu je 43 MW Leistung
in vertikaler Anordnung eingebaut. Die
Inbetriebnahme ist 1984 vorgesehen.

5.2 Geologische Verhältnisse:

Im Bereich des Krafthauses wurde mit 16
Bohrungen die Tiefenlage des Gebirges
erkundet. Zwei Bohrungen wurden tiefer
in den Fels abgeteuft, davon eine 10m
unter die Schachtsohle. Der Fels besteht
aus dünn gebankten Mergeln mit verein=
zelten Kalk- und Sansteinzwischenlagen.
Dieses anstehende Felsgestein ist stark
durchbewegt.

5.3 Ausbruch und Sicherung:

Zuerst wurde auf Vorplatzniveau ausge=
hoben, dann der Felsschacht abgeteuft
und über den Unterwasserkanal geschut=
tert, der den Schachtring beckenseitig
aufschlitzt. Sofort nach dem jeweiligen
Abschlag wurde mit Ankern, Baustahlgitter
und Spritzbeton gesichert.

5.4 Felsmechanische Überlegungen:

Der anstehende Flysch hat als ganzes ei=
ne geringe Gebirgsfestigkeit, die starke
Durchbewegung und Verfaltung läßt eine
ausgeprägte Anisotropie nicht in Erschei=
nung treten. Für die felsmechanischen Be=
rechnungen kann dieses Gebirge als quasi
isotrop angesetzt werden. Gemäß den Er=
fahrungen bei Rodund II wurde ein modi=
fiziertes Berechnungsmodell den stati=
schen Überlegungen zugrundegelegt.

1. Systemankerung:
Eine Minimalankerung verhindert im Ver=
bund mit Baustahlgitter und Spritzbeton
das Herausbrechen einzelner, nur durch
ihr Eigengewicht belasteter Felskeile.
Ausgeführt wurden Dywidag-Einstabanker
St 835/1030, Ø 26,5 mm, auf 335 kN vor=
gespannt und mit abwechselnd 5m und 7m
Länge im Abstand 2,3/2,3m versetzt. Als
Flächenbewehrung zwischen den Ankern
waren Baustahlgitter AQ 35 M IV, eine
Schubbewehrung 4Ø8 Torstahl 50 am Anker=
kopf und Spritzbeton mit mindestens 10cm
Stärke erforderlich.

2. Gleitkeil- und Schachtkronensiche=
rung:

Der Krafthausschacht des Walgauwerkes
ist kein in sich geschlossener Ring, son=
dern wird durch den 16m breiten Unter=
wasserkanal beckenseitig aufgeschlitzt.
Im kreisförmigen Schachtbereich wurde
der Gleitkeil als von der Schachtlaibung
und zwei mit Winkel 90°-ϱ zueinander ge=
neigten Gleitflächen begrenzte Pyramide
angesetzt. An den Wänden des Unterwasser=
kanales wurde der Gleitkeil als auf der
Spitze stehende Pyramide mit dreieckiger
Grundfläche angesetzt, deren bergseitige
Kante gemäß einer Maximum-Minimum-Betrach=
tung 45°-ϱ/2 gegen die Vertikale geneigt
ist. Die daraus zur Systemankerung zu=
sätzlich erforderliche Ankerung wurde in
der Felskrone angeordnet. Damit wird au=
ßerdem die von Natur aus größere Auflok=
kerung im Kronenbereich abgedeckt und die
örtliche Rückverankerung für Beanspru=
chungen bei den verschiedenen Montage=
vorgängen erreicht. Im Schachtbereich wur=
den die beiden oberen Ankerreihen mit
Dywidagankern St 835/1030 Ø32mm, 490 kN
vorgespannt und mit abwechselnd 7m und
9m Länge im Abstand 2,3/2,3m versetzt,
gesichert. Im Eckbereich Schacht-Unter=
wasserkanal wurde diese Ankerung auf
ganze Wandhöhe durchgeführt, zu Recht,
wie die Messungen bewiesen.

5.5 Messungen:

Es wurden 8 Stück Zweifachextensometer
mit Klemmverankerung in 4m und 10m Tie=
fe eingebaut. Über elektrische Wegauf=
nehmer werden die Längenänderungen an
einer zentralen Meßstelle abgelesen. So
wurde vor und nach jedem Abschlag, je=
doch mindestens einmal wöchentlich, mit
Fertigstellung des Ausbruches alle 14
Tage gemessen. Mit Invardraht wurde
einmal monatlich die Lage der Meßanker=
köpfe in Bezug auf außerhalb des Schach=
tes liegende Festpunkte eingemessen,
sodaß die echten Verformungen des Ge=
birges bekannt sind. Mit dem Hochbeto=
nieren des Schachtringes werden diese
Meßanker ausgebaut und stehen für ande=
re Zwecke zur Verfügung. Bisher lassen
die Beobachtungen folgendes erkennen:

1. Das Kurzzeitverhalten ist bei al=
len Meßstellen gleich, zwei bis drei
Monate nach Ausbruch und Setzen der An=
ker sind die Hauptverformungen abge=
klungen. Danach sind im Schachtring
keine nennenswerten Verformungen mehr
zu verzeichnen, in den Ulmen des Unter=
wasserkanales jedoch dauern die Ver=
schiebungen in den Hohlraum mit 2 bis
3mm je Monat an.

2. Bei der rechnerischen Erfassung der
Verschiebungen sind hier beim Walgauwerk

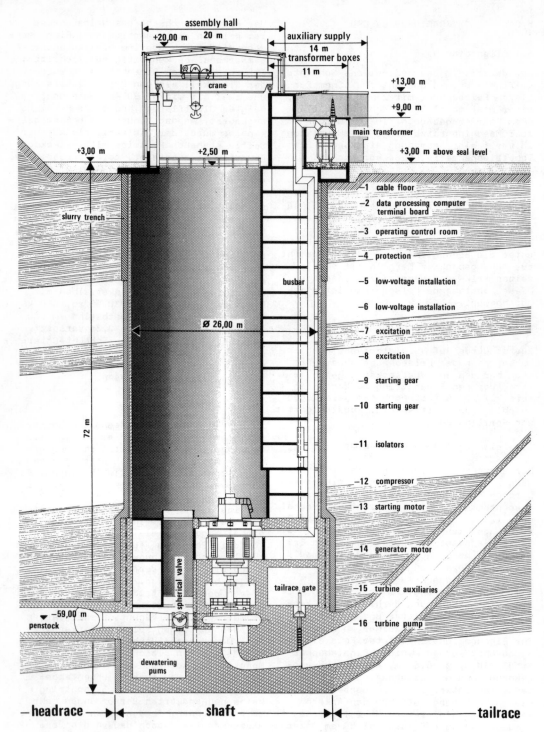

assembly hall
+20,00 m
20 m

auxiliary supply
14 m
transformer boxes
11 m

crane

+13,00 m
+9,00 m

main transformer

+3,00 m
+2,50 m
+3,00 m above seal level

slurry trench

−1 cable floor
−2 data processing computer terminal board
−3 operating control room
−4 protection

busbar

−5 low-voltage installation
−6 low-voltage installation

Ø 26,00 m

−7 excitation
−8 excitation
−9 starting gear
−10 starting gear

72 m

−11 isolators
−12 compressor
−13 starting motor
−14 generator motor

spherical valve

tailrace gate

−15 turbine auxiliaries

−59,00 m
penstock

−16 turbine pump

dewatering pums

—headrace—►◄— shaft —►◄— tailrace

Fig. 4 Schnitt durch Schacht 1 des Doppelschachtkrafthauses Ain Sukhna der Repub=
lik Ägypten

zwei sich überlagernde Effekte zu beob=
achten: Nicht nur infolge des Schacht=
ausbruches tritt eine Verschiebung zum
Hohlraum ein, sondern auch durch den
Abtrag der Überlagerung auf Vorplatz=
niveau, der durch die Entlastung des
Gebirges in vertikaler Richtung eine
Entspannungsbewegung in horizontaler
Richtung provoziert. Die größte Verfor=
mung hat im linken Unterwasserulm 4 cm
erreicht, was der Wandhöhe und der ge=
ringen Gebirgsfestigkeit des Flysch ent=
spricht. Es wird getrachtet, möglichst
bald den Unterwasserkanal zu betonieren,
um die Ausbildung einer tiefliegenden
Gleitfuge durch diesen Sohlschluß zu
vermeiden.

3. Die geringen Verschiebungsunter=
schiede zwischen Hohlraumrand und den
4m im Gebirge liegenden Meßpunkten zei=
gen deutlich, daß die Verankerung die
oberflächennahen Gebirgszonen wesent=
lich vergütet.

4. Die Verformungen der 10m tief im
Gebirge liegenden Meßpunkte sind mit
bis zu 3 cm noch ziemlich groß und deu=
ten an, daß wie bei Rodundwerk II die
horizontalen Verformungen zum Hohlraum
hin sehr weite Gebirgszonen erfassen.
Nach unseren Berechnungen wird in der
Horizontalen eine Ausdehnung erreicht,
welche der zweifachen Schachttiefe ent=
spricht.
Beim Hochbetonieren des Schachtringes
werden Teleformeter eingebaut, welche
über die Beanspruchung des Betonschacht=
ringes Aufschluß geben werden.

5.6 Felsmechanische Erkenntnisse:

Der Schlitz des Unterwasserkanales ist
mit den lotrechten Ulmen gegenüber dem
Schachtring eine sehr ungünstige Form,
die beim Walgauwerk nur im Bauzustand
auftritt und wegen der wesentlichen Er=
leichterung des Schachtausbruches in
Kauf genommen werden mußte. Mit dem Be=
tonieren des Unterwasserkanales und dem
Einschütten wird der Schachtring wieder
geschlossen. Da im Schachtbereich selbst
die Verformungen abgeklungen sind, ist
es zulässig, den beim endgültigen Aus=
bau hochbetonierten Schachtring auf Was=
seraußendruck und Temperaturänderung al=
lein zu bemessen und für Langzeitverfor=
mungen des Gebirges noch eine Reserve
bereitzuhalten.

6 DAS SCHACHTKRAFTHAUS AIN SUKHNA

Für die Republik Ägypten wurde im Rahmen
der Verbundplan Ges.m.b.H. Austria von

den Vorarlberger Illwerken eine Studie
über das Schachtkrafthaus Ain Sukhna am
Golf von Suez durchgeführt. Es sind zwei
Ausbaustufen mit je einem Schacht von
74m Tiefe und 28m Durchmesser, in dem je
zwei vertikale Maschinensätze unterge=
bracht sind, vorgesehen. Eine Montage=
halle mit Kran soll beide Schächte über=
decken und zum Meer hin ist das Betriebs=
gebäude mit den Transformatoren angeord=
net. Gemäß den bisherigen Bohrungen ste=
hen im Krafthausbereich söhlig gelagerte
Sandsteine, Tone und Dolomite an. Die
spezifischen Eigenschaften des Gebirges,
horizontale Lagerung, die Nähe des Mee=
res und die große Tiefe der Schächte
schaffen hier wieder etwas andere Aus=
gangsbedingungen als bei Rodund II oder
Walgau, die Vorgangsweise, die felsme=
chanischen Probleme zu lösen, wird je=
doch dieselbe sein:

1. Es wird eine Minimalsicherung gegen
das Abgleiten einzelner Felkeile einge=
baut.

2. Durch Messungen wird die Wirkungs=
weise der Sicherung überprüft und die
Reaktion des Gebirges auf den Ausbruch
beobachtet.

3. Der im Zuge des Schachtausbaues von
unten hochzubetonierende Schachtring
wird auf Wasseraußendruck und Tempera=
turschwankungen dimensioniert, wobei
eine den Messungen entsprechende Re=
serve für Langzeitverformungen des Ge=
birges bereitgehalten wird.

4. Bis Generatortischoberkante wird
kraftschlüssig an den Fels anbetoniert,
die Dichtung wird durch ein im Schacht=
ring einbetoniertes Blech mit beidsei=
tig aufgeschweißten Kopfbolzendübeln
gebildet. Je nach den tatsächlichen Ver=
hältnissen wird über Generatortisch eine
komprimierbare Drainfolie zwischen Pri=
mär- und Sekundärauskleidung des
Schachtes eingebaut werden.

5. Durch ein beim Hochbetonieren ein=
zubauendes Meßsystem wird das Langzeit=
verhalten des Schachtes untersucht.

7 ZUSAMMENFASSUNG

An den Beispielen der Krafthauskavernen
Kops und Langenegg sowie der Schacht=
krafthäuser Rodund II, Walgau und Ain
Sukhna wurde eine Bemessungsmethode
vorgestellt, welche folgende Grundsätze
verfolgt:

1. Auf Grund von Voruntersuchungen
wird eine möglichst günstige Lage des
Hohlraumes im Gebirge gewählt.

2. Eine Minimalsicherung wird errech=
net, deren System eine Anpassung an

505

örtliche Schwächezonen und nachträgli=
che Verstärkungen erlaubt.

3. Aus Messungen am Bauwerk selbst
und dem Vergleich mit theoretischen Be=
rechnungen während der ersten Ausbruch=
phasen werden die felsmechanischen Wer=
te rückgerechnet (Modell im Maßstab
1 : 1).

4. Die Minimalsicherung wird den am
Bauwerk beobachteten Werten angepaßt
und durch Langzeitmessungen die Stand=
sicherheit des Hohlraumes nachgewiesen.

8 LITERATURHINWEISE

Diem, F.u.Wisser, E., 1970, Sicherung
und Verhalten des Felshohlraumes der
Maschinenkaverne Kops, ÖZE, H.7.
Diem, F. 1981, Bauwerkskontrollen wäh=
rend der Bauausführung und nach Fer=
tigstellung der Kraftzentrale Ro=
dund II, ÖIZ.

Ehrle, W. 1970, Die Baudurchführung der
Kraftzentrale Kops, ÖZE, H.7.
Loacker, H. 1970, Zur Geologie des
Kopswerkes, ÖZE, H.7.
Stefko, E. 1968, Bautechnische Probleme
und Besonderheiten beim Kopswerk der
Vorarlberger Illwerke, Österreichi=
sche Wasserwirtschaft H.11/12.
Stefko, E.u.Innerhofer, G., 1972, Das
Pumpspeicherwerk Rodund II, Österrei=
chische Wasserwirtschaft H.7/8.
Wisser, E. 1972, Eine einfache Methode
zur rechnerischen Ermittlung der Ver=
schiebungen eines Hohlraumrandes,
Rock Mechanics H.4.
Wisser, E. 1977, Design and observation
of the underground power station Lan=
genegg, International Symposium on
Field Measurements in Rock Mechanics,
Zürich.
Wisser, E. 1982, Der Bau des Kavernen=
krafthauses Langenegg, Bauingenieur.

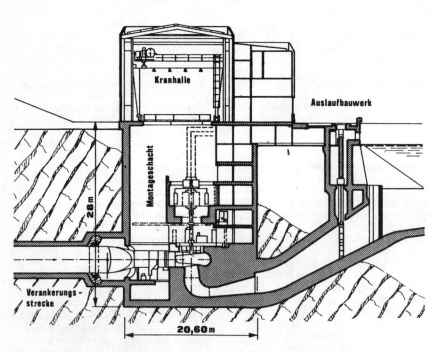

Fig.5 Schnitt durch den Krafthausschacht des Walgauwerkes der
Vorarlberger Illwerke AG.

BATH COUNTY PUMPED STORAGE PROJECT (VIRGINIA, USA), UNDERGROUND FEATURES

Pumpspeicherprojekt Bath County (Virginia, USA), unterirdische Entwurfsaspekte

Dimensionnement et exécution des travaux souterrains du projet de la centrale de pompage de Bath County (Virginia, USA)

A.ZAGARS
Harza Engineering Co., Chicago, Illinois, USA

SUMMARY:
Design and construction aspects of the permanent underground features for a large hydroelectric pumped storage project are presented. All principal underground features are constructed in sedimentary rock formations consisting of thinly interbedded sandstone, siltstone, claystone and shale beds. In-situ testing results are summarized and results are related to design approach taken. Primary rock support system consists of shotcrete and pattern rockbolting. Concrete lining is provided throughout for hydraulic reasons and to assure permanent structural integrity of the conduit surfaces. Penstock bifurcations are located deep in the rock mass to simplify design and achieve economy. Steel-lined penstocks are designed accounting for rock assistance where the rock is sound. Drainage tunnels are provided to control external pressures on the penstocks. Tunnel and shaft excavation methods, rates of advance and rock bolt installation procedures are discussed.

ZUSAMMENFASSUNG:
Die Aspekte des Entwurfes und des Ausbaues der permanenten untertägigen Bauwerke eines grossen hydroelektrischen Pumpspeicherwerkes sind dargestellt. Alle untertägigen Bauwerke sind in sedimentären Felsformationen, bestehend aus dünnen Wechselschichtungen von Sandstein, verfestigten Schluffmergel, Tonstein und Schieferton, ausgebaut. Felsmechanische Untersuchungen sind zusammengefasst und die Resultate mit der Entwurfsweise in Beziehung gesetzt. Das Hauptsystem der Felsabstützung besteht aus Spritzbeton und Systemankerung des Felses. Durchgehende Betonauskleidung für hydraulische Zwecke und um andauernden Bestand der Ausbruchsflächen zu sichern ist vorgesehen. Zur Vereinfachung des Entwurfes und aus ökonomischen Gründen sind die Abzweigungen der Druckleitungen tief in dem Gebirge angeordnet. Der Entwurf der Stahlverkleidung der Druckleitungen berücksichtigt die Mitwirkung des Gebirges wo der Fels tragfähig ist. Dränage Stollen sind für die Kontrolle von Aussendruck auf die Stahlpanzerung der Druckstollen vorgesehen. Der Bauvorgang für den Ausbruch, Vortriebsleistung und Verfahren für die Versetzung von Felsankern ist erläutert.

RESUME:
Les études et techniques de construction des installations souterraines pour une importante usine d'accumulation d'énergie par pompage hydraulique sont présentées. Toutes les installations principales sont construites dans la roche sédimentaire composée de couches entrecroisées de grès, silices, schistes, et argiles. Les résultats des essais in-situ sont résumés et comparés aux études effectuées. La méthode principale de soutien de la roche consiste de béton projeté et de boulons. Pour satisfaire aux conditions hydrauliques et assurer l'intégrité structurale, un revêtement en béton est utilisé sur toutes les surfaces. La culotte des conduites forcées est située dans la masse rocheuse pour simplifier les études de construction et pour des raisons économiques. Les conduites forcées en acier sont conçues en tenant compte de la résistance de la roche. Des tunnels de drainage contrôlent les pressions externes sur les conduites forcées. Les méthodes d'excavation de tunnel et des puits, les cadences de progression et les procédés d'installation de boulons sont traités.

1. INTRODUCTION

The Bath County Pumped Storage Project, located about 13 km north of Mountain Grove in northwestern Virginia, is presently under construction by the Virginia Electric and Power Company (VEPCO). When completed in 1986, it will have the world's largest pumped storage installation of 2100 MW. Presently, the project is about 62 percent complete with almost all underground excavation finished. Construction started in the spring of 1977 and continued on full-scale basis through May 1980 when, for economical reasons, all underground and fill construction was suspended. Full-scale activities resumed in the spring of 1982.

This discussion deals with the design and construction aspects of the project's permanent underground features consisting of power tunnels with flow shafts, bifurcations, penstocks, surge shafts and penstock drainage tunnels to control groundwater effects.

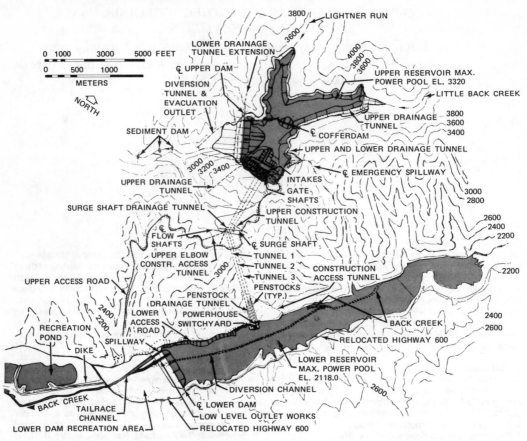

Figure 1. General plan.

2. BRIEF DESCRIPTION OF PROJECT GEOLOGY

All project underground features are situated in sedimentary rock formations of the Devonian age. The lower level features (Fig. 2, profile) are contained within the Millboro/Brallier formation which consists of thinly interbedded siltstone, sandstone and claystone. The medium hard, dense and thin-bedded siltstone is the predominant rock of the formation. Siliceously cemented, hard and rather thinly bedded sandstone, and the medium soft claystone form the interbeds of the formation. The beds are severely folded, forming sharp synclines and anticlines along the west bank of the valley over a width of about 110 m. Thereafter the rock is fresh, thinly bedded and dipping gently (about 8 to 10°) in northwesterly direction.

The contact between the underlying Millboro/Brallier formation and the overlying Chemung formation intersects the vertical flow shafts at approximately their mid-height such that all upper level underground features are contained in the Chemung formation which is approximately 600 m thick. Weathering in the Millboro/Brallier zone reaches about 15 m and varies between 15 to 30 m in the Chemung formation. Laboratory tests on core samples indicated minimum rock strengths for

sandstone, siltstone and claystone/shale of about 66, 40 and 35 MPa, respectively.

3. SUBSURFACE EXPLORATION

Subsequent to prefeasibility field exploration efforts, consisting of geologic mapping, some core drilling, seismic refraction surveys, bore hole geophysical tests and test pitting, the final foundation exploration efforts included about 15,000 lin. m of core drilling and driving of a 300 m long exploratory tunnel which was intended to serve later as a drainage tunnel over the penstocks (Fig. 2, 4).

Initial studies considered an underground powerhouse and the exploratory drilling efforts were carried out accordingly. However, the early project licensing and completion schedule set by the owner did not allow for sufficient time for the driving of a pilot/exploration tunnel into the intended underground powerhouse area. Consequently, a project concept was developed based on a conventional surface type powerhouse and the exploratory drilling program was revised to suit. The results of the exploration justified conclusions that no major geologic faults, that could affect the design of the project features, existed in the project area and that the rock formation

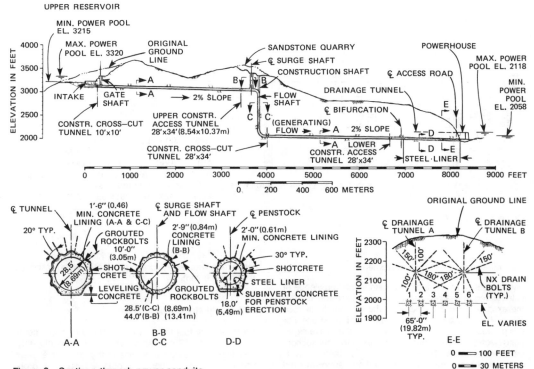

Figure 2. Sections through power conduits

was suitable for construction of the project underground features.

4. IN-SITU TESTING

4.1 Exploration Tunnel

The north penstock drainage tunnel was excavated during the pre-licensing period (early in 1973) to determine the quality of the rock mass through which the penstock tunnels would be driven, to gain some knowledge in regard to the tunneling characteristics, and to perform series of in-situ rock-mechanics tests to obtain the necessary parameters for the design of the power tunnels and penstocks. It should be noted that VEPCO, to benefit from contractor's input at an early stage of the studies, engaged the services of the general construction contractor at the beginning of the engineering studies for the licensing of the project. The tunnel subcontractor was engaged shortly thereafter and was available for excavation of the exploratory tunnel. The 1.98 by 2.7 m size of the 300 m long tunnel was selected to fit the size of the mucking equipment (Wagner ST-2) used by the contractor. An enlarged 38.4 m long semicircular section having a somewhat larger radius (5.79 m) than the excavation for the power tunnels was provided near the far end of the exploratory tunnel to gain better insight in regard to the rock stand-up capability for the full tunnel size.

4.2 In-situ Tests

The tunnel geology was mapped and additional geologic data were obtained from three exploratory holes drilled from the tunnel invert to slightly below the penstock tunnel grade, and from the numerous core holes drilled for installation of multiposition extensometers.

The following investigations were conducted:

1. Monitoring of rock movement during and subsequent to excavation.
2. Determination of in-situ stress by method of overcoring.
3. Determination of deformability characteristics of the rock mass.
4. Measurements of tunnel temperature, water seepage and humidity.
5. Measurements of water pressures in rock joints.
6. Rock bolt pull-out tests; shotcrete evaluation.
7. Monitoring of rates of advance for the drill-and-blast excavation, optimum round power factors and overbreak (by the contractor).
8. One test on jacking a tunneling shield into rock (by the contractor).

Detailed discussion of the in-situ testing and the results obtained is beyond the scope of this presentation. Therefore, only a summarized discussion of the testing activities and results is given in the following sections.

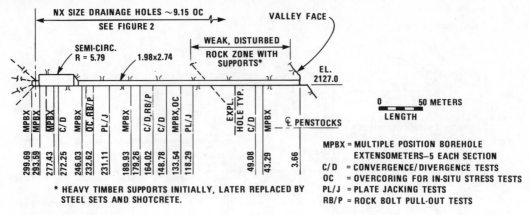

Figure 3. Exploration tunnel

4.2.1 Measurement of rock movement

These tests were conducted to gain some knowledge of time-related stress redistribution around the tunnel after the excavation and to measure the magnitude of rock movements caused by the redistribution of the stress. For this purpose, twenty six-point mechanical and five eight-point electronic extensometers, in sets of five per section, were installed in NX-size holes. Fourteen convergence/divergence measurement stations supplemented the above measurements. Tape extensometers for measuring between embedded bolts were used for the latter purpose. Terrametrics Inc. supplied all instruments. Initially, the length of the extensometers was equivalent to two tunnel widths for the horizontal and three tunnel widths for the vertical extensometers, with an intermediate length for the two inclined extensometers in the roof. These lengths were increased up to four tunnel widths in an attempt to obtain zero movement between the deepest anchors, but some movements were recorded even at that depth. Relative movements were generally less than 1 mm and of consistent pattern from station to station. They occurred during the first 8 m of advance beyond the extensometer. A ring of compressive strain appeared to concentrate around the opening. The dial type readout gage was sensitive to about 0.025 mm.

One set consisting of five eight-point electronic extensometers was installed in the enlarged tunnel portion. Two horizontal, two sloped 45° and one vertical instrument comprised the set. The depths were 19.8, 24.4 and 30.5 m for the horizontal, inclined and vertical instruments, respectively. This set was installed after the excavation of the enlarged section had been advanced about 1 m past the station of the instruments. Initial movements during stress redistribution reached 5 mm near the face in the crown instrument. Stability in relative movements of a magnitude of about 1.3 mm set in when the heading was about 9 m (about 1.7 R) from the instrument station.

The tape convergence measurements showed results inconsistent with those obtained from the extensometers because of difficulties encountered in protection of the measuring eyes during construction. The maximum horizontal convergence at the beginning of the enlarged tun-

nel section was recorded about 1.8 mm which stabilized at about 0.8 mm.

4.2.2 In-situ stress measurements

A total of sixty-four tests for in-situ stress measurements by overcoring (152 mm dia) an EX-size (38 mm dia) hole, after first measuring the strains in the latter hole, were attempted at two stations. Acceptable results were obtained from forty-four of these tests and forty cores were used to determine the elastic modulus of the rock. Based on unconfined pressure tests in the laboratory on sandstone and siltstone/claystone core samples (5 and 11 tests, respectively), average values for modulus of elasticity were 51×10^3 MPa for the sandstone and 49×10^3 MPa for the siltstone/claystone. Poisson's ratio was determined to be 0.17 and 0.26, respectively, for the two rock types tested.

The gage used for these measurements was furnished by Terrametrics, Inc. and was capable of measuring deformations of three axes, 60° apart, simultaneously. The gage sensitivity corresponded to a deformation of approximately 0.15×10^{-3} mm. The tests started approximately 3 m into the holes from the tunnel face. At the test station nearest to the valley bank, the vertical stress amounted to twice the overburden stress, whereas the horizontal stress (normal to tunnel axis and parallel to the valley bank) was measured to be 2.8 times the overburden stress. The principal stress directions coincided with the vertical and horizontal directions. The stress parallel to the tunnel axis was slightly (about 10%) lower than the stress normal to the axis. The directions of the principal stresses at the second test station located about 85 m deeper into the mountain deviated from the vertical/horizontal directions by about 50°, with the vertical stress component being about 1.5 times that of the overburden stress.

4.2.3 Rock deformability measurements

These tests, conducted at two stations, were performed to assess the deformability of the rock mass which eventually would be subjected to internal hydrostatic operating pressures in the water conduits. Uniaxial loads were applied against the rock mass by jack pressures between the walls, at approximately the midheight, and between the invert and the roof along the center line of the tunnel. The resulting deformations were measured with electronic eight-point extensometers. The jacking tests were made on prepared surfaces about 0.30 m from the rock face (disturbed rock removed). Deformations were measured with 7.6 m long extensometers anchored at 0.3, 0.6, 0.9, 1.2, 1.8, 2.4, 4.9 and 7.3 m from the prepared rock faces. One 870 mm dia bearing plate at each end of an adjustable jacking frame retained flat jacks of the same size. Grout pads were poured between the rock faces and the flatjacks mounted on the frame. Test pressures were applied in 1.38 MPa (200 psi) increments with the maximum pressure reaching 6.9 MPa (1000 psi) and developing a total force of approximately 4.1 MN.

Rock moduli of deformation were calculated for the rock mass between the face and the first anchor (0.30 m thickness) and the face and the last anchor (7.3 m thickness) as tabulated below.

1. Modulus of deformation for the first 0.30 m of rock from the tunnel face in 1000 MPa (145038 psi).

Station	Left Wall	Right Wall	Invert	Roof
118.29	16.20	18.95	10.00	Instrument Failure
231.11	8.96	20.34	8.94	7.58

2. Modulus of deformation for the rock mass between the rock face and the last anchor.

118.29	21.03	22.76	21.37	10.33
231.11	23.78	54.82	22.06	14.82

As described under project geology, the bedding planes were dipping gently into the mountain and thus they were almost parallel with the tunnel invert and roof. Consequently, the test pressures applied on the walls acted parallel with the bedding whereas they were directed essentially normally to the bedding in the invert and the roof. Accordingly, the higher values for the modulus deformation were found in the walls, as expected. Because of the thinly bedded and slabby rock, the disturbance from blasting was greater in the roof and the invert than in the walls.

Based on the above tests and considering that in the penstock tunnels (6.7 m excavated diameter) the disturbed zone would be deeper than in the exploration tunnel, it was considered prudent to select for rock modulus of deformation a relatively low value of 5.2×10^3 MPa (750,000 psi) for a 1.20 m thick zone surrounding the tunnels. A value of 27.6×10^3 MPa (4,000,000 psi) was assigned to the rock mass beyond the disturbed zone. This value was near or below the values found for the deeper zones tested. It was also decided that the downstream end of the penstocks would have to be designed without rock assistance because of the poor rock exposed in the tunnel.

4.2.4 Rockbolt pullout tests

Pullout tests were performed on five types of rockbolts from three manufacturers at stations 164.02 and 232.62 in the exploration tunnel (Figure 3). Two nongroutable types (with long cone/shell and short cone/shell as anchorage heads) and one groutable type (with long cone/shell head), all of the same manufacturer, were tested against two brands of rock bolts using polymer resin for anchorage (Celitite Inc. and DuPont Systems).

All bolts were approximately 1.5 m (5 feet) long and were tested in the tunnel crown normally to the rock bedding planes. The mechanically anchored bolts were tested for varying shell expanding torques in relation to the anchorage force developed. Similarly, the amount of resin was varied for the Celtite and DuPont bolts to establish relationship between the amount of resin used for the anchorage of the bolt and the force developed. From the mechanically anchored bolts, the bolts with the long cone/shell anchorages exhibited good, consistent performance but the setting torques had to be consistently near the maximum recommended value of about 475 Nm (350 ft-lb). The groutable bolt indicated only slightly higher anchorage capacity than the bolts anchored only mechanically. This observation finds explanation in the relatively short length of the bolts which is insufficient to develop substantial additional anchorage through the grout. Also, the resulting working load of the bolt is smaller because of the cored grouthole through the center of the bolt.

For the Celtite system, a single cartridge of polymer resin was insufficient to provide good anchorage in 41.3 mm (1-5/8 in) hole, but with two cartridges it outperformed other bolt types tested. However, a single cartridge, probably, would suffice for the hole size of 35 mm recommended by Celtite. It was concluded from the tests that the Celtite system was perferable since it indicated higher load carrying capacity and required only about 40% of the time needed for the installation and grouting of the bolt with the mechanical anchorage head.

4.2.5 Shotcrete tests

Shotcrete application was tested at two locations in the exploration tunnel. An approximately 16 m long section near the center of the tunnel, and a 6.4 m long section in the tunnel enlargement were shotcreted to check shotcrete application to the rocks encountered in the tunnel. The thickness varied between 50 and 75 mm in the small section and between 75 and 100 mm in the enlarged section. The test-mix consisted of uniformly graded 3/8 in (10 mm) maximum size aggregate using nine sack (43.6 kg) mix, with w/c ratio of 0.5 and 2.5% accelerator. Observed rebound was minimal and the applied shotcrete set up quickly. Coring indicated good quality shotcrete, well bonded to the rock.

These tests were conducted in the spring of 1973 and no shotcrete spalling or popping has been observed to date.

5. DESIGN ASPECTS

The results of the exploratory core drilling and the associated water pressure testing in the exploratory holes indicated that the fresh rock in both rock formations, the lower Millboro/Brallier and the upper Chemung forma-

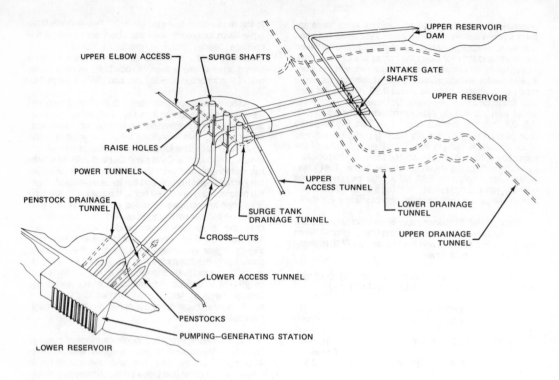

Figure 4. Isometric view of underground features

tion, were, for all practical purposes, impermeable. It was concluded that the rock mass could contain water under the hydraulic operating pressures in the power conduits where sufficient rock cover existed over the conduits and in absence of any weak rock zones. Also, it was concluded that, because of insufficient rock cover, the penstocks would need steel liners for most of their length. Furthermore, the downstream ends of the liners would need to be designed to resist full internal pressures.

5.1 Power tunnels and penstocks - general

The power tunnels and penstocks were sized on basis of hydraulic transient studies to obtain acceptable flow conditions in the water conduit system and to obtain compatible regulating characteristics for the pumping/generating units of the plant. Before these studies commenced, the decision was made that all power conduits would be concrete lined, with steel liners where required, to obtain greater hydraulic efficiency than with unlined conduits, thus resulting in smaller conduit sizes and reduced excavation quantities. Also, concrete-lined conduits would provide greater safety against degradation of the tunnel faces than unlined or shotcrete-lined conduits.

Because of the expected good rock quality, only minimum rock support requirements were anticipated. However, considering the fairly large size of the tunnels and also considering their service conditions, shotcrete application and pattern bolting in the crown was included

in the design for the full length of the tunnels.

5.1.1 Shotcrete design

The design of shotcrete is more an art than science. It is based mostly on observations and evaluation of past experiences. The design approach is also dictated by the purpose of shotcrete application. Shotcrete may be used as a sealer of the excavated rock face to maintain natural moisture conditions, or used as temporary or permanent support of the rock face under varying loading conditions - support of loosening rock fragments, gravity loads from larger wedges or providing balancing skin pressure in conjunction with rock bolts, supports etc. At Bath County, the tests in the exploration tunnel indicated that air-slaking will not be a problem. However, because of the thinly interbedded and closely jointed rock, fragmentation along the tunnel sides, and some slabbing along the roof could be expected. Also, because of the tunnel size, a general support of the excavated rock face appeared to be in order. Besides, the contractor recommended the use of shotcrete throughout the works for safety of his personnel.

Inward deformations of the tunnel face, after the shotcrete is applied, generate radial pressures on the shotcrete, because of the shotcrete interlocking with the rock and shotcrete's capability to resist shear along its contact with the rock prevent it from deforming circumferentially (tangentially). Consequently, a quasiring action in the shotcrete is effected. The bond between shotcrete and rock prevents the shotcrete from buckling in most cases. Thus, a true ring-action is also prevented and the shotcrete really becomes captive in the rock face and forms the structural skin of the latter.

For documentation purposes, the ring analysis assuming a radial skin pressure of 0.1 MPa (14.5 psi) indicated the need for a 25 mm thick shotcrete lining. To account for the roughness in the rock face, additional 50 mm were added to the theoretical value thus arriving at a total thickness of 75 mm. This result was compared with published data correlating shotcrete requirements with rock quality expressed in terms of RQD (Rock Quality Designation). In rock with good core recovery (high RQD values), past experience indicated shotcrete requirements in the range of zero to 75 mm and thus confirms, in this instance, the ring analysis approach described above.

5.1.2 Rockbolt design

Since the power tunnels and penstocks will be subjected daily to hydraulic surge effects during the lifetime of the project, the tunnel design should ensure stable rock conditions along the tunnels. The primary concerns were in the area of the tunnel crown since in that area the rock is more susceptible to loosening because of gravity effects. The latter, combined with dynamic surge effects during the daily reversal of operating modes from pumping to generating and vice versa, could become detrimental in any section along the power conduits. These above considerations lead to the conclusion that pattern rockbolting in the crown area of the penstock and power tunnels would be provided in addition to the shotcrete treatment which alone, with rockbolting only where needed, may have been sufficient for comparable size tunnels designed for service in dry conditions.

To determine the rock bolt requirements, rock loads were estimated on basis of published data correlating the RQD values with Terzaghi's rock load factors (Deere, Peck, Monses and Schmidt, University of Illinois 1969). The resulting bolt requirements and lengths were compared with information on precedent designs published in "Underground Rock Chambers" by ASCE (Cording, Hendron, Deere 1971). Procedures in the design of the rockbolts for the flow shafts were similar to those used for the tunnels.

Dywidag threadbars with a yield strength of approximately 413.69 MPa (60,000 psi) were used throughout the design. Full encapsulation of bolts were specified for corrosion protection.

The rockbolt requirements for the penstock bifurcations (Fig 5) were dictated by the relatively flat configuration of the cavern and by the fact that the rock would be faced only with a 0.60 m thick concrete lining that itself would depend for its structural support on the rock. It was conceivable that unbalanced hydrodynamic surge effects could, during the service life of the project, loosen an unsupported rock mass envisioned as being included under a parabola with a height above the springline equivalent to three-fourths of the width of the bifurcation cavern. The rock bolts in the roof were designed to support that rock mass from the rock above. The sides and the invert were provided with a nominal amount of bolt support.

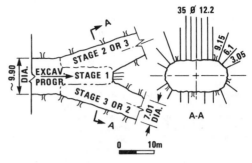

POWER TUNNEL—PENSTOCK BIFURCATION

Figure 5. Rock support in bifurcations

The surge shaft rock bolt requirements were designed along the same principles as used for the tunnel support, recognizing the fact that, in general, rock bolt requirements for shaft supports are less than for tunnels, because of the absence of direct gravity effect in the rock mass towards the interior of a vertical shaft. The nearly horizontal bedding planes are intersected with nearly vertical joint systems rendering the rock mass around the surge shafts to resemble a columnar matrix. Such individual columns along the shaft face are held in place by interlocked wedging action and the radial and tangential stresses resulting from the excavation. However, the same stress effects may also be the cause for dislodging of some of the column elements during the deformation and readjustment process along the face. It was felt that a face support of approximately 0.1 MPa, to maintain structural integrity at the face and to generate rock support around the 15 m dia excavation, was in order. This requirement was met with 35 mm dia 4.6 m long, high strength grade (f_y = 414 MPa) rockbolts spaced 15^0 circumferentially and 1.8 m oc vertically. The bolt length was doubled for the bottom one-third of the shaft to account for load concentrations at the surge shaft and tunnel intersection. Additional bolts were provided in the tunnel roof and walls at the intersection with the surge shaft.

5.1.3 Concrete lining design, tunnels and shafts

As mentioned in the preceding section, the decision had been made to concrete-line all water conduits for hydraulic efficiency (with the resulting decrease in conduit size and excavation volumes). Also, the lining would provide, in composite action with the applied shotcrete, the added insurance against degradation of the conduit faces (and possible rock-falls) under service conditions of the plant. With the rock bolts and shotcrete providing for an early support of the rock, the concrete lining does not support any rock loads per se, especially when the lining is placed after the radial deformations in the tunnels have subsided. Under such conditions, the design of the tunnel lining is reduced to selecting a nominal thickness, compatible with the size of the tunnel and convenient for concrete placement to assure acceptable quality of the lining.

513

Thus, the selection of the lining thickness was based on judgement and application of precedent experience. Initially, a lining thickness of 0.61 m (24 in) was selected for the power and penstock tunnels, however, this was reduced to 0.46 m (18 in) for the power tunnels after the initial excavation had exposed rock of consistently good quality. The lining thickness in the penstock tunnels was maintained at 0.61 m to provide sufficient clearance between the steel liners and the rock face for access during installation of the liners. Generally, the concrete lining is unreinforced, except in the penstock tunnels upstream of the steel liners, in the bifurcations, flow shaft elbows and in zones where weak rock has been encountered during excavation. The nominal reinforcement will consist of circumferential 36 mm bars spaced 0.3 m oc, and longitudinal 25 mm bars also at 0.3 m oc. All reinforcement is of high strength grade with $f_y = 414$ MPa.

5.1.3.1 External hydrostatic pressure considerations in the lining design

The ground cover above the lower tunnels, immediately downstream of the vertical flow shafts, is about 350 m high with perched groundwater levels at somewhat lesser heights above the tunnel. Trapped pore water pressures of the magnitude of the operating heads and exceeding those of the groundwater pressures, could act upon the tunnel lining externally during fast withdrawals of water from the power tunnels. For the worst case of external pressure being equivalent to the head differential resulting from the maximum level in the upper reservoir, the maximum stresses at the inside face of the lining would be in the order of about 42 MPa. These stresses would exist in a free-standing cylinder, separated from the shotcreted rock surface and free to deform circumferentially and radially. However, since the circumferential (tangential) deformations of the lining are inhibited by the interlocking effect with the rock and by the shear restraint along its outside face, some of the stresses resulting from the external pressures will be dissipated into the shotcreted rock face which surrounds the concrete lining. Thus, contrary to some expressed opinions that a tunnel lining is a free body in the surrounding rock and acted independently therefrom, it is actually captive in and interlocked with the surrounding rock mass (assuming adequate contact grouting in the crown), with no freedom to deform independently. These considerations lead to the conclusion that a design of concrete lining for external pressures, based on contemporary methods that consider free standing cylinders subject to shear and moment effects, appear unwarranted. Consequently, the lining is unreinforced and both circumferential cracking from shrinkage and radial cracking from internal pressure effects are accepted. The cracking is also considered to have the beneficial effect of relieving the external pressures.

The external pressure design of the concrete lining for the penstock bifurcations, because of the horizontally oblong shape of the bifurcation cross-sections (Fig. 5, 6), dictated somewhat different approach than for the tunnel lining discussed above. Early in the conceptual design studies it was decided that, because of the relatively large size of the power tunnels and the penstocks, the power tunnels should not be bifurcated near the powerhouse where the rock (a) was expected to be of poor quality and (b) did not have much cover for construction of caverns of the size dictated by steel penstock bifurcations (including their customary crotch

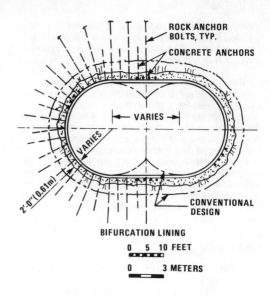

Figure 6. Bifurcation lining

reinforcements) and the related provisions for their erection. It was considered prudent to locate the bifurcations in the rock mass, upstream of the steel-lined penstocks, such that all unbalanced forces acting along the sections of structural discontinuity in the bifurcations can be delivered directly into the rock. Also, to simplify construction of the three bifurcations, the usual bifurcation geometry was simplified in that the roof and invert areas were formed as flat planes instead of being intersecting conical surfaces. The concrete lining of uniform 0.61 m (24 in) thickness was provided on basis of the same reasoning as applied in tunnel lining design - to increase hydraulic efficiency (with resulting reduction of the cavern size) and to protect the cavern surface against degradation. Because of the flat invert and roof areas, the adopted lining design precluded its design as a self supporting shell frequently used in other bifurcation designs. Moreover, because of the relatively long spans (up to 18 m) the lining must be supported from the rock against external hydrostatic effects during unwatering of the penstocks. Calculations indicated that even with an anchor spacing of only 0.75 m, and the anchors stressed to yield stress, the maximum supportable external hydrostatic pressure is equivalent to a head of only about 75 meters. In the initial design, it was assumed that any excessive pressures would result in the cracking of the lining and simultaneous relief of the excessive pressures. But, since the lining is also reinforced to provide for structural integrity and control excessive and concentrated cracking under internal pressures, this approach appeared to be somewhat counterproductive and leaving the designer in very little control of the design itself. Therefore, in lieu of some unknown pressure relief-effect through the expected cracking at random, the lining will be provided with weep holes approximately 2 m oc, drilled through the lining and approximately 0.6 m into the rock. Pressure relief through weepholes has been used successfully in tunnel portal design under high heads, tunnel invert design, draft tube floor design, retaining wall design and in similar applications. It is realized, however, that the provision of weepholes through the lining introduces full operating hydrostatic pressures into the rock mass surrounding the bifurcations. This fact would appear, at first glance, to be objectionable. However, the entire tunnel design is based on the conclusion that the rock is watertight and, therefore, the tunnels upstream of the bifurcations are unreinforced, subject to cracking and thus contributing to the exposure of the rock mass to hydrostatic pressures inside the tunnel. Notwithstanding this reasoning, consolidation grouting to 3 m depth, along the entire surface of the bifurcations, will be provided, prior to drilling of the weep holes, as an added precaution to improve the watertightness of the disturbed rock zones around the bifurcations. Rock bolts, with hooked extensions, will provide one half of the lining anchorage; the other half is provided by hooked anchor bars alternating with the rockbolts.

The design of the surge shaft lining against external pressures is based on the same principles as described for the tunnel lining design.

mately 100 m length would have to be designed to resist full internal pressures without rock assistance because of the poor rock conditions expected in that area. On the other hand, good rock conditions were expected beyond the poor rock zone and, therefore, for reasons of economy, the effect of rock assistance was considered in the design of the steel liners for internal pressures in this area (Fig. 7). The most downstream section, which connects to the pump/turbine guard valve, was designed for a relatively low stress of 145 MPa to control deformations and thus to make the design of this section more compatible with that of the guard valve body. The adjoining transition section and an approximately fifty-nine meter long section connecting to the transition were designed for factor of safety of 3 with respect to the ultimate strength (795 MPa) of the quenched and tempered steel A517. At the upstream end of this section the F.S. was stepped down to 2.5 to account for added safety because of deeper rock cover.

The upstream part of the penstocks (Fig. 7) was de-

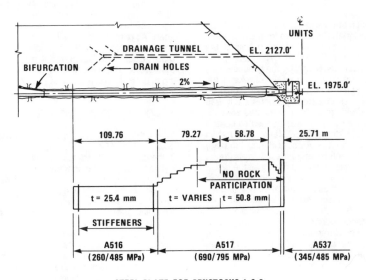

STEEL PLATE FOR PENSTOCKS 1 & 2
OTHER PENSTOCKS SIMILAR

Figure 7. Penstock liner

5.1.4 Penstock design

The six penstock tunnels, of varying lengths because of the topography, are steel-lined for the most part of their lengths. In general, the steel liner terminates where the ground cover is at least forty percent of the static head plus surge effects of one unit. The concrete lining between the bifurcations and the steel liners is reinforced because it was considered prudent to control cracking under internal pressures in this area. A sunburst type cut-off grout curtain and seepage cut-off collars are provided at the upstream end of each penstock. It was obvious, from the geology exposed in the exploration tunnel, that the downstream end of the steel liner of approxi-

signed accounting for rock assistance compatible with rock deformability as determined from the in-situ plate bearing tests. The section between the upstream and downstream liner sections described above served to effect gradual transition in plate thicknesses. In the design of the upstream section by classical deformation compatibility methods the rock carried about 73% of the internal pressures.

To determine the effect of rock participation, a 1.2 m thick disturbed rock zone with a rock modulus of deformation $E_r = 5.2 \times 10^3$ MPa (750,000 psi) was assumed. For the outer rock mass an $E_r = 27.6 \times 10^3$ MPa (4,000,000 psi) was used. Ac-

515

tually, for this zone, one half of the latter value would not give appreciably different results because the deformability of the disturbed zone governs the design. The design was tested for two values of moduli of elasticity for the concrete lining. In the first attempt, a modulus of 20.7 x 10^3 MPa (3 x 10^6 psi), which corresponds to a concrete strength of approximately 18.6 MPa, was used. In the second attempt, the concrete lining was assumed of the same quality as that of adjoining disturbed rock zone. This approach was made to compensate for some uncertainties in regard to the rock quality behind the disturbed zone, or in the disturbed zone itself, and to account for some degree of plastic deformations in the rock that can be expected during the many loading cycles over the life span of the project. The latter approach yielded about 10 to 12% higher steel stresses than with the higher value for modulus of deformation and was used to determine the minimum requirements for the steel thicknesses.

5.1.4.1 Design of penstock liner for external pressures, drainage tunnels

Early penstock design studies indicated that it would be uneconomical to design the steel liners for the maximum groundwater pressures that may develop behind the steel liner. It was also realized that hydrostatic pressures higher than those generated by the groundwater, resulting from seepage through possible cracks in the concrete lining upstream from the steel liner, could be present during penstock unwatering. Therefore, it was felt that a positive drainage system, combined with appropriate cut-off grout curtains, was needed to control the magnitude of the external hydrostatic pressures in the area of the steel liners. Also, considering the plant size and prohibitively high revenue losses even during the shutdown of only one unit, it was felt that the provisions made should be open for inspection at any time and also should afford access for maintenance and for modifications to the drainage facilities should the need arise. Drainage tunnels, with drain holes drilled into the rock from such tunnels, were considered as most suitable to satisfy the above requirements. Two drainage tunnels designated "A" and "B" of a modified horseshoe shape, 1.98 m wide and of 2.74 m height were provided at the powerhouse yard level.

Tunnel "B" was excavated early (spring 1973) for the purpose of rock exploration and in-situ testing. Tunnel "A" was excavated in summer 1977. The drainholes have been drilled in the pattern shown on Figures 2 and 7. Groundwater, seeping directly from the surrounding rock into the tunnels, will be collected in a gravel layer placed directly on the excavated invert. The drainholes would drain onto the concrete paving which covers the gravel layer. With these provisions, the maximum external hydrostatic pressure head is limited to about 46 m over the penstock centerline. The steel liners were checked against that head for a factor of safety against buckling of 1.5. Only the 25 mm plate of the upstream part of the penstocks requires stiffeners. Grouting pressures in the penstock area are limited to about 0.28 MPa to prevent penstock buckling during grouting.

The drainage provisions described above will serve not only to control the external water pressures above the penstocks, but, perhaps even more importantly, will limit the saturation of the hillside above the penstocks only to the level of the drainage tunnels which are set only about 2.8 m above the maximum operating pool elevation in the lower reservoir.

5.1.5 Surge shaft lining

The 13.41 m dia concrete-lined surge shafts are approximately 100 m high and are formed almost entirely in the rock. The excavated face is reinforced with rockbolts as described earlier. During operation of the project, the interior of the shaft will be exposed to daily occurrence of dynamic surge effects which would tend to cause disintegration in a rock face which consists of thinly bedded rock interbeds and closely spaced joints. A shotcrete treatment would serve well to seal the rock face for dry service conditions, but it was felt that the shotcrete could pop off under operating conditions with the risk of fallen chunks being carried into the turbines. Consequently, a concrete lining of 0.76 m (2.5 ft) thickness was considered appropriate as a permanent lining of the shafts. It is reinforced through the top 15 m of the shaft where the rock is somewhat weathered and more fractured than at lower elevations. Also, the bottom 21 m of the shaft are reinforced to account for the higher magnitude of the dynamic surge effects at the bottom of the shaft. All reinforcement is in the exposed face only and consists of No. 11 (35.8 mm dia) circumferential bars 0.30 m oc, and No. 8 (25.4 mm dia) vertical bars 0.46 m oc. The remaining portion of the surge shaft lining is unreinforced and some cracking will be accepted.

6. CONSTRUCTION ASPECTS

When the project construction activities were slowed down in June 1980, all underground excavation, except in the power intake transition area, was completed. The subcontractor for the underground excavation work was well organized and performed ahead of schedule. The rock excavated easily and presented no special support problems except in areas of occasional mud seams. Specified shotcreting and pattern rock bolting sufficed to make the rock self-supporting and to preserve its integrity along the excavated faces. By now, the earlier excavated tunnel sections have been exposed for three years. Instrumentation and visual inspection of the shotcreted surfaces indicate very good condition, except in some areas of the diversion tunnel where some loosening in the slabby rock of the tunnel roof, as evidenced from rock falls on the invert, has taken place.

6.1 Power and penstock tunnel construction

These tunnels were constructed by conventional drill-and-blast, top heading and bench method. A weekly progress of approximately 15 m was made in excavation of the top heading (between the crown and 3.7 m below the springline) of the power tunnels by working a three-shift day, 40 hr week. Subsequently, the remaining bench section (about 1.3 to 1.5 m thick) was excavated at a rate of approximately 90 to 100 m per week. Field-fabricated, six-drill, two-deck jumbos and Wagner ST-8 muckers of about 6 m^3 capacity were used for the tunnel operations. The standard procedure was to shoot a round of approximately 3 m depth, scale loose rock and shotcrete the roof, muck excavated material and shotcrete more, as needed. Four to six rockbolts were installed for safety during the drilling of the next round. The average time required for a round was about 3 hours to drill, one half hour to load and blast; scaling, shotcreting and mucking took another 2.5 hours. Perimeter hole spacing was about 0.45 m and production hole spacing 0.75 m. While this pattern produced the best results production-wise, it may not have given the best results in regard to the presplitting of the rock along the perimeter.

Some problems were encountered with running water and several soft seams. Fortunately, most of the water drained out quickly. Spiling bolts, in conjunction with closely spaced rockbolts placed through the mat of the spiling bolts, were used in the crown of the softer zones with very good success. Subsequently, the soft material will be over-excavated and replaced with a concrete cap. The tunnel lining will be reinforced and consolidation grouting will be attempted in such areas.

Dywidag threadbar type rockbolts, in conjunction with DuPont resin for anchorage and encapsulations, were used for most of the underground construction because their continuous thread-like deformations offer great flexibility in installation and, also, smaller bar-sizes can be used because the threads do not undercut the nominal diameter. All pattern rockbolts, provided as permanent rock support, were fully encapsulated in polymer resin to provide corrosion protection because of the aggressive water at the project site. Installation of the standard 3 m long bolts and 6 m (uncoupled) bolts was a routine matter. Longer bolts, such as for the bifurcations, required couplings and the holes had to be drilled larger. To reduce the hole size, special high strength, smaller size couplings were used which also allowed for easier penetration through the polymer cartridges during insertion of the bolt. The hole size used was about 57 mm dia. Initially, difficulties were experienced with the loading of the cartridges and with having enough cartridges to load a hole because, generally, drilling operations increase the theoretical size of the hole and more cartridges than specified were needed. Also, assurance had to be obtained that the bolt was fully surrounded by the resin. To that end, field tests were conducted by simulating installation procedures in a suspended plastic pipe. The bolts appeared to be well coated but not necessarily filling the pipe completely, however, there was more than sufficient length of complete contact with the pipe walls to develop sufficient anchorage length. The cartridges were loaded in pairs by supporting them on a plastic cap, slightly larger than the hole diameter, and by pushing that set (two cartridges - resin and catalyst - and the cap at the near end) into the hole with a plastic pipe. The cap prevented the pipe from penetrating into the cartridges and supported the latter by friction along the perimeter of the hole. The caps became shredded when the bolt was spun through the cartridges.

It was observed that, for better penetration of the cartridges, the far end of the bolt had to be sharpened because the square end would push and jam the plastic separations between the cartridges (provided with DuPont cartridges to prevent contact between resin and catalyst) into the vicinity of the far end of the hole. This condition rendered a part of the anchorage embedment of questionable quality. The bearing plate was held against the rock to prevent resin runouts. Where incomplete encapsulation was observed, new overlapping bolts were installed. The hole was first loaded with anchorage cartridge (2 min. setting time), followed with encapsulation cartridges (15 min. setting time). The latest time for tensioning was 13 min., maximum, after inser-

tion of the bolt. Impact wrenches (Chicago Pneumatic) were used for tensioning all short (small-size) bolts, although, torque wrenches were used at the start of construction. Skidmore-Williams calibrator was used with the former. The long (large-size) bolts were jacked with air jacks. All bolts were tensioned with a force developing 0.6 Y.P. stress.

6.2 Surge and flow shaft construction

Construction of the 100 m high surge shafts preceded the flow shaft construction. They were constructed by the raise-bore, slash-down method which was initiated by drilling a 300 mm dia pilot hole through the center of the shaft for connection and guidance of the raise-boring equipment (Ingersol Rand Rotary Raise Bore, 2.75 m dia). The next step was to raise-bore the 2.75 m dia shaft from the upper power tunnels followed by drilling and blasting around the raise-bore and mucking the material down to the upper power tunnels. The drilling rate of the 300 mm pilot hole was about 2.1 m/hr. and that of the raise-bore about 0.9 to 1.5 m/hr. in sound rock. Excavation rate to full diameter was between 2.4 and 3 m/day.

Work in the 300 m high flow shafts proceeded in a similar manner as for the surge shafts. The upper tunnels were excavated into the upper elbows and 2.75 m dia construction access shafts were raise-bored from the elbows to the surface in line with the flow shafts. Drilling of a pilot hole preceded this operation. Also, a construction access tunnel was driven from the upper reservoir access road to the upper elbows of the flow shafts to gain staging areas for the Ingersol Rand drilling machine over the flow shafts. The pilot holes were drilled to the lower power tunnels for raise-boring to the staging area at the upper elbow level. Drilling and blasting started from this level and the mucking down the raise-bore was accomplished with Wagner ST-8 mucker. Progress for full-section excavation was about 4.2 m/day. All shaft excavation proceeded as planned except that the initial efforts to drill the 300 mm dia pilot holes with a truck-mounted drill were unsuccessful because the alignment of the hole could not be controlled. On the other hand, the Ingersol Rand drilling machine performed very well. Also the power intake gate shafts were excavated in similar fashion.

6.3 Bifurcation construction (Figure 5)

Construction of the bifurcations started from the power tunnel end once the power tunnel headings, starting from the lower construction tunnel, had been advanced to the bifurcations. The bifurcations were excavated in stages. Initially, a 4.9 m wide drift was excavated along the center line of a bifurcation to the full height of the top heading. The roof of this drift was secured with four longitudinal rows of 12.2 m long bolts spaced about 1.5 m oc each direction. Two sets of pipe cluster extensometers, each consisting of five single pipes (0.93; 7.6; 15.2 and 24.4 m long) were provided one on each side of the drift to observe deformations during subsequent work. Scaling and shotcreting preceded the bolting. Subsequently, the sides, one by one, were blasted into the drift and supported as before. It is believed this construction procedure resulted in the least rock disturbance along the bifurcation surface and limited the roof deformations to a minimum. The initial deformation after the full width of the cavern was excavated amounted to about 10 mm.

CONCLUSION

In total, twenty different tunnels and shafts, with a total length of approximately 18 km, have been excavated at the site. Their present condition, with the primary support being rock bolts and shotcrete, and having not received permanent concrete lining as yet, is excellent. The contractor, Gates & Fox from Loomis, California deserves a credit for a job well done. Contractor's advisor in geotechnical area was A. A. Mathews, Inc. of Rockville, Maryland. General Contractor acting as VEPCO's agent is Daniel Construction Company of Greenville, South Carolina. Chicago Bridge and Iron is responsible for the steel penstocks. VEPCO Consulting Board consists of Dr. R. B. Peck (Foundations, Embankment), F. B. Slichter (Structures), W. V. Conn (Geology), G. J. Vencill (Equipment). Harza Engineering Company, Chicago, Illinois has the overall design responsibility for all permanent project features.

THE METHOD OF EVALUATION FOR THE STABILITY OF KARST CAVERNS
Methode zur Beurteilung der Stabilität von Kavernen im Karst
La méthode d'évaluation de la stabilité des cavernes dans le karst

ZHU JINGMIN & XIAO ZHIZHONG
Chongqing Institute of Architecture & Engineering, China

SYNOPSIS

In the present paper an appreciation table is suggested in which the stability of
karst caverns is classified into four ranks. By the use of orthotropic finite element
analysis stresses and displacements around a karst cavern are obtained. In examining
the stability of a whole cavern, Mohr-Coulomb strength theory is applied to check the
stability of rock and weak structural faces. In respect to analyzing the stability
of part of a cavern, the theory of "block equilibrium" is adopted. The stability of
caverns are measured in-situ with the pressure cells. Actual examples are illustrated.

INHALTZUSAMMENFASSUNG

In diesem Artikel wird eine Tablle aufgestellt, in der die stabilität des Karstes in
vier Klassen unterteilt wird mit der ortho-anisotropischen Finite-Element Methode
werden die Spannungen und Verschiebungen zweiter Ordnung des umschließenden Gesterins-
körpers berechet. Durch Untersuchungen der Festigkeit des Gesteins und der schwachen
Strukturflächen mit der Mohr-Coulomb Theorie wird die Gesamtstabilitat des höhenums-
chließenden Gesteinskorpers bewertet, und die teilweise Stabilität wird dann mit der
"block-equilibrium Theorie untersucht. Die Stabilitat des Gesteinskörpers wird durch
Messung mit der "Druckbüchsen" verfolgt.

SOMMAIRE

Les présents papiers vous montront le tableau de degré évaluant la stabilité en quatre
degrés. On calcule et analyse des éléments limitatifs et orthoanisotropiques afin
d'obtenir le déplacement et la contrainte secondire d'une caverne. Pour évaluer la
stablite en ensemble de la caverne, on emploie la théorie de l'intensité Mohr-Coulomb
à examiner l'intensité des rocjes et de la surface de structire faible, et d'après la
théorie "équilibre bloc", évaluer la stabilité des parties localisées de cette caverne.
Prendre sur place la "boite à presser" pour examiner la stabili té dé la caverne en
question.

1 INTRODUCTION

Karst caverns are formed by dissolution
and erosion along the slits of soluble
rock by filtering ground water. In the
process of dissolution and erosion the
unstable blocks of caverns will collapse,
thus their cross-sectional areas will
further increase.

There are many karst caverns scattered
over all districts in Chongqing, China.
For energy savings and cultivated land
conservation these karst caverns may be
utilized for underground storage of petroleum or gas, for treatment of waste

material or for other purposes. As a
matter of fact several karst caverns have
been converted into parks as well as
underground factories, etc. Hence, it is
becoming very important to use these resources more efficiently and rationally.

How to determine whether the surrounding
rock of karst cavern is stable is a question to be solved before making the decision to use it. As the process by which
karst caverns are formed is quite different from that of man-made ones, the way
to evaluate the stability of the former
is slightly different. It depends essentially on the qualitative engineering

Table 2.1 Stability index of karst cavern

Conditions	Stable	Basically stable	Less stable	Unstable
Geological structure	No fualt and fold, only slightly fissured, filled and cemented very well, and no unstable block exposed.	With a few faults and/or folds, but more fissures, filled and cemented well, a few unstable blocks exposed.	With more faults and/or folds and fissures, a few fissures are open, filled though cemented poorly, some filled by water, many unstable blocks exposed.	With major faults and or heavily forded, highly fissured and open, unfilled and cemented poorly, some filled by water, a great many unstable blocks exposed.
Rock properties	Very thick or thick inclined strata or beds, the continuity of rock masses is perfect, strikes intersect with tunnels' axis.	Thick or medium inclined strata or beds, fairly continuous, strikes intersect with tunnels' axis.	Medium and thin, broken gently inclined strata or beds strikes parallel to tunnels' axis.	Thin or medium nearly horizontal strata or beds with intercalated shale layer, highly broken, strikes parallel to tunnels' axis.
Ground water, karst and underground river	No water dripping from roofs, no karst water on bases and no underground river near by, only a few karst caves.	Little water dripping from roofs, little karst water appeared on bases and fairly many karst caves, no underground river.	Fairly more water dripping from roofs, karst water appeared on bases, many karst caves and modern or ancient underground rivers, but easy to treat.	Water heavily dripping from roofs, a good many karst caves, much more karst water and modern underground river, but difficult to treat.
State of the roof	Covered with calcium shells, no fresh mark of collapse, rock mass interlocks with good arching action in the roof.	Covered with calcium shells over two-thirds of the roof, no fresh mark of collapse, rock mass interlocks with good arching action in the roof.	Covered with calcium shells about one half of the roofs, and some fresh mark of collapse observed in rock mass isolated points, interlocks with poor arching action.	Covered with calcium shells only on partial roof, more fresh surfaces of collapse, no arching action in the rock mass.
Rockfall	Only a few rockfalls observed, but no unstable rockfalls at present.	A number of rockfalls observed, but no unstable rockfalls at present	A good number of rockfalls observed and rock falls may occur at isolated points.	A great number of rock-falls observed and large rockfalls may occur.
Treatment before use	May be used after a slight treatment.	May be used after a certain treatment.	May be used after a greater treatment.	Treatment is very difficult, must not be used.

Table 2.2 Rank of karst caving and rockfall*

Rank	A few	some more	many	A good many
Karst caves	< 4	4— 8	8—12	>12
Rockfalls	< 6	6—10	10—15	>15

* Numbers per 100m of tunnel length

Table 2.3 Index to degree of fissuring

Type	Coefficient of fissure(Kmp)	Fissure width
Non fissured	< 2%	Most of fissures width is less than 1^{mm}.
Some fissuring	2— 5%i	More than 50% fissures width is less than 1^{mm}.
Fissured	5—10%	10—20% fissures width is 20—100^{mm}.
Highly fissured	10—20%	All fissures are compact.

Table 2.4 Thickness classification of bedded units

Name	Very thick	Thick	Medium	Thin
Thickness(m)	> 1	0.5—1	0.1—0.5	0.05—0.1

Table 2.5 Case histories of evaluation for the stability of karst cavern

No.	1	2	3	4
Cavern size	Length about 45m, span 8—17^m, height 8—12m, overburden thickness 15—30^m.	Length 359m, span 15—20^m, mean height 15m, overburden thickness 20—25m.	Length 20m, span qm, height 6.5m, overburden thickness 5—15m.	Length 330^m, span 6—22m, height 18—20m, overburden thickness 20—48m.
Geologic structure	No fault and fold.	A small fault and a gentle fold.	A gentle fold but no fault.	A bedding fault in the roof, a thrust fault in the north portal handle it easy, no fold.
Rock Properties	Thick or medium Jialinjang limestone of the triassic System, rock masses are perfect, strikes intersect with tunnels' axis, dip angle 16°—19°.	Thick or medium Jialinjiang limestone of the Triassic System, rockmass are fairly perfect except for the roof of east section, strikes parallel or intersect with tunnel's axis, dip angle 14°.	Thick or medium Jialinjiang limestone of the Triassic System, rockmasses are inperfect, strikes intersect with tunnel's axis, dip angle about 14°.	Thick and medium with a few thin Jialinjiang limestone of the Triassic System, rock masses are broken, strikes about parallel to tunnel's axis, dip angle about 60°.
Condition of fissure	Few fissures, filled with calcspar and cemented well, rock masses are cut by the structual faces gently.	Some fissuring, filled and cemented well except for the roof of east section, rock masses are cut by the tectonic discontinuity,	Some fissuring, a part filled and cemented well, rock masses of the roof are cut by the joint sets or fissure systems.	Beddings and tectonic fissures developed well, many fissures are filled and cemented with calcium except for the bedding fault, rock masses are cut by the joint sets in the whole cavern.
Ground water	No dripping water on the roof and walls, no underground river under the bases.	A little dripping water on the roofs, no karst water in the bases, but a little saturation water in the soil.	Some dripping water in the east side of the cavern gate, no ground water in the base.	Much dripping water on the roof and more on the bedding fault, a lot of karst water in the base.

Table 2.5 (Continue)

No.	1	2	3	4
Karst and under-ground river	Small karst caves passed through the south wall, no can-tilever walls.	A few karst caves in the roof and walls, no under-ground river, a few cantilever walls.	No karst cave in the roof and walls except for the wall of south end, no underground river.	Some vertical small karst in the roof and some big karst in the walls, a ancient underground river amd a modern under the base, but handle it easy.
State of the roof	Rock masses of the roof and the walls support each other well, with calcium shells on the roof, no fresh collapsed mark, arch roof unformed.	Calcium shells on the roofs, no fresh collapsed mark, arch roof formed well except for the roof of east section.	A part of the roof cemented with cal-cium, no fresh mark of rock fall, a old rock lining.	Cemented with cal-cium and no fresh mark of rock-fall, rock masses support each other well except for a part place, arch roof formed.
Rockfall	Small rock-fall at the portal of ca-cern.	Fairly many rock-falls, but may be handled, no present rock-falls filled, clay cemented with calcium over the bases.	Some rock-falls at the portal and the end wall, but may be treated easily, no rock-fall filled and some pebbly layer in the base.	Fairly many rockfall, distributed over the whole cavern, but can be treated, some small rockfalls fil-led, a slide slope on the north portal.
Class of stability	Stable	Basically stable	Basically stable	Less stable
Plane figure				

geologic appraisal combined with rockmass mechanics quantative evaluation.

This paper is intended to make a discus-sion on the following subjects: the eng-ineering geologic stability index of a karst cavern, stresses in surrounding rock, global or local stability of sur-rounding rock, as well as long time mo-nitoring the stability in-situ. Illus-trated actual examples are cited.

2 APPRAISAL OF ENGINEERING GEOLOGIC STA-BILITY OF KARST CAVERN

The main factors influencing stability of karst cavern are the nature of rock forma-tion, geological structure, hydrogeological condition, state of cavern roof, unstable rocks, etc. These factors have a close tie with the stability of the surrounding rock.

In accordane with the preceding five main factors affecting stability, we have made a complete analysis of many actual karst caverns in Chongqing and proposed a sta-bility index as the criteria to determine the stability of karst caverns for various uses, see table 2.1. The stability is classified into four ranks: ie, stable, basically stable, less stable and unstable.

Indices of karst cave and unstable rock classification are shown in table 2.2; indices of degree of fissuration in table 2.3; indices of rock thickness classifi-cation in table 2.4.

In the classification of rock inclina-tion, it is called an "inclined state" when the angle of slope of the rock is above $15°$, and a "flat state" when below $15°$. In the classification of water dripping, it is called a "little dripping" when the fissure water percolating gently from only very few isolated points on the roof, a "heavy dripping" when percolating from several points with a few streaming, and a "serious dripping" when the water spreading over one half of the roof with large streams.

It is to be noted that the stability index is suitable only for minor earthquake zones.

Four typical karst caverns are listed on the last column of table 2.5 to illustrate application of the stability index. All of them satisfy the stability criteria and have been in good condition.

3 STRESS ANALYSIS OF SURROUNDING ROCK

The crux of stability of karst caverns is the contradiction of the stress of surrounding rock with the strength of rockmass. The general procedure of rock mass mechanics evaluation is as follows:

1. To determine the dimension of the cavern, the bedding strike, the dip angle and the fissural density by dint of the engineering geologic investigations.

2. To determine the in-situ state of initial stress in the rock masses.

3. To measure the rock mass mechanics parameters by means of field and lab tests.

4. To carry out the in-situ measurement, the model test and the finite element analysis for the determining of the stresses in the surrounding rock.

5. To establish a long run field monitoring system.

At first, it is necessary to model the medium of rock mass for computing the stresses in the surrounding rock. Both discontinuity and continuity of the rock mass must be taken care of because the nature of rock mass is determined by the geologic structure and the stress state. Therefore, it may be considered appropriate that rock mass may be taken as a quasi-continuous medium. The surrounding rock of karst cavern may be simulated by the orthotropic model according to some field measurement.

For example, the karst cavern No. 4, shown in Table 2.5, may be considered. The surrounding rock mass consists of thick and medium thick Jialinjiang limestone with a strike of N 350°E and a dip angle of about 60°. The bed is comparatively regular with only a fault in the roof, the greater part of which is cemented with calcium shell, as shown in Fig 3.1.

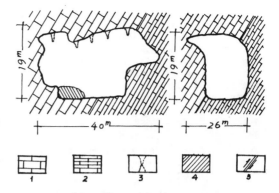

Fig 3.1 Geologic cross-section at No. 5 and No. 26 along the cavern axis. 1-thick limestone, 2-medium thick limestone, 3-stalactite, 4-rockfall, 5-bedding fault.

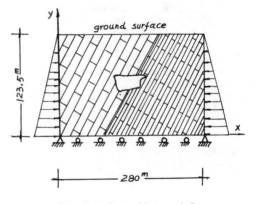

Fig 3.2 Computing model

The computing model is shown in Fig 3.2. For comparison, the coefficient of ground reaction is taken to be $\lambda_1 = 0.3986$, $\lambda_2 = 1$, $\lambda_3 = 2$. respectively.

The mechanical properties of rock have been measured in the field and in the lab, but not that of the bedding which are estimated from engineering geologic-analogic method. The mechanical parameters of Jialinjiang Limestone are shown in Table 3.1. The unit weight of the rock is $\gamma = 2.675$ T/m^3, the dip angle $\theta = 60°$. The overburden is 47.5m thick for No.5 and 40.5m thick for No. 26.

Orthotropic finite element analysis used to determine stresses and displacements around cavern. The principal stress distribution in surrounding rock is shown in Fig 3.3 and Fig 3.4; the tangential stress distribution around cavern is shown in Fig 3.5 and Fig 3.6. The tangen-tial stresses around cavern for cross-section No. 5 are recorded in Table 3.2, in which the plus sign of stress is for compression.

Table 3.1 The mechanical parameters of Jialinjiang Limestone

E_1	E_2	M_1	M_2	G
420000	280000	0.30	0.25	96000

Note: elastic meduli are in kg/cm^2

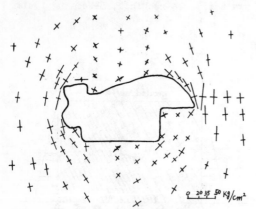

Fig 3.3 Principal stress distribution for cross-section No. 5

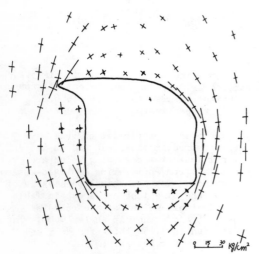

Fig 3.4 Principal stress distribution for cross-section No. 26

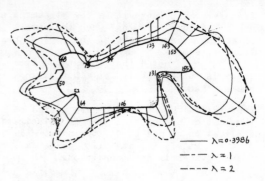

$\lambda = 0.3986$
$\lambda = 1$
$\lambda = 2$

Fig 3.5 Tangential Stress distribution around cavern for cross-section No. 5

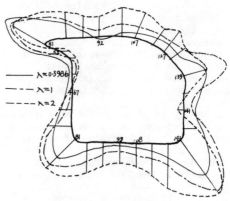

$\lambda = 0.3986$
$\lambda = 1$
$\lambda = 2$

Fig 3.6 Tangential Stress distribution around cavern for scross-section No. 26

Table 3.2 Tangential Stresses around cavern for cross-section No. 5

No.	155	153	143	48
λ_1	65.4	25.27	23.99	46.71
λ_2	106.5	31.3	35.28	81.61
λ_3	138.7	41.73	49.31	51.68

Note: Stress unit kg/cm^2

The stresses of the wall around the cavern for cross-section No. 5, measured in-situ by the method of stress relief, is shown in Table 3.3

Table 3.3 Experimental data of stresses around cavern

No.	155	153	143
σ_1	130	108.1	62
σ_2	48.6	69	54
α	28'	$-21°$	$24°$

Note: Stress unit kg/cm2

Comparison of stresses in the Table 3.2 with that in Table 3.3, it may be seen that the stresses measured in-situ are about 60-130kg/cm2 and the stresses computed with the coefficient of ground reaction λ_2=1 are about 40-110kg/cm2, thus the result computed by the orthotropic finite element analysis is principally agreed to the data measured in-situ.

4 EVALUATION OF GLOBAL AND LOCAL STABILITY FOR THE SURROUNDING ROCK OF CAVERN

When unstable blocks are exposed by excavation, local or even global instability of surrounding rock may occur. Hence, it is necessary to evaluate global and local stability of the surrounding rock. Their inter-relations are very similar to the well known "theory of key stone".

4.1 Strength criteria of rock mass

Rock mass is a natural geologic body. It have passed through a long historic process and experienced all sorts of geologic action, hence there remained various marks of geologic structure.

At present, Mohr-Coulomb theory is usually used as the strength criteria of rock and weak structural faces and may be expressed by the following equation:

$$\frac{\sigma_1 - \sigma_3}{2c\,ctg\varphi + \sigma_1 + \sigma_3} \leq \sin\varphi \qquad (4.1)$$

Where c=cohesion of rock, φ =angle of friction.
  Strength criteria of weak structural faces may be expressed as:

$$\frac{(\sigma_1 - \sigma_3)\sin2\beta}{2c_1ctg\varphi_1+(\sigma_1 - \sigma_3)\cos2\beta+\sigma_1+\sigma_3} \leq tg\,\varphi_1 \quad (4.2)$$

Where c_1=cohesion of weak structural faces, φ_1 =angle of friction, β =angle of weak structural faces with σ_3 .

For a given state of stress, whether the breaking occurs in the rock or along the weak structural faces may be determined from the following formula:

$$\varphi_1 < \beta < \pi/2 \qquad (4.3)$$

4.2 Evaluation of global stability for surrounding rock

Karst cavern No. 4 is taken as an example. The parameters of rock strength measured in-situ are φ =55° and c=25kg/cm2; those for the bedding fault as estinated by engineering geologic evaluation are φ_1 = 38° and c_1=5kg/cm2. It is seen from Fig 3.6 and Fig 3.7 that the maxionum stress is at the point 155 of cross-section No. 5 (see Fig 4.1 a).

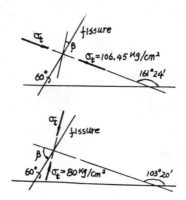

Fig 4.1. Stability examination of surrounding rock

It is seen from Fig 4.1 a, β =11°24', i.e. $\beta < \varphi_1$, therefore, the strength criteria of rock (4.1) may be used to check the stability of surrounding rock mass:

$$\frac{\sigma_1 - \sigma_3}{2c\,ctg\varphi + \sigma_1 + \sigma_3} =0.76797$$

$$\sin\varphi=\sin55°=0.81915$$

$$\therefore \frac{\sigma_1 - \sigma_3}{2c\,ctg\varphi + \sigma_1 + \sigma_3} < \sin\varphi \qquad (4.4)$$

It is seen from Fig 4.1 b, β =76°30', i.e. $\beta > \varphi_1$, therefore, the strength criteria of weak structural faces (4.2) may be used to cheek the stability of surrounding rock mass:

525

$$\frac{(\sigma_1 - \sigma_3)\sin2\beta}{2c_1ctg\,\varphi_1 +(\sigma_1 - \sigma_3)\cos2\beta+\sigma_1+\sigma_3}=0.72644$$

$$tg\ \varphi_1 =tg38°=0.78128$$

$$\therefore\ \frac{(\sigma_1 - \sigma_3)\sin2\beta}{2c_1ctg\,\varphi_1 +(\sigma_1 - \sigma_3)\cos2\beta+\sigma_1+\sigma_3} < tg\,\varphi_1\quad(4.5)$$

It may be concluded that Karst cavern No. 4 satisfies strength criteria and the whole cavern is stable.

4.3 Evaluation of local stability for surrounding rock

The crux of local stability for surrounding rock is the contradiction of sliding of rock block against the resistance offered by the adjacent blocks. Sliding forces include the weight of unstable block Q, static hydraulic pressure H or dynamic hydraulic pressure as well as earthquake force and structural stress, etc., and may be expressed as $f(Q. H. J ...)$; stabilizing forces include the reaction forces: friction N $tg\varphi$ and cohesion c, etc., and may be expressed as $F(Ntg\varphi .c)$. The critenria of local stability may be expressed as follows:

$$F(Ntg\varphi .c)> f(Q.H.J...)\quad(4.6)$$
or
$$K=\frac{F(Ntg\varphi .c)}{f(Q.H.J...)} > 1\quad(4.7)$$

Where K is called the stability coefficient.

Computing model of plane problems for local stability of cross-section No, 5 is shown in Fig 4.2

In the state of Fig 4.2 a,b, substituting the stabilizing force F and the sliding force f into formula (4.7) results:

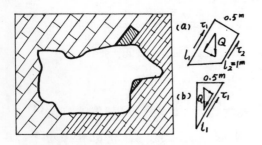

Fig 4.2 Evaluation of local stability of surrounding rock

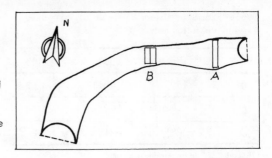

Fig 5.1 The plan arrangement of pressure cells

$$K=\frac{F}{f} = \frac{Qcos\theta tg\varphi_1 +c_1\,l_1 +c_1\,l_2}{Qsin\theta}=1.31\quad(4.8)$$

and

$$K=\frac{F}{f} = \frac{Qcos\theta tg\varphi_1 +c_1\,l_1}{Qsin\theta}=1.56\quad(4.9)$$

respectively.

It is seen from the above that No.2 Karst cavern satisfies the criteria of global and local stability, there-fore, the surrounding rock of this cavern is in good condition.

5 LONG TIME MONITORING THE STABILITY OF KARST CAVERB IN-SITU

Lining and column pressure cells were used for monitoring the stability in-situ. Lining pressure cell is principally used to cover large supporting area while column pressure cell is used for small supporting area.

The arrangement of pressure cell for the karst cavern No. 2 (see table 2.5) is shown in Fig 5.1. Four Lining cells were installed in the reinforced Lining of cross-section A and twelve column cells on the reinforced concrete frame of longitudinal section B.

The pressure-frequency curves of pressure cells are shown in Fig 5.2b and Fig 5.3. The frequency-time curves of pressure cells are shown in Fig 5.2 c and Fig 5.4.

Pressure cell No. 11 was unloaded and its frequency didn't change evidently in a year (see Fig 5.2). During the first five

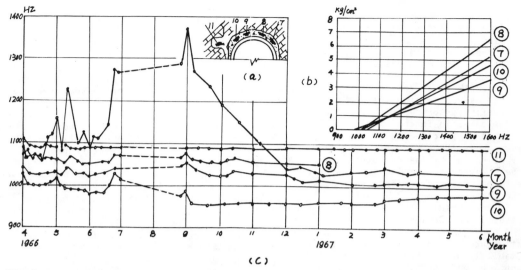

Fig 5.2 Lining pressure cells of cross-section A.(a) The plan arrangement of pressure cells, (b) Pressure-frequency curve, (c) Frquency-time curve.

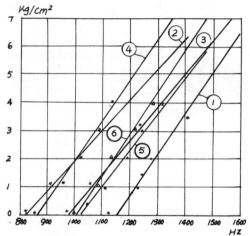

Fig 5.3 Pressure-frequency curve of column pressure cells

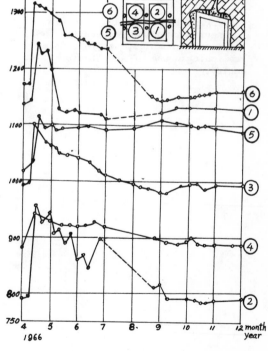

months after installation the frequencies changed irregularly, and then all reached the stable condition. It may be concluded that the stability of karst cavern No. 2 is in good condition.

Fig 5.4 Frequency-time curve of column pressure cells

6 SUMMARY

In the present paper engineering geologic appraisal combined with rock mass mechanics evaluation has been taken in appreciating the stability of karst caverns. It may be concluded as follows:

1. Based on engineering investigation we have made a complete analysis of eighteen actual karst caverns in Chongqing and proposed the table of stability index for karst cavern, in which the stability is classified into four ranks. It was shown to be ceasible in engineering application.

2. It is proposed in this paper that the surrounding rock mass of karst cavern may be simulated by the orthotropic model and the stresses computed by orthotropic finite element analysis agrees essentially with the stresses measured in-situ.

3. In examining the stability of a karst cavern, Mohr-Coulomb theory may be used as the strength criteria for rock and weak structural faces. In respect to the local stability of cavern, the theory of "block equilibrium" was adopted.

4. It is a feasible method to monitor the stability in-situ with the pressure cells.

7 REFERENCES

Chongqing Institute of Architecture and Engineering, Tungji University, 1981, Rock mass-mechanics, Beijing, China Publishing House of Architectural Industry.

Sun Renbo, 1965, Experimental research on mechanical properties of karst cavern's limestone, Chongqing Institute of Architecture and Engineering press.

Sun Renbo, 1972, Insitu, measurement of earth pressure on karst caverns, Chongqing Institute of Architecture and Engineering press.

Xiao Zhizhong, 1965, Evaluation of geological engineering for the stability of karst caverns, Chongqing Institute of Architecture and Engineering press.

Zhu Jingmin, 1972, Evaluation of rock mechanics for the stability of a karst cavern's engineering, Chongqing Institute of Architecture and Engineering press.

Zhu Jingmin, 1981a, Theory of elastoplastic and viscoelastoplastic stress-strain model for rock, Journal of the Chongqing Institute of Architecture and Engineering , 1981, 3.

Zhu Jingmin, 1981b, Evaluation method of rockmass mechanics for stability of karst caverns, Chongqing Institute of Architecture and Engineering press.

Zhu Jingmin & Bai Yuanchang, 1980, Evaluation for the stability of rock caverns and structural design and construction, Journal of Underground Engineering, 1980, 12.

Zhu Jingmin, Dou Jiazhen & Zhong Yongqun, 1981, Orthotropic Finite element analysis for the stability of rock caverns, Chongqing Institute of Architecture and Engineering press.